D1215295

ALUMINUM

Vol. II. Design and Application

ALUMINUM

Vol. I. Properties, Physical Metallurgy and Phase Diagrams

Vol. II. Design and Application

Vol. III. Fabrication and Finishing

ALUMINUM

Vol. II. Design and Application

Prepared by engineers,
scientists and metallurgists
of Aluminum Company of America

Edited by
Kent R. Van Horn
Vice President—Research and Development
Aluminum Company of America
Past President, American Society for Metals

AMERICAN SOCIETY FOR METALS
Metals Park, Ohio

Distributor outside the United States and Canada:
Chapman & Hall, Limited
11 New Fetter Lane
London EC4, England

Library of Congress Catalog Card Number:
66–16222

Printed in the United States of America

Preface to Volume Two

THIS three-volume work was written by Aluminum Company of America personnel at the invitation of the American Society for Metals. A general preface to the three volumes appears in Volume I.

This volume is concerned with design and applications. The first four chapters are introductory or basic; the next five are concerned with design factors; and the four that follow relate to structures. The next six chapters discuss transportation applications; the final six deal with applications in other fields. Chapter lengths and details of treatment are not in direct proportion to distribution ratios of aluminum tonnage in the market, but rather are related to the potential number of users in the fields of application discussed — as befits the aim of this book.

For many applications, two or more alloys or tempers are indicated, which may signify a need for alloy variation to accommodate design differences. For other applications, alloy selection is not critical; a number of alloys may be almost equally suitable, with choice depending on cost or other commercial considerations. In many instances in which only one alloy is cited for a specific application, others may be even more satisfactory under the stated conditions.

Extensive cross references in this volume direct the reader to related information. But the reader should consult the index to insure maximum awareness of all information presented on a particular subject.

References and the text were revised on proofs to include data as recent as 1966. No pretense of an extensive bibliography is made, but patents are included in the selected references, in keeping with the purpose of this work. However, no significance concerning scope or patent protection is intended. Credit is given in captions for illustrations derived from the literature or obtained from other companies.

THE COMMITTEE of Alcoa personnel appointed to guide the preparation of this work consisted of: WILLIAM R. BUTLER, Manager, Application Engineering (upon Mr. Butler's retirement, in July, 1965, WAYNE C. KEITH assumed his company responsibilities and the work on the committee); MAURICE W. DAUGHERTY, Secretary, Alcoa Research Laboratories; J. HOWARD DUNN, Manager, Alcoa Process Development Laboratories; ERNEST C. HARTMANN, Director of Research; HOWARD J. ROWE, Secretary, Research and Development Committee; LAURENCE S. SEWELL, JR., Manager of Special Services, Public Relations Department; and KENT R. VAN HORN (*Chairman*), Vice President, Research and Development.

Maurice W. Daugherty reviewed, with Ernest C. Hartmann, the 26 chapters originating from the Alcoa Research Laboratories. Mr. Daugherty then devoted six months beyond his normal retirement to the special editing and coordination of the 14 chapters on industry applications. He also read the page proofs of all volumes for general technical sense. Laurence S. Sewell edited all chapters for clarity and also selected and arranged many of the photographs. James M. Houck, Assistant Head of the Engineering Department, Alcoa Research Laboratories, supervised the drafting of charts and drawings. James L. Brandt, Manager of Technical Information, Alcoa Research Laboratories, assisted the authors in checking and expanding the ASM-prepared index and also in adding pertinent recent references.

THESE VOLUMES do not pretend to be encyclopedic. They do represent an attempt to assemble useful, current information, primarily from American sources, to benefit the fabricator and consumer, and to reflect the views of the American aluminum industry as a whole — not solely those of the 96 Alcoa authors. Wherever more than one viewpoint was found to prevail, the authors tried to write the chapters so as to present all significant views.

Pittsburgh
February, 1967

KENT R. VAN HORN
Editor

Contents

Chapter 1

Historical Development of Aluminum Production and Application

J. H. DUNN and L. S. SEWELL, JR.

The historian who would trace the story of aluminum has a comparatively easy task. It is not referred to in the writings of the "ancients", nor in classical records; aluminum is a product of the present age. — JUNIUS D. EDWARDS (1930)

IN 1886, in a woodshed at Oberlin, Ohio, and in a tannery at Gentilly, France, two young men almost simultaneously unlocked the door to low-cost production of aluminum from its oxide. Charles Martin Hall, in February 1886, and Paul Louis Toussaint Heroult, in April 1886, determined that molten cryolite was an effective solvent for the electrolysis of alumina. The age of light metals was born.

From the first moment that aluminum was isolated and its properties determined, there was no doubt in the minds of the early scientists that it was a material of significant potential value. The advantageous characteristics of aluminum are partly inherent in the material, and are partly the result of extensive research and development work in industry laboratories. One of its chief advantages is lightness; others include resistance to corrosion, nontoxicity, workability (it can be fabricated by more different methods than any other metal), high strength-weight ratio in alloys, attractive appearance, susceptibility to an almost infinite range of finishes, high electrical conductivity, high

J. H. Dunn is manager, Alcoa Process Development Laboratories, Alcoa Technical Center, Pittsburgh. L. S. Sewell, Jr., is manager, special services, Public Relations Dept., Aluminum Company of America, Pittsburgh.

conductivity for heat, efficient reflection of light and heat, nonmagnetism, and availability in a wide range of basic forms.

In addition to having favorable properties, aluminum has experienced a remarkably stable price history from the time it was first made available at a price to make volume use possible. In 1854, aluminum was almost literally worth its weight in gold, selling at $17 an ounce. Today aluminum is sold in primary ingot form at less than 25¢ per pound.

Whether the selected starting point is the mid-1800's — its first availability as a metal, in tiny globules — or the late 1800's — when it first became available in ingot quantity — the history of aluminum is relatively brief. It reflects a growth paralleled by few (if any) major materials used by man. Aluminum today is second in production among metals, behind only iron and steel.

Early History of Aluminum (1)

The Latin name "alumen" was first employed by Pliny. The chemical "alum" had been used for centuries, but it was not until 1722 that Friedrich Hoffman concluded from experiments that the base of alum was a true and distinct "earth". Before the end of that century, the name of the earth had been Anglicized to "alumina".

In 1807, Sir Humphrey Davy became convinced that alumina had a metallic base. He attempted to reduce it by heating it with potash and an "electrolyzing" mixture. Although his efforts were unsuccessful, he named the material he could not secure "alumium". In his later writings, Davy changed the name to "aluminum", to correspond with the name of the oxide, alumina.

The spelling history of aluminum is a complicated one. The spelling and pronunciation "aluminium" came into use in Europe in the early 1800's. Subsequently, both "aluminum" and "aluminium" were employed. In 1925, the American Chemical Society settled the problem for the United States, by designating the official spelling as "aluminum". The accepted spelling in most other countries today is "aluminium".

Davy's unsuccessful efforts to isolate aluminum were of definite value, since they defined an approach to separating the metal from the oxide. The next major milestone was 1825, when Danish scientist H. C. Oersted announced to the Royal Danish Academy of Sciences that he had obtained the "metal of clay".*

*As translated and published in Reference 1, page 2.

He had done so by heating potassium amalgam with aluminum chloride, and distilling the mercury from the resultant aluminum amalgam, obtaining a small lump of metal with the color and luster of tin.

Two years later, Frederick Wöhler repeated Oersted's experiments in his Berlin laboratory. When Wöhler did not secure aluminum in a direct repetition of Oersted's experiments, he substituted metallic potassium for potassium amalgam and obtained aluminum as a gray powder.

By 1845, Wöhler succeeded in producing aluminum in slightly larger amounts: He reported some particles as large as "big pinheads"! Because of the oxide film on the particles, he was unable to make them coalesce. He hammered out two metallic globules, with a combined weight of 32 mg, and proceeded to measure specific gravity, ductility, and air stability of the metal. He also demonstrated that it melted before a blowpipe flame, and he showed the chemical relationship of aluminum to other metals and compounds. These pivotal experiments by Wöhler provided the first awareness of the remarkable lightness of aluminum.

In 1854, H. Sainte-Claire Deville announced an improvement in Wöhler's process, in a presentation before the French Academy of Sciences. Sainte-Claire Deville had substituted sodium for potassium, and developed a process wherein the globules of aluminum would coalesce. By this method, he was able to obtain "mammoth" pieces of aluminum, the size of marbles — perhaps one thousand times greater than the largest previously available pieces of the metal.

These discoveries by Sainte-Claire Deville marked the beginning of the chemical (as opposed to electrochemical) aluminum industry. They triggered great experimental activity.

Sainte-Claire Deville felt that aluminum should be available in bar and ingot form, and started work toward this goal. He received a grant from the French Academy for research on the production of aluminum. Intrigued by the potential of aluminum as a material for fabricating helmets and armor, Napoleon III financed Sainte-Claire Deville to continue his experiments on a larger scale. The work was carried on at the Javel Chemical Works; the process appeared practical but expensive.

In 1855, bars of aluminum produced at Javel were displayed at the Paris Exposition. This first public introduction of the light metal was one of the sensations of this most sensational fair.

Sainte-Claire Deville obtained financial backers and began manufacturing aluminum the following year. The process was improved enough that the price was reduced from almost $90 a pound (equivalent) at Javel to $27 a pound two years later in a plant at Nanterre. Then began the use of fluorspar and cryolite as fluxes. With these and other technical improvements, the price was down to an equivalent of $17 by 1859.*

Because sodium was a key element in the process — and vastly more expensive than the aluminum ores — Sainte-Claire Deville began as early as 1854 to experiment with processes for extracting sodium. He was seeking to reduce its cost, since nearly 3 lb was required for each pound of aluminum produced.

Ironically, the solution to the lower-cost production of sodium was found in the 1880's, on the eve of the discovery of electrolytic smelting processes that were to eliminate the sodium process from commercial consideration. H. Y. Castner of New York developed a radically improved method of producing sodium, reducing the cost from about $1 a pound to about 25¢. The Aluminium Company, Limited, started production at Oldbury, near Birmingham, England, in 1888, using Castner's sodium process and Sainte-Claire Deville's reduction method. Production reached 500 lb per day in 1889.

Castner invented yet another, still cheaper process of producing sodium (by electrolysis of sodium hydroxide). But by 1891, competition from the new electrolytic processes for aluminum had overwhelmed the Aluminium Company operation. They ceased production after a total three-year output of 250,000 lb.

There were scores of other projects involved in the early, intense investigation of aluminum and methods to extract the metal from ores. The electrolytic smelting technique by no means came as an instantaneous flash of light in the late 1800's: As early as 1854, both Sainte-Claire Deville and Robert Wilhelm Bunsen (of burner fame) coincidentally explored electrolytic production methods for aluminum. At that time, batteries were the only source of current, and the cost was prohibitive. The later development of dynamo sources of electrical energy again turned the eyes of researchers to this approach.

The first American aluminum production was by Cowles Electric Smelting and Aluminum Company, in Cleveland. In

*Sainte-Claire Deville's book, "De l'Aluminium, ses Proprietes, sa Fabrication et ses Applications", was the first important book published on aluminum (1859).

1885, Eugene H. and Alfred H. Cowles patented a process of producing aluminum alloys by electrothermal reduction of a mixture of alumina, carbon, and a heavy metal, such as copper. Alloys containing up to 40% aluminum were made, but the average aluminum content of their product was much lower. In 1886, Cowles was successfully using this process in a plant at Lockport, New York. Their principal product was aluminum bronze, a copper-aluminum alloy containing 10 to 20% Al.

The Hall Discovery (2)

The epochal discovery by Charles Martin Hall is in the full tradition of Edison, Steinmetz, and the legion of other young scientific geniuses who led the United States and the world into the twentieth century and the modern industrial age. Driven only by his imagination and determination, working in literally a woodshed laboratory with makeshift equipment, Hall found at 22 a secret that for decades had eluded top scientists.

Hall was born to invent something. It happened to be aluminum that captured his attention. As a youth, he had a certain fame in his neighborhood, based on the sounds, smells, and occasionally even sights (a puff of smoke) from his experiments in a cupola atop his parents' Oberlin, Ohio, home. After bedtime, instead of swashbuckling tales, he read and reread one of his preacher father's college chemistry texts, from which he first became intrigued by the scientific challenge and economic potential of improving on Wöhler's process.*

After graduating from Oberlin in 1885, Hall continued full time his prior part-time experiments with alumina reduction. Hall correctly analyzed the initial problem: Alumina was readily available at low cost and in high-purity form. Its high melting point, 2050 C (3722 F), deterred its electrolysis in the fused condition. Hall believed that he should seek a fused salt that would dissolve alumina in substantial quantities, assuming that he could then electrolyze the oxide in solution. A requirement

*In his 1911 Perkin Medal acceptance speech, Hall reported this, deglamorizing the legend that Oberlin chemistry professor, F. F. Jewett, had first turned Hall's attention to aluminum with a statement to his class that fame and fortune awaited the discoverer of an economical method of reducing aluminum. While Professor Jewett undoubtedly made such a statement, its effect on Hall was to reinforce a conclusion he had already made during his bootleg, afterhours reading of the chemistry text during his early teens.

was that the salt have higher stability than alumina, so that the solvent would not decompose before or during the reduction.

The discovery unfolded in a two-week period in February 1886. It began when Hall concluded his long and painstaking trial-and-error search by determining that molten cryolite would

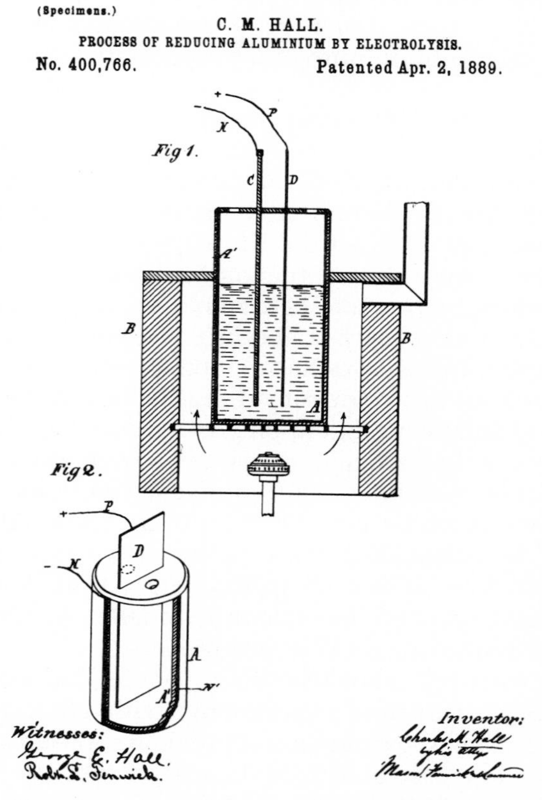

Fig. 1. Drawing of aluminum reduction cell that accompanied the specifications for Charles Martin Hall's patent

dissolve alumina. Six days later he had built a crude clay cell. He passed a direct current of electricity through the molten bath of dissolved alumina. The result was failure: No aluminum was secured. Hall reasoned that the problem lay with the crucible, not with the contents, and began a round-the-clock project to build a carbon cell. On February 23, 1886, 13 days after he had isolated cryolite as the necessary solvent, Hall produced the first shining buttons of aluminum by his revolutionary new process.

Hall's fused electrolyte met in every respect the needs defined when he set his research goal. Cryolite offered additional advantages: a reasonably low melting point, a low operating voltage (approximately 6 volts), and specific gravity sufficiently low for the reduced aluminum to sink to the cell bottom through the electrolyte and be protected by it (Fig. 1).

The Raw Material

Aluminum is the most abundant of all metallic elements. Of the solid portion of the earth's crust to a depth of ten miles, an estimated 8.05% is aluminum. Only oxygen (46.68%) and silicon (27.60%) are more abundant. Next to aluminum is iron (5.03%), followed by calcium (3.63%), sodium (2.72%), potassium (2.56%), and magnesium (2.07%).

Aluminum is an important constituent of virtually all common rocks. It is especially abundant in clay, shale, slate, schist, granite, syenite, and anorthosite. In a content ranging from 15 to 40%, alumina (Al_2O_3) is present in feldspars, micas, and clay, the most abundant minerals with a high alumina content.

The pre-eminent aluminum ore was discovered in 1821 by the French chemist P. Berthier, who analyzed specimens found near Les Baux, in southern France. The name "bauxite" was later applied to the material, from the name of the area in which it was discovered.

Bauxite cannot be precisely defined; it was long used widely in a general sense to identify the various kinds of aluminum ores found in the various parts of the world. Perhaps the best definition is that bauxite is an aluminum ore of a varying degree of impurity, in which the aluminum is present largely as hydrated oxide, the single major constituent.

The bauxites of various areas have similar composition and impurities. The physical appearance of bauxite, however, varies greatly, as does its chemical composition: It may be dense and hard, or it may be soft and earthy. The color of bauxite is related primarily to iron oxide content. If low in iron, bauxite is white, gray, or cream; with moderate iron content, it is pink, yellow, light brown, or light red; if high in iron, it is dark red or brown.

The mining of bauxite varies greatly in technique because of the great variety of types of deposits throughout the world. Most bauxite is mined in open pits after the overburden is stripped, as much as 50 ft or more of overburden being removed at some sites. Large shovels or drags are commonly used to remove ore. The ore from a given field is transported to a central collecting point for processing.

In ore-field processing of bauxite, crushing, washing, drying, pulverizing, and calcining may be involved. The nature of the ore itself, and the subsequent processes and their location, determine which, if any, of these are involved at a given site. Bauxite is sometimes refined to alumina at the ore field, and it is sometimes transported to a refining plant adjacent to a single smelter or centrally located to serve several smelters.

There is a wide range of alkaline, acid, and electrothermal methods of refining bauxite, clay, or other ores to obtain alumina. The method employed commercially today by the aluminum industry in the United States is the "original" Bayer process — and the modified combination process.

In the Bayer process, patented in Germany in 1888 by Karl Josef Bayer, bauxite is digested under pressure with hot sodium hydroxide solution, forming dissolved sodium aluminate. After filtering (the residue is discarded as "red mud"), the solution is cooled and agitated with a seed charge of alumina hydrate. Dissolved hydrate crystallizes out, is filtered and washed, and heated in kilns to drive off the combined water, converting it to alumina.

The major challenge of the Bayer process is that (as a rule of thumb) each pound of silica in the bauxite combines with about 1 lb of alumina and 1 lb of soda to form a "desilication" product. The alumina and soda thus combined are lost in the red mud waste. The Alcoa-developed combination process (3) employs a lime-soda-sinter cycle to enable ores with higher silica content to be refined economically. In this operation, red mud is treated to reclaim alumina and soda as sodium aluminate, which is pumped back into the Bayer process stream. This process is essential to the economical use of low-grade (high-silica) bauxites.

Smelting

Three approaches to the production of aluminum metal from ores or from its oxide have been the subject of intensive research. The first of these is the sodiothermic technique, characterized by the work of Sainte-Claire Deville. The second is the electrolytic process, reflected in the discoveries of Hall and Heroult. The third approach is carbothermic smelting.

Fig. 2. Pittsburgh Reduction Company's Smallman Street, Pittsburgh, plant. (Top) Reproduction of early engraving showing the potroom in 1888. (Bottom) One of the smelting pots in the plant.

Sodiothermic methods have been commercially abandoned, because of the greater economies of the electrolytic process. Carbothermic techniques, on the other hand, have continued to be a subject of intense interest to research scientists both within and outside the aluminum industry. Their great attraction is the possibility of bypassing the conventional alumina refining cycle and of starting with ores less rich in aluminum than bauxite. These processes reduce the aluminum first to high-iron-silicon alloys, and then decrease the impurities in the second stage. The search for an economical and satisfactory carbothermic smelting technique has literally been unceasing. Hall himself began investigating this technique virtually the first moment his electrolytic process was in successful operation. Despite the long years, intensive effort, and considerable investment represented in this effort, carbothermic smelting is not yet commercially useful. In 1965, every pound of aluminum produced commercially in the world was produced by the Hall-Heroult electrolytic method (4).

Although unchanged in principle, the Hall process of today differs greatly in detail from the original process (Fig. 2). Sizes of pots, current densities, pot linings, anode materials, and many other aspects of the smelting process have been subject to unending investigation, refinement, and improvement.

In a modern smelter, alumina is dissolved in smelting pots filled with molten cryolite. High-amperage low-voltage direct current is passed through the bath. Metallic aluminum is deposited at the bottom of the pot (which serves as a cathode), while the freed oxygen combines with the carbon anode and is released as carbon dioxide.

The smelting process is continuous. Periodically, molten aluminum is siphoned from the cell. The metal is either cast into ingot, charged into holding furnaces for pre-casting alloying, or transported to users in molten form. As the alumina in the bath is consumed by reduction, additional quantities are added. As necessary, aluminum fluoride is added to restore the chemical composition of the bath, since some aluminum fluoride is lost by combining with soda in the alumina and by hydrolysis from moisture in the air. (An "acid bath" condition, which provides optimum reduction efficiency, is attained by adding an excess of aluminum fluoride.) Heat generated by the electric current maintains the cryolite bath in a molten condition, so new alumina charges are dissolved as introduced.

Smelting pots are deep, rectangular steel shells lined with carbon, through which the electric current flows. When the smelting process is taking place, the layer of metallic aluminum deposited on the bottom of the pot serves as cathode. Current is introduced to the pot through anodes — a set of carbon blocks suspended in the pot. Some smelting operations employ the Soderberg anode, a self-baking continuous carbon anode formed from a controlled supply of paste.

Long rows of smelting pots, electrically connected in series, are known as "potlines".

Approximately 0.5 lb of carbon is consumed for every pound of aluminum produced, and manufacture of carbon anodes is an important auxiliary activity at most smelters.

Power is one of the most costly "ingredients" of aluminum metal. (Transportation is another.) Over the last three or four decades, the amount of electrical energy necessary to produce a pound of aluminum has been driven down constantly. In 1930, more than 12 kwhr of power was required to produce a pound of aluminum, but now less than 8 kwhr is required.

The Early Aluminum Industry in America (5)

At the time of Hall's discovery in 1886, aluminum was available to anyone who could use it at $8 a pound. Its properties of light weight, reasonable strength, and stability had been known for some years. But young Hall's process for making low-cost aluminum was new, commercially untried, and a seemingly risky investment.

Hall first took his process to the Cowles Company, in July 1887. He worked there for a year, leaving because he received no real encouragement in perfecting his process.

He brought his great discovery to Pittsburgh in July 1888. Here Hall found a young metallurgist who knew something of aluminum and understood the problems that would confront a pioneering project to develop his process. This man, Alfred E. Hunt, and a group of young Pittsburghers financed Hall. With the forming of the Pittsburgh Reduction Company on September 18, 1888, the potential of Hall's development became a reality.

The first works of the Pittsburgh Reduction Company was two rooms in a building on Smallman Street. Operations started on Thanksgiving eve, November 28, 1888. First metal was tapped the following day.

Fig. 3. Reproduction of an early drawing, showing powerhouse and upper and lower works (at left) of the Pittsburgh Reduction Company facility at Niagara Falls

A daily production of 20 to 50 lb of aluminum, to sell at a profit of several dollars a pound, looked very promising to the new company. Although operation was on a small scale, the cost of production was less than half that of the best competitive process. While the Hall-process metal at $5 a pound could undersell all other aluminum, there was a very limited market at that figure, so the price was reduced to $4, and again to $2 in half-ton lots, to increase use and to stimulate demand.

By the middle of 1890, it became necessary to enlarge the original works. The added equipment was in operation by September, giving the company a daily production of about 475 lb. This plant was used until March 1891, when its operations were discontinued and production began in a new plant on the Allegheny River, at New Kensington, 20 miles northeast of Pittsburgh. The New Kensington Works produced 1000 lb of aluminum per day in 1893 and 2000 lb per day by 1894.

When the Niagara Falls power development was inaugurated, the aluminum industry was its first customer. On June 28, 1893, the first power contract was made with the Niagara Falls Power Company. A new electrolytic smelter was designed, constructed, and put into operation at Niagara Falls on August 26, 1895. The following year, on November 21, a second plant started making

Transit is the first product known to have been fabricated from aluminum in this country (1876); along with opera glasses (1879), it predates Hall's discovery. Items made between 1888 and 1900 include cigar case (1892), license tag for hired carriages (1898), medal (1889), combs, and matchbox.

Fig. 4. Early uses of aluminum in the United States

aluminum at that location (Fig. 3). In succeeding years, other additions were made to the Niagara Falls Works, and the production of aluminum greatly expanded.

On January 1, 1907, the Pittsburgh Reduction Company changed its name to Aluminum Company of America.

Early Markets for Aluminum

The honor of being the first "user" of aluminum belongs to the Infant Prince Imperial of France, who received in 1855 a baby rattle formed from aluminum made by Sainte-Claire Deville. The first assembly of fabricated aluminum in the United States

Fig. 5. Reproduction of etching from 1884 issue of Leslie's Weekly, showing placing of aluminum cap atop the Washington Monument. Sketch was made on the scene; ceremony took place during a severe wind storm.

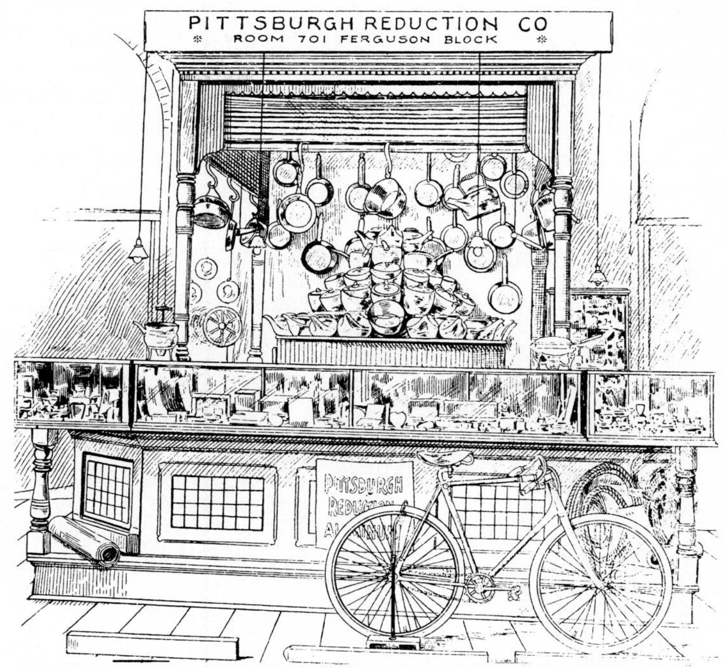

Fig. 6. Sketch of Pittsburgh Reduction Company's exhibit at the 1894 Pittsburgh Exposition. All major consumer products made from aluminum at that time were shown.

that can be documented was in 1876: an engineer's transit, composed primarily of aluminum castings and aluminum tube (Fig. 4). It was exhibited at the Philadelphia Centennial Exposition that year. The first "architectural" application of aluminum also predates the Hall process: On December 6, 1884, a 100-ounce cast aluminum pyramid was mounted on the tip of the Washington Monument (Fig. 5), after a previous showing in Tiffany's Fifth Avenue window. (This installation was inspected during its 50 and 80-year anniversaries, and both times was found to be in excellent condition.)

There is no mystery to the slow growth of aluminum uses in the early years: The cost was too high. In the first five years of production, the young Pittsburgh Reduction Company drove the price down again and again. On October 16, 1889, they offered aluminum for $2 a pound in 1000-lb lots, and $3 a pound in smaller quantities. In 1891, the price was $1.50. By 1893, it was

75¢. Even though aluminum cost but a fraction of its initial price, and far less than the selling price before electrolytic production was undertaken, it was still too expensive for tonnage uses of the metal. After aluminum had been available in quantity for five years, its uses were essentially confined to novelties, surgical instruments, and steel deoxidizing. During the early days, many companies tried to gain promotional value

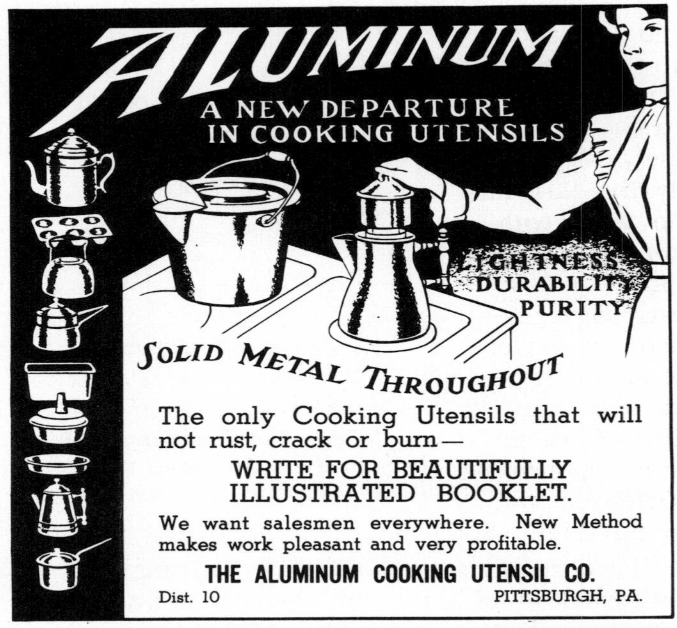

Fig. 7. Advertisement for aluminum utensils, which appeared in the March 1902 Ladies' Home Journal

merely from the novelty of the use of aluminum, manufacturing a host of trinkets such as coins, combs, collar buttons, and tea balls (Fig. 6).

Cast cooking utensils, introduced in the 1890's, became aluminum's first major application (Fig. 7).

Although slow, growth during the first 15 years of aluminum production in the United States was steady. In 1903, 6.5 million pounds was consumed — 1.8 million in the form of ingot (principally for castings), 2.2 million pounds as sheet, and 2.4 million as wire.

In the decade following 1900, the uses of aluminum included

utensils, military equipment (tent pins, canteens), marine and aeronautical components, surgical and sickroom equipment, engineering and scientific instruments, wire products (brushes, dog muzzles, bird cages), bottle caps, powder and paint, lithographic printing, and metallurgical application as a reducing or deoxidizing agent.

During the industry's first two decades, electrical conductors represented the largest-growth application of aluminum. The initial installation of aluminum as a conductor was as bus at Pittsburgh Reduction's own Niagara Falls Works, in 1895. The original sale for electrical transmission was for telephone wire erected in the Chicago stockyards in 1897. The first electrical power transmission lines of aluminum were sold in 1899. Following this sale, the interest in aluminum grew rapidly and intensely. By 1901, Pittsburgh Reduction had hired cable supervisors to work with the many utilities beginning to install conductors of aluminum.

Aluminum was tried on land, on sea, and in the air during these early days. As the cost of the metal dropped, bicycle manufacturers explored its advantages and installed a broad range of aluminum components. Early automobile manufacturers made wide usage of the light metal. The Wright brothers' 1903 Kitty Hawk flight was powered by an engine largely of aluminum supplied by Pittsburgh Reduction Company. The yacht "Defender", built in 1895 for the International Cup Races, featured aluminum alloy plates and deck angles, as well as cast fittings; it followed by one year construction of an aluminum-hulled torpedo boat for the French Navy (Fig. 8). These early uses were prophetic of major future applications.

Aluminum's entry into the packaging field came in 1898, when the first jar covers of aluminum were made. This started the aluminum closure industry, a major and important market for aluminum today. Aluminum foil was not produced in this country until 1913, a quarter century after the Hall process was placed in operation. Its initial use hardly presaged its importance today, since it was first employed as identifying leg bands for racing pigeons!

Just prior to the first World War, major annual consumption of aluminum included the automobile industry (15,500 tons), utensil manufacturing (12,000 tons), and steel deoxidizing (5000 tons) — accounting for about two thirds of total output. Aluminum conductors were a large part of the remainder.

Fig. 8. Reproduction of old lithograph showing an aluminum-hulled steam-turbine torpedo boat designed in 1894 for the French Navy by Sir Alfred Yarrow

The year 1914 marked the beginning of World War I and a period of dynamic growth for the aluminum industry. Consumption had expanded notably since the money panic of 1907, but military uses for aluminum were about to increase demand sharply, and require the building of new facilities that would more than double production over the ensuing five years.

During World War I, approximately 90% of all aluminum output was consumed by the military. Total United States military requirements for aluminum were 65,800 tons in 1918 and 76,200 tons in 1919, including export to the Allies. Three major military uses were production of ammonal (high explosive made of aluminum powder and ammonium nitrate), aircraft engines, and motor transport. The famous Liberty engine, developed during the war, required 300 lb of rough-finished castings. There was wide use of aluminum for mess, personnel and horse equipment, and ammunition cases.

The Industry in the 1920's and 1930's

In the era following the first World War, the use of aluminum expanded greatly. In this period, aluminum was at times in short supply, as more and more manufacturers and users recognized its versatility and applied it to their products. Among many milestones that might be cited were these outstanding technological influences: the formal organization of research and development programs; the development of heat treatable, high-strength alloys; "alclad" products; the extrusion process; and anodic coatings.

Aluminum Company of America was still the only domestic producer of aluminum, as it was to be until the second World War. As a result, this growth period necessarily must be closely associated with the history of one company.

Although the aluminum industry was actually founded on research — Charles M. Hall's invention — and although Hall and others conducted an extensive research effort, a formal research organization was not formed by Alcoa until 1918. By 1930, this group had expanded to include more than 150 people and was moved into new headquarters at a different location in New Kensington, Pa. It constituted the finest research facility of any metal manufacturer at that time and was among the first of the campus-type sites. This activity continued to keep pace with the expanding aluminum business, and numerous acknowledgments have cited its basic and applied research programs as principal motivating forces in the tremendous growth of the industry.

Closely coupled with the use of research were kindred programs broadly classified as "development". In these areas, specialized groups of engineers were established to promote the use of aluminum in specific fields by providing assistance in design and processing. The industry early learned that it was not sufficient simply to make aluminum available. It had to survey uses and markets, provide design and fabrication assistance, and anticipate problems so as to have answers ready.

During World War I, attention was focused on an alloy known as duralumin, which had been invented by a German, Alfred Wilm. This discovery opened an entirely new field — the use of aluminum for high-strength applications — for this heat treatable alloy provided properties very similar to those of structural steel. Soon Alcoa was producing its version of this alloy, originally known as 17S, and from then on large numbers of heat treatable alloys of various types were developed for both wrought and cast products. The availability of aluminum alloys "as strong as steel" was a real milestone.

Some of the new heat treatable alloys were not as resistant to corrosion in some environments as was desirable. As a result, the principle of anodic protection was applied for sheet products by cladding a thin layer of pure aluminum to each side of a strong alloy core. During corrosive attack, the pure aluminum cladding sacrificially protects the strong alloy core, including sheared edges where the strong alloy is exposed. This widely used class of product is called "alclad".

The extrusion process (Volume III, Chapter 3), although not limited to aluminum, is particularly adaptable to it, permitting displacement of metal into almost any conceivable cross section. The development of the modern extrusion technique during the 1920's was of great significance to the growth of aluminum. It provided manufacturing economies and design efficiency not possible in steel, for example, although limited amounts of steel are extruded today.

The anodic process for artificially thickening the natural oxide film on aluminum is another significant process born of research. It produces a hard, wear-resistant finish that improves resistance to corrosion. In addition, color may be introduced or even developed from the alloy itself during the anodizing process. In the same way that extruding provides unique fabricating advantages for aluminum, anodizing permits finishing characteristics not available to other metals.

Such technological advances, coupled with the inherent properties of aluminum, helped accelerate its acceptance.

Also, during the 1920's and 1930's — due largely to influences similar to those previously related — aluminum started to compete in broad new fields. In railroad transportation, aluminum began to be used for passenger cars, coal cars, tank cars, and others. On shipboard, aluminum came into demand for deck houses, life boats, bulkheads, and furniture. Structural applications for bridges, flood-control bulkheads, and dragline booms appeared. Truck bodies, freight trailers, dump bodies, and tank trailers of aluminum became popular.

In a move typical of the industry's aggressive developmental efforts, a large rolling mill to produce structural shapes of aluminum was built at Massena, N.Y., without a single order on the books. It was built in anticipation of the role aluminum could play in this field, so that proper material would be available in the sections and lengths required, at the lowest possible cost.

Architectural applications of aluminum included spandrels, window frames, store fronts, roofing, shingles, and rain-carrying equipment. For some of these building products, economics did not then favor aluminum; their production was discontinued, to be re-established later under more propitious conditions.

The modern airplane was born in this period, graduating from the earlier fabric-and-wood designs to virtually all-metal structures, with few people suspecting the tremendous impact the next war would have on both the aluminum and aircraft industries.

The use of aluminum in passenger cars did not share this growth. Into the early 1920's, automotive uses had represented the single largest application of aluminum. Aluminum sheets formed more easily than steel; aluminum castings were used for crankcases; and many other uses were in vogue. But the development of deep-drawing steels that could be welded together in smooth and involved surfaces at a lower cost relegated aluminum to the background. During the late twenties and thirties, some use for aluminum was found in radiator shells and cylinder heads, but these, too, passed from use. Aluminum pistons in some models were about all that remained until the surge that brought aluminum into this picture again after World War II.*

Aluminium Ltd. Another significant event in the 1920's concerned the spin-off of most of the foreign properties and operations of Aluminum Company of America and their transfer to the newly formed Aluminium Ltd., a Canadian corporation; stockholders of Alcoa were issued stock in the new company. A number of reasons occasioned this change. It was believed that the foreign properties were not being given sufficient attention and were not being adequately developed, and that the job could be done more effectively by a foreign corporation devoting its major attention to this task. Nationalistic spirit, both in the United States and abroad, and internal conditions in Alcoa made this a favorable time to create a foreign company. Aluminium Ltd. expanded rapidly and became an important factor in world markets, and today it is a dominant competitive force in the world industry.

The Anti-Trust Case. A recital of significant events during the 1930's would not be complete without mention of the anti-trust case brought against Alcoa by the United States Government. This suit was of considerable influence on subsequent developments in the domestic aluminum industry.

*An interesting sidelight during this period related to some aluminum cars that Alcoa sponsored during the 1920's. A prominent English automotive engineer was hired to design an aluminum automobile. Several such cars were built, utilizing aluminum for every conceivable application. They performed splendidly, but were too expensive, and only one all-aluminum car remains today, as a museum piece.

In April 1937, the Department of Justice filed a sweeping bill of complaint against Alcoa, asking that the company be dissolved. The general charges were monopolization of the production of aluminum ingot and of raw materials from which it was made and of products into which it was fabricated, as well as conspiracy with foreign producers. The trial lasted 26 months, including brief recesses, making it the longest in the history of Anglo-Saxon jurisprudence up to that time. In 1941, Judge Caffey found Alcoa innocent of all the charges of monopolization and conspiracy that the Department of Justice had made (6).

The Department of Justice appealed the case to the Supreme Court. Because a quorum of justices qualified to hear the appeal was lacking, the case was certified to the Second Circuit Court of Appeals by special enabling legislation. The decision of this court (7) upheld Judge Caffey on all counts except as to the alleged monopolization of the aluminum ingot market, and an alleged exercise of such monopoly power in effecting a "squeeze" or narrow spread between the price of ingot and the price of certain gages and sizes of sheet. The court found monopolization of the ingot market to have existed as of August 14, 1940 (the date the testimony closed), by virtue of the power which Alcoa had to exclude others, notwithstanding that it did not knowingly or intentionally exclude any other producer or potential producer. However, at the time of the decision, new aluminum ingot plants had been built as part of the war effort, and the court recognized that the post-war situation might be entirely different. Final judgment was withheld until disposal of the wartime plants, and the case was returned to the District Court. Judge John C. Knox filed an opinion on June 2, 1950 (8), and in 1951, 14 years from the start of litigation, entered a decree under which the structure of Alcoa was left intact, but the case was kept open for an additional period of five years to maintain surveillance over competitive conditions. In June 1957, a motion to continue this surveillance was denied by Judge Cashin (9).

The 1951 decree, while not disturbing Alcoa's structure, did require certain individuals who held large blocks of stock in both Alcoa and Aluminium Ltd. to dispose of one or the other, this to be accomplished within the next ten years, so it was not until January 1961 that the matter was finally and completely laid to rest, almost 24 years from the initiation of the suit.

The Aluminum Association began in the 1930's. Formed in 1933 as the "Association of Manufacturers in the Aluminum

Industry", the group of 13 companies was organized as part of the depression-born National Recovery Administration program. In 1935, the present name was adopted and the purpose of the Association was defined as being "to promote the general welfare of the aluminum industry, of the members of it, and all others affected by it, and to increase the usefulness of the industry to the general public". Among its most important activities have been standardization of aluminum alloys and products, and collection and dissemination of industry statistics.

The first industry standard developed by the Aluminum Association was entitled "Drafting Standards for Aluminum Extruded and Tubular Products", followed by "Nomenclature for Wrought Aluminum Mill Products". Certainly, one of the most important accomplishments was its "Alloy Designation System for Wrought Aluminum and Aluminum Alloys". Today, work of the Association encompasses registration of new alloys as they are introduced to the public, publishing mechanical-property data, statistical compilations, and a wide range of other standards, plus broad industry promotional activities.

The Second World War

As World War II started in Europe in the autumn of 1938, no one could visualize fully the impact this was to have on the American aluminum industry. In April 1939, Congress authorized the Army to acquire 6000 airplanes in the next two years, and the Navy to procure 3000 planes in the next five years. By 1943, a single month's goal was approximately 9000 planes. Because aluminum alloys constituted a high percentage of the weight of a typical airplane, and because the war was to develop into a struggle largely dominated by aircraft, most wartime production of aluminum had to be utilized for this purpose alone. Although Alcoa was rapidly expanding its own facilities and, in fact, had an inventory of more than a year's supply of metal at the beginning of 1939, the demands were to be far greater than one company could meet.

By 1941, government authorities recognized the probable scope of the war in the air, and approved the first government aluminum program. Two major steps were involved. (*a*) Private industry expanded as rapidly as possible. Alcoa was already under way with a $300,000,000 program, and Reynolds Metals Company entered the business of producing aluminum, assisted by a loan from the Reconstruction Finance Corporation. (*b*) The Defense Plant Corporation let contracts for the construction of aluminum plants, some of which were located to utilize available, but expensive, excess power in large industrial centers. Alcoa had the responsibility of designing, constructing and operating 40 government plants in 25 different locations.

At the peak of the war, 1,250,000 tons of aluminum was available annually, including metal purchased from Canada. Total American production in 1939 had been 163,500 tons. The growth in six years was an amazing sevenfold increase.

A grand total of 304,000 military airplanes was produced in the United States in 5½ years, requiring 1,750,000 tons of aluminum. It was estimated that 85% of the war output went into the aircraft program. In 1943, basic metal supply began to exceed demands. By 1944, cutbacks in output were in effect and some plants were closed.

Disposal of Surplus Capacity. Although the aluminum industry had been largely dominated by a single company until World War II, the United States Government emerged as the largest owner of aluminum producing and fabricating plants at the end of the war. Not all of the government facilities were suitable for peacetime production, but many were economically desirable. The annual capacity of government-owned aluminum producing plants capable of competitive operation was 276,000 tons, compared with Alcoa's 325,000 tons and 81,000 tons for Reynolds.

In addition to disposing of the surplus plants, the government's aim was to increase the number of competitors in the aluminum industry. One roadblock with regard to certain alumina-producing plants was Alcoa's patent on the combination process. In view of the public considerations involved, Alcoa agreed to grant royalty-free licenses to the government to pass on to any competitors.

By mid-August 1946, all aluminum plants owned by the government under the Defense Plant Corporation had been declared surplus. By May 1946, over 40% of the total government capacity — all the most economic plants except one — had been disposed of to competitors of Alcoa, generally on a lease-purchase basis. At the end of 1945, the annual relative capacities for producing aluminum in the United States were: Alcoa, 50.6%; Reynolds, 29.4%; Kaiser Aluminum & Chemical Company, 20%.

The establishment of two new major producers completed the

competitive fabric of the industry. The primary producers not only faced each other, but also the secondary (scrap) smelters, importers of foreign primary and secondary metal, and, above all, the vigilance and energy of producers of all other basic materials, especially steel, copper, and plastics. As aluminum had carved out many markets from uses primarily enjoyed by other materials, its growth spurred vigorous counterattack.

The Aluminum Industry Since 1945

Cessation of World War II released large quantities of aluminum for the domestic market, with the supply of aluminum on an entirely different basis, not only from the standpoint of primary producers, but because of the large amounts of war surplus and scrap. In their war activities, many manufacturers became intimately acquainted for the first time with the properties of aluminum, and had learned to design for it and to fabricate it. Use of aluminum increased greatly.

The Korean Conflict. In the midst of this period of increased use of aluminum, the Korean conflict broke out in 1950. The United States aluminum industry was encouraged by the government to expand its smelting capacity. Although the government did not invest any money in the expansion during the Korean War, it did provide incentives in the way of accelerated depreciation considerations and metal stockpile purchase contracts. During this period, Alcoa expanded its smelting capacity by 205,000 tons, Reynolds by 180,000 tons, and Kaiser by 228,200 tons. Anaconda Aluminum Company entered the field with a 60,000-ton smelter, although production did not begin until 1955. Likewise, Harvey Machine Company (later Harvey Aluminum Company) began production in 1958.

The Government Stockpile. A recent and dominant factor in the economics of aluminum is the government stockpile of strategic materials. Starting in 1945, the government had built up stocks of materials as a safeguard to assure a supply in case of emergency. In the aluminum industry, contracts were made with existing and new suppliers for shipments to the stockpile, encouraging entry of new primary producers through assurance of at least a partial market. As of December 31, 1962, the amount of aluminum in the national stockpile was 1,127,000 short tons, and an additional 843,000 tons was in Defense Production Administration (DPA) inventory. As world conditions changed, this inventory was considered excessive, and reduction is being made through open sales, most of it absorbed by primary producers at current market prices.

Diversification of Power Sources. The cost of producing aluminum has always been closely associated with the availability of large quantities of low-cost power. As a consequence, smelting plants were initially located near sources of cheap hydroelectric power. Other sources of power were sought as the disadvantages of hydro power became evident: susceptibility to weather, interruptible contracts, and a shortage of desirable new sites. Coal-fired steam first was used as a source of power at the Reynolds smelting plant at Listerhill, Ala. This power was supplied under a contract with the TVA, starting in 1941. Natural gas was used

Table 1. Primary Aluminum Installed Capacity in the United States

Company	Year of first primary production(a)	Annual rate in short tons(b)			
		Capacity June 1966	Expansion by June 1968	Capacity June 1968	Total, %
Aluminum Company of America	1888	1,050,000	50,000	1,100,000	34.0
Anaconda Aluminum Co.	1955	100,000	...	100,000	3.1
Consolidated Aluminum Corp.	1963	62,000	44,000	106,000	3.3
Harvey Aluminum, Inc.	1958	88,000	...	88,000	2.7
Intalco Aluminum Corp.	1966	76,000	76,000	152,000	4.7
Kaiser Aluminum and Chemical Corp.	1946	650,000	...	650,000	20.2
Ormet Corp.	1958	184,284	36,850	221,134	6.8
Reynolds Metals Co.	1941	725,000	90,000	815,000	25.2
Total		2,935,284	296,850	3,232,134	100.0

(a) Various sources. (b) As reported to the Aluminum Association.

Table 2. Aluminum Production Statistics

Item	Production, in 1000 short tons; price, in ¢/lb					
	1955–59 average	1960	1961	1962	1963	1964
United States						
Primary production	1682	2014	1904	2118	2313	2553
Price of ingot, average	26.2¢	26.0¢	25.5¢	23.9¢	22.6¢	23.7¢
Secondary recovery(a)	338	329	340	462	506	552
Imports for consumption, crude and semicrude	271	196	255	373	466	453
Exports, crude and semicrude	82	384	238	259	292	349
Consumption, apparent(b)	2191	2016	2320	2705	3019	3216
World production	3855	4985	5210	5555	6095	6730

(a) By reporting companies, aluminum content. (b) Measured by quantity of primary sold or used plus secondary recovery and net imports.

SOURCE: "Bureau of Mines Yearbook", 1964 preprint, p 1

at the Alcoa-built, government-owned facility at Jones Mills, Ark., beginning in 1942; electric power was generated with internal combustion engines fueled by the gas. In 1948, Alcoa began construction of a plant at Point Comfort, Texas, again utilizing natural gas burned in internal-combustion engines for power. After the outbreak of the Korean hostilities, Kaiser and Reynolds also used natural gas in new facilities. Later, a plant was built by Alcoa at Rockdale, Texas, that employs lignite (a low-grade coal) as fuel for steam generation. Kaiser, at Ravenswood, W. Va., and Alcoa, at Warrick, Ind., both built plants using power supplied from bituminous-coal-fired steam electric-generating facilities. Thus, the limitations of hydroelectric power were circumvented, and plants could be located with greater regard to markets and supplies of fuel and raw materials.

Production of Aluminum and Aluminum Products

Production Capacity Summary. Table 1 lists the capacities of various aluminum producers in the United States, including actual capacity and that planned for June 30, 1968. The year of first primary production for each company is indicated.

Salient Aluminum Statistics, 1955 to 1964. Table 2 lists some important data for recent years concerning production of pri-

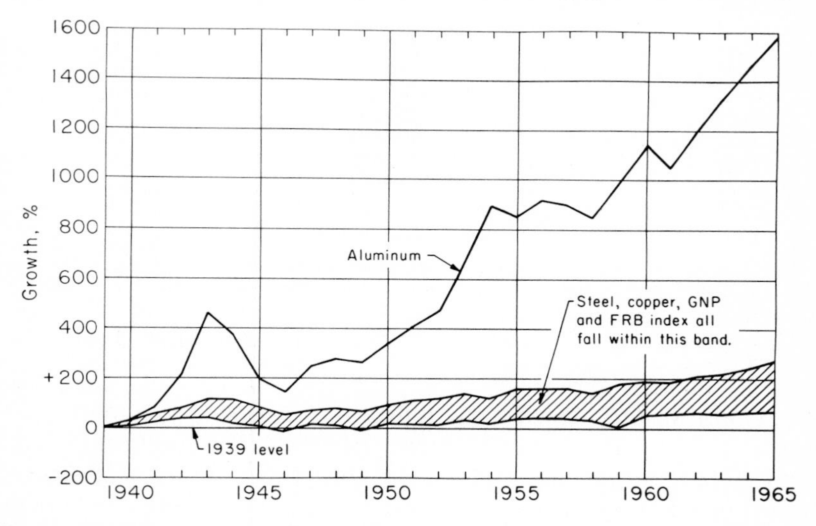

Fig. 9. Growth of aluminum output compared to steel, copper, GNP *(gross national product, in 1958 constant dollars), and* FRB *index (U.S. industrial production). The 1965 figures are preliminary.*

Table 3. Number of Companies in the United States Producing Principal Aluminum Products in Selected Years(a)

Product	World War II	1956	1966
Primary ingot	3	4	8
Secondary ingot	46	74	80
Sheet	8	18	35
Foil	5	11	19
Rolled and continuous cast rod and bar	2	3	12
Bare wire	10	13	46
ACSR and bare cable	(b)	13	20
Wire and cable, insulated or covered	12	32	27
Extruded shapes	9	81	145
Drawn tube	(b)	18	19
Powder and paste	11	10	11
Forgings	48	45	44

(a) Includes companies producing solely for their own use. (b) Not reported.

SOURCE: "Aluminum Factbook", 1963, and "Directory of Aluminum Suppliers", 1966, Business & Defense Services Administration, United States Department of Commerce

Table 4. Average Prices for Primary Aluminum, 1940 to 1965

Year	Price, ¢ per lb	Year	Price, ¢ per lb
1940	18.8	1955	21.9
1941	16.5	1956	24.0
1942	15.0	1957	25.4
1943 to 1947(a)	14.0	1958	24.8
1948	14.7	1959	24.7
1949	16.0	1960(b)	26.0(c)
1950	16.6	1961	25.5
1951	18.0	1962	23.9
1952	18.4	1963	22.6
1953	19.7	1964	23.7
1954	20.2	1965(d)	24.5

(a) Beginning with 1943, prices quoted are for primary pig; previously, virgin ingot. (b) Beginning with 1960, prices quoted are for unalloyed ingot; pig price discontinued. (c) Corrected. (d) Added.

SOURCE: "Metal Statistics 1965", American Metal Market, p 541

mary aluminum, secondary aluminum recovery, imports, exports, prices, and consumption. In 1964, production in the United States was about 38% of the world total. The United States produces far more aluminum than any other country, with the USSR second (based on estimates), followed by Canada and France, in that order.

Growth Compared to Other Metals and Indices. Figure 9 depicts the relative growth of aluminum, copper, and steel, as well as other indices, starting before World War II.

Growth of Mill Product Manufacturers. The spectacular growth in primary aluminum capacity in this country has been

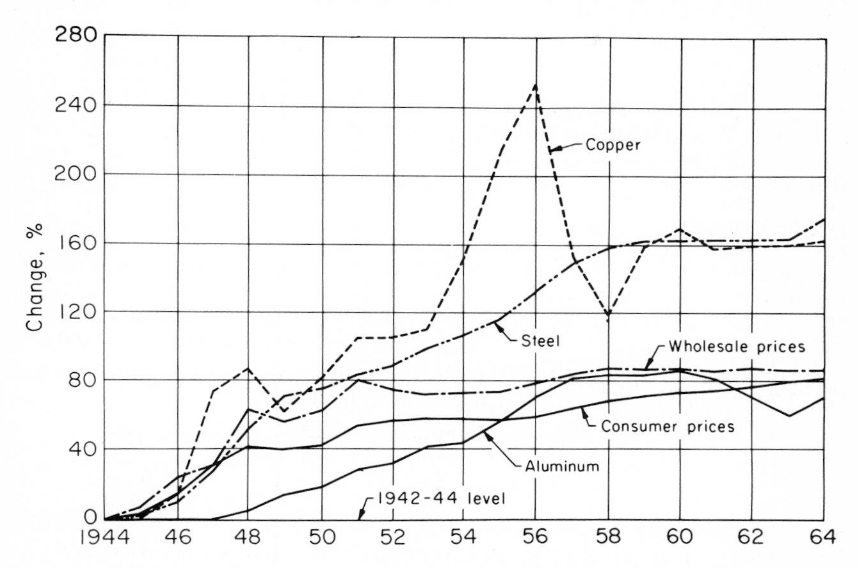

Fig. 10. Changes in prices of aluminum, copper, steel, wholesale commodities, and consumer goods in the United States since 1944. The 1942–1944 price level serves as a base.

Table 5. Price Relationships of Several Metals Related to Specific Gravity

Metal	Price 1965, ¢ per lb	Pounds per cu in.	Comparative price on a volume basis
Aluminum(a)	24.5	0.097	1.00
Copper(b)	35.2	0.323	4.77
Lead(c)	15.0	0.409	2.72
Magnesium(d)	36.0	0.063	0.91
Carbon steel(e)	4.2	0.284	0.50
Stainless steel(f)	28.0	0.288	3.38
Zinc(g)	14.5	0.258	1.57

(a) Aluminum: 99.5% unalloyed ingot; average 1965 price. (b) Copper: electrolytic copper in New York; average 1965 price. (c) Lead: St. Louis; average 1965 price. (d) Magnesium: 99.8% ingot; average 1965 price. (e) Carbon steel: bessemer and open-hearth steel billets at $84 per ton. (f) Stainless steel: 304 reroll ingots; average 1965 price. (g) Zinc: East St. Louis; average 1965 price.

SOURCE: American Metal Market

Table 6. United States Shipments of Aluminum Mill Products and Castings

Product	Shipments, 1000 tons 1955	1960	1965(a)
Sheet and plate	672.3	694.1	1365.9
Foil	99.1	144.5	202.8
Rolled rod and bar, including continuous cast(a)	55.0	46.5	82.5
Wire, bare, conductor and nonconductor	30.8	27.7	42.5
ACSR and aluminum cable, bare	78.5	91.5	215.3
Wire and cable, insulated or covered	19.8	30.2	64.7
Extruded shapes	341.2	425.5	771.5
Drawn tube	33.6	30.2	41.4
Welded tube	12.8	12.9	46.8
Powder and paste	17.9	16.4	29.8
Forgings and impacts	35.2	25.0	47.6
Sand castings	82.7	64.9	137.4
Permanent mold castings	149.1	129.0	165.4
Die castings	177.6	192.8	401.8
Total	1805.6	1931.2	3615.4

(a) Preliminary. (b) A small quantity of structural shapes is included with rolled bar in 1955 and 1960 and with extruded shapes in 1965.

SOURCE: Aluminum Association

accompanied by a great expansion in the number of facilities producing mill products. Such growth is indicated in Table 3.

Price History

In 1920, the price of primary aluminum was 33.3¢ a pound; in mid-1964 it was 24.0¢. From 1920 until 1943, the general trend was downward, reaching a low of 14.0¢ in 1943, holding at that level for several years, increasing to 26.0¢ in 1960.* The price at the end of 1965 was 24.5¢. The year-by-year figures from 1940 to 1965 are shown in Table 4. Comparisons with other materials and indices are shown in Fig. 10. The war years 1942–1944 were selected as the base because processes were controlled.

Price Relationships Based on Specific Gravity. Prices of various materials are often more meaningful when viewed in the light of the specific gravities involved. As a comparison on this

*Some confusion in the listing of prices results from the definitions of pig and ingot. Prior to 1943, prices were quoted as "ingot", whether alloyed or not. Starting in 1943, the price was quoted as "pig", which referred to unalloyed metal. In 1960, the basis again became ingot (99%+ virgin ingot); the designation (and price for) pig was discontinued.

Table 7. Estimated End-Use Distribution Total of Aluminum Industry Shipments by Major Categories, 1962 to 1965

End use	Total shipments — 1962		1963		1964		1965	
	1000 tons	%	1000 tons	%	1000 tons	%	1000 tons	%
Building and construction	676	23.4	773	24.2	841	23.4	933	22.9
Transportation	675	23.4	756	23.6	799	22.4	924	22.7
Consumer durable goods	320	11.1	326	10.4	383	10.7	422	10.3
Electrical	314	10.9	352	11.0	419	11.7	540	13.2
Machinery and equipment	210	7.3	231	7.3	252	7.0	285	7.0
Containers and packaging	193	6.7	246	7.7	287	8.0	328	8.1
Exports	207	7.2	235	7.4	291	8.1	287	7.0
Other	287	10.0	270	8.4	313	8.7	360	8.8
Total	2882	100.0	3189	100.0	3585	100.0	4079	100.0

SOURCE: Aluminum Association

basis, the prices of several metals on a per pound and on a cubic-inch basis are shown in Table 5. Note that these prices are based on ingots and billets. Other forms compare similarly.

Aluminum Products and Uses

Distribution of Aluminum Shipments by Product. The breakdown shown in Table 6 indicates distribution of aluminum mill product shipments exclusive of ingot. The predominance of the production of sheet and plate over the years is clearly evident. In the ten-year period from 1955 to 1965, sheet and plate production increased over 100%, and aluminum cable production almost tripled. Production figures for castings over the same period indicate a substantial growth in the production of sand and permanent mold castings, and an increase of over 100% in die castings.

Distribution of Aluminum Shipments by Major Industrial Markets. A breakdown of the end-use distribution of aluminum shipments by major industrial markets is shown in Table 7. Discussions of the applications of aluminum in these various fields are covered in detail in Chapters 10 to 25 in this volume.

Future Growth. The interplay of a multitude of influences makes the projection of the growth of any material into the future hazardous and conjectural. Some estimates have been

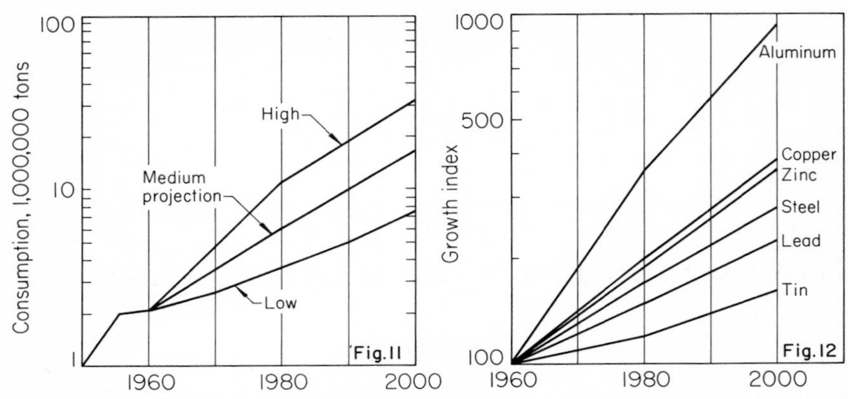

Fig. 11. Predicted consumption of aluminum, including exports (10)
Fig. 12. Predicted growth in consumption of principal metals (10)

made as carefully and soundly as possible within the limits of available data and practicable methods. The most comprehensive recent study of this type is "Resources in America's Future" (10). Figure 11, from this source, gives estimates of the total future end-use consumption of aluminum to the year 2000. The relative predicted growth (consumption) of several principal metals is shown in Fig. 12; data are based on the median predictions for these periods.

References

1 J. D. Edwards, F. C. Frary, and Z. Jeffries, "Aluminum and Its Production", McGraw-Hill, New York, 1930. The entire book provides amplification of this chapter.
2 J. D. Edwards, "The Immortal Woodshed", Dodd, Mead, New York, 1955
3 J. D. Edwards, Combination Process for Alumina, Metals Technology, 12, Technical Publication 1833 (April 1945)
4 P. T. Stroup, Carbothermic Smelting of Aluminum, Transactions of the Metallurgical Society of AIME, **230**, 356 (1964)
5 C. C. Carr, "Alcoa, An American Enterprise", Rinehart, New York, 1952, p 23–134
6 United States vs Aluminum Company of America et al, 44F. Supp 97
7 United States vs Aluminum Company of America et al, 148F. 2d, 416
8 United States vs Aluminum Company of America et al, 91F. Supp 333
9 United States vs Aluminum Company of America et al, 153F. Supp 132
10 H. Landsberg, L. Fischman, and J. Fisher, "Resources in America's Future", Johns Hopkins Press, 1963, p 36, 310

Chapter 2

Commercial Forms of Aluminum Alloys

W. R. BUTLER

MILL PRODUCTS of aluminum vary from foil thinner than tissue paper to plate 6 in. thick, and from wrist-thick stranded electrical power transmission conductor to magnet wire finer than human hair. Available forms are discussed in this chapter.

Ingot

Ingot, from which all other aluminum products are made, is generally supplied in one of seven commercial forms.

Unalloyed Ingot. Unalloyed aluminum ingot is furnished in sizes ranging from small notched bars weighing a pound or less to large ingots weighing a ton or more. Unalloyed ingot may vary from about 98 to 99.999% Al; 99.5% Al is the most common grade. Electrical conductor (EC) ingot and rotor ingot for motors are special grades in which impurities objectionable for these applications are controlled. Other special grades are used for the deoxidizing and aluminizing of steel (see Chapter 25).

Rich Alloy Ingot. Although unalloyed ingot is often used as produced, it is more often necessary to alloy it with other elements such as chromium, copper, iron, magnesium, manganese, nickel, silicon, titanium, and zinc. To accomplish this easily in production, rich alloy ingot, or "hardener", is employed; hardeners contain from less than 1% to as much as 50% of alloying elements.

Casting Alloy Ingot. Large quantities of scrap are consumed in the production of casting alloy ingot. When the impurity

Before his retirement in July 1965, the author was manager, Application Engineering Div., Aluminum Company of America.

limitations on such alloys permit the introduction of large amounts of scrap, the resulting product is referred to as secondary casting alloy ingot. When the composition limits restrict the use of scrap, the product is designated as primary or virgin casting alloy ingot. There are many areas of overlap between primary and secondary.

For melting in large furnaces, casting alloy ingot generally is supplied in 30 or 50-lb interlocking bars. Other popular ingot sizes are 6 and 10 lb. Even smaller notched bars or "sticks" are sometimes required by the small-production die caster who does his melting at the casting machine.

Extrusion ingot is usually furnished in cylindrical form, both solid and hollow. It varies in outside diameter from 3 to 33 in. This product is most often made by the direct chill (DC) casting process (Volume III, Chapter 3) or by some modification thereof. It is sawed to lengths varying from several inches to several feet, conforming to the requirements of the press in which it will be extruded. With certain alloys, extrusion ingots are often soaked or preheated before shipment to the extruder. This treatment, sometimes called homogenizing, permits higher extrusion speeds, improved surface finish on the extrusions, and longer die life. When extrusions of the highest quality are required, as in strong alloy aircraft parts, extrusion billets may be scalped before shipment to remove surface liquation.

Hollow ingots are used to extrude tube and other hollow shapes. These ingots are normally cast to the required dimensions in the direct chill casting machine, but manufacturing limitations often require machining of the inside diameter.

Forging Ingot. Although most small forgings are produced from rolled or extruded stock, cast ingots are often used for large forgings. To prevent irregularities in the cast surface from affecting the quality of the forgings, these ingots are always scalped before shipment. Forging ingot is generally supplied in cylindrical form, 1 to 2 ft in diameter and 1 to 4 ft long.

Sheet and Wire Bar Ingot. Ingot for the production of sheet is available in a wide range of cross-sectional dimensions, and in weights up to about 10,000 lb. The most common sizes are 12 by 36 in. and 12 by 48 in., in any length up to 146 in. Scalping of the rolling surfaces and homogenizing may be required, depending on the alloy. Wire bar ingot for the production of rolled shapes and wire is supplied as square, cylindrical or rectangular direct chill castings, generally 6 or 7 in. square in section. These ingots are almost always scalped.

Hot Metal. Molten metal is sometimes transferred directly in insulated ladles from the smelter to the customer's plant, occasionally at distances up to several hundred miles.

Castings*

In order of commercial importance, the three major forms of aluminum castings are: die, permanent mold, and sand.

Die casting is inherently suited to large-quantity production of both ornamental and structural aluminum parts. If the quantity permits investment in a die, if wall thicknesses can be reduced as much as the casting process permits, and if objectionable undercuts are not present in the design, aluminum castings can usually be produced by this process at a lower cost than by any other method.

The practical minimum wall thickness that can be die cast usually is governed by the necessity of filling the die properly and by the surface finish required. Under the most difficult conditions, a wall $9/64$ to $5/32$ in. thick may be needed to permit metal flow in the die. In a casting less than about 6 by 6 in. over-all and where its form promotes good casting conditions, walls may be as thin as 0.050 to 0.065 in.

The largest aluminum die casting on record measures 49.75 by 51 in. in a projected view and weighs 47.7 lb. This casting was made on a machine having a locking pressure of 4500 tons. Engine block castings weighing almost 70 lb (including 14 lb of inserts), but having less projected area, have been made on smaller machines.

Permanent Mold Castings. In the permanent mold process, cast iron molds and cores are generally used; less frequently, steel and inlays of other metals are employed. Molten aluminum is poured into the mold cavity under a normal gravity head. In special cases, a small amount of pressure is applied to the mold through the application of vacuum, by pumping the molten metal, or by centrifugal force. In the semipermanent mold process, cores of dry sand or other expendable material are employed, overcoming many of the design limitations imposed by metal cores.

Permanent mold castings are metallurgically superior to die or sand castings, having greater soundness, pressure tightness, and higher strength. Greater speed of production and thinner walls

*Detailed information on aluminum castings is given in Volume I, Chapter 8; Volume II, Chapter 5; Volume III, Chapter 2.

($\frac{1}{8}$ to $\frac{3}{16}$ in.) generally result in lower cost per piece than with sand castings. Dimensional tolerance control and surface finish are better than for sand castings, but not as good as obtainable in die castings. The chilling effected by the metal mold results in higher strengths than for similar parts cast in sand. Relatively

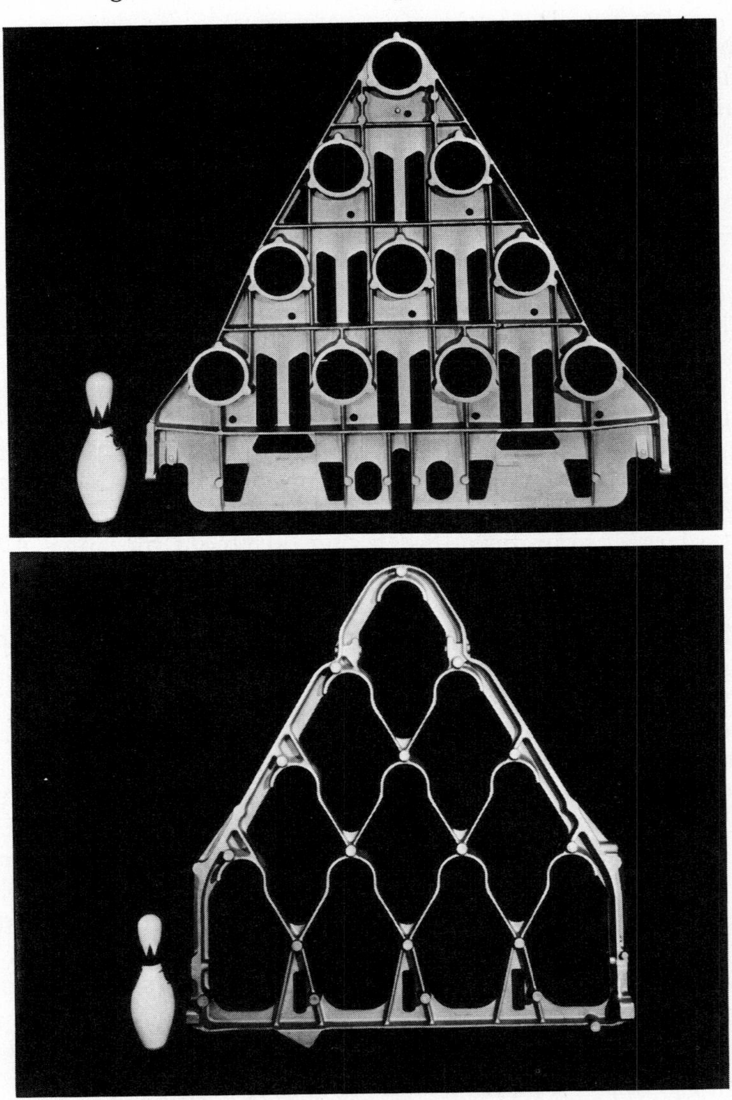

Fig. 1. Large permanent mold castings (6 ft high) are assembled to produce an automatic pinsetter for bowling alleys.

slow, progressive solidification prevents the gas entrapment that often occurs in die castings. Among the largest permanent mold castings ever produced are the bowling pinsetter frames shown in Fig. 1. These parts are more than 6 ft high and weigh about 100 lb per set (one of each).

Sand Castings. The sand casting process is the most versatile method of producing a cast aluminum shape and is characterized by universal adaptability. It is employed to produce small quantities of identical castings, parts requiring intricate coring, and very large castings. Modern high-speed molding equipment and methods produce sand castings relatively cheaply.

Many large floor-molded aluminum sand castings have been produced: A tire mold used for curing earthmover tires is a typical example. The casting is 9 ft in diameter and weighs almost 20,000 lb; the alloy used was 355-T77. Machining fixtures 6 ft wide by 18 ft long but weighing less than this tire mold have also been cast in sand. These fixtures, for machining aircraft wing panels, are ¼ in. thick in some areas. This is considered the minimum for large aluminum sand castings.

Other Cast Forms. Direct chill castings — both solid and hollow, having round, rectangular or odd-shaped sections — are used because of their outstanding mechanical properties after heat treatment and their sound structure. Mechanical properties approach those of wrought products except that the elongation is lower. Cast tool and jig plate and large sizes of cast bus bar are commonly made by this process. When thin walls and close dimensional tolerances are required, and if the quantity does not warrant die casting, shell mold casting, plaster mold casting, or investment casting are often employed. The last two processes are also used where difficult undercuts and intricate coring are required. The centrifugal casting process is used for the production of large aluminum alloy tubes and rings.

Sheet and Plate

Aluminum that is 0.250 in. or more thick is classified as plate; sheet is 0.006 to 0.249 in. thick. Sheet is supplied either flat rolled or in coils. Sheet and plate are also available in circular and odd-shaped blanks that are sheared, blanked, sawed, or routed to size or specified configuration.

Sizes and Tolerances (1). Aluminum alloy sheet and plate are available in very large sizes. For example, sheets for commer-

Table 1. Commercial Finishes of Aluminum Alloys

Finish designation	Alloys	General surface characteristics	Surface stains
Mill finish	All alloys	Uncontrolled surface appearance that may vary from sheet to sheet	May not be entirely free of stains or oil residue
Skin-quality finish	All heat treatable alloys in O and T tempers	High degree of surface quality on one side. Surface imperfections detracting from uniform appearance are controlled to a minimum on this side. Other side is equal to or better than mill finish.	Heat treatment stains held to a minimum, as are other surface imperfections
One-side-bright mill finish	1100, 3003, 5005, 5257, 5357, 5457, 5557, 5657	Moderate degree of brightness on one side only. Finish on reverse side is uncontrolled.	Bright side free of oil residue-type stains; has residual oil
Standard one-side-bright finish	1100, 3003, 5005, 5257, 5357, 5457, 5557, 5657	Uniformly bright finish on one side. No control on reverse side.	Bright side free of oil residue-type stains and pits
Standard bright finish	1100, 3003, anodized and reflector sheet	Relatively bright appearance on both sides. Less lustrous than one-side-bright mill finish.	Both sides free of oil and residue-type stains
Controlled finish	Heat treated tempers of bare heat treatable alloys in flat sheet only	Special heat treatment and quench employed to minimize extent of oxide discoloration on the surfaces of the sheet	Heat treat stains and yellowish oxide stains are controlled to a minimum.
Uniform mill finish	1100, 3003, 5005	Sheet having uniform matte finish for nameplates, dials and other decorative applications. May vary from sheet to sheet.	None permitted; may have residual oil

cial trailer roofs are furnished as wide as 108 in. Plates are available 12 ft wide by 45 ft long or larger, depending on thickness, alloy, and temper. Single coils of sheet weighing 8000 or 10,000 lb are not uncommon. Plate thicknesses up to 6 in. are commercially available in certain alloys.

These large sizes are not furnished in all alloys, tempers, and finishes and cannot be procured from all suppliers. Generally, however, sheet and plate sizes obtainable in aluminum alloys exceed those available in other nonferrous metals and approximate those produced in steel. Tolerances are about the same as those in other metals.

Alloys used in the production of sheet and plate can be divided into non-heat-treatable and heat treatable.

The standard non-heat-treatable alloys in which sheet and plate are supplied are EC metal, 1060, 1100, 3003, alclad 3003, 3004, alclad 3004, 3105, 5005, 5050, 5052, 5082, 5083, 5086, 5154, 5252, 5254, 5257, 5357, 5454, 5456, 5457, 5557, 5652, 5657, 6011, and 8280.*

The standard heat treatable alloys regularly supplied as sheet and plate are: 2014, alclad 2014, 2024, alclad 2024, 2219, alclad 2219, 6061, alclad 6061, 6070, X7005, 7039, 7075, alclad 7075, 7079, alclad 7079, 7139, 7178 and alclad 7178.**

Commercial Finishes. A complete discussion of the finishes that are applied to sheet and plate products after rolling can be found in Volume III, Chapter 16. However, these products are often used in one of the many finishes supplied by the mill. The standard mill-supplied finishes are described in Table 1.

Protective Coatings. Interleaving paper is often used in shipping sheet and plate products. Standard interleaving is an anti-tarnish, noncorrosive kraft paper.

Oiling is employed as an alternate method to protect sheet and plate. The oil used has a mineral oil base and about 200 sec viscosity. It is compounded to provide maximum resistance to water penetration and minimum irritation to the skin of those who may handle the material. Sheet and plate products for overseas shipment are generally oiled.

*The tempers in which these alloys are furnished, as well as their compositions, are described in Volume I, Chapter 4. Alclad products are discussed in Volume I, Chapters 7 and 9. Compositions of the non-heat-treatable alloys are given in Volume I, Chapter 9, Table 1.

**Tempers and compositions for heat treatable alloys are described in Volume I, Chapters 5 and 9.

Gummed protective tape is sometimes applied to flat sheet and plate as surface protection during transit and subsequent handling. It is not recommended where more than 90 days may elapse between the time of application and removal.

A transparent vinyl strippable coating, applied during mill fabrication, affords a practical finish protection for a number of sheet products in transit and during plant handling and fabricating operations. It is applied in a film thickness of approximately 1.5 to 2.0 mils and can be removed by hand or by an air blast introduced between the coating and the metal.

Specialty Products. Many special grades of sheet and plate are supplied to meet the requirements of specific applications.

Anodizing Sheet. For the application of protective and decorative coatings by the anodizing process.

Prepainted Sheet. A baked synthetic resin enamel finish is applied to one or both sides over a chemical conversion coating. This sheet can be formed by conventional metalworking equipment without destroying the finish, and it can be punched or drilled without disrupting the coating. It is available in a variety of colors, all of which are controlled as to uniformity, hardness, and adhesion.

Reflector Sheet. For use in the manufacture of reflectors. It is available in various grades suitable for diffuse and specular finished reflectors.

Lighting Sheet. Reflector sheet (either diffuse or specular) is prefinished for use in trough-type reflectors and other reflector applications where severe forming is not required.

Recording Sheet Circles. Used by the recording industry to produce master-copy recordings and high-quality transcription records, and for data recording and storage in memory units. These products are furnished with a high degree of flatness and freedom from surface defects.

Brazing Sheet. Nonclad or special clad sheet for brazing purposes. Clad brazing sheet is coated on one or both surfaces with an alloy having a distinctly lower melting point than the parent or core alloy. The unclad product is furnished in alloys having a low melting temperature. It is used in furnace brazing applications as an alternative to a brazing alloy cladding and has the same function.

Litho Sheet. One side has optimum freedom from surface imperfections; supplied with a maximum degree of flatness, for use as a plate in offset printing.

Patterned Sheet. Raised or indented pattern on one or both surfaces affords a broad range of designs and textures for decorative purposes; available in both coiled and flat sheet forms.

Vinyl-Coated Sheet. Permanently bonded laminate of aluminum sheet and vinyl film. This product is available in coiled or flat sheet form and generally can be fabricated with conventional metalworking tools.

Porcelain Enameling Sheet. Specifically designed to provide maximum porcelain enamel adherence. Available in various grades, with closely controlled compositions. Furnished either plain or in embossed patterns.

Trailer Roof Sheet. Wide, relatively light-gage 3003 or 5052 alloy sheet used by the truck-trailer industry for one-piece roofs. Available in thicknesses from 0.032 in. and in widths up to 102 in. in coiled or flat form.

Rural Roofing Sheet. Standard sizes of formed or corrugated sheet for roofing or siding on farm and light commercial buildings. Available in thicknesses of 0.0175, 0.019, 0.0215 and 0.024 in. and in a number of standard corrugations. Usually pattern is embossed.

Decorative Panel Sheet. Standard sizes of embossed-and-formed 0.0215-in. sheet with trapezoidal corrugations. Prepainted in many different colors, for industrial and residential building applications.

Industrial Roofing Sheet. Standard sizes of formed sheet, plain or embossed, for use as roofing or siding on general industrial buildings. It is available in prepainted colors.

Tapered Sheet and Plate. A rolled or machined product with the thickness tapered from one end to the other in the direction of rolling. The taper may be uniform from end to end or for only part of the length. Important uses include aircraft wing skin and large storage tanks.

Armor Plate. Wrought aluminum alloy plate for military vehicle armor. It meets United States Army Ordnance ballistic requirements and possesses adequate formability and welding characteristics for vehicle manufacture. Characteristics are defined by ordnance specifications.

Tread Plate. Sheet or plate with a raised, figured pattern on one surface to provide improved traction, or with abrasive granules imbedded in the surface.

Stainless-Clad Aluminum. Although it has other applications, this product was designed to provide a stainless steel inner liner for cooking utensils. It is produced in 3004 alloy with a 0.010-in. layer of 18–8 stainless steel roll bonded to one or both sides.

Boral Sheet and Plate. This product is a composite material with a core of boron carbide (B_4C) dispersed in commercially pure aluminum and clad on both sides with aluminum, and it is employed as a neutron shielding medium. It can replace large amounts of concrete or earth as a shielding medium and is therefore used where space and weight are factors.

Tooling Plate. A wrought or cast plate product for tool and jig applications. It is produced to provide maximum stability for machining purposes. The cast plate is machined on both surfaces to obtain superior flatness.

Traffic and Street Sign Blanks. Standard sign blanks are precut from 6061-T6 alloy sheet in configurations and thicknesses established by the United States Bureau of Public Roads.

Tube-in-Sheet. By inserting long strips of resist (carbon-plastic-plaster "cores") in a sheet ingot, parallel passages are obtained in a sheet rolled from this ingot. Hydraulic or pneumatic pressure is used to expand the passages.

Roll-Bond Evaporator Sheet. Internal pressure is also applied to expand the maze of complicated passages in refrigerator evaporator sheet. This product is produced by bonding two sheets together under roll pressure after a stop-off has been printed on one of the sheets. This is done hot after both sheets have been wire brushed.

Foil*

Commercial aluminum foil ranges in thickness from 0.00017 to 0.0059 in. and in width from 0.250 to 61 in. It is produced with two sides bright or one side bright and one satin finished. The latter, common for thicknesses less than 0.001 in., is produced by pack rolling: Two sheets of foil are passed through the rolling mill at the same time. The faces in contact with the rolls have a bright, specular finish, while the mating faces have a satin finish. Foil more than 0.001 in. thick is normally rolled in single sheets and is available with two sides bright.

Most foil applications are confined to 1145 alloy and to the O and H19 tempers. Household foil and other flexible packaging materials are almost always in the O temper, and various types of heat-and-serve rigid containers are in the H19 temper; 3003-H19 is also used in rigid containers.

The ease with which foil can be coated, printed or combined by laminating with many flexible and rigid materials has greatly broadened the range of applications. It is available with heat-seal coatings, decorative lacquers, and a wide selection of protective coatings, films, and adhesives of varied compositions and thicknesses. These coatings are designed to enhance or protect surface appearance, achieve easy printability, increase rigidity and strength, and prevent chemical attack. The use of thinner gages of foil in combination with paper and other materials generally results in a less expensive product. For example, foil 0.0007 in. thick is generally considered to be the lightest gage that is impermeable to moisture-vapor transmission. However, when aluminum foil is combined with other materials, moisture impermeability can be obtained with lighter and less expensive gages of aluminum.

When the "feel" of soft aluminum wrapper foil is compared to that of hard strong-alloy foil, it is almost incomprehensible that both products are made from the same basic metal. As shown in

*In Volume I, Chapter 9, information is given on physical, mechanical and chemical properties of the alloys commonly used for foil.

Table 7, Chapter 9, Volume I, aluminum foil is furnished in strengths varying from those approximating lead to those of steel. Hard foils find wide use in adhesive-bonded honeycomb, artificial Christmas trees, sound transducer and receiver diaphragms, instrument needles, and rigid containers.

Wire, Rod and Bar

Although many wire, rod and bar products are made by hot extrusion, a sequence of rolling and drawing operations is generally the preferred method for producing these commodities. When a rolled and drawn product is employed, a greater range of tempers in the non-heat-treatable alloys becomes available, as well as closer dimensional control.

The principal alloys commercially produced in wire, rod and bar are: EC, 1100, 1345, 2011, 2014, 2017, 2024, 2117, 2219, 3003, 5005, 5050, 5052, 5056, alclad 5056, 5083, 5086, 5154, 5254, 5454, 5456, 5652, 6053, 6061, 6066, 6101, 6201, 6262, 7001, 7072, 7075, 7079, 7178, No. 716 brazing and No. 718 brazing. The following alloys are furnished in the form of welding wire: 1100, 2319, 4043, 5183, 5356, 5554 and 5556.

Wire is generally round, but it may be square, rectangular or hexagonal in section. It is, by definition, less than 3/8 in. in diameter. Aluminum wire is supplied commercially in diameters of less than 0.001 in. Flattened wire is available 0.020 to 0.187 in. thick and in widths of 0.063 to 1.000 in. Wire is furnished straightened and cut-to-length as well as in coils or spools.

Rod and Bar. Rod is any round section 3/8 in. or more in diameter. Bar is any section other than round with the greatest dimension across flats 3/8 in. or more. Rod and bar usually are supplied in straight lengths approximately 12 ft long. Redraw rod is furnished in large coils and is generally 3/8 in. in diameter.

Specialty Products. Several wire, rod and bar products are used as a starting point in the manufacture of other commercial forms. Forgings and pressings are produced from rolled forging stock. This is available as Class 1 forging stock, where dimensional tolerances are not important, and Class 2 stock, which is controlled to closer tolerances, for use in a closed die. Both are furnished in 5/8 to 8-in. diameters, or in squares or rectangles of equivalent cross section.

Coiled rivet wire and rod, furnished in sizes 0.061 to 1.000 in. in diameter, are used in the manufacture of cold headed products such as rivets, nails, screws and bolts—which are often considered standard mill products. Although 1100, 5052 and 5056 alloys are standard rivet wire and rod alloys, a heat treatable alloy such as 2024, 2117, 6061 or 7075 is generally supplied to provide good machinability for secondary operations and strength in the upset products.

Screw-machine stock is rod or bar supplied solid or hollow and chamfered for fabrication on automatic screw machines. Because of superior machinability and chip characteristics, 2011 alloy in either the T3 or T8 temper is most commonly employed. Alloys such as 2017, 2024, 6061, and 6262 are frequently used to provide higher strength or superior corrosion resistance. Standard screw-machine stock is supplied either round or hexagonal in sizes of 0.125 to 3.000 in.

Aluminum wire is stranded to produce ACSR (aluminum conductor, steel reinforced) or all-aluminum conductors for electrical power transmission and distribution. It is regarded as a standard mill product. Rolled or extruded bar is employed as electrical bus conductor and is a standard commercial product.

Specialized forms of aluminum wire include welding electrode for tungsten or consumable arc welding, brazing rod, armor rods for electrical overhead conductors, and tie wire.

Extrusions

Extruded shapes are furnished in EC, 1100, 2014, 2024, 3003, 5083, 5086, 5154, 5254, 5454, 5456, 6061, 6063, 6066, 6262, 7001, X7005, 7075, 7079 and 7178 alloys. Alloy 6063 is the most popular, because it is easy to extrude and develops relatively good mechanical properties after quenching at the press.

The maximum size of extrusion that can be produced on a press of any given capacity depends on the wall thickness and the alloy specified. Heavy-walled extrusions weighing 50 to 100 lb per ft are produced in soft alloys on a 14,000-ton press. However, when wide widths and relatively thin walls are required in strong alloys, the maximum weight can drop to 1 to 2 lb per ft. Widths of nearly 3 ft can be produced.

Cost Considerations. A solid aluminum shape can usually be produced at a lower cost per pound than a semihollow shape, and a semihollow shape for less than a hollow shape. Because of its lighter weight per foot, however, the total cost of a hollow shape may be less per piece than a corresponding solid shape designed to perform the same function.

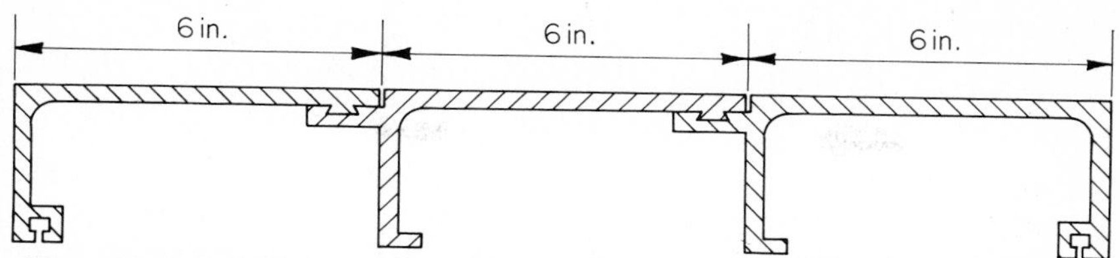

Fig. 2. Roll-locked extrusions combining three shapes in a panel

The average "thinness" of an extruded shape, measured in terms of a "factor", also affects the price. This factor is determined by dividing the perimeter of the cross section of the shape (in inches) by its weight per linear foot (in pounds) and is expressed as the nearest whole number. A thin shape with a high factor costs more per pound than a heavy section with a lower factor, but it may cost less per foot because of its lighter weight.

The size of the circumscribing circle that completely encloses the cross section of a specific shape is also an important cost factor, as well as a limiting factor in selection of press equipment. Shapes with a circle size of 6 to 8 in. are generally less expensive per pound than smaller or larger shapes.

Sections having circumscribing circles that exceed economical extrusion sizes can be produced as roll-locked extruded shapes; combinations of two or more 6-in. interlocking shapes can be rolled together to form a single panel unit, as shown in Fig. 2. Another system often employed to produce a flat shape wider than the capacity of the press on which it is made is to extrude it in the form of a V or a W and then flatten the shape. Die costs for most aluminum extruded shapes are relatively low. Therefore it is economical to produce a special shape to suit each special application. Typical examples, showing some of the advantages of using special shapes, are delineated in Fig. 3.

Finishes. Mill supplied finishes are classified in four basic groups identified by number; these finishes apply to exposed surfaces only. Finish is also an important cost consideration.

Finish No. 1. Standard finish where appearance is not otherwise specified. It is applicable to all alloys and tempers. Unexposed surfaces are also supplied in this finish.

Finish No. 2. Standard finish where good appearance is a requirement. This applies to 1100-F, 3003-F, 6063-T6, and 6063-T42.

Finish No. 3. Special finish designed for subsequent polishing. This finish can be specified for 1100-F, 3003-F, 6063-T4, 6063-T42, 6063-T5, and 6063-T6 alloys and tempers. It is restricted to solid shapes and applies to a specified portion of the exposed surface.

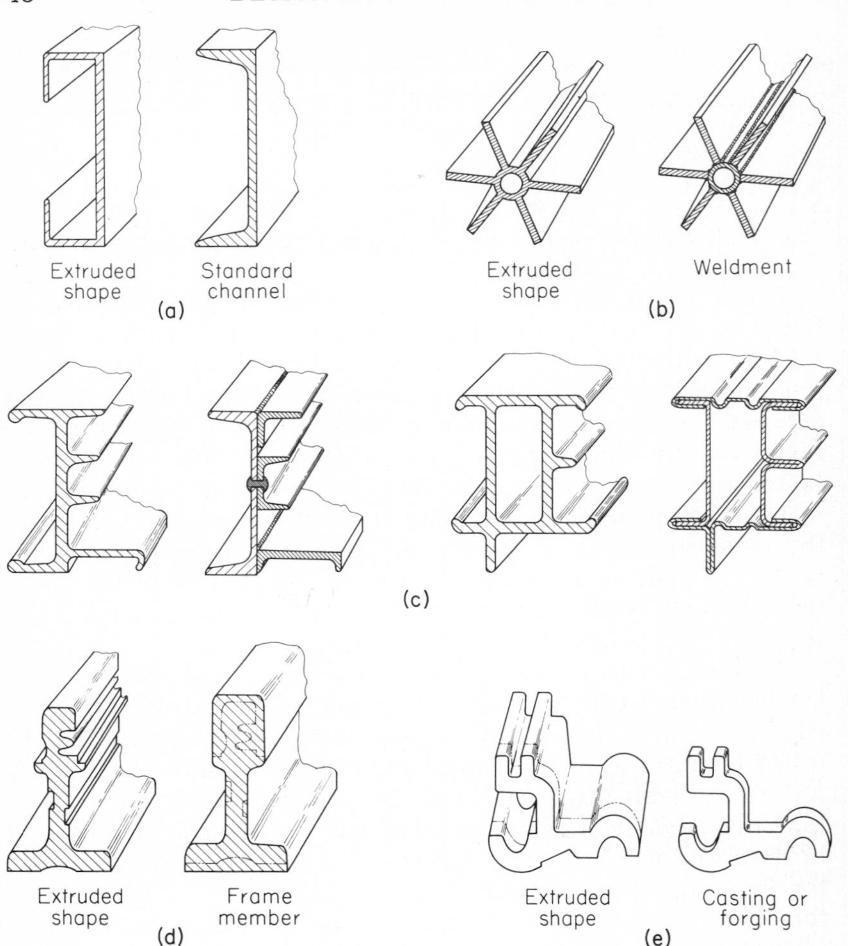

(a) Extruded shapes withstand greater stresses than standard rolled shapes, because of more efficient disposition of metal. As a long column, the extruded shape will support almost twice as great a load as the standard channel.

(b) In addition to increasing strength and accuracy, extruded shape cuts costs by eliminating welding.

(c) Assemblies of rolled steel shapes or crimped hollow sections are often redesigned into a single aluminum extruded shape having greater stiffness, strength and simplicity of construction.

(d) Aluminum extruded shape eliminates costly machining operations when used to replace heavy iron or steel frame member.

(e) Parts with cross sections that are symmetrical in one plane are produced more economically as short sawed-off sections of an extruded shape than as a casting or forging.

Fig. 3. Examples where special extruded shapes are economical

Finish No. 4. Eleven special finishes, and finishes similar to No. 2 and 3 for use where those finish designations are not applicable.

Structural Shapes

A comprehensive line of structural shapes is available in aluminum alloys, ranging in size from ¾-by-¾-in. angles to 12-in. I-beams. Structural shapes are produced in alloys 5083, 5086, 5454, and 5456 for welding; in alloys 2014, 6061, and 6066 for riveting and bolting; and in EC metal for bus conductor.

Where large quantities of standard shapes can be produced at one time, they are generally rolled (as in steel). Structural shapes smaller than 9 in. wide are more often extruded. Small quantities of shapes in special sizes or special alloys are always extruded.

Tube and Pipe

Aluminum and aluminum alloy tube is generally round, but it is commercially available in many different shapes such as square, rectangular, octagonal, and oval. When furnished in sizes designated as nominal pipe sizes or by ASA schedule numbers, it is called pipe. It is manufactured by drawing, extrusion, welding, and (to a minor degree) impact extrusion.

Drawn tube is generally produced by drawing extruded tube through dies on drawbenches. It is seamless and is produced in smaller diameters and with thinner walls than extruded tube; also, it is held to closer tolerances and has better surface appearance than extruded tube. Drawn tube in non-heat-treatable alloys can be produced in work hardened tempers not obtainable in extruded tube. Standard drawing tools are available to fabricate any outside diameter from ⅛ to 7 in.

Extruded tube comes directly from the extrusion press. It is a less-expensive product than drawn tube. Manufacturing limits and tolerances are broader than those for drawn tube. Extruded tube can be made in outside diameters up to 24 in. and the larger sizes can be offered in longer lengths than drawn tube.

Welded aluminum tube is produced from coiled sheet by induction welding or high-frequency resistance welding. Welding is the most economical method for producing alclad tube. Welded tube can generally be furnished with dimensional tolerances approaching those available in drawn tube and, in large quantities, at a lower price. Welded tube can be drawn after welding, to produce smaller sizes to closer tolerances than those attainable in the as-welded product.

Hooker tube is fabricated by the forward impact extrusion technique (Volume III, Chapter 4). Tubes approximately 5 to 6 ft long are produced with close tolerances. Small-diameter tubes having wall thicknesses less than 0.010 in. are sometimes produced most economically by the Hooker process.

Aluminum tube of small diameter is also available in coiled form. This product is produced by extrusion, drawing, swaging or welding.

Tubes of large diameter, such as those used for papermill rolls, are made by centrifugal casting. Cast tube having even heavier walls is produced by the direct chill process.

Forgings and Pressings

Aluminum alloy forgings and pressings are produced commercially in conventional hammer equipment, on hydraulic and mechanical presses, in ring rollers, and on upsetters. They may be classified as die forgings, hand forgings, and rolled rings.

Die Forgings. Depending upon the amount of machining necessary to obtain a finished part, aluminum die forgings and pressings are categorized as (*a*) blocker, requiring the most machining; (*b*) conventional, providing a good balance between die cost and machining cost; or (*c*) precision forgings and pressings. Precision forgings are of advantage where it is desirable to obtain thin web sections and thin, accurate ribs with a minimum of machining. Draft angles are controlled to less than 1° if desired; corner fillets can be held to a minimum.

Aluminum die forgings having a projected area close to 6000 sq in. and weighing as much as 3400 lb are produced; also, lengths up to 252 in. are furnished.

Hand forgings are produced by working aluminum stock between flat dies or other simple tools that shape the piece roughly to the required contour. Prototypes are frequently made as hand forgings to reduce delivery time. Slabs as large as 7 in. thick by 120 in. wide and 450 in. long, weighing over 35,000 lb, are available in the form of hand forgings.

Rolled Ring Forgings. Precision ring rolling equipment is available to produce rolled rings in a wide range of diameters up to 150 in., in any wall thickness and alloy. Larger rings can be fabricated by forging over a mandrel (Volume III, Chapter 5).

Impact Extrusions

Starting point for all impact extrusions ("impacts") is an aluminum or aluminum alloy slug, which may be cast, blanked from plate, or sawed from rod. The slug provides a closely controlled volume of metal in a precise, predetermined shape. Inserted in the die, either automatically or by hand, it is the reservoir of metal that forms the finished extrusion.

Impacts are categorized by the direction in which the metal flows in relation to the stroke of the punch.

The most common method of impacting is the reverse process. The collapsible tube and a host of other impacts, such as electronic condenser cans, are made by metal flow-back around the punch, counter to the direction of the punch stroke. If there is an orifice in the punch, metal also flows upward into the punch, forming a double-walled part.

When there is no aperture between punch and die wall but apertures in the die, metal flows forward through the die, in the same direction as the punch stroke. Typically, flanged tubes are made by forward impacting, with the flange formed in the die and the tube extruded through the die.

When metal flows both up around the punch and down into the die, the part is designated a combination impact. Parts hollow on both ends, with a solid midsection web, are typical products of this method.

When metal flow is lateral, perpendicular to the direction of the punch stroke, the part is termed a lateral impact extrusion. Lateral features may be obtained in combination with any of the other impact types.

Press equipment currently available imposes size limits on impacts. Present limits are given in Chapter 7 of this volume.

Particles, Powder and Paste

There are many commercial forms of divided aluminum, particles ranging from globules 0.5 in. in diameter to minute flakes that are only a few microns thick. The methods used to produce this range of products are as diversified as their applications (Volume I, Chapter 10).

Coarse Particles. The coarsest products are called granulated ingot, grained ingot, and shot, although the steel producers who use them for deoxidizing liquid steel often refer to all three products as "shot". Granulated ingot is a semiflat sphere 0.20 to 0.56 in. in diameter, and grained ingot comes in a rough, granular form that is 5 mesh and finer. Shot is more nearly spherical in shape and is furnished in sizes from 4 to 14 mesh, based on Tyler screen sieves.

Other products in the coarse-particle category are needles approximately 1/16 to 1/4 in. long, and coarse cast flakes ranging in size from approximately −4 to +50 mesh.

Fine Powders and Paste. Powder produced by atomizing may be granular or spherical. It is commercially available in particle sizes ranging from −12 mesh (with a substantial portion through −325 mesh) all the way to 100% through −325 mesh. Because of the method by which it is made, atomized powder is dry and does not contain lubricants. A very thin oxide film forms naturally on each particle in processing. This film acts as a protective coating.

The particles in paste and flake powder are flakelike in shape and are, for the most part, −325 mesh. This flake material is much thinner than the granular or atomized form, so that mesh size is not a valid comparative measure of relative particle size.

Most flake pastes and powders are produced in a ball mill. They contain, in addition to the oxide that is formed on the surface, a sufficient quantity of lubricant to provide leafing.

Flake powders used for dusting greeting cards and wrapping papers are much coarser than the pigment grades. They are available in many sizes and vary from −4 to −100 mesh.

Dyed aluminum flake powders are also available, especially in gold, for decorative applications.

A special ball-milled powder is furnished for the production of the aluminum powder metallurgy products described in Volume I, Chapter 10. Alloy powders are also specially produced for welding and for compacting into bearings and into other parts requiring an alloy unobtainable by any other process.

Reference

1 Standards for Aluminum Mill Products 1966, The Aluminum Association, New York, 1965

Chapter 3

Factors That Determine the Applications of Aluminum

K. F. THORNTON

THE ONLY valid reason for choosing a material is that it performs required functions at the lowest over-all cost. This result can be achieved in three general ways: First, the chosen material may be lower in first cost. Second, it may be more economical in the long run because of lower maintenance costs. Third, it may have special characteristics peculiarly suiting it to the application. Although this third factor may be combined with one or both of the others, discussion is simplified by considering each factor separately (1).

First Cost

There are a few applications for which aluminum is more economical than practical alternates simply on the basis of ingot price; electrical conductor is the outstanding example. Copper is the only other general-purpose metal used for conductors, and aluminum is less expensive even on a per-pound basis. To make a realistic comparison of the basic cost of copper versus aluminum for conducting electricity, the conductivity and density of the two materials must be considered. Electrical conductor (EC) grade aluminum is rated at 63% IACS (International Annealed Copper Standard). Combining this conductivity measure, which

NOTE: Every topic mentioned in this chapter is treated in detail elsewhere in these volumes. For reference to more complete information, the reader may consult the indexes.

The author is chief engineer, Product Development Div., Aluminum Company of America, New Kensington.

is on a volume basis, with the densities of the two metals yields the result that 0.48 lb of aluminum has the same conductive capability as 1 lb of copper. To complete the cost comparison it is, of course, necessary to make allowances for fabricating both materials into final form. The complete analysis of cost usually leaves aluminum with a clear advantage when the conductors are large, as for transmission or distribution lines. For smaller conductors, such as house wiring, the saving in cost of the wire is generally not sufficient to justify the effort required of the small user to learn to handle a new material. With very fine wire, such as is employed for winding fractional horsepower motors for household appliances, fabricating costs overshadow metal cost, and copper is normally used. This example of electrical conductors illustrates one type of relationship of metal cost to over-all cost of final product.

A similar situation exists in the competition between zinc and aluminum in die castings. Aluminum is cheaper on a volume basis, and this results in a price advantage for aluminum in large castings. Smaller parts, and those that have very thin sections, usually cost less in zinc because its lower casting temperature permits longer die life, better lubrication, and thinner sections. Aluminum die castings have the advantage of light weight, but zinc is more economical to chromium plate. Automotive usage of the two materials reflects these influences.

Stainless steel is frequently in competition with aluminum for parts and structures requiring resistance to weathering or other corrosive environments. The ingot price advantage of aluminum is maintained in fabricated products such as sheet and plate.

There are a few applications where lead and aluminum are in competition; price favors aluminum. Although these two metals are similar in their ability to withstand the effects of time and atmosphere, they are otherwise so different that comparisons are difficult, unless a specific application is considered.

Steel has (and, no doubt, will continue to have) the largest share of the metal market, largely because of its ability to fulfill so many, varied requirements at the lowest cost. Aluminum is more economical than steel only when one or more of its special characteristics can be utilized.

Although basic material cost is always important, it is not unusual for unique fabricating capabilities to assume equal significance. The extrusion process, highly developed and very economical for aluminum, permits fabrication of thin, complicated, and even hollow, shapes for little if any higher cost than flat rolled sheets. This capability has led to the wide use of extruded shapes for items such as windows, ladders, and truck bodies. The application of special shapes has provided strength with minimum material and (perhaps of even greater economic importance) simple assembly of the various parts.

The ease and speed with which aluminum can be rolled to very thin foil (0.00035 in. is common) underlie its extensive use in many applications where other materials might be competitive on a performance basis.

The automobile industry is making extensive use of the special capability of aluminum alloys in die castings. The metal itself is more expensive than cast iron. However, a saving results from the die casting process, compared to sand casting as employed for iron, and additional saving results from the elimination of most of the expensive machining required for iron. The die cast aluminum part requires only drilling of some holes (most are cast over core pins), reaming of others, and threading those that require it. Components such as flywheel housings and transmission cases are made in aluminum at a competitive price.

Cost Over Service Life

A most important factor contributing to the increasing use of aluminum for outdoor structures is the low cost of keeping it presentable in appearance and sound structurally, with minimum expense for field chipping, spot priming, and repainting. Many highway accessory items, such as signs, railings, and lighting standards, are so expensive to paint in the field that the cost of a single repainting equals the additional price of aluminum. Sometimes the cost of shutting down equipment for painting or other maintenance is an important consideration. Aluminum structural alloys have been used in outdoor electric switching stations on this basis for nearly 20 years.

The widespread use of aluminum for house siding, rain-carrying equipment, and other items for residential construction stem from consumer appreciation of the ease of maintaining aluminum.

Originally, aluminum was used for bodies for trucks and trailers because of its light weight. An unexpected advantage was revealed after a few years of experience. The riveted aluminum construction was much easier to repair in a small shop or garage than competing spot welded, light-weight steel bodies. Panels and stiffeners damaged in minor collisions can be removed by cutting rivets and sawing with woodworking equipment. The replacement parts can then be securely and neatly built into the structure using either hand-driven rivets or bolts. The reduced cost of repairs and the long service life have been important factors in extending the use of aluminum to types of truck bodies and trucking jobs where weight saving alone would hardly justify it.

The good resistance of aluminum to weathering results in a long service life that is seldom limited by corrosion.

A final consideration in the over-all cost of any piece of equipment or structure is its residual or scrap value. Aluminum can be remelted with little loss due to oxidation, and even rather complex structures such as aircraft justify the effort of reclaiming them for the metal values contained. Good melting scrap is readily marketable, and this factor should be considered in assessing the over-all cost of an aluminum structure.

Performance

Every application of aluminum involves consideration of its performance compared to that of other materials. Some of the basic characteristics of aluminum alloys as they apply to performance in specific applications are given in Table 1.

Light weight is the basic reason for using aluminum in all types of transportation equipment, as well as in moving and movable parts in general. The list of applications predicated on lightness is almost endless, but other capabilities are usually required, to the extent that it is sometimes difficult to assign a top priority. An example is the combined effect of modulus of elasticity and weight. Aluminum has about one third the weight and one third the modulus of steel. In a flat sheet, bending stiffness increases as the cube of the thickness. Thus, an aluminum sheet of equal weight per square foot is nine times as stiff as its steel counterpart. Equal stiffness requires a thickness factor equal to the cube root of 3, or 1.44. This is the source of the often used "40% rule" (increase thickness 40%) for transposing a steel design to aluminum. Accumulated experience with aluminum alloys favors consideration of gage-for-gage substitution in applications that defy analytical design in terms of known load and deflection requirements.

The universal use of aluminum for aircraft structures probably represents the most exacting — and at the same time the most economically rewarding — use of the highest-strength aluminum alloys where weight saving is the primary requirement. A

Table 1. Typical Applications and Considerations Involved in the Use of Aluminum

Application	Pertinent characteristics: Favorable	Pertinent characteristics: Unfavorable
Electric transmission lines	Low first cost Conductivity Resistance to corrosion Good joints Steel reinforcing Large diameter Light weight	Low strength
Truck trailer van bodies	Light weight Easy fabrication Easy repair Resistance to weather Adequate strength Paint not required	Higher cost
Residential windows	Resistance to weather Low cost Easy fabrication Paint not required	High thermal conductivity Wear strips required
Diving boards	Low modulus of elasticity High strength Resistance to corrosion Easy fabrication No warping or splitting	Higher cost
Automotive trim	Attractive finish Avoids selective attack on body steel Easy forming Low cost	Dent resistance Some cleaners harmful
Automotive transmission cases (die cast)	Low cost Machining reduced High production Light weight	Low modulus of elasticity Thermal expansion
Automotive pistons	Thermal conductivity Light weight Low cost	Thermal expansion
House siding	Holds paint well No splitting or burning Nails don't show	Higher cost Thermal expansion Dent resistance
Truck wheels	Light weight Thermal conductivity True running	Higher cost Less resistance to abuse

conservative figure for the value of a pound of "lightness" in a modern long-range civil transport is $2500. In more workaday applications, aluminum is used almost exclusively in the housings of portable power tools, ranging from the ¼-in. drill in the home workshop to the lumberman's gasoline-powered chain saw, and in outboard motors.

Resistance to weathering is equal in importance to light weight in number of applications and volume of metal consumed. Those aluminum alloys that are especially formulated for outdoor exposure are regularly used without paint or other protective finish. Numerous installations have been exposed for 30 years with no loss of structural integrity, an acceptable level of architectural appearance, and no maintenance other than the cleaning effects of rain. Included are cast bridge rails on the Outer Drive in the Chicago Loop district, wrought bridge rails on the Smithfield Street and other bridges in the Pittsburgh area, and cast spandrels on monumental buildings, including New York's Empire State Building.

Closely associated with its resistance to weathering is the performance of aluminum in combination with organic coatings. Properly applied paint coatings on aluminum exhibit maximum adhesion, and local penetrations of the coating seldom expand. This characteristic is largely responsible for the extensive application of aluminum siding for residences.

High electrical conductivity was touched on in the preceding sections. Even when reasonable conductor size and nonmagnetic characteristics are of no concern (as in the third rail for electric railroads using direct current), aluminum can provide a given current-carrying capacity at a lower per-foot cost than steel, copper, or any other material.

High thermal conductivity of aluminum parallels its high electrical conductivity. Heat exchange equipment, including cooking utensils, requires many other characteristics; thus, thermal conductivity does not control the application to the same extent that electrical conductivity does in its field. However, aluminum is used where the basic function is conduction of heat; its other capabilities contribute to the final choice.

The chief function of the cast aluminum sole plate in a hand iron is the conducting of heat from the heating element to the cloth. The light weight is attractive to the housewife, and manufacturing economy (the element is "cast-in", and no protective finish is required) results in a favorable price.

High specific heat helps to maintain a uniform temperature in the hand iron. The specific heat of aluminum alloys is 0.215 cal per g, compared to 0.117 for steel and 0.249 for magnesium. On a volume basis, the heavier metals have a higher capacity.

The low modulus of aluminum causes complications in applications where space is strictly limited and deflection also must be held to a minimum. Such conditions are rare, and they are perhaps balanced by other situations where a large elastic deflection is desirable. Aluminum diving boards utilize the large deflection resulting from low modulus, and truck bodies for hauling rock also exploit the increased energy absorption in resisting permanent denting. It is interesting to note that a considerable group of important structural materials have nearly the same ratio of modulus of elasticity to density. Steel, aluminum, magnesium, and titanium are close. Wood is not far from this range. Copper, lead, and cast iron are much heavier in relation to modulus, whereas beryllium is lighter by a factor of about 4 in relation to its modulus of elasticity.

Aluminum alloys, in general, are somewhat less permeable to magnetic fields than air (paramagnetic). Uses resulting from this characteristic are not many, but permeability is an important contributing characteristic in some applications.

The coefficient of thermal expansion for aluminum alloys in general is about double that of carbon steel, 1½ times that of 18–8 stainless steel and copper, and slightly more than that of brass or bronze. Assemblies involving different materials require consideration of these differences. One approach is to provide free movement, but it is also appropriate in many combinations to fasten the dissimilar metals together tightly and permit the changes in relative length to be expressed as elastic stresses. These stresses are seldom high enough to be troublesome unless they produce undesirable warpage of the assembly in the manner of a thermostatic strip.

Aluminum forms only nontoxic salts. Cooking utensils, both domestic and institutional, rely on this capability. Aluminum is also nontoxic to molds, bacteria, and similarly sensitive organisms, and it is often used in growing them.

Low-temperature applications of aluminum rely on the fact that aluminum does not become brittle at temperatures at least as low as −423 F (the boiling point of hydrogen).

High reflectance for visible, ultraviolet and infrared radiation makes aluminum the choice for many types of reflectors.

Table 2. Approximate Properties of Common Metals(a)

Metal	Weight, lb/cu ft	Modulus of elasticity, million psi	Poisson's ratio	Coefficient of expansion, millionths/°F(b)	Specific heat, cal/g	Conductivity Thermal(c)	Electrical(d)
Aluminum(e)	169	10	0.33	13	0.215	0.53	58%
Magnesium(e)	109	6.5	0.35	15	0.249	0.38	39
Titanium(e)	283	16.8	...	5	0.126	...	2
Yellow brass	529	15	0.33	11	0.09	0.28	27
Copper(e)	560	16	0.33	9	0.092	0.94	103
Malleable iron	456	25	0.17	7	0.122	...	..
Lead(e)	708	2.6	0.43	16	0.031	0.08	8
Monel	551	26	0.39	8	0.127	0.06	4
Carbon steel	490	29	0.28	7	0.117	0.12	13
Zinc(e)	446	..	0.11	22	0.092	0.27	28

(a) For other metals and alloys, see Metals Handbook, 8th Edition, Vol 1, 1961, American Society for Metals. (b) For temperatures between 68 and 212 F. (c) Calories transmitted per second through a plate 1 cm thick per square centimeter of its surface, for a temperature differential between the two faces of the plate of 100 °C. (d) Volume conductivity at 20 C in % IACS. (e) Pure or commercially pure.

Aluminum is receptive to a number of unique finishes, including anodic oxide coatings, chemical conversion coatings, and special finishes for reflectors involving a combination of electrolytic or chemical brightening for high reflectance and an anodic coating for long life even in outdoor exposure.

Some other characteristics of aluminum that do not warrant discussion here but should be mentioned are: short half life of aluminum 28, low absorption for x-rays, high affinity of oxygen, high resistance to sparking, and colorless corrosion products.

Table 2 compares several physical properties of aluminum with those of nine competitive metals.

Strength

Strength rarely overshadows other requirements to the extent that selection can be based on strength alone. Consideration must usually be given also to environmental factors, special characteristics required, manufacturing processes, and cost.

A first look at the mechanical property tables reveals two facts: There is a wide range of strengths from which to choose, and there is considerable duplication in strength values. Typical yield strengths vary from 4000 to 78,000 psi and tensile strengths from 10,000 to 88,000 psi. Elongation values range from 4 to 43% (in 2 in. on 1⁄16-in. sheet specimens). Alloys and

Table 3. Aluminum Alloys and Tempers Having Identical Yield Strengths

Yield strength			
28,000 psi	29,000 psi	30,000 psi	31,000 psi
2EC-T6	3004-H34	5086-H32	5052-H34
5005-H18	Alclad 3004-H34	5154-H32	5652-H34
5052-H32	5050-H38	5254-H32	6063-T6
5083-H112		5357-H38	6463-T6
5557-H38		5454-H32	
5652-H32		5457-H38	

tempers having the randomly selected yield strengths of 28,000, 29,000, 30,000, and 31,000 psi are listed in Table 3. Choice among these 19 alloys and tempers obviously must be based on something other than yield strength.

The stronger aluminum alloys are usually higher in price, because they are harder and slower to fabricate into sheet, extrusions, forgings and other mill products. A weaker alloy at the same price would not have a market unless it had some other special attribute. Also, cold worked alloys are less expensive than those that are heat treated to attain their final strength. For non-heat-treated sheet, the several standard work-hardened tempers of a specific alloy, although covering a considerable range of strength, usually are priced the same (Table 4).

Fatigue strength involves three principal considerations: alloy, metallurgical quality, and design. The tabular data and Fig. 1 show a range of 3000 to 24,000 psi in the fatigue limit of aluminum alloys. Substandard quality (involving discontinuities

Table 4. Price per Pound for 30,000-Lb Quantity, Mill Finish (1965)

Alloy	Temper	Flat sheet, 48 by 144 in. by 0.030 to 0.120 in. thick	Coils, 24 in. wide by 0.030 to 0.096 in. thick
1100, 3003, 5005	O, H12, H14, H16, H18	39 to 40¢	34¢
3004	O, H32, H34, H36, H38	41 to 46¢	37 to 39¢
5456(a), 5083(a)	O, H323, H343	50 to 52¢	46 to 48¢
5257, 5357, 5457, 5557, 5657	O, H25, H26, H38	49 to 50¢	42 to 43¢
6061	T6	45 to 51¢	43 to 47¢
2024, alcad 2024	T3	50 to 62¢	49 to 55¢
7075, alcad 7075	T6	52 to 69¢	50 to 59¢

(a) Minimum thickness, 0.047 in.

revealed by ultrasonics) lowers the fatigue strength measurably if the principal stresses are in the most unfavorable direction. Also, when a reasonable level of quality is maintained, no amount of metallurgical maneuvering will consistently produce

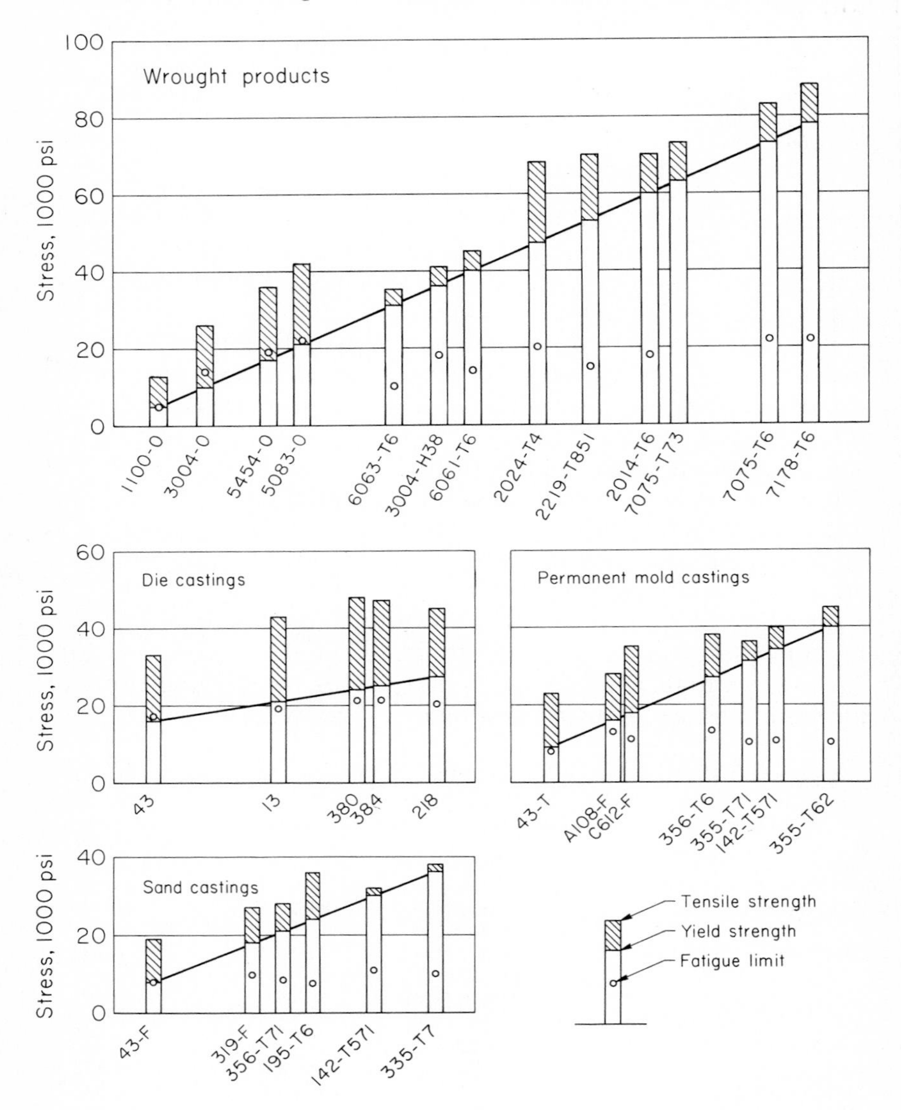

Fig. 1. Comparison of tensile strength, yield strength and fatigue limit for aluminum alloys

higher fatigue strengths. In contrast, design details are very potent in affecting fatigue performance. Sharply notched fatigue specimens provide an indication of the nominal stresses that an ordinary structure may be expected to withstand in fatigue. Although it is difficult to approach the smooth-specimen fatigue strengths under service conditions, it is usually easy to gain a significant improvement in fatigue performance through careful attention to design details. The first step is to avoid asymmetric loading and stress concentrations due to small radii in re-entrant corners. A more sophisticated procedure, which usually requires verification by test, is the use of compressive prestressing of the specific surfaces where fatigue cracks are most likely to occur. Shot or hammer peening and surface rolling are the most commonly used mechanical methods of inducing local plastic deformation so as to improve resistance to fatigue.

Resistance to Corrosion

Atmospheric weathering is the most frequently encountered corrosive environment; as discussed previously, many applications of aluminum stem directly from good performance in the atmosphere. Extruded shapes or tubes used outdoors are normally alloy 6063 if strength is of less importance than price. Greater strength for extrusions can be obtained in alloy 6061, with little reduction of weathering resistance, a slight increase in price, and minimum extrudable thickness. For outdoor applications of sheet and plate, one of the many cold worked alloys is used where price is more important than strength (6063 is available only in extrusions and tubes). Alclad 3004 provides an excellent combination of strength, resistance to corrosion, and price, and it is used extensively for industrial roofing and siding. For unpainted outdoor structural applications that require higher strength, heat treated alloy 6061 sheet or plate is regularly employed, with little reduction in weathering capability or increase in cost.

The only aluminum alloys normally painted for outdoor applications are the aluminum-copper (2*xxx*) and the Al-Zn-Mg-Cu (7*xxx*) series. With alclad coating, these alloys also are used outdoors without paint, as for the external surfaces of most aircraft. The first and usual function of the cladding is to provide a physical coating that is very resistant to weathering and does not peel or chip under any circumstances. In addition, the cladding alloy is always chosen to be anodic to the core. Hence, at cut edges and any other place where the surface layer may be penetrated or removed, electrolytic protection is provided for the core at the expense of the coating. This sacrificial effect prevents perforation of the core material until a considerable area of the cladding has been consumed. Even when the core alloy is one that has good inherent resistance to corrosion, the ability to forestall penetration indefinitely is important.

Stress-corrosion cracking involves: (*a*) a material susceptible to this type of corrosion; (*b*) enduring tensile stress of sufficient magnitude at the surface of the metal; and (*c*) a corrosive environment. The time required to produce a stress-corrosion crack is a complicated function of these factors.

Susceptibility to stress-corrosion cracking depends on alloy, temper, and direction of loading with respect to grain orientation. Alloys in the 2*xxx* and 7*xxx* series are the only ones susceptible in regularly used tempers. Artificial aging generally reduces susceptibility, and special aging treatments can effectively remove susceptibility at the expense of maximum strength. The T73 temper makes alloy 7075 particularly resistant to stress corrosion. The 5*xxx* alloys containing more than 3% Mg can be made susceptible to stress-corrosion cracking by various combinations of cold work and aging. However, use of the commercially recommended tempers and service temperatures below 150 F prevents stress-corrosion cracking.

It is rare for stress-corrosion failures in service to result from longitudinal stresses, and the long-transverse direction is almost as safe. Failure is almost always due to a load in the short-transverse direction because of the shape of the grain structure.

The stress causing stress corrosion is usually one not contemplated in the design — for instance, stress from pressed-in bushings, tapered threads, misfits, and sometimes quenching stresses that are exposed and altered by machining. These can sometimes be avoided by suitable design and manufacturing control, or by shot peening or other plastic deformation of the surface.

The degree of corrosiveness of the environment has its greatest effect on the length of time before failure occurs. Thus, organic or other finishes delay stress-corrosion cracking, but they are not effective in preventing it if the other conditions are such that a failure would occur in a short time on uncoated material. Coatings help but do not solve the problem.

Special Characteristics

Low density is an attribute of all aluminum alloys. In the 1*xxx*, 3*xxx*, and 6*xxx* series, the weight per cubic inch is 0.098 or 0.099 lb. The 5*xxx* series ranges from 0.095 to 0.098, with the higher magnesium contents accounting for the lower densities. The 2*xxx* and 7*xxx* series range from 0.099 to 0.103. This characteristic rarely forms the basis for an engineering choice of one aluminum alloy in preference to another, but it is sometimes important from a cost standpoint.

High electrical conductivity is a specialized characteristic, so significant that two alloys are controlled in composition for the electrical industry. EC grade has a guaranteed conductivity of 63% IACS, and 2EC ranges from 55 to 60%, depending on temper. The latter is a heat treatable aluminum-magnesium-silicon alloy of specific interest for bus bar in sizes too large to be cold worked economically to the hard temper. A small loss of conductivity over EC is traded for the higher strength of 2EC.

The other alloys range in typical conductivity from 62%, for high-purity alloys such as 1060-O, down to 29%, for several of the high-magnesium alloys.

Thermal conductivity parallels electrical conductivity in the individual alloys. However, no specialized industrial market has developed around this characteristic on a quantitative basis. The values are 0.50 to 0.57 cal per cm per sq cm per °C per sec for the 1*xxx* alloys, down to 0.28 or 0.30 for the high-magnesium group.

Low modulus of elasticity is common to all aluminum alloys. Most engineering calculations employ the rounded off value of 10 million psi, either in tension or compression. This is the actual average value for alloys in the 1*xxx*, 3*xxx*, and 6*xxx* groups. The 5*xxx* series ranges from 10.0 to 10.3 million, with the higher-magnesium alloys having the higher moduli. The 7*xxx* group averages 10.4 million, and the 2*xxx* series, 10.6 million. The tension modulus is about 1% less than the average figure usually listed, and the compression value about 1% higher. Alclad sheet has a primary modulus in effect when both core and cladding are in the elastic stress range and a secondary one in effect when only the core is in the elastic range.

For engineering purposes, all aluminum alloys may be considered to have the same specific heat.

The range of variation in coefficient of thermal expansion for most aluminum alloys, excepting those high in silicon, is about 5%, usually not enough to be significant.

Low-temperature properties of all aluminum alloys are such that they are suitable for the same equipment, service, and fabricating procedures as for use at ordinary temperature levels. Tankage and other welded equipment are an important part of the cryogenic market, and alloy 5083 is the predominant selection for such uses.

In the kilovoltage range normally used for radiography, pure aluminum absorbs about one twelfth as much x-radiation as does steel. There are significant differences among the alloys, depending on the density and quantity of the alloying elements. Compared to high-purity aluminum as 1.0, alloy 3003 has an absorption of about 1.12; alloy 5086, about 1.02; and alloy 7075, about 2.00. In absorption of beta radiation, the variation among alloys is only 1 or 2%.

Although the half-life of aluminum 28, the principal isotope, is 2.27 min, aluminum alloys have longer half-lives due to alloying elements or impurities. Alloys in the 2*xxx* and 7*xxx* series have the slowest rate of decay and 6063 has the most rapid rate. Certain impurities such as cobalt, lithium, cadmium and boron are sometimes controlled for maximum rate of decay.

Aluminum is used for growing delicate cultures, because of its nontoxicity. For this specialized application, alloying constituents or impurities known to be harmful to the organism involved are carefully avoided. For example, manganese inhibits the growth of the culture that produces citric acid, and alloys other than 3003 are used for this purpose. For more general use, such as handling food, all alloys are equally nontoxic.

For normal engineering applications, all commercial alloys have equally advantageous paramagnetic properties.

Neither alloying constituents nor impurities have any appreciable effect on the kinetics of the reaction between aluminum and oxygen present in other metals. However, in the deoxidation of steel, a commercially pure grade of aluminum is employed.

Cost of Alloys

In the earlier discussion, cost was considered largely from the standpoint of pure aluminum compared to other metals. In choosing the best alloy for a specific part, considerations of performance, life, maintenance, processing, and fabricating are of primary importance. However, there are differences in the cost of various alloys. Table 4 lists actual price ranges for some mill-finish sheet, as an illustration of the range generally to be expected. A comparison based on price and strength shows, for example, that 5456 is a better buy than 3003 if tensile strength of welded joints is the critical factor. The strength ratio is 16,000 to 46,000 psi, or 2.87, in favor of welded 5456, and the price ratio is 39 to 50, or 1.28, in favor of 3003.

Other characteristics of various alloys may be compared in the same way, for selecting the most economical alloy.

Process Selection

In general, aluminum can be worked by all the processes that are employed for other metals. However, some advantages may be exploited with aluminum and, conversely, aluminum is at a competitive disadvantage in other processes. Resistance spot welding and soldering are examples of the latter.

Forming or shaping of parts is the first item to consider in process selection. There are usually two basic questions to be resolved: How far can the metal supplier process the part toward completion, and at what level of production quantity does a given fabricating sequence become justified. An outstanding example of special capability of aluminum is extrusions, where the die cost is so small that moderate production quantities are sufficient to permit the use of individually designed sections that eliminate machining and have built-in features to facilitate assembly. Pressure die castings require greater production to support the cost of tools, but machining and shaping costs are reduced, and the cost of the final part is less.

Bending, drawing, stretch forming, shear spinning, and many other metal deformation processes are used effectively on aluminum. Balancing the strength required in the finished part against the ductility needed for forming, so as to select the most suitable alloy, is a problem that sometimes requires solution by trial. When a cold worked (non-heat-treated) alloy is to be used, allowance must be made for variations in forming characteristic among lots of the same temper. For example, the variation from one lot to another may be as great as the nominal difference between the H36 and H38 tempers.

Sometimes, forming may involve such severe plastic deformation that only an annealed or freshly quenched, heat treated material will suffice. Even in this event, a wide range of tensile strength in the finished part is available. Without recourse to heat treatment, the choices range from tensile strengths of 10,000 to 42,000 psi (EC to 5456) in the original stock. Some zones of the finished part are work hardened to greater strength, and the strength is seldom uniform throughout the part. Should higher strength be required, heat treatable alloys can be used, even if the forming is severe. First consideration should be given to freshly heat treated stock, formed within half an hour of quenching. If the forming is too severe or takes too long, the last resort is to start with a heat treatable alloy and solution heat treat the partially formed workpiece. Solution heat treatment of the final part should usually be avoided if possible, because of the distortion that results from quenching. This distortion ranges from moderate for stocky, symmetrical parts to severe for large, gently curved parts made from minimum-gage sheet. All forming should be completed before artificial aging, as forming is easier in this condition.

Aluminum has some special machining characteristics. Usually, the highest cutting speed available on the machine tool is not too fast for aluminum. Another advantage is that heat treated products can generally be supplied in a mechanically stress-relieved condition that virtually eliminates warpage resulting from relief of residual stresses during the machining operations. For some parts, the chip characteristic associated with the term "free cutting" is desirable; alloys 2011, 6262, X310, and X335 have this property.

Assembly of parts may be accomplished by any conventional method. Mechanical fasteners made of aluminum are available and should be given first consideration to retain resistance to corrosion, good appearance, and light weight. A wide range of such fasteners is available. Bolts, machine screws, and wood screws are made from alloy 2024-T4. Rivets range in shear strength from 11,000 psi for alloy 1100 to 38,000 psi for 2024-T31 (which must be in the freshly heat treated condition for driving). Should aluminum fasteners be unsuitable, consideration should be given to stainless steel, which is compatible with aluminum from a corrosion standpoint, despite the separation of the two metals in the electrochemical series. Commercially plated steel fasteners usually rust after a few years of outdoor exposure and should not be employed where enduring good appearance is important.

The art of fusion welding of aluminum has made great advances in recent years, both from the standpoint of processes and suitable alloys, and general use of this joining technique continues to expand. Welding by either the metal-arc or tungsten-arc process utilizes argon or helium shielding and works best for intermediate metal thicknesses (0.060 to 1 in.). Only a few aluminum alloys are considered to be unweldable on a commercial basis, the most difficult and unsatisfactory being 7078, 7075, 7079 and 2024. The Thor and Titan rockets are welded from alloy 2014, which requires extreme care to avoid cracking and to maintain the expected weld strength. Alloy 2219-T87 is nearly as strong and much less of a problem in welding. The 5*xxx* alloys are progressively easier to weld (fewer problems with cracking) as the magnesium content is increased. As a group, they are outstanding in their performance for dump truck bodies, medium-size boats, and other all-welded structures. As these alloys are not easy to extrude, it is common to find 6061-T6 shapes welded to 5*xxx* sheet and plate.

Shrinkage resulting from the heating and cooling cycle involved in making a weld is a very important problem in welding, but it does not appear to be a function of alloy.

Brazing has been highly developed for aluminum, and special alloys and fluxes are available. The most outstanding use of brazing is for heat exchangers; brazing is employed also to assemble small tanks and other parts, generally in large production quantities. Each part ordinarily requires some setup and learning time. Heat is applied in an air furnace, by a flux bath, or by a hand-manipulated torch. The process is limited to alloys of low and intermediate strength by the melting temperature of available filler alloys.

The use of adhesives for fastening aluminum is growing rapidly. The same precautions in regard to cleanness and surface preparation as are used with other metals are required for highest-strength joints. Many applications do not require maximum strength (or reliability), and these may be bonded under less rigorous conditions. It is frequently possible to develop the full strength of the strongest alloys in properly designed and executed adhesive-bonded joints for up to ⅛-in. metal thickness.

Finishing. Some finishes are used entirely to protect against corrosion — for example, the paint on the inside of an aircraft wing. The cleaning and pretreatment procedures are as important as the paint itself. The best protection results from painting the parts in detail prior to assembly. Zinc chromate primer is most frequently used for this protective finish.

An extremely wide range of decorative finishes is used on aluminum. Organic coatings, vitreous enamel coatings, electroplating, anodic oxide coatings, chemical conversion coatings, and mechanically applied textures have extensive application. The latter are frequently combined with a coating to provide texture in addition to color. Regardless of finish, the inherent resistance of aluminum to weathering results in maximum life for that particular system.

Occasionally, there is need for a finish that is primarily of value from a functional standpoint. For example, aircraft landing gear parts are given a thick, hard chromium plate, which is subsequently honed to provide maximum resistance to wear on the telescoping parts. The message on a highway sign is a functional finish, although the ability to maintain an acceptable appearance for years without maintenance is the reason for using aluminum for the sign structure.

When anodic oxide coatings are applied as final finishes, the base alloy is all-important. As a base for paint, oxide coatings are effective regardless of alloy.

Porcelain (vitreous) enamel is used primarily for some architectural panels and for highway signs. Special alloys, often modifications of 3003 and 6061, assure good adhesion and provide adequate strength after the firing operation.

Special alloys, developed and used for automotive and household appliance trim, have been designed to approach the appearance of chromium plate and to exceed its service performance at a lower cost. Alloy 5053, made from super-purity aluminum and magnesium, is the top alloy in this field (at a premium price). Alloys 5257, 5457 and 5657 are used in large volume and are receptive to a durable, bright finish.

Reference

1 Wrought Aluminum and Its Alloys, Materials in Design Engineering, **61**, 117–132 (June 1965)

Chapter 4

Significance of Mechanical Properties in Design and Application

MARSHALL HOLT, J. G. KAUFMAN and G. W. STICKLEY

A DETAILED understanding of the mechanical properties of aluminum alloys is needed by the designer (for choice of alloy and establishment of allowable stress values), as well as by the aluminum producer (for control of the fabrication processes). Although quality control is usually based on room-temperature tensile properties, design specifications must include the full complement of allowable stress values, including compression, shear and bearing, for various loading and environmental conditions. In tests to determine properties, the magnitude and significance of the values obtained may depend somewhat on the design of the specimen, its location in the product, and the testing procedure that is employed.

Nature of Mechanical Properties

Variations in test results are to be expected, because no two production lots are exactly alike and because the evaluation of properties is, at best, a statistical procedure. To obtain meaningful information for the quality control of aluminum alloy products, standard tests are made on standard specimens taken from specified locations in successive production lots. Experience has shown that data obtained in this way fall into relatively narrow bands and that they are amenable to statistical analysis. Specifi-

The authors are with the Mechanical Testing Div., Alcoa Research Laboratories, New Kensington. Marshall Holt is chief; J. G. Kaufman and G. W. Stickley are assistant chiefs.

cation requirements are established so that only production lots of commercial quality will be accepted. The properties of virtually all lots are greater than the specified minimum values. In compilations of mechanical properties, it is necessary to differentiate between specification requirements and "typical properties", which are values at or near the median of all the test values.

ASTM standards (2) describe test procedures for evaluating a variety of properties. These methods should be followed closely. Furthermore, sampling and testing procedures always should be described in presentations of data.

Sampling for Testing. Because properties may vary in the piece, sampling procedures must define the location and orientation of test specimens. Generally, specifications for wrought aluminum alloy products require specimens taken with the longitudinal axis parallel to the direction of maximum flow during the metalworking process (with-grain or longitudinal direction). For heat treated sheet and plate wider than 9 in., the specimen axis is transverse to the direction of rolling and parallel to the rolled surface (long-transverse direction). For some thick hand forgings, specimens are taken from all three principal directions. The locations within the thickness and width of the part from which specimens are to be cut are included in the specification.

In castings and die forgings, it may not be feasible to remove specimens from the manufactured part, so alternate procedures are provided. Castings specifications generally require separately cast test bars, which are highly specialized castings; for forgings, test bars may be machined from prolongations or from separately forged coupons. All portions of a complex casting or forging do not develop the same mechanical properties, since rates of cooling and amounts of working in various locations differ. However, meeting specification requirements by successive lots assures that composition, fabrication procedure, and heat treatment have been controlled within satisfactory limits. For castings and forgings in which properties at certain regions are critical, the purchaser and producer should agree on the sampling and test procedures and the properties to be achieved.

Effects of Specimen Orientation. In comparison with other metals, the differences in properties associated with the direction of metal flow are usually small enough so that aluminum alloys can be considered essentially isotropic. However, in thick plate, forgings, and extrusions, the properties in the transverse direction in some cases may be appreciably lower than those in the longitudinal direction; representative values are shown in Table 1 (1). For these products, it may be necessary to take the anisotropy into account in the design of parts subjected to sustained high stress in the short-transverse direction.

Variation in properties through the cross section of a product is not generally of much consequence, but for structural members obtained by substantial machining of a product this variation may have to be considered. The critical section of a machined member could be at the point of minimum strength in the original product.

Size of Test Specimen. Whenever possible, tensile specimens described as standard (0.5-in. diameter or width) are used. Sheet-type specimens can be taken from some products; round specimens are often more practical and economical. For sheet-type and round specimens, there should be little or no differences in the values of tensile strength and tensile yield strength. The elongations of sheet-type specimens usually are lower than those of round specimens.

When it is necessary to test subsize tensile specimens, the largest specimen of proportionate dimensions is used. In measuring small dimensions and changes in these, the size of the

Table 1. Minimum Tensile Properties of Aluminum Alloy Plate, Hand Forgings and Extrusions (1)

Direction	Plate(a) 7075-T651	Plate(a) 7079-T651	Hand forgings(b) 7075-T6	Hand forgings(b) 7079-T6	Extrusions(c) 7075-T6511	Extrusions(c) 7079-T6511
Tensile Strength, Psi						
Longitudinal	72,000	71,000	73,000	72,000	81,000	79,000
Long-transverse	73,000	73,000	71,000	70,000	66,000	70,000
Short-transverse	65,000	68,000	69,000	67,000	...	...
Yield Strength, Psi						
Longitudinal	64,000	64,000	61,000	61,000	72,000	70,000
Long-transverse	62,000	63,000	59,000	59,000	57,000	62,000
Short-transverse	55,000	59,000	58,000	56,000	...	...
Elongation in 4D, %						
Longitudinal	5	6	9	9	7	7
Long-transverse	3	6	4	5	1	4
Short-transverse	1	2	3	4	...	...

(a) Thickness, 2.001 to 2.500 in. (b) Thickness, 2.001 to 3.000 in.; maximum cross-sectional area, 256 sq in. (c) Thickness, 1.500 to 2.999 in.; maximum cross-sectional area, 20 sq in.

graduations of the measuring device may control the accuracy of the measurement; it is thus undesirable to use specimens with a test section smaller than 0.25 in. in diameter or width. Much greater skill is required in machining smaller specimens to insure that the machining technique (for example, tailstock pressure, depth of cut, finish, and heating) does not significantly influence the test results.

Design Values vs Specification Values. If a production lot meets the specification requirements, the purchaser can be reasonably sure that it will behave in fabrication and in service in about the same manner as other lots that have met the same specification. Meeting these requirements, however, does not imply that those properties were necessary for the application, nor does it insure satisfactory performance in other applications. The purchase specification does not provide all the information needed to establish design values.

Stress-Strain Curves and Elastic Constants

Stress-strain curves (Fig. 1) provide considerable information for comparing alloys and for design. They are developed for axial (tension or compression) or shear loadings (torsion) and are continuous records of the relation between stress and strain.

In the region of small plastic deformations, the departure of

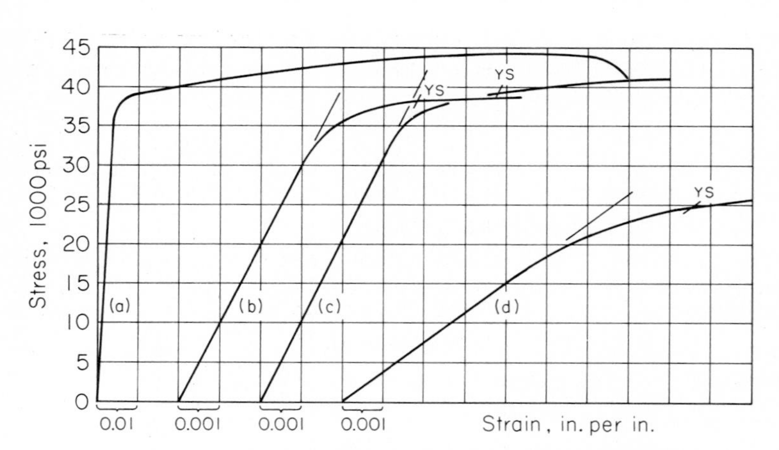

Fig. 1. Stress-strain curves for drawn tube of alloy 6061-T6. (a) Complete tensile curve, gage length of 8 in.; (b) expanded tensile curve, gage length of 8 in.; (c) compressive curve; (d) shear curve.

the stress-strain curve from the initial straight line usually is gradual; for a few alloys, particularly some of the 5*xxx* in the annealed temper, the departure may be abrupt (Fig. 2). The magnitude of the plastic strain developed before the stress again increases with increasing strain usually is less than 1%; for mild steel, this may be as much as 5%.

Elastic and Proportional Limits. Although these properties generally differ only slightly, if at all, their definitions are not the

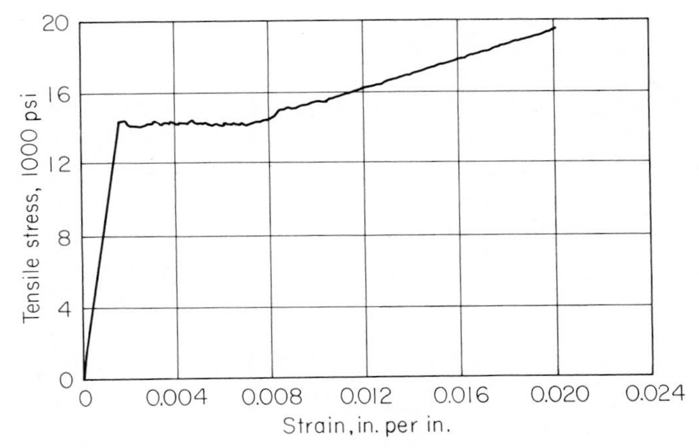

Fig. 2. Stress-strain curve for rod of alloy 5052-O

same. Elastic limit is the limit of elastic action and may be higher than the proportional limit, which is the limit of proportionality of stress to strain. The determination of either generally is impractical, because the shape of the curve in this region is highly affected by the sensitivity of measuring and plotting the strains and of representing the plotted points with a curve. In addition, the determination is affected by the scales employed, as shown in Fig. 1, where two scales of abscissas are used for the tensile data. Also, these properties may vary considerably depending upon residual stresses, which in turn may vary widely among, and within, pieces and lots of the same alloy and product. For these reasons, the elastic and proportional limits are of little practical interest, and the yield strength, to be defined subsequently, is a more important property.

Modulus of Elasticity and Poisson's Ratio. The moduli of elasticity of aluminum alloys are dependent mainly upon composition; they are virtually independent of temper, product, and direction of working. Although published values for modulus of a stated alloy may vary considerably, the wide range is mainly the result of variations in accuracy and sensitivity of testing equipment, skill in testing, method used, and interpretation of results.

The moduli of elasticity of selected alloys under tensile and compressive loading (Young's modulus) and under shear loading (shear modulus or modulus of rigidity) are listed in Table 2. Moduli in compression are about 2% higher than in tension.

The moduli in tension and in shear are related as follows:

$$G = \frac{E}{2(1 + \mu)}$$

in which G = modulus of elasticity in shear in psi, E = modulus of elasticity in tension in psi, and μ = Poisson's ratio.

For aluminum alloys, the value of Poisson's ratio is about one third. Hence, the modulus of elasticity in shear is about three eighths of the modulus of elasticity in tension.

The modulus of elasticity is used in equations for elastic deflection and elastic buckling strength of structures. For

Table 2. Moduli of Elasticity of Selected Aluminum Alloys

Alloy	Modulus, million psi: Tension, E	Compression, E_c	Shear, G	Alloy	Modulus, million psi: Tension, E	Compression, E_c	Shear, G
1100	9.9	10.0	3.8	5052	10.1	10.2	3.8
2020	11.1	11.4	4.2	6061	9.9	10.1	3.8
2024	10.5	10.7	4.0	7075	10.3	10.5	3.9

stresses above the elastic range, the tangent modulus and the secant modulus sometimes are utilized as the "effective moduli", especially in buckling problems. Figure 3 shows how these two properties are determined from a stress-strain curve. Above the elastic range, they are stress dependent; in the elastic range, they are identical with the modulus of elasticity.

Typical and Minimum Stress-Strain Curves. The most valuable part of the stress-strain curve extends to slightly beyond the yield strength (strains generally less than 1%). However, there are some uses for complete stress-strain curves (Fig. 1).

The application of stress-strain curves in design and alloy selection demands that the curves be representative of all lots of a specific product. Because of the variable nature of production lots, the stress-strain curve determined for a single lot may not be representative of other lots, and so "typical" and "minimum" stress-strain curves are employed. These curves are developed from data from tests of many lots (3). Typical strengths and curves represent expected average behavior, while minimum strengths and curves show the level of behavior that all lots are expected to meet.

Nominal Versus True Stress-Strain Curves. In developing stress-strain curves for mechanical property considerations, the stresses usually are based upon the original cross-sectional area, although the area actually changes as the test proceeds. Similarly, the strains are based upon the original gage length. Curves

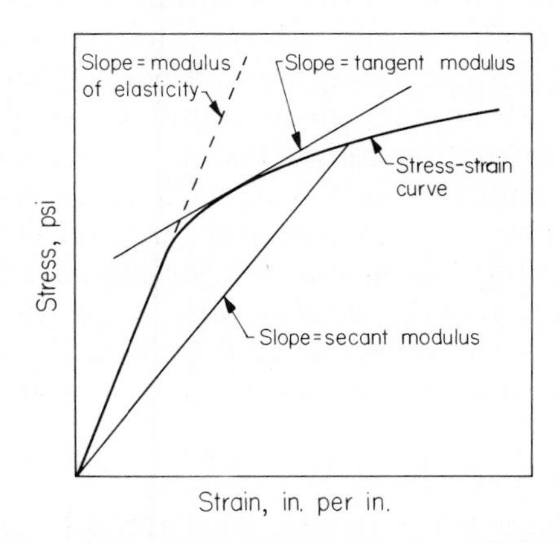

Fig. 3. Determination of tangent modulus and secant modulus from the stress-strain curve

developed with these definitions usually are referred to as "nominal" or "engineering" stress-strain curves. There are applications, however, where it is advantageous to consider the deformation based on the instantaneous area, and the strain based on the instantaneous gage length. Curves developed with these definitions are referred to as "true" stress-strain curves (4). Up to the point of necking (in the range of uniform elongation), the nominal and true curves are related algebraically and one can be developed from the other.

For stresses in the range of elastic action and even up to the yield strength, there is no significant difference between the nominal and true stress-strain curves (Fig. 4). For stresses greater than the yield strength, the difference between the two curves gradually increases; it is greatest in the range of and beyond the point where the maximum load occurs. In the nominal tensile stress-strain curve, the maximum load determines the maximum stress, that is, the tensile strength. For most aluminum alloys, fracture takes place at a subsequent smaller load; the amount of the decrease after passing the maximum load depends also on the testing equipment and procedure. In the true stress-strain curve, the maximum load determines only another point on the curve of increasing stress with increasing strain, and fracture occurs at a higher stress, the true fracture strength. These differences are associated with the facts that (*a*) longitudinal strain and lateral contraction are nearly uniform along the gage length until the maximum load is developed, and (*b*) additional strain and contraction are concentrated within a short portion of the gage length and a neck is formed. Computations made in developing the nominal curve do not take the nonuniform deformation into account, as is done in developing the true curve. Unless otherwise qualified, all references in this chapter are to nominal stresses and nominal strains.

Strain-Hardening Coefficient. On log-log coordinates, the portion of the true tensile stress-strain curve beyond the yield strength usually can be represented by a straight line. This line can be represented by the equation:

$$\sigma_t = K(\epsilon_t)^n$$

in which σ_t = true stress in psi, K = strength coefficient in psi, ϵ_t = true strain, and n = strain-hardening coefficient. The value of n generally approximates the true strain at fracture (4).

The strain-hardening coefficient sometimes is considered to be an index of the formability and of the toughness of a material, but there seems to be little practical use of these concepts.

Tensile Properties

Standard procedures for tensile tests are given in ASTM E8 (2), and, unless the test conditions are described as differing from the standard test conditions (plane stress), ASTM definitions are implied.

For aluminum alloys, the yield strength is generally defined by an offset in the stress-strain curve equal to 0.2%. For some purposes, and in some foreign countries, the yield strength is defined by other values of offset, such as 0.1 and 0.01%, the latter being a close approximation of the elastic limit.

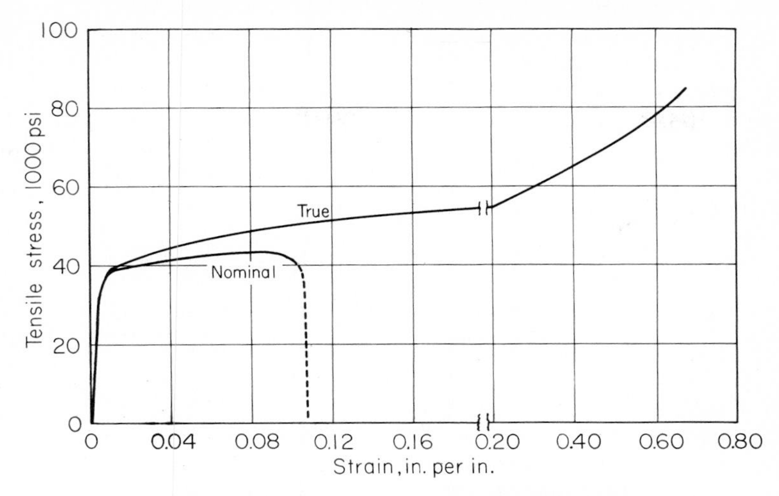

Fig. 4. Stress-strain curves for rod of alloy 6061-T6

The designer must deduce allowable stress values from the values of tensile strength and yield strength determined by standard test procedures (2). For example, the ASME Boiler and Pressure Vessel Code (5) has four criteria for establishing the allowable stress value, two of which apply to the tensile strength and yield strength. In these, the allowable stress value shall not exceed one fourth of the tensile strength or two thirds (for nonferrous alloys) of the yield strength.

Values of elongation and reduction of area often are considered measures of ductility or workability. If the specimen necks substantially in fracturing, it follows that the elongation value depends strongly on the gage length (Fig. 5). On the contrary, if the specimen fractures with only insignificant necking, the elongation value is virtually independent of gage length. The data in Fig. 6 show the variation in elongation along a specimen. Elongation is nearly uniform except within about 1 in. of the fracture (region of the neck).

The elongation in "zero" gage length is computed from the reduction of area, with the assumption of constant volume (Volume I, Chapter 6, Fig. 18).

The aluminum industry relies heavily on tensile properties and makes tests on most production lots. Therefore, data on tensile properties are more abundant than on other properties. The data from these are used for quality-control purposes and analyzed statistically to determine the normal ranges of values.

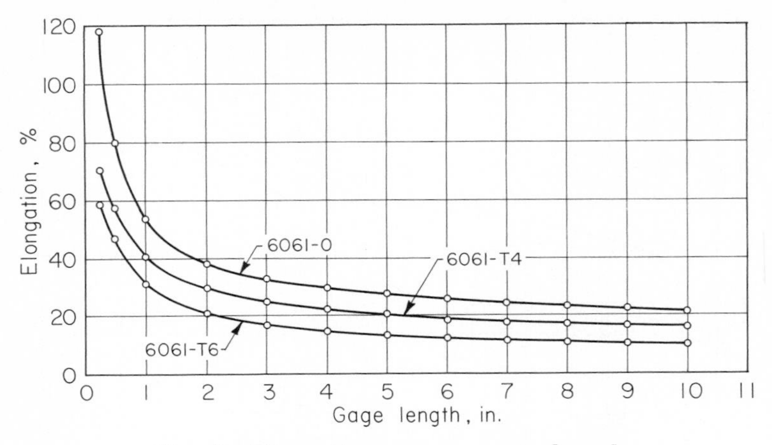

Fig. 5. Elongation versus gage length for different tempers of rod of alloy 6061

The results of these continuing analyses are the basis for revisions of specification values and for the establishment of design values. Expected minimum values of other properties (for example, compressive, shear, and bearing) are derived from the minimum tensile properties by applying empirical factors developed from specific interrelated tests.

Compressive Properties

Under compressive loading, aluminum alloys may fail by one of four general types of behavior. Relatively short members (slenderness ratio less than about 10) of very ductile alloys deform by shortening continuously into a flat wafer, perhaps with eventual development of edge cracks. In contrast, short members of very-high-strength alloys may fail by shearing or splitting after considerable deformation. Members with thin webs or walls may fail by local structural instability and long members by lateral deflection.

Compression tests of small specimens provide valuable information for design to avert these types of failure. The significant properties usually determined are compressive modulus of elasticity and yield strength (stress at an offset of 0.2%). Compressive stress-strain curves (Fig. 1) are employed to develop curves of tangent and secant moduli as a function of stress (Fig. 3). For alloys with low capability of deformation, the compressive strength may also be obtained.

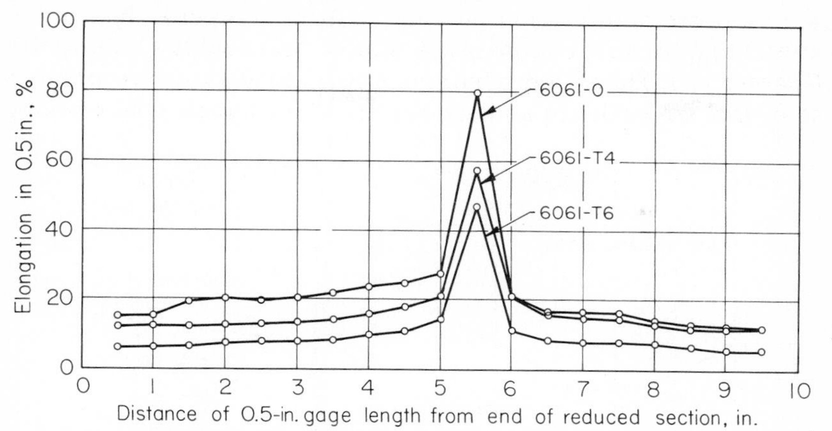

Fig. 6. Elongation of different tempers of rod of alloy 6061

For most aluminum alloys and products, the compressive yield strength is about equal to or greater than the tensile yield strength. Therefore, in lieu of compressive data, the compressive yield strength generally is assumed to be equal to the tensile yield strength; also, the tensile and compressive stress-strain curves normally may be assumed to be the same.

When aluminum alloys have been cold worked by stretching (for straightening or stress relieving), the tensile yield strength is increased but the compressive yield strength in the direction of stretching may be reduced to a level lower than that of the tensile yield strength; this is an illustration of the Bauschinger effect. The compressive yield strengths in directions normal to the direction of stretching are increased slightly. For certain 2*xxx* series alloys in the T3 or T4 temper (for example, 2024 and 2219), the reductions in longitudinal compressive yield strength may be appreciable (as illustrated for 2024 in Fig. 7). In addition, if the stretching is done after artificial aging, the effect may be large, even for alloys not considered to be affected greatly by cold work (as illustrated for 2014-T6 in Fig. 7). If stretching of heat treatable alloys is performed as an intermediate operation (between solution heat treatment and artificial aging, T*x*51 temper), most or all of the effects of stretching are removed by the aging, the directional differences are almost eliminated, and the tensile and compressive yield strengths are usually equal within about ±3%.

To relieve internal stress, aluminum alloy forgings sometimes are cold worked by compressing (Tx52 temper), instead of stretching, because compression is more practicable (Volume III, Chapter 10). The effects of compressive cold working on compressive yield strength are analogous to those of tensile cold working

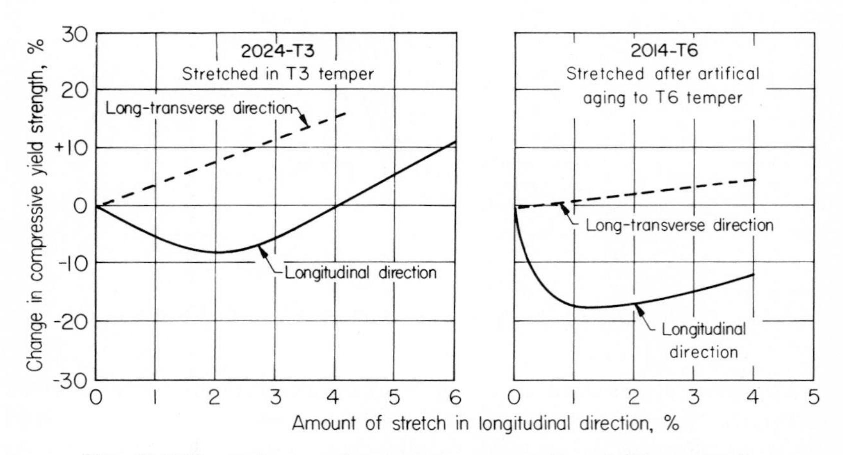

Fig. 7. Effect of stretching on compressive yield strength

on tensile yield strength. That is, compressive cold working causes an increase in compressive yield strength and a decrease in tensile yield strength in the direction of working. Compressive yield strengths in directions normal to the direction of loading are reduced 3 to 5% by deformations of 1 to 3%.

Shear Properties

Shear strength has several interpretations, such as the force required to shear cylindrical members on transverse sections, the force required to punch holes in plate and structural shapes, and the resistance to failure of members under torsional loads.

The shear strengths of metals can be determined by a number of methods, including those in which (*a*) the material is sheared on one plane (single-shear) or two planes (double-shear), (*b*) a hole is punched (punching-shear or blanking-shear), and (*c*) torsional loads are applied. These methods provide useful data, but the values are not identical, because the loading conditions do not always represent pure shear. The tests should be made so as to avoid stresses other than shear stresses and so that the specimens actually fail in shear. In single-shear tests, these conditions commonly do not prevail because of the eccentricity of loading and the resulting rotation of the member into a position to better accommodate the loading.

In double-shear tests and also in blanking-shear tests of sheet, only the ultimate shear strength is determined. On the contrary, in torsional tests of circular tubes, it is feasible to measure the shear strains, plot the shear stress-strain curve, and determine the shear yield strength at 0.2% offset. Shear stress-strain curves (Fig. 1) have many of the characteristics of tensile and compressive stress-strain curves.

The value of ultimate shear strength is a function of the dimensions of the specimen or member. In double-shear tests, the values obtained depend on the spacing of the shear planes and the stiffness of the tool (6). Values obtained with a rigid tool with relatively large spacing between planes average about 10% higher than those obtained with rivet-testing devices with less rigidity and in which shear planes are only one diameter apart.

In torsion tests, the strain is not uniform across the section, and a meaningful value of shear strength cannot be determined by inserting the maximum torque into the equation for elastic stress. The error is less in tests of tube than in tests of solid rods, because the stress is relatively more uniform over the cross section; the error decreases with wall thickness until buckling is encountered.

The shear strengths of aluminum alloys average about 60% of the tensile strengths; the range is from about 55 to 80%. The lower percentages are applicable to high-strength wrought alloys, especially in extrusions, and the higher percentages to annealed or low-strength wrought alloys and some casting alloys.

The shear strengths of some aluminum alloy products also vary with the plane of shear and direction of loading. For example, in plate the shear strengths on planes parallel to the surface average about 15% lower than those on planes normal to the surface. For planes normal to the surface, the shear strengths are about 10% higher when the loads are applied parallel to the surface than when applied normal to the surface.

Hardness

Hardness values usually are of little direct value to the designer, but sometimes they are useful for quality control, particularly during fabrication of semifinished parts.

The hardness of aluminum alloys generally is measured as

resistance to indentation under static load, by tests such as Brinell, Rockwell, and Vickers (2). Less common tests are the Knoop indentation, the Shore scleroscope rebound, and scratch hardness tests.

In Brinell tests of aluminum alloys, a standard combination of load and ball (500-kg load on 10-mm ball, or an equivalent) must be used. Otherwise, different values may be obtained and the differences are not the same for all alloys (Fig. 8). Values for certain other metals, such as steels, are not comparable with those for aluminum alloys. When this test is properly made, the hardness numbers for different wrought aluminum alloys and tempers are comparable, and there is a broadly defined, linear relationship between hardness and tensile strength (Fig. 9).

The Rockwell test also is employed frequently and advantageously for process-control testing. However, there are no linear relationships with other mechanical properties, and no single Rockwell scale can be used for all alloys or, in some cases, for all tempers of the same alloy. Figure 10 shows approximate relationships between tensile strength and Rockwell E values for different tempers. Figure 11 shows approximate Brinell-Rockwell relationship for several Rockwell scales.

Hardness tests of aluminum alloys may be used satisfactorily for various purposes, provided the results are carefully interpreted. If the composition of an alloy is known, such tests generally indicate whether the metal is in the annealed or heat treated condition. Hardness values may indicate within accepta-

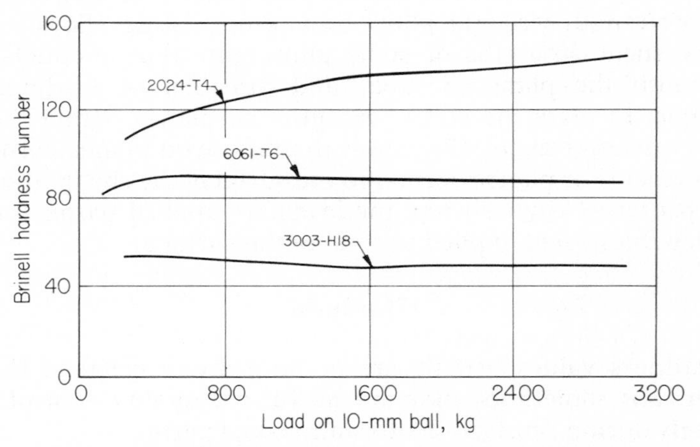

Fig. 8. Brinell hardness versus load on a 10-mm ball

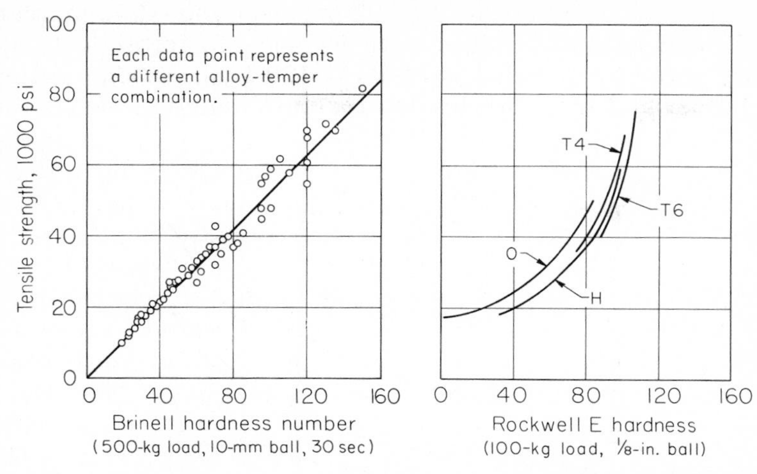

Fig. 9. Tensile strength versus Brinell hardness of wrought aluminum alloys

Fig. 10. Tensile strength versus Rockwell E hardness of aluminum alloy sheet

ble limits whether certain heat treating operations have been performed properly. Also, the tests frequently are used to separate mixed lots of alloys with sufficiently different compositions and tempers.

Hardness tests of aluminum alloys are much less informative than tension tests. They can give some indication of the tensile strength, although the hardness numbers may actually prove to be misleading in this respect. Useful relationships with yield strength and ductility have not been found. Hardness tests are not always reliable as a final inspection test for quality of aluminum alloy products. For this purpose, the tension test is preferred.

The many compositions and tempers of wrought aluminum alloys result in a wide variety of combinations of tensile strength, yield strength, and elongation, as well as pronounced differences in cold working capacities. It, therefore, is not possible to obtain any simple accurate conversion factor or chart relating these factors to hardness.

Hardness tests of coated aluminum alloys generally are unsatisfactory, because the test measures the average hardness of only a relatively small volume of metal near the surface. Alclad coatings usually are much softer than the core material, and the actual thickness of coating varies with the total thickness. In tests of some alclad 2024-T3 0.032-in. sheet and 0.250-in. plate, the Brinell hardness values were 98 and 55, respectively; the typical value for nonclad 2024-T3 is 120 Bhn. Anodic coatings are harder and more brittle than the base material; hence, they

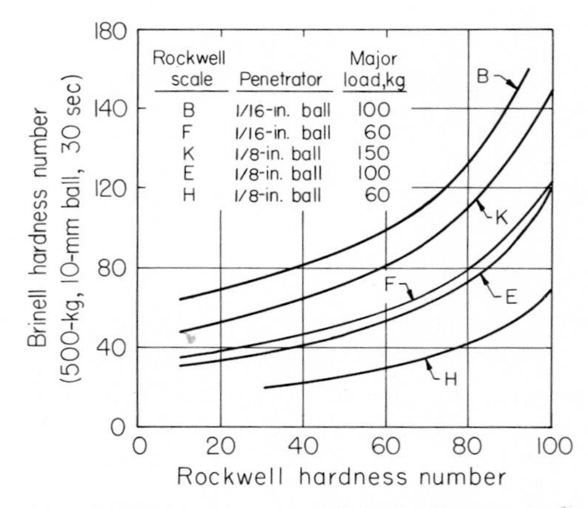

Fig. 11. Approximate correlation between Brinell and Rockwell hardness of wrought aluminum alloys

may have a significant effect on the results of hardness tests. For example, Vickers hardness numbers (5-kg load) of 89 and 105 were obtained on bare and coated sheet, respectively.

Bearing Properties

The bearing properties of aluminum alloys are used in the design of riveted, bolted, and pinned joints, or where edgewise loads are applied by pins or rods. They are established as the resistance of specimens to crushing against a round, hardened steel pin tightly fitted in a hole in the specimen and loaded in the plane of the specimen.

The relation between the load and the deformation of the hole has many of the characteristics of a tensile stress-strain curve. The bearing yield strength is the stress at a permanent set equal to 2.0% of the pin diameter. The maximum load before fracture defines the bearing strength. Both bearing strength and yield strength are based on the area of the projection of the contact surface (diameter of pin multiplied by thickness of specimen). Bearing values depend on the test conditions and the proportions of the specimens (7). To obtain uniform results, bearing specimens and fixtures should be cleaned thoroughly (for example, ultrasonically) and care should be taken to avoid touching the bearing surfaces before the test is performed (8).

Formability

Significance of Laboratory Tests. Formability is defined as the relative ease and success with which a metal can be shaped through plastic deformation. Aluminum is among the most workable common metals. It can be formed by processes involving tensile, compressive, shearing, or bending forces, or by combinations of these. There is, however, no universal measure of formability, and various types of tests are used. A test may be applicable only when it closely simulates a specific forming operation.

Tensile Tests. Elongation in the tensile test is one of the most commonly used measures of formability. The value usually obtained, however, represents a composite of characteristics, dependent to some extent on the size, shape, and gage length of the test section. This value is governed by two factors: the uniform elongation, which is independent of gage length, and the localized elongation in the vicinity of the fracture, which is

Table 3. Indices of Formability From Tensile Tests of Several Wrought Aluminum Alloys (0.5-In.-Diam Specimens)

Alloy and temper	Ratio of yield strength to tensile strength	Elongation, %			Reduction of area, %
		In 0.5*D*	In 4*D*	Uniform	
1100-O	0.39	147	53	35	88
1100-H12	0.89	130	25	12	76
1100-H18	0.92	...	23	9	73
2024-O	0.36	50	22	13	43
2024-T36	0.84	45	17	12	17
2024-T4	0.62	46	23	14	34
2024-T6	0.80	35	15	7	26
2024-T86	0.95	53	9	3	25
6061-O	0.36	118	38	20	75
6061-T4	0.67	70	30	13	54
6061-T6	0.87	58	21	8	49
6061-T91	1.00	35	9	0.2	34
7075-O	0.45	...	20	10	40
7075-W(a)	0.48	48	26	19	37
7075-T6	0.86	...	19	8	31

(a) Tested 4 hr after quenching

dependent on the extent of necking. Uniform elongation is representative of the characteristics needed in stretching operations, whereas localized elongation represents those needed in severe bending or forging. These two types of elongation may rate materials differently (Table 3). For example, experience has shown that 2024-T4 is better than 2024-O for forming by stretching, whereas 2024-O is better for forming by bending.

Reduction of area and ratio of yield strength to tensile strength, also obtained from the tensile test, are sometimes employed as measures of formability. Reduction of area is related closely to localized elongation. Workability is normally greater for those alloys with low ratios of yield to tensile strength.

Bend tests are made sometimes to evaluate formability and are of value in establishing limiting shop practices. One such test reveals the smallest radius over which a metal can be bent without fracture; the values vary, not only with alloy and temper, but also with thickness or diameter. Guided and wrap-around bend tests with prescribed radii are used to establish the quality of welds and, thus, the qualifications of welding procedures and welders.

Cupping tests are used to evaluate the formability of sheet by stretching with a punch. The more popular of this variety of tests are the Erichsen and Olsen tests (2). In both, a cup is formed by making a spherical indentation in a thin test specimen with a punch and die mounted in a press. The unit of measurement generally is the depth of the cup when fracture occurs. The Mullen test (2) is often applied to foil, and the hydrostatic pressure is the index of formability. After trial runs of a particular forming operation have shown that a specific alloy and temper are satisfactory, these cupping tests may be useful supplementary tests for quality control.

Another form of cupping test is made to determine the degree of draw possible with a certain value of hold-down pressure, type of lubrication, forming pressure, and punch-and-die clearance. Experience is required to correlate data with plant practices.

Creep and Creep-Rupture Properties

In the preceding discussions of tensile, compressive, and shear properties, it is implied that the stress is increased continuously and that the accompanying strains are independent of time under any specific stress. If, however, a stress less than the

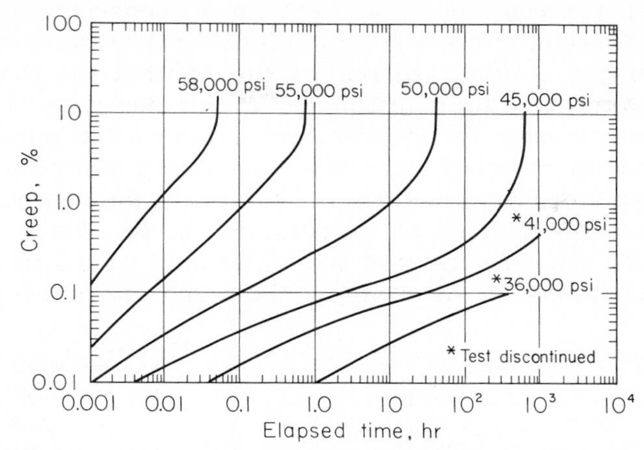

Fig. 12. Creep-time curves for 2024-T851 plate, 0.875 in. thick, at 300 F, in the longitudinal direction

ultimate strength is maintained for a period of time, the strain increases continuously (Fig. 12). If the stress is high enough or held long enough, the specimen eventually fails in the mode that would occur under continuously increasing loading. In this respect, the behavior of aluminum is like that of other metals.

Significance of Laboratory Tests. Creep strength cannot be expressed by a single number, but it must be related to time, amount of deformation, and temperature. Similarly, creep-rupture strength must be related to time and temperature. Strengths are lower for longer times and higher temperatures (Fig. 13).

At stresses less than about the yield strength, the amount of creep at room temperature is very small. Room-temperature creep thus is seldom used in establishing working stresses. At elevated temperatures, however, the amount of creep within the anticipated life of a structure or machine part may be significant; the creep strength corresponding to the tolerable amount of deformation therefore must be considered an upper limit of the working stress. For example, Section VIII of the ASME Boiler and Pressure Vessel Code (5) sets the creep strength associated with a minimum creep rate of 0.1% in 10,000 hr as one limit on the allowable stress value. However, criteria of this type neglect much of the primary creep and imply that a certain amount of deformation is tolerable. Another approach to the consideration of creep in design is to specify the total creep and the associated time as a criterion for establishing the allowable stress.

Similarly, creep-rupture strength can be considered in establishing allowable stress values by specifying the time to fracture. For example, another criterion of the ASME code (5) is the stress to produce rupture in 100,000 hr. But, designers of rockets might be concerned with rupture lives of only a few minutes.

The use in design of allowable stress values derived from the creep and creep-rupture strengths has led to the misconception that creep occurs only at temperatures in the "creep range". Employing other fractions of the tensile and yield strengths or other conditions for determining the creep and stress-rupture

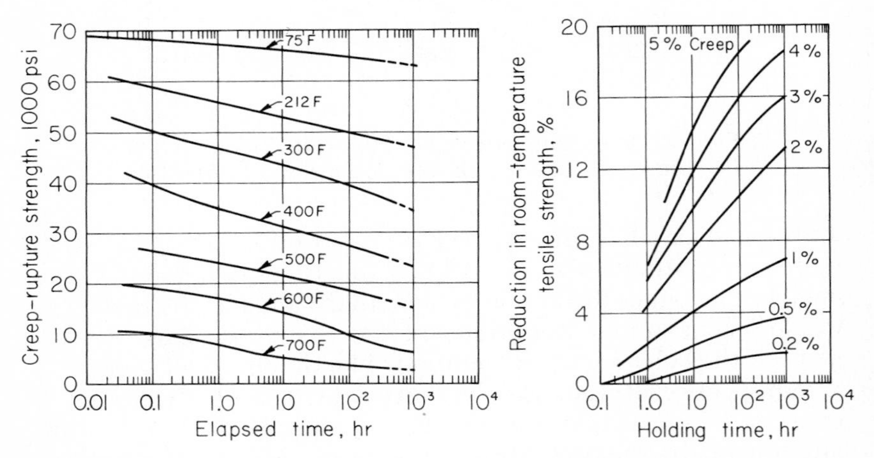

Fig. 13. Creep-rupture strengths of 1-in. plate of 2219-T851 at various temperatures, in the longitudinal direction

Fig. 14. Per cent of creep damage versus holding time for various creep strains at 300 F for alloy 1060-H19

strengths might lead to another range of temperature in which the creep characteristics control the allowable stress values — thus, to a different "creep range".

Methods of Extrapolation. Since it generally is impractical to continue creep and creep-rupture tests beyond a few thousand hours, it is necessary to determine strengths by extrapolating available data. Several procedures have been suggested for making such extrapolations, notably those by White, Clark, and Wilson (9), Larson and Miller (10), Manson and Haferd (11), and Orr, Sherby, and Dorn (12). Since there are no data from tests of extremely long duration with which to evaluate these methods of extrapolation, they should be used with caution.

Effects of Prior Creep. Creep strains generally are accompanied by changes in the grain structure and in the subsequent mechanical properties. Test results given in Fig. 14 indicate that creep developed in 1060-H19 over long exposure periods causes a greater loss in strength than the same amount of deformation developed at the same temperature over a shorter period but at a higher stress (13). Creep at higher temperatures causes a greater loss in strength than the same deformation at lower temperatures; in fact, creep at room temperature, like cold work, seems to have a strengthening effect. As seen in Fig. 14, the decrease in strength associated with creep strains of 0.2% (the offset used to define yield strength) is not more than 2%.

Creep strains in alloys 2020, 2024, and 2219 also are associated with some decrease in tensile strength; however, the decreases are less than 5% for strains as great as 0.5%.

Relaxation. In contrast to creep, which is the time-dependent strain resulting from stress, relaxation is the time-dependent decrease in stress under conditions of constraint. Relaxation is a complex interaction of (*a*) creep strain, (*b*) the accompanying direct relief of the stress, and (*c*) the indirect relief of load through relief of elastic stress in adjacent members. Design for relaxation is difficult, because of the problems in obtaining suitable information on relaxation characteristics; this arises because of the need for extremely sensitive automatic feedback mechanisms with rapid response, and the strong dependence of relaxation phenomena on the characteristics of the testing equipment. Freudenthal (14) has suggested that relaxation curves for aluminum alloys could be based on the stress-rate effects on inelastic straining, which have been determined in tests with linearly increasing or decreasing stresses.

Fatigue Properties

Like other metals, aluminum fractures when subjected to repeated loadings of sufficient magnitude and duration. The stresses are lower than those required for static failure; for long-life failure, the stress may be in the elastic stress range. The cycles of loading in service may be of constant maximum stress or of constant maximum strain, or, as usually occurs, reflect a wide range of loading conditions. The variations in loading conditions may be solely the result of mechanical conditions, or they may be the indirect result of different thermal conditions.

The cyclic stresses may be in tension, compression, shear, or combinations of these. The highest stresses, those of most importance, usually are localized and associated with design features, surface conditions, and internal characteristics that are effective stress concentrators. In fact, stress concentrators often are more important than the basic fatigue strength of the alloy.

Fatigue strength cannot be expressed by a single number. The number of cycles must be stated and the stress cycle must be described in terms of the maximum and minimum stresses or by one of these stresses and the ratio or difference of the stresses. Importance of number of cycles and stress ratio will depend on the type of structure under consideration.

The most commonly quoted fatigue property of aluminum alloys is the fatigue limit, defined as the strength at 500 million

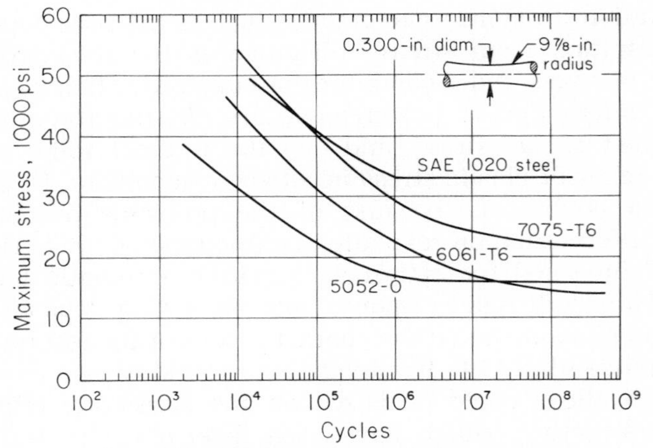

Fig. 15. Rotating-beam fatigue curves for some aluminum alloys and mild steel

cycles, under reversed bending stresses, maximum and minimum stresses equal but opposite in sign, $R = -1.0$ (Tables 3, 4, and 5, Volume I, Chapter 8, and Tables 4, 5, 6, 10, and 11, Volume I, Chapter 9). This is determined from a curve (*S-N* diagram) developed by making one or more series of tests at various stresses and plotting the stress, *S*, against the number of cycles, *N* (Fig. 15). As can be seen in Table 4, the rotating-beam fatigue limits of the heat treated alloys are about 0.3 times the tensile strengths; for many of the annealed non-heat-treatable alloys, the ratios are about 0.5.

Table 4. Relationship Between Fatigue Limit and Tensile Strength for Some Aluminum Alloys

Alloy and temper	Typical fatigue limit(a), psi	Typical tensile strength, psi	Ratio of fatigue limit to tensile strength
1100-O	5,000	13,000	0.38
3003-O	7,000	16,000	0.44
3004-O	14,000	26,000	0.54
5050-O	13,000	21,000	0.62
5052-O	16,000	28,000	0.57
5052-H34	18,000	38,000	0.47
5052-H38	20,000	42,000	0.48
5056-O	20,000	42,000	0.48
5083-O	22,000	42,000	0.52
5086-O	21,000	38,000	0.55
2014-T6	18,000	70,000	0.26
2024-T4	20,000	68,000	0.29
2219-T62	15,000	60,000	0.25
6061-T6	14,000	45,000	0.31
7075-T6	22,000	83,000	0.27
7079-T6	22,000	78,000	0.28
7178-T6	22,000	88,000	0.25

(a) Determined from rotating-beam tests at 500 million cycles

The shear fatigue strength for a stated stress ratio is about 0.6 times the corresponding value for axial tensile and compressive stresses.

There are differences in fatigue properties of nominally identical lots of an alloy; however, the data lie within a relatively narrow band, as in Fig. 16, which contains the results of tests of 16 lots of various products of 6061-T6. These differences in fatigue properties can seldom be related to variations in production operations, or to the other characteristics of the material, such as tensile strength, elongation, grain size, and direction of metal flow.

The *S-N* curves for aluminum alloys differ in shape from those for some steels, as indicated in Fig. 15. The curve shown for steel contains a sharp break; the fatigue limit is defined by 10 million cycles of stress. With most aluminum alloys, there is no such break, and the curves do not become horizontal at less than 500 million cycles. The aluminum-magnesium alloys are exceptions, in that their *S-N* curves are essentially horizontal beyond 1 million cycles (see curve for 5052-O in Fig. 15).

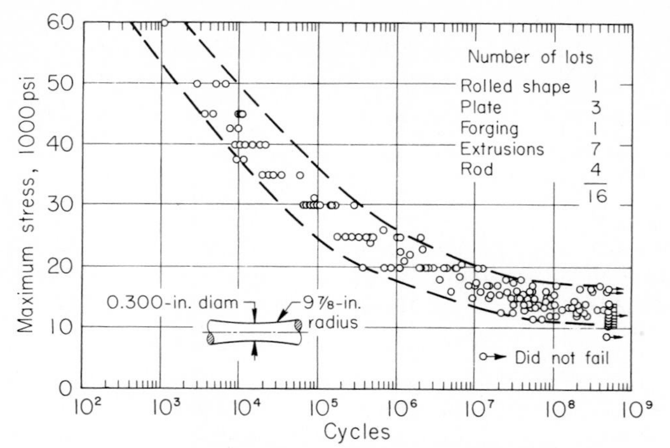

Fig. 16. Rotating-beam fatigue band for products of alloy 6061-T6, in the longitudinal, long-transverse, and short-transverse directions

Data obtained in tests of machined smooth specimens are of interest for comparative purposes, although they generally are not directly useful in the design of structural members. Tests of specimens with machined notches are used to obtain relative measures of notch sensitivity of different alloys and tempers; such tests may be of value in considering stress concentrations approximately equal to that of the notch employed in the tests. As with data from many other types of test, they are useful primarily in comparing alloys with respect to inherent fatigue strength and notch sensitivity. Data from fatigue tests of actual structural members, which contain the design discontinuities that will be encountered in service, are the most helpful kind.

Fracture Characteristics

Fracture characteristics involve those properties by which the resistance to rapid crack propagation and low-ductility fracture (without appreciable plastic deformation) can be evaluated. Information concerning fracture characteristics is used to develop structures or components where maximum resistance to low-ductility fracture is required, by providing criteria to rate materials and establish allowable stress values. This information is of maximum importance for those conditions where fracture with little or no prior yielding would result in total loss of the assembly ("catastrophic" failure).

Elongation and reduction of area from the tensile test, as measures of ductility, are indices of fracture characteristics; the ratio of yield strength to tensile strength and the magnitude of the area under the tensile stress-strain curve also serve this function. However, these properties seldom are sufficiently descriptive of the general behavior of materials to be useful to the materials engineer or designer concerned with low-ductility fracture (15). As a result, more specialized criteria, such as fracture toughness, tear resistance, and notch sensitivity, are needed. These can be divided into (*a*) measures of capacity to absorb energy, and (*b*) indices of notch toughness.

Ability to Absorb Energy. The magnitude of the area under the tensile stress-strain curve provides a measure of the capacity of a material to absorb energy under simple tensile loading.

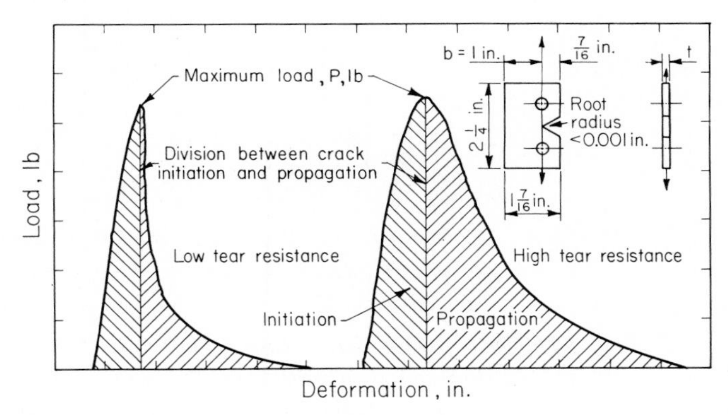

Fig. 17. Tear-test specimen and load-deformation curves

Although this area may be useful for some purposes, it generally is not reliable as an indicator of resistance to rapid crack propagation. Other measures of energy-absorption capacity define better the fracture behavior of aluminum alloys.

Charpy and Izod notched-bar impact tests have been employed widely to determine the transition temperature in ferritic steels. Because these tests are used widely in the steel industry, they are sometimes suggested for aluminum alloys. However, the aluminum alloys do not exhibit a transition temperature, and notched-bar impact-test values for most alloys are nearly constant over the temperature range from room temperature to −452 F. Consequently, the test has no value for this purpose. Since many aluminum alloys are so tough they do not fracture completely in notched-bar impact tests, no valid data are obtained for these alloys. Comparison of notched-bar impact test results for different metals has no recognized value; even within the aluminum alloy systems, comparisons are unreliable. Certainly, the notched-bar impact test does not provide data that can be used to measure impact resistance of structures.

The search for the explanation of the sudden failures of welded steel ships during the 1940's led to the development of the Navy tear test by Noah Kahn of the Brooklyn Naval Shipyard (16). A modification of this test has been used to rate aluminum

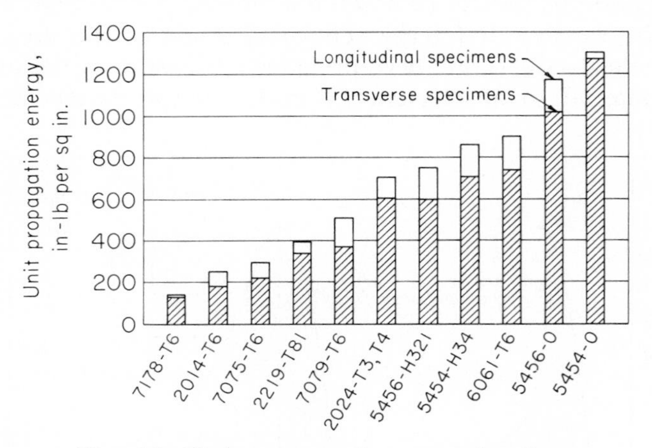

Fig. 18. Unit propagation energies from tear tests of 0.063-in. aluminum alloy sheet

alloys (15). Measures of the energies required to initiate and propagate cracks in specimens of the design shown in Fig. 17 are obtained by determining the areas of appropriate regions under the load-deformation curve; examples are shown in Fig. 17. In place of the keyhole notch in the Navy specimen, a sharp notch is used, because it affords increased sensitivity in measuring the energy required to propagate the crack. The energy required to propagate a crack in the tear test divided by the net cross-sectional area of the specimen is referred to as "unit propagation energy" (Fig. 18).

Although the tear test provides only a merit rating for aluminum alloys, the unit propagation energy from the test is related directly to the strain-energy release rate for alloys that conform to the fracture-mechanics theory (17). This indicates that the tear test provides a realistic measure of resistance to rapid crack propagation, lending confidence to its application in rating the many aluminum alloys that do not conform to the stringent conditions of the fracture-mechanics theory.

Test procedures and parameters have been developed (17) that relate fracture strength to size of flaw or crack, or to design detail, thus providing a measure of "fracture toughness". These procedures are useful to designers of structures that are highly stressed in tension, with a relatively large reserve of stored elastic energy in the system, and that utilize the high-strength aluminum alloys. They are not useful for the design of most civil-engineering structures.

Most aluminum alloys do not exhibit rapid crack propagation under elastic conditions, but instead they yield generally, even in the presence of severe stress raisers (15). For these alloys, the fracture-mechanics approach is not applicable and, if it is attempted, the results will be misleading. The high-strength heat treatable aluminum alloys, however, are amenable to the fracture-mechanics approach.

The most useful information for the application of fracture mechanics to design is the stress-intensity factor, K. This represents the relationship between the uniform gross tensile stress, σ, and the length, $2a$, of a crack or flaw in the field of elastic stress. The critical stress-intensity factor, K_c, (at the onset of unstable crack propagation) decreases with increase in metal thickness and approaches a constant minimum value, which is identified as K_{Ic} and is associated with fracture under entirely plane-strain conditions.

When members containing through-the-thickness cracks are loaded increasingly in tension, there is generally a period of slow crack growth until the crack reaches a critical length. Then rapid crack propagation occurs in the essentially elastically stressed material. For relatively thin members, the amount of slow crack growth may be large and the fracture is of a shear type. In these cases, plane-stress conditions exist, and fracture is controlled by the value of K_c. With greater thicknesses, the degree of constraint increases and the state of stress approaches plane strain. The amount of slow crack growth prior to rapid crack propagation decreases and there is a gradual transition to flat fracture. For thick sections, slow crack growth is negligible and fracture is controlled by K_{Ic}.

The small burst of unstable crack growth that sometimes precedes slow crack propagation, and also the unstable growth of part-through cracks or cracks emanating from fully embedded discontinuities in structures of all thicknesses, are also broadly controlled by plane-strain toughness, K_{Ic}.

Representative K_{Ic} values for some alloys are listed in Table 5 and in Ref 15.

Notch toughness represents a measure of fracture characteristics based solely upon the effect of stress raisers on the load-carrying capacity of materials, without any consideration of the energy dissipation.

A common criterion of notch toughness is the ratio of the net fracture strength of a notched specimen to the tensile strength of the material (notch-strength ratio). This is pertinent where a measure. of structural efficiency is desired. Thus, for riveted joints, the ratio of the net strength at fracture to the tensile strength (or preferably to the design stress) is the logical criterion. In fatigue loading, the ratio of the fatigue strength of notched specimens to that of smooth specimens for a given number of cycles, or the inverse ratio (the effective strength-reduction factor), is used. In creep-rupture loading, the ratio of the rupture strengths of notched specimens to those of smooth specimens for a specific rupture life is the logical criterion.

Table 5. Representative Values of Plane-Strain Stress-Intensity Factor, K_{Ic}, for Some Sheet and Plate Alloys(a)

Alloy and temper	K_{Ic}, psi $\sqrt{in.}$ Longitudinal	Long-transverse
2014-T6, -T651	28,000	25,000
2024-T3, -T4, -T351	50,000	45,000
7075-T6, -T651	28,000	25,000
7075-T73, -T7351	35,000	32,000
7178-T6, -T651	23,000	21,000

(a) Average values from tests of center-notched, notched-round, single-edge-notched, and surface-flawed specimens.

A criterion of notch toughness pertinent to evaluations of inherent fracture characteristics might be based on the capacity of a material to deform plastically in the presence of a stress raiser and thus to redistribute load to adjacent material or components. For this purpose, the ratio of the net fracture strength of a notched tensile specimen to the tensile yield strength (notch-yield ratio) is significant (18), since the yield strength, more than the tensile strength, is a measure of the lowest stress at which appreciable plastic deformation occurs. If the strength of a notched specimen equals or exceeds the tensile yield strength, fracture is accompanied by appreciable general yielding; if it is appreciably less, fracture develops with little plastic deformation.

The notch-yield ratio provides more consistent ratings for aluminum alloys, regardless of specimen design, than does the notch-strength ratio (18). Furthermore, ratings based upon notch-yield ratio are consistent with those derived from tear and fracture-toughness tests, providing further support for their use when evaluating the basic fracture characteristics of materials.

There has been considerable controversy as to the optimum type of specimen and notch shape for evaluating notch toughness. Very sharp notches (notch-tip radii $\leq$0.001 in.) are favored by many to represent a theoretical crack. Others regard the sharply notched specimen as unrealistic and prefer relatively mild notches. The sharp notches generally provide the greatest range of notch-yield ratios for a specific group of aluminum alloys; hence, they are the more discriminating. The sharper notches also provide ratings, when based upon notch-yield ratio, that closely conform to those based on tear and fracture-toughness tests. ASTM testing procedures have recognized this in specifying notch-tip radii $\leq$0.0007 in. for specimens used in screening tests to evaluate notch toughness (17).

Evaluations of notch toughness for rating alloys are directly applicable to the design of only those structures that are actually represented by the shape of the notch, such as tests of bolted joints. Similarly, it usually is unrealistic to set an acceptance limit for notch-strength or notch-yield ratio, such as unity, and state that alloys and tempers with lower ratios are unsatisfactory.

Damping Capacity

The damping capacity of a material is its ability to absorb vibrational energy and, therefore, to damp out or resist the development of vibrations. It is sometimes referred to as internal friction. Damping capacity can be measured by a variety of tests; the results depend on test method and magnitude of the maximum stresses developed. Consequently, damping capacity is expressed in various ways and the measured values are not readily converted from one unit to another. Furthermore, the data seldom are applicable directly to the design of a structure; they usually are of value only to merit-rate the alloys.

One common means of evaluating relative damping capacity is to determine the rate at which free vibrations decay in free-free (simple) beam or fixed-free (cantilever) beam specimens. Log decrement (δ) is the simplest measure of damping capacity from this test. Specific damping capacity, based on the percentage of total potential or kinetic energy in the system dissipated in each cycle of vibration, may be estimated as 200 δ for values of δ less than 0.1. The damping capacity increases with the maximum stress during the cycle of vibration; the rate of increase is much greater for stresses above the elastic limit of the metal. For this reason the lower-strength aluminum alloys and those with soft alclad coatings have much higher damping capacities than the high-strength bare alloys.

It is important to recognize that the vibration characteristics of most structures are less dependent on the damping capacity of the alloy than on features in the design, particularly the joints.

Effects of Strain Rate

Tensile tests for purposes of material qualification and evaluation are usually made at strain rates in the range from 0.001 to 0.1 in. per in. per min, so that fracture occurs within 1 to 3 min after the beginning of loading. Although this range is considered as "standard" or "static", it represents only a narrow band in a wide range of strain rates that are encountered, extending from those in relatively long stress-rupture tests, where fracture may develop after hundreds of thousands of hours, to those in explosive fractures that develop in milliseconds. Although this may be considered as a continuous range, the effects of strain rate can be discussed in two sections: (*a*) the effects of rates less than those normally used in conventional tensile tests, and (*b*) the effects of rates higher than those normally employed.

Low Strain Rates. In tensile tests at room temperature, aluminum alloys are not considered to be sensitive to strain rates less than 0.01 in. per in. per min (2).

As the strain rate is reduced below the practicable limit of a tensile test, the condition approaches that in which the load on the specimen remains constant and the creep rate becomes the strain rate. Hence, the subject merges with that of creep and creep-rupture.

High Strain Rates. The term "impact", as applied to strain rate, is not clearly defined; in fact, a test made at an "impact" rate actually is made at a specific strain rate represented by some point in the spectrum of rates. For aluminum, a high rate generally increases both ultimate and yield strengths, and ductility. For strain rates up to about 0.01 in. per in. per min, the effects are small, however, and can be ignored. At higher rates, the effects are increasingly significant. Although the amount of the increase dependent upon strain rate appears to differ with alloy and temper, the over-all effect is essentially the same. Data are insufficient to establish the variations in the trends for specific alloys or tempers.

The increases in properties of aluminum alloys with increases in strain rate are more pronounced at elevated temperatures than at room temperature; in general, the effects increase with temperature.

As the strengths of aluminum alloys at high strain rates are at least as high as those in "static" tensile tests, the use of the static test values in design represents a conservative approach for high-strain-rate applications. Few attempts are made to take advantage of the higher properties at the higher strain rates.

Effects of Environment

Most material specifications are concerned with a special, but readily available, set of environmental conditions: room temperature and normal atmosphere. However, many service applications involve deviations from these conditions, and it thus is necessary to know the effects of variations in environment on properties.

The most significant environmental factor is temperature. Room temperature represents only one point (or a small range) in the scale between absolute zero and the melting range of a metal; so the properties of the metal at room temperature represent points on smooth curves covering the entire range, as illustrated in Fig. 19. Nevertheless, it is convenient to discuss the effect of temperature by subdividing temperature into those ranges below and above room temperature.

Temperatures Below Room Temperature. The strengths of aluminum alloys increase with decrease in temperature. The increases at −50 or −100 F are almost negligible, but at lower temperatures they become increasingly significant. The tensile strengths and tensile yield strengths of most aluminum alloys at −320 F average about 30 and 20%, respectively, higher than those at room temperature; at −423 F, they average about 50 and 35% higher. The actual differences vary appreciably with composition and temper. The strengths of aluminum alloys at low temperatures are not influenced by length of exposure at those temperatures, with the exception of a few alloys in the freshly quenched temper that age harden at room temperature. Refrigeration retards aging of these alloys, but does not completely prevent the process. The strengths of aluminum alloys at room temperature after exposure to low temperatures are not influenced by the exposure.

The elongations of most alloys increase with reduction in temperature, at least to −320 F. With further decrease in

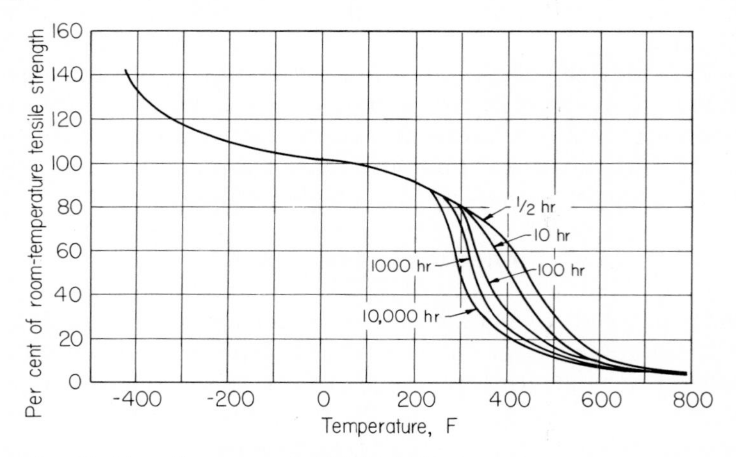

Fig. 19. Tensile strength of 2014-T6 at various temperatures

temperature, the elongations of some alloys decrease slightly, but usually not below the room-temperature values. For a few high-strength heat treated alloys, elongations remain about the same or decrease gradually with temperature.

The shear and fatigue strengths of aluminum alloys increase with decrease in temperature. The amounts of the increases are of the same order as those in tensile strengths, and the ratios of the properties remain virtually constant.

Moduli of elasticity — in uniaxial tension and compression and in shear — also increase with decrease in temperature at a nearly linear rate, as shown in Fig. 20. This indicates that Poisson's ratio is essentially the same as at room temperature.

The toughness or fracture characteristics of many aluminum alloys, as measured by the results of tear tests (unit propagation energy) or notch-tensile tests (notch-yield ratio), remain about the same or improve with decrease in temperature, as shown by representative data in Fig. 21 and 22. For the high-strength 7*xxx* series alloys, however, there is a gradual decrease in toughness with decrease in temperature, the extent of which varies with composition and temper (Fig. 22). This indicates that care should be exercised to avoid severe stress raisers in these alloys in cryogenic applications.

Temperatures Above Room Temperature. The strengths of aluminum alloys generally decrease with increase in temperature above room temperature, except that in some cases the effects of age hardening offset the other effects of exposure

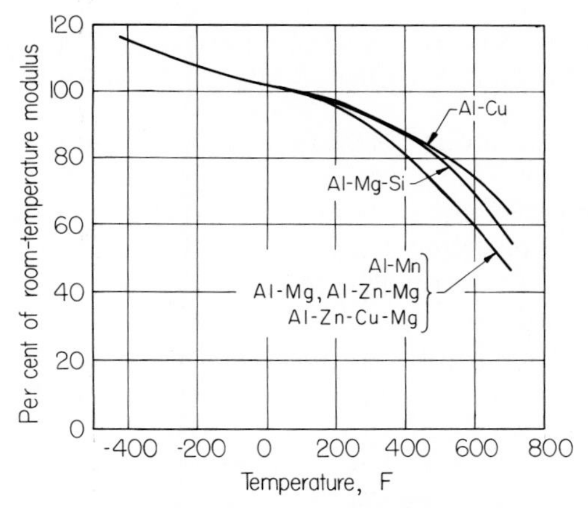

Fig. 20. Modulus of elasticity of aluminum alloys at various temperatures

within narrow temperature ranges for various holding periods. The length of the exposure is important in the case of cold worked or heat treated alloys (Fig. 19), but it has little or no effect on the properties of annealed alloys. The time-temperature dependence of strengths requires that the properties over the entire period of the exposure be considered in selecting the alloy, in establishing allowable stress values, and in determining section sizes.

Shear, bearing and fatigue strengths appear to vary with temperature in much the same way as tensile strengths; ratios of these strengths to tensile strengths generally may be considered constant. Similarly, ratios of the tensile and compressive

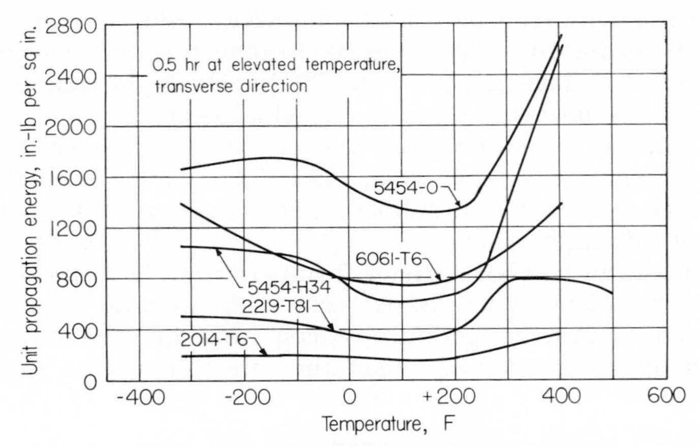

Fig. 21. Unit propagation energies of 0.063-in. aluminum alloy sheet at various temperatures

yield strengths are about the same at elevated temperatures as at room temperature. As a result, it is possible for designers to deduce compressive, shear, bearing and fatigue design properties at elevated temperatures from knowledge of the ratios of the properties at room temperature and the tensile properties at elevated temperatures.

The ductility of aluminum alloys, as measured by elongation and reduction of area, generally increases with increase in

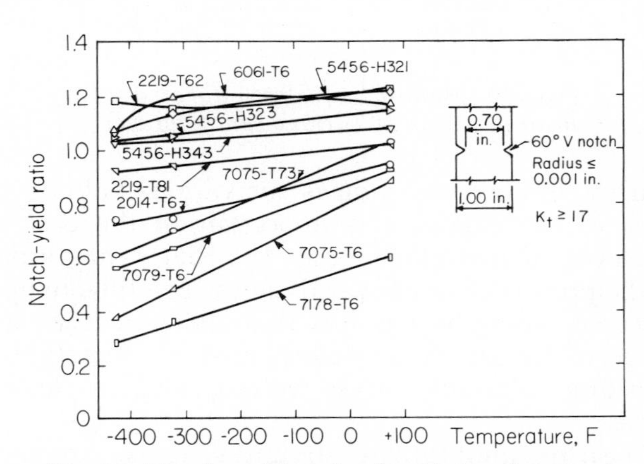

Fig. 22. Notch-yield ratios for 1/8-in. aluminum alloy sheet; average of longitudinal and transverse directions. Notch-yield ratio = notch-tensile strength divided by tensile yield strength.

temperature and with length of exposure at temperature. Exceptions to these trends parallel those with respect to strength. The ductility of heat treatable alloys exposed after solution heat treatment decreases until the maximum strength is attained, and then increases with overaging. The ductility of annealed alloys is not affected by length of exposure.

Toughness, as indicated by tear resistance or notch toughness, follows the same general trends with respect to temperature as does ductility, as measured by elongation and reduction of area. The changes in toughness are usually more pronounced. The implications to the designer are clear; if the toughness of fully age-hardened aluminum alloys is satisfactory at room temperature, no problem should generally be anticipated because of elevated-temperature exposure. For alloys that artificially age harden, however, the toughness in the corresponding fully aged condition must be considered.

Because of the time-temperature dependence of the properties of aluminum alloys at elevated temperatures, various parametric procedures have been suggested for unifying, interpolating, and extrapolating them, and for calculating the effects of complex exposures (combinations of different elevated temperatures and times). These procedures include those considered descriptive of creep and creep-rupture behavior, but they are generally less successfully used. Nevertheless, certain variations of these procedures have been incorporated into handbooks for designers; it

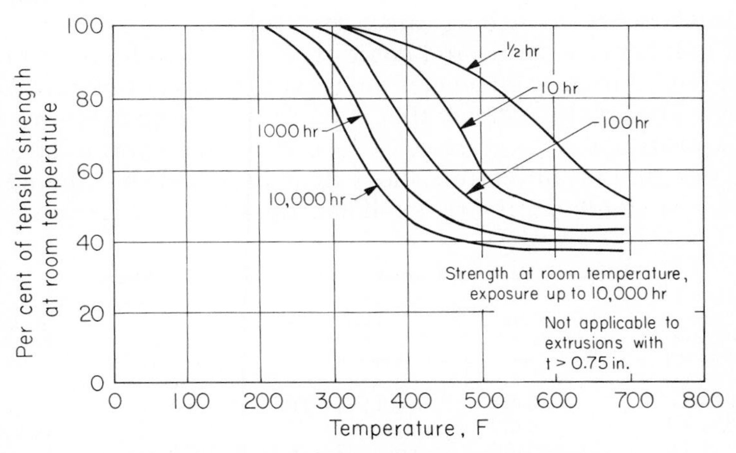

Fig. 23. Tensile strength of 2014-T6 at room temperature after exposure at elevated temperature

is important that the designers utilizing these procedures recognize that, at best, they provide only estimates of the properties, with no consistent degree of accuracy or assurance of safety.

Similar trends apply to the properties of aluminum alloys determined at room temperature after elevated-temperature exposure, as indicated by Fig. 23. There is one important exception: The modulus of elasticity is not affected permanently by elevated-temperature exposure; it returns to the room-temperature value after exposure.

Surrounding mediums represent a broader environmental factor than temperature, to the extent that the previous discussion of mechanical properties was based on the assumption of a normal indoor atmosphere, uncontaminated and at moderate humidity. If the surrounding medium is other than normal atmosphere, the effect on the properties may be significant.

There are three basic variations of the surroundings that are of practical importance: vacuum, gaseous, and liquid environments. (The effects of corrosive environments are discussed in Volume I, Chapter 7.)

There are relatively few data available on the effect of a vacuum on mechanical properties. The available data indicate that strength and ductility are either unaffected or increased by the vacuum, presumably because of the complete exclusion of moisture and other corrosive elements. Fatigue strengths are usually reported to be higher in a vacuum than in normal atmosphere, although it has been suggested that there may not be any benefits where long times are involved.

A number of gaseous and liquid mediums have been evaluated with regard to their effects on the tensile properties of aluminum alloys. The results indicate that exposures to those mediums that are known to induce corrosion cause some reduction in strength and ductility of aluminum alloys. It is expected that the effects would be significantly greater if the duration of exposure were

Table 6. Fatigue Limits of Bare and Alclad Sheet

Bare alloy and temper	Fatigue limit(a), psi	Clad alloy and temper	Cladding alloy	Fatigue limit(a), psi
2014-T6	18,000	Alclad 2014-T6	6053	15,000
2024-T3	18,000	Alclad 2024-T3	1050	13,000
7075-T6	20,000	Alclad 7075-T6	7072	13,000

(a) Completely reversed flexure; 500 million cycles

for a substantial period of time before testing. Similarly, exposure to these mediums should decrease the fatigue strength and creep-rupture strength.

Nuclear radiation, a source of considerable concern with some metals, has little or no deleterious effect on the mechanical properties of aluminum and its alloys. The strengths of aluminum alloys in the annealed temper are increased and elongations are decreased, which is similar to the changes resulting from cold working. The properties of alloys in the high-strength tempers are not significantly affected (19).

Surface Condition and Coatings

Most aluminum alloys are sufficiently ductile that there is usually no appreciable influence of surface conditions on strength or ductility in tensile tests, except if specimen preparation introduces heating or working.

For a few high-strength aluminum alloys in the T6 temper, such as 2020 and 7178, shearing may produce minute edge cracks. These edge cracks are effective stress raisers and reduce the tensile strength and elongation; this influence is greater on stress-rupture and fatigue strengths.

The surface residual compressive stresses produced by shot peening or surface rolling may increase the fatigue strength significantly (Volume III, Chapter 10). The effects may not always be significant in complete structures that contain design and fabrication stress raisers.

With soft alclad coatings there are reductions in tensile strength and yield strength proportional to the coating thickness. The corresponding reductions in fatigue strength are larger, being as much as 35%, as shown in Table 6.

Anodic coatings have no appreciable effect on tensile properties, but they may reduce the fatigue strength as much as 30% depending on factors such as thickness and sealing of coating.

References

1 "Metallic Materials and Elements for Flight Vehicle Structures", MIL-HDBK-5 (Aug 1962, and revisions June 1965); "Standards for Aluminum Mill Products", Aluminum Association, New York, 1966
2 "ASTM Standards", American Society for Testing and Materials
3 R. L. Templin, E. C. Hartmann, and D. A. Paul, Typical Tensile and Compressive Stress-Strain Curves for Aluminum Alloy 24S-T, Alclad

24S-T, 24S-RT, and Alclad 24S-RT Products, Tech Paper 6, Aluminum Company of America (1942)

4 J. Marin and M. G. Sharma, Material Rating Based Upon True Stress-Strain Properties, Welding J, Res Suppl, **23**, no. 8, 375s–378s (1958)

5 "ASME Boiler and Pressure Vessel Code", Section VIII, Par UA-601, American Society of Mechanical Engineers, New York (1965)

6 J. G. Kaufman and R. E. Davies, Effects of Test Method and Specimen Orientation on Shear Strength of Aluminum Alloys, Proc ASTM, **64**, 999–1010 (1964)

7 R. L. Moore and C. Wescoat, Bearing Strengths of Some Wrought Aluminum Alloys, NACA Tech Note 901 (1943)

8 G. W. Stickley and A. A. Moore, Effects of Lubrication and Pin Surface on Bearing Strengths of Aluminum and Magnesium Alloys, Mater Res Std, **2**, 747–751 (1962)

9 A. E. White, C. L. Clark, and R. L. Wilson, The Fracture of Carbon Steels at Elevated Temperatures, Trans ASM, **25**, 863–884 (1937)

10 F. R. Larson and J. Miller, Time-Temperature Relationship for Rupture and Creep Stresses, Trans ASME, **74**, 765–775 (1952)

11 S. S. Manson and A. M. Haferd, A Linear Time-Temperature Relation for Extrapolation of Creep and Stress-Rupture Data, NACA Tech Note 2890 (March 1953)

12 R. L. Orr, C. D. Sherby, and J. E. Dorn, Correlations of Rupture Data for Metals at Elevated Temperatures, Trans ASM, **46**, 113–128 (1954)

13 K. O. Bogardus, M. S. Hunter, M. Holt, and G. R. Frank, Jr., Effects of Prior Creep on the Tensile Properties of Cold-Worked Unalloyed Aluminum, "Proc Joint Intern Conf Creep", Institution of Mechanical Engineers, London, England, 1963, p 1-17 to 1-31

14 A. M. Freudenthal, The Phenomenon of Stress Relaxation, Proc ASTM, **60**, 986–999 (1960)

15 J. G. Kaufman and Marshall Holt, Fracture Characteristics of Aluminum Alloys, Tech Paper 18, Aluminum Company of America (1965)

16 N. A. Kahn and E. A. Imbembo, A Method of Evaluating Transition from Shear to Cleavage-Type Failure in Ship Plate and Its Correlation with Large-Scale Plate Tests, Welding J, **27**, 169s–182s (1948)

17 Reports of Special ASTM Committee on Fracture Testing of High-Strength Sheet Materials: first report — ASTM Bull, no. 243, 29–40 (1960) and no. 244, 18–28 (1960); second report — Mater Res Std, **1**, 389–393 (1961); third report — Mater Res Std, **1**, 877–885 (1961); fourth report — Mater Res Std, **2**, 196–203 (1962); fifth report — Mater Res Std, **4**, 107–119 (1964). "Fracture Toughness Testing and Its Application", ASTM STP 381 (1964).

18 J. G. Kaufman and E. W. Johnson, The Use of Notch-Yield Ratio to Evaluate the Notch Sensitivity of Aluminum Alloys, Proc ASTM, **62**, 778–791 (1962)

19 J. G. Watson, J. L. Christian and J. W. Allen, A Study of the Effects of Nuclear Radiation in High Strength Aerospace Vehicle Materials at the Boiling Point of Hydrogen, General Dynamics Research Report ERR-AN-085 (Sept 27, 1961); Mat Design Eng, Materials Selection Issue, **60**, No. 5, 38 (Mid-Oct 1964)

Chapter 5

Design Factors for Castings

E. V. BLACKMUN

DESIGNERS and other engineers whose work is closely related to the activities of design departments are concerned primarily with the capabilities of aluminum alloy castings, and the practicability of their production by available foundry processes. It is the purpose of this chapter to provide an understanding of the benefits of relating the design of castings to the factors affected by the characteristics and capabilities of the principal aluminum casting processes (Volume III, Chapter 2). In so doing, this discussion supplements and augments the information in the "Casting Design Handbook" (1).

In the design of aluminum alloy castings, functional requirements and appearance are the primary considerations, along with certain factors imposed by the casting processes.

Several examples of accepted design details are shown in Fig. 1: methods of joining walls, blending bosses and flanges, and beading holes to obtain quality parts. The recommended dimensions are averages, and the use of either larger or smaller numerical factors may result in casting defects.

Die Castings

The general rules of good casting design (Fig. 1) apply to die castings. Table 1 provides tolerance data for die castings.

Wall thickness should be as nearly uniform as possible. The practical range of wall thickness is influenced by the necessity to

The author is technical manager for ingot sales, Aluminum Company of America, Pittsburgh.

fill the die cavity. When the conditions of metal flow are difficult, a wall of 0.150 to 0.180 in. may be needed. When the casting is small and its shape permits straight-line flow of metal from the gates, the minimum wall thickness may be 0.090 in. Surface requirements also affect the minimum economical wall thickness. A surface that is to be polished must be reasonably free of flow lines and small casting imperfections. This quality of surface is more readily obtained with 0.100 to 0.125-in. sections than with thinner ones.

The surface roughness of die castings is directly dependent on the original finish of the die and the number of castings that have been produced. Parts made from new or repolished dies can

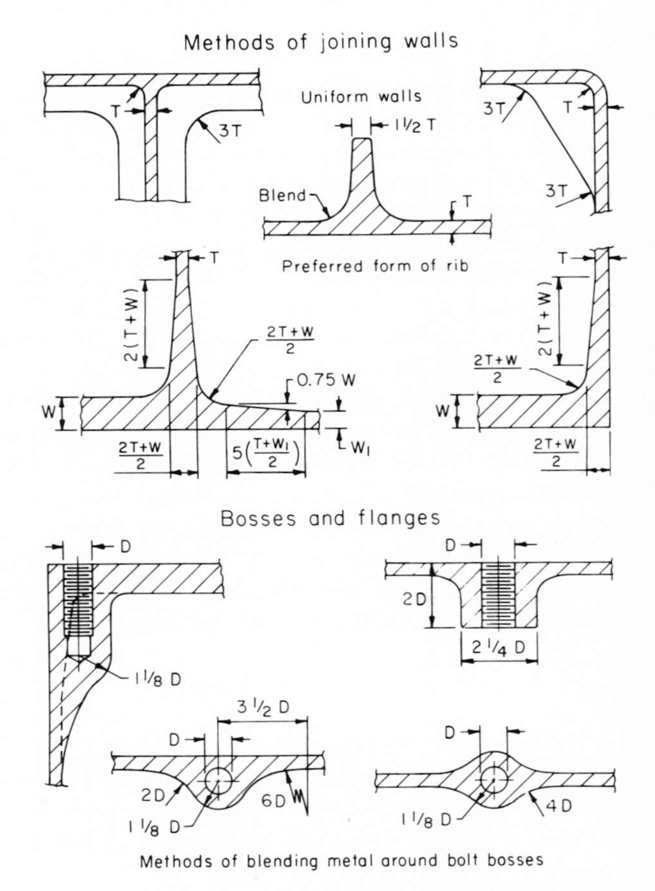

Fig. 1. Suggested design details

have surface roughness values as low as 24 micro-in. As the die surface deteriorates from contact with the molten aluminum alloy, the average roughness value increases. Often, when maximum surface roughness value of the casting reaches 125 micro-in., the die is repolished. With strictly functional parts, it is acceptable to have higher roughness values and localized thread-like ridges due to heat-check cracks in the die.

Finish machining allowance for die castings is low — 0.020 to 0.040 in., depending on size; this is one of the cost advantages of die castings. Furthermore, the 0.040-in. allowance should not be exceeded, because heavier machine cuts expose internal porosity, resulting in unsatisfactory appearance and loss in strength.

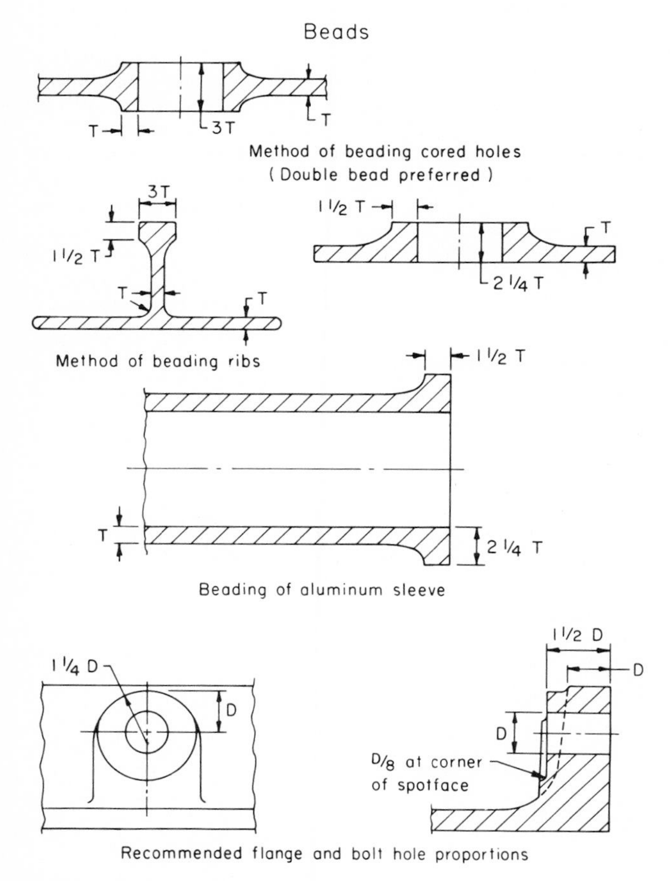

for aluminum alloy castings

Table 1. Suggested Dimensional Tolerances for Die Castings

Type A Dimension: Between two points in same part of die, not affected by parting plane or moving parts

Specified dimension, in.	Tolerance, ±, in. Critical	Noncritical
Up through 1	0.004	0.010
Over 1 to 12	0.004 + 0.0015 in./in. over 1 in.	0.010 + 0.002 in./in. over 1 in.
Over 12	0.0205 + 0.001 in./in. over 12 in.	0.032 + 0.001 in./in. over 12 in.

Type B Dimension: Across parting plane. A-type dimension plus following:

Projected area of casting, $A_1 \times A_3$, sq in.	Additional tolerance for parting plane, in.
Up through 50	0.005
Over 50 to 100	0.008
Over 100 to 200	0.012
Over 200 to 300	0.015

Type C Dimension: Affected by moving parts. A-type dimension plus following:

Projected area of casting affected by moving part, $A_3 \times G$, sq in.	Additional tolerance for moving part, in.
Up through 10	0.005
Over 10 to 20	0.008
Over 20 to 50	0.012
Over 50 to 100	0.015

D Dimension: Draft

Depth of draw, in.	Draft, deg Critical	Noncritical
Up through 0.1	6	18
Over 0.1 to 0.5	3	6
Over 0.5 to 1.0	2	3
Over 1.0 to 3.0	1	1½
Over 3.0 to 9.0	¾	1

E Dimension: Minimum wall thickness, 0.090 in.

F Dimension: Allowance for finish

Maximum dimension, in.	Nominal allowance, in.
Up through 5	0.020
Over 5 to 12	0.030
Over 12 to 18	0.040

Minimum diameter of cored holes, 0.140 in.

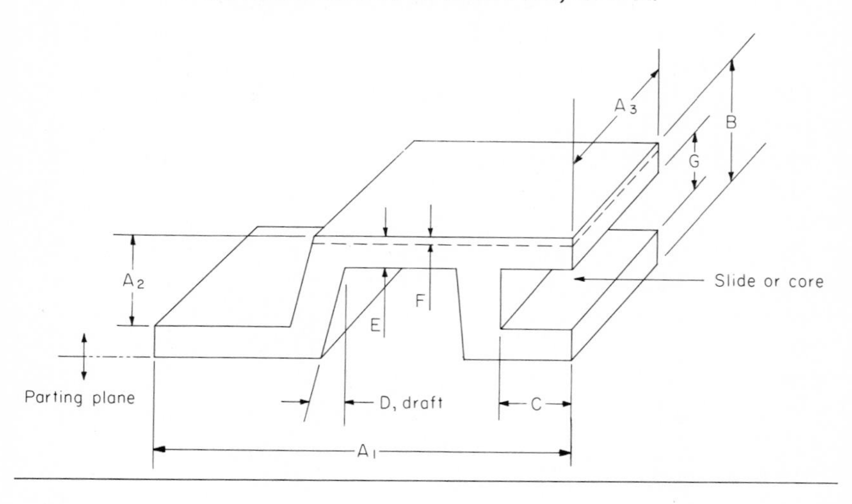

Commercial aluminum die castings generally are designed and produced to tolerance limits derived from a basic linear tolerance of ±0.004 in. per in. of dimension (Table 1). These tolerances agree with those included in the Engineering Standards of the American Die Casting Institute (2). These Engineering Standards also include statements of policy for die retention, price quotation, and other factors of importance to a clear understanding between the user and producer of die castings.

Choice of alloy is discussed in detail in Volume I, Chapter 8. However, it is unsatisfactory to select an alloy on the basis of engineering or service characteristics alone, because adaptability to the process is a major factor in determining the quality and serviceability of the parts. As an example, selection of 218 alloy for its attractive combination of tensile properties in separately cast test bars may be unwise, because it may shrink-crack during casting of complex shapes.

Die castings are not always pressure tight, particularly when extensive machining is required to complete the finished parts. Machinability and resistance to corrosion are determined by the alloy, rather than by any inherent difference between die casting and other casting processes. Extensive machining operations usually are not required on die castings. The machining ordinarily consists of light turning, reaming, edge milling, disk grinding, and the tapping of threads. For many applications, the natural finish of aluminum alloys, as produced from the dies, is satisfactory. A wide range of mechanical, chemical, or organic finishes may be applied with a minimum of surface preparation.

Welding of die castings, for assembly to other products or for repair, is not common. Even small amounts of carbonized lubricant in these castings, a normal occurrence, seriously deter production of sound welds. Mechanical joining methods are preferred.

The surface skin of die castings is very dense and fine grained, whereas the internal structure often is porous. With this characteristic structure, aluminum die castings are capable of carrying high sustained loads as well as cyclic (fatigue) loads. Once the dense surface skin is removed by machining, the tensile and fatigue strengths are reduced to levels comparable to those of sand castings. Die castings are machined only to provide accurate fitting to other parts of an assembly.

With the modern cold-chamber die casting machines, castings weighing a fraction of a pound to 125 lb are possible (Fig. 2).

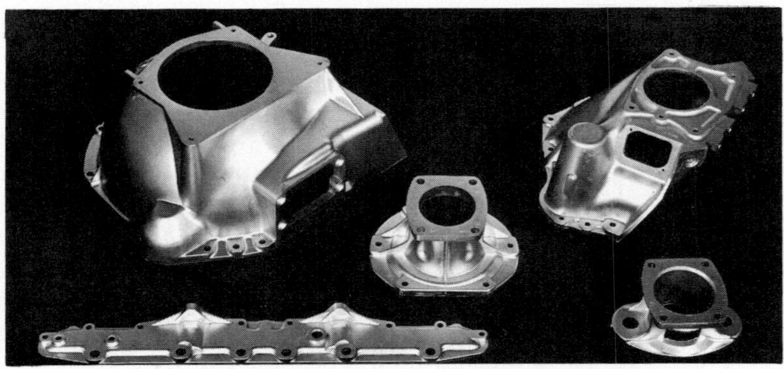

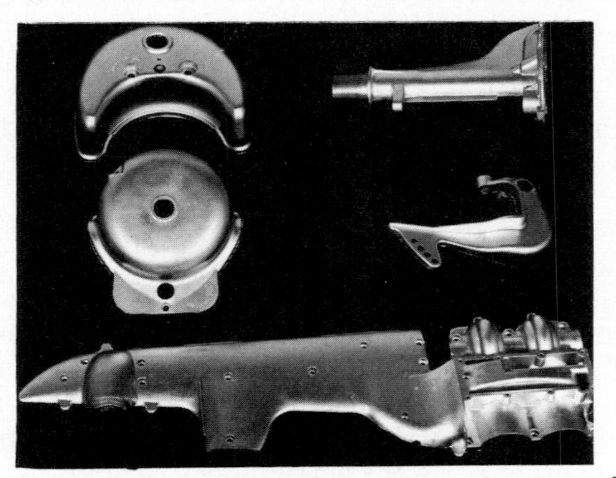

Fig. 2. Typical aluminum die castings: (top) small engine parts; (center) automobile engine and transmission parts; (bottom) outboard motor parts

Permanent Mold Castings

The general design requirements shown in Fig. 1 apply also to permanent mold castings.

Maintaining section uniformity not only helps simplify gating and feeding but also equalizes solidification rate, important in preventing cracking and internal shrinkage. However, a gradual increase in thickness toward a junction with heavy sections assists considerably in obtaining high-quality parts; in service, the blending distributes load stresses over a larger area of the casting, often eliminating undesirable stress concentrations.

The effect of casting size makes it difficult to define minimum section thickness for the permanent mold process. A section thickness of 0.140 in. over an area 3 in. or less in width usually is the minimum. For areas 3 to 6 in. in width, the minimum section thickness is 0.160 in. A minimum of 0.188 in. is required if the shortest dimension of an area exceeds 6 in. The minimum diameter for cored holes depends on hole depth and location with respect to various sections of the mold. Best design practice is to have no cored holes less than 0.375 in. in diameter. Smaller holes are produced more economically by machining.

The suggested dimensional tolerances given in Table 2 are based on recommendations of the Aluminum Association.

Finish machining allowances for permanent mold castings are greater than those for die castings. For castings up to 6 in. long, a minimum allowance of 0.030 in. should be provided. For castings over 18 in. long, the minimum machining allowance is 0.090 in. On surfaces of semipermanent mold castings formed by sand cores, 0.060 in. minimum should be provided.

The surface finish of permanent mold castings is governed by control of mold coatings, which are essential to the process. Typical cast surfaces range from 150 to 400 micro-in. Surfaces at sand or plaster cores reflect core material smoothness.

The pressure-tightness, welding, and machining characteristics of permanent mold castings are affected substantially by the choice of alloy and the ability of the foundry to produce quality parts. Careful consideration of relative alloy ratings for these characteristics (Volume I, Chapter 8) is important in applications where liquids or gases are held under pressure. Equally important to casting quality is the design and foundry engineering of parts so that they can be cast without excessive surface or internal defects.

Table 2. Suggested Dimensional Tolerances for Permanent and Semipermanent Mold Castings

Type A Dimension: Between two points in same part of mold, not affected by parting plane or moving parts

Specified dimension, in.	Tolerance, ±, in. Critical	Noncritical
Up through 1	0.010	0.015
Over 1	0.010 + 0.0015 in./in. over 1 in.	0.015 + 0.002 in./in. over 1 in.

Type B Dimension: Across parting plane. A-type dimension plus following:

Projected area of casting, $A_1 \times A_3$, sq in.	Additional tolerance for parting plane, in.
Up through 10	0.010
Over 10 to 50	0.015
Over 50 to 100	0.020
Over 100 to 250	0.025
Over 250 to 500	0.030

Type C Dimension: Affected by moving parts. A-type dimension plus following:

Projected area of casting affected by moving part, $A_3 \times G$, sq in.	Additional tolerance, in. Metal core or mold	Sand core
Up through 10	0.010	0.015
Over 10 to 50	0.015	0.025
Over 50 to 100	0.015	0.030
Over 100 to 500	0.022	0.040
Over 500 to 1000	0.032	0.060

D Dimension: Draft

Location	Draft, deg Critical	Noncritical
Outside surface	2	3
Recesses	2	5
Cores	1	2

E Dimension: Minimum wall thickness

Maximum dimension, in.	Minimum wall thickness, in.
Up through 3	0.140
Over 3 to 6	0.160
Over 6	0.188

F Dimension: Allowance for finish

Maximum dimension, in.	Nominal allowance, in. Metal core or mold	Sand core
Up through 6	0.030	0.060
Over 6 to 12	0.045	0.090
Over 12 to 18	0.060	0.120
Over 18 to 24	0.090	0.180

Minimum diameter of cored holes, 0.375 in.

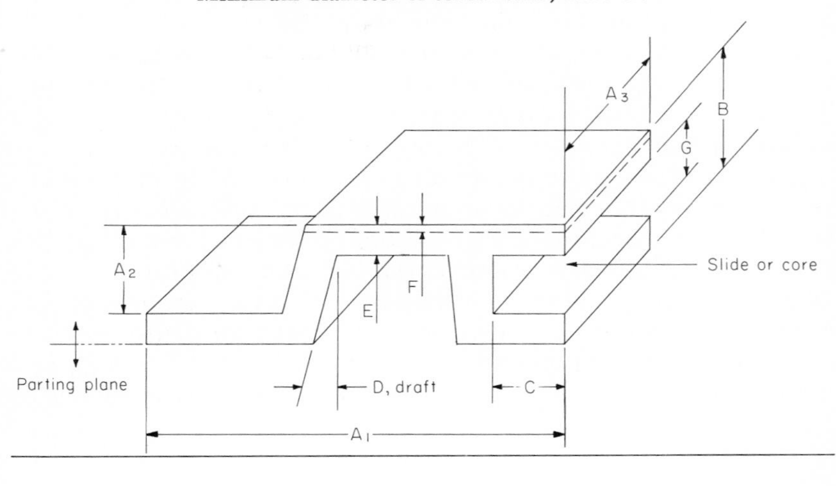

Although the first cost of the permanent mold and the accessory equipment may be higher than patterns and materials for sand casting, the higher production rates of permanent mold casting usually make it more economical than sand casting when sizable quantities are involved. Furthermore, machining costs for permanent mold castings are less, because of the closer dimensional tolerances and the accurately dimensioned and located holes provided by metal cores.

Most permanent mold castings weigh less than 20 lb, but castings weighing 50 to 200 lb are not uncommon, particularly when the semipermanent mold process is used (Fig. 3). Parts of simple design weighing several hundred pounds have often been

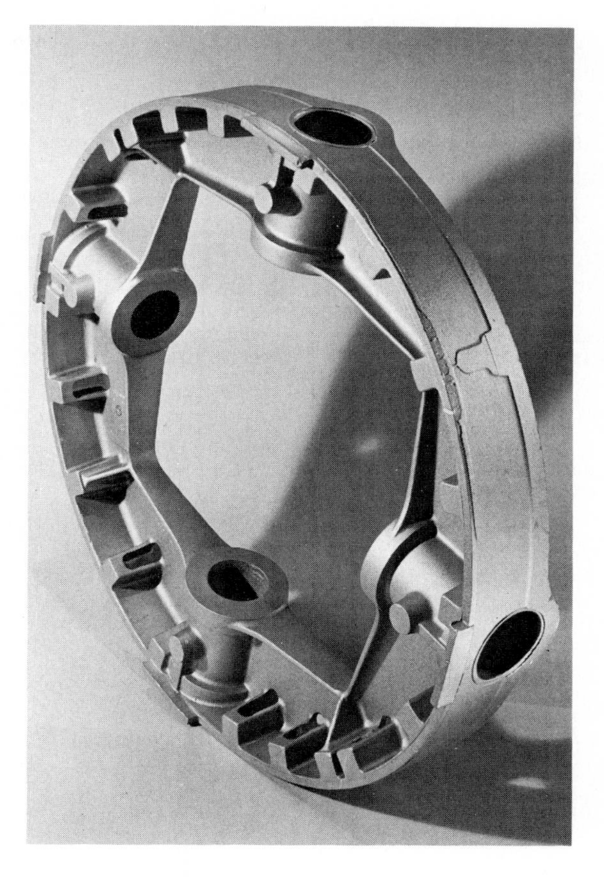

Fig. 3. Permanent mold cast missile ring showing intricate design and cored sections. Casting weighs 53 lb and is 32 in. in diameter.

Table 3. Suggested Dimensional Tolerances for Sand Castings

Type A Dimension: Between two points in same part of mold, not affected by parting plane or core

Specified dimension, in.	Tolerance, ±, in. Critical	Noncritical
Up through 6	0.030	0.040
Over 6 to 12	0.030 + 0.003 in./in. over 6 in.	0.040 + 0.004 in./in. over 6 in.
Over 12	0.048 + 0.002 in./in. over 12 in.	0.064 + 0.002 in./in. over 12 in.

Type B Dimension: Across parting plane. A-type dimension plus following:

Projected area of casting, $A_1 \times A_3$, sq in.	Additional tolerance for parting plane, in.
Up through 10	0.020
Over 10 to 50	0.035
Over 50 to 100	0.045
Over 100 to 250	0.060
Over 250 to 500	0.090

D Dimension: Draft

Location	Draft, deg Critical	Noncritical
Outside wall	2	3
Recesses	3	5
Cores	2	3

E Dimension: Minimum wall thickness, 0.150 in.

Type C Dimension: Affected by core. A-type dimension plus following:

Projected area of casting affected by core, $A_3 \times G$, sq in.	Additional tolerance for core, in.
Up through 10	0.020
Over 10 to 50	0.035
Over 50 to 100	0.045
Over 100 to 500	0.060
Over 500 to 1000	0.090

F Dimension: Allowance for finish

Maximum dimension, in.	Nominal allowance, in.
Up through 6	0.060
Over 6 to 12	0.090
Over 12 to 18	0.120
Over 18 to 24	0.180

Minimum diameter of cored holes, 0.250 in.

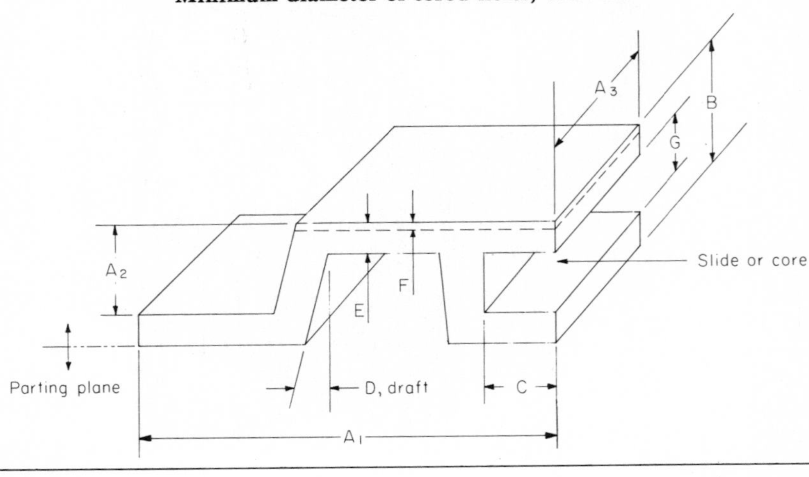

produced. Very large castings are produced only in sand, because of their complexity, the need for extensive sand coring, and the high cost of permanent mold tooling.

Sand Castings

General guides to design requirements are described in Fig. 1 (page 108). Casting in sand molds is not a precision process, because of variables in ramming the sand onto the pattern, drawing the pattern, setting the cores, and expansion of the sand as the casting is poured. Size and parting plane location are the major factors in determining tolerances for aluminum alloy sand castings. Additional variations are introduced by trimming and heat treating. The generally accepted dimensional tolerances for sand castings given in Table 3 are those recommended by the Aluminum Association. All tolerances listed are for castings made in green sand molds, with or without dry sand cores. Closer tolerances are possible when the entire mold is of dry sand.

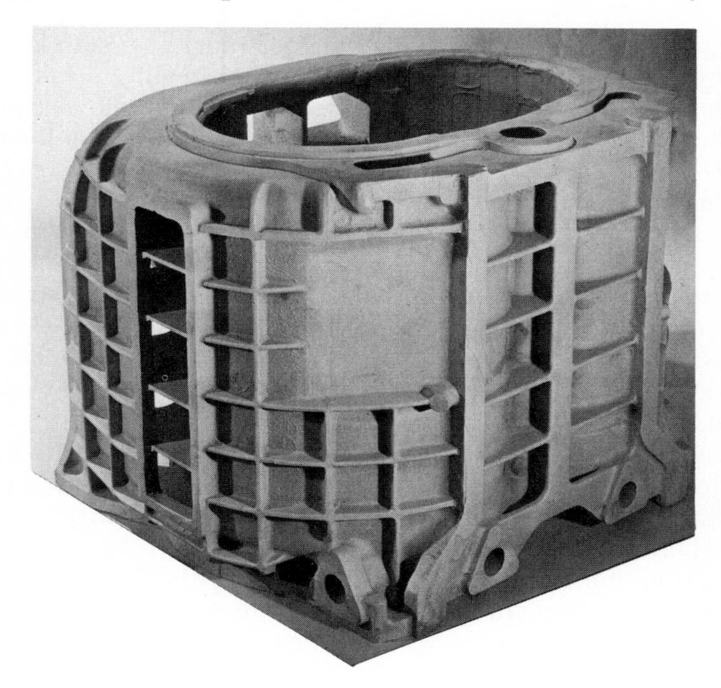

Fig. 4. Cored sand casting, weighing 250 lb, is housing for a diesel engine blower.

A minimum wall thickness of 0.150 in. is normally applicable to design and production of sand castings. Thinner sections can be cast if areas are not too large and part shape permits adequate metal flow and feeding of the thinner section. Heavier sections present no problems in filling, but require control of solidification temperature gradients to prevent shrinkage or gas porosity.

When machining is required, to provide close fits to other parts, it is normal to allow 0.060 to 0.180 in. for finish on surfaces with maximum dimensions between 6 and 24 in. Larger castings usually require 0.250 in. or more finish allowance.

Physical characteristics of the sand, quality of the pattern surface, and molding techniques govern the surface smoothness of sand castings. Although fine sand produces a relatively smooth surface, its use is limited to small or simple castings with few changes in section thickness. Larger castings require coarser sand to provide the mold permeability needed for better soundness and freedom from large surface irregularities. Normal surface on aluminum alloy sand castings ranges from 250 to 500 micro-in. However, random occurrence of small areas rougher than the average makes surface roughness standards of little value as design criteria or specification requirements.

The casting characteristics of sand casting alloys have a marked effect on part quality, and are rated in Volume I, Chapter 8, Table 7.

The influence of solidification rate on soundness is greater than in permanent mold castings. For structural applications, many purchasing and engineering specifications recognize this variation in sand castings by using a design allowable stress of 75% of the minimum yield strength of separately cast test bars plus a factor of safety based on experience. The mechanical and physical properties of separately cast test specimens are given in Volume I, Chapter 8.

The sand casting process is used primarily for small quantities of identical castings from single or multiple patterns, for parts requiring intricate coring, and for large, complex castings (Fig. 4). There is virtually no maximum size or weight for a sand casting; aluminum parts weighing over 18,000 lb have been cast. When casting design, including intricate coring, is suitable to modern high-speed molding machines, movement of molds on conveyors, and automatic pouring and knockout, production costs as low as those of permanent mold or even die casting can be realized.

Plaster Mold Castings

The greater insulating value of plaster, as compared to sand or metal mold materials, permits the casting of thinner sections, as well as adjacent thick and thin sections. More severe radii and rib-to-wall ratios are often permissible than those shown in Fig. 1. In fact, sharp corners can be cast.

The insulating effect of plaster permits using a greater range of thermal gradients during solidification. Composite molds of plaster, sand and metal permit optimum solidification sequence and produce excellent soundness and mechanical properties.

All-plaster molds or plaster sections in sand or metal molds may eliminate or reduce machining in cored holes or other sections requiring close tolerances. Although very close machining tolerances may not be met fully with plaster molds, the plaster process frequently can produce a casting of sufficient accuracy to eliminate machining operations.

Dimensional tolerances for aluminum parts cast in plaster molds are shown in Table 4. Noncritical linear tolerances not affected by parting planes are comparable to those attainable in die casting. Because of the low chilling rate of plaster molds, walls as thin as 0.060 in. can be cast in small parts. A draft angle of 2° usually is specified, but often zero draft can be maintained.

The excellent reproducibility of dimensions is an advantage of the plaster process. When working to critical tolerances, such as ±0.005 in. per in., it is necessary to estimate the shrinkage allowance closely. The pattern then is modified slightly on the basis of sample castings.

A notable characteristic of the plaster mold process is the smooth as-cast finish obtainable. A surface finish of 125 micro-in. is typical; a 50 to 60-micro-in. finish is attainable.

Factors Influencing Characteristics. Aluminum alloy plaster mold castings develop mechanical properties similar to those of sand castings. When the section thickness of plaster castings is less than 0.250 in., the mechanical properties are approximately equal to those of sand castings. The properties are somewhat lower for castings having a section thickness of 0.5 to 1 in. As with the sand and permanent mold methods, some specifications for plaster castings require that for specimens machined from castings, the average tensile and yield strengths shall not be less than 75% and elongation not less than 25% of the minimum requirements for separately cast specimens.

Table 4. Suggested Dimensional Tolerances for Plaster Castings

Type A Dimension: Between two points in same part of mold, not affected by parting plane or core

Specified dimension, in.	Tolerance, ±, in. Critical	Noncritical
Up through 1	0.005	0.010
Over 1	0.005 + 0.001 in./in. over 1 in.	0.010 + 0.002 in./in. over 1 in.

Type B Dimension: Across parting plane. A-type dimension plus following:

Projected area of casting, $A_1 \times A_3$, sq in.	Additional tolerance for parting plane, in.
Up through 10	0.005
Over 10 to 50	0.010
Over 50 to 100	0.020
Over 100	0.030

D Dimension: Draft

Location	Draft, deg Critical	Noncritical
Outside surface	0	2
Recesses	0	2
Cores	0	2

E Dimension: Minimum wall thickness, 0.060 in.

Type C Dimension: Affected by core. A-type dimension plus following:

Projected area of casting affected by core, $A_3 \times G$, sq in.	Additional tolerance for core, in.
Up through 10	0.005
Over 10 to 50	0.020
Over 50 to 100	0.030
Over 100	0.045

F Dimension: Allowance for finish

Maximum dimension, in.	Nominal allowance, in.
Up through 5	0.020
Over 5 to 12	0.030
Over 12 to 18	0.040

Minimum diameter of cored holes, 0.250 in.

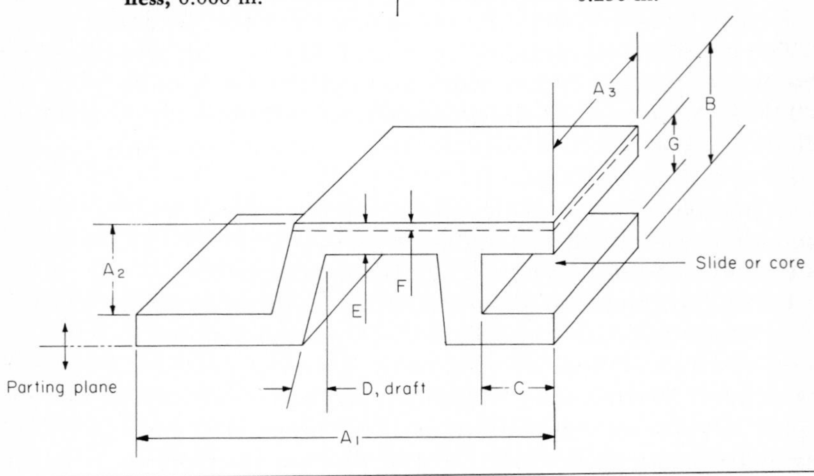

All the aluminum alloys that can be cast successfully in sand molds are suitable for casting in plaster molds. However, certain alloy groups are preferred because of their superior casting characteristics. Alloys 43, A344, 355, Red X-8 and 356, which are rated highest for fluidity and resistance to hot cracking (Volume I, Chapter 8, Table 7), are the best for plaster or composite mold casting. Aluminum-silicon alloy 43 is satisfactory when high mechanical properties are not required. The aluminum-silicon-copper alloys 354, 355 and Red X-8, and the aluminum-silicon-magnesium alloys of the 356 type, have excellent characteristics for casting in plaster, and provide high mechanical properties, because they usually are heat treated.

Process Capabilities. The plaster process is used in casting bladed, rotating parts; molds for rubber and plastics; and precision electronic parts, such as wave guides. The casting of all types of impellers, open-blade and shrouded, utilizes the ability of the process to produce adjacent thick and thin sections. Thin blade sections formed by plaster cores have excellent surface finish and tolerances of about ±0.005 in. Blade thickness often tapers to less than 0.040 in. at leading or trailing edges. Only minor polishing is required to produce surface finishes as smooth as 30 micro-in.

Blade spacing is limited only by the strength of plaster cores. Although impeller designs usually provide 0.125 in. between blades, closer spacing is feasible. Bladed parts commonly are cast up to 16 in. in diameter; a few have been made as large as 72 in. in diameter.

Plaster cast aluminum molds for tires and other rubber parts and for plastics combine precision with high thermal conductivity. Intricate tread design, including back draft and small undercuts, is made possible by using soft rubber linings in the plaster core boxes. Many hundreds of small steel stampings are inserted in the rubber-lined pattern and cast into the mold, to produce the tire tread. The plaster molds may be produced in one piece or assembled from segments of the tire circumference.

For electronic applications, aluminum plaster castings combine precision with high reflectance to microwaves. Intricate inside passages are held within ±0.005 in. or less; consistent smooth finish of about 63 micro-in. is obtained. Design of microwave guides often precludes any internal machining, because surfaces are inaccessible. In general, the plaster process permits casting intricate precision parts such as shown in Fig. 5.

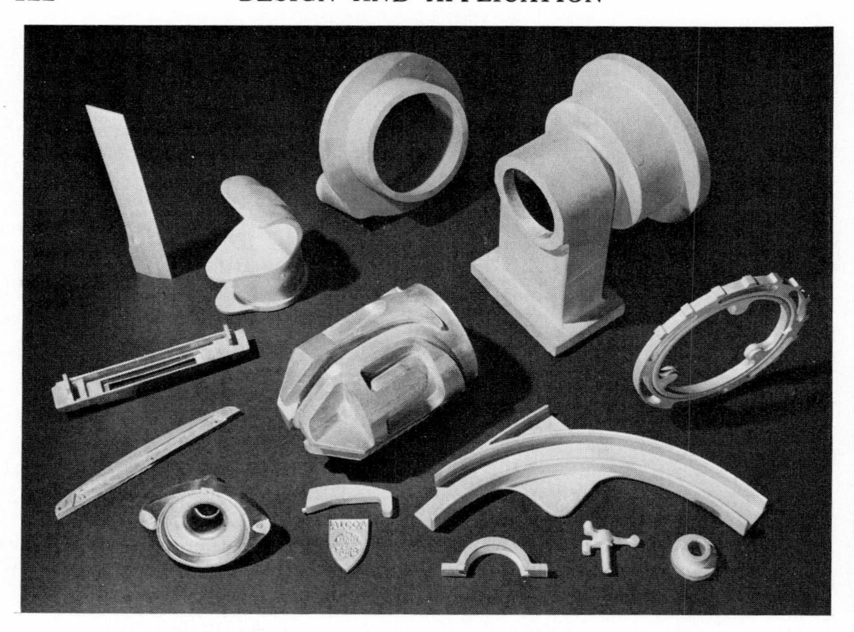

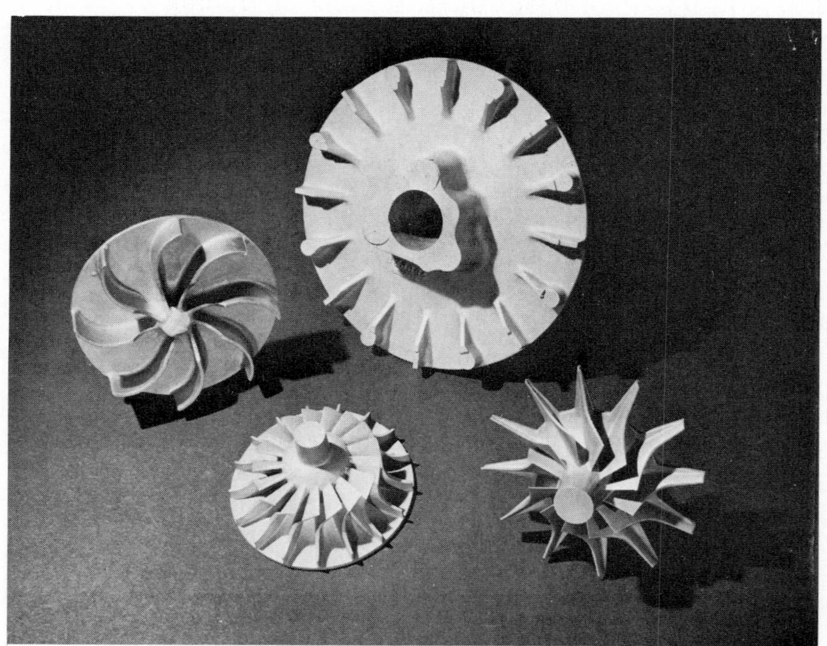

Fig. 5. Plaster mold castings: (top) typical small parts; (bottom) supercharger impellers

Premium-Quality Castings

Premium-quality casting techniques utilize a number of conventional foundry processes in a selective manner, so as to produce a cast product with the most desirable characteristics of each process. Thus, premium-quality castings have a combination of features not often produced by any one casting method. This technique was developed to meet the exacting quality and reliability demands of aerospace and electronics industries.

The precision or accuracy of premium-quality castings depends largely on the care with which models and patterns are made. Fixtures often are required to assemble mold components and qualify the critical dimensions of finished castings. Metal, cast plastic, and rubber patterns are preferred. Wood patterns seldom are satisfactory except for prototypes or a small number of castings. Accurate and rigid molding machines are equally important in premium-quality casting, particularly to maintain dimensional control.

The cost advantage of a premium casting, instead of a fabricated assembly of high-strength wrought forms, often lies in the elimination of machining operations.

Intimate knowledge of each basic casting process is essential, because designing premium-quality castings assumes that limitations of any one process can be reduced. For example, the limitations illustrated in Fig. 1 must be removed if machining is to be decreased or eliminated. Similarly, design objectives with respect to precision only can be accomplished by lowering the critical tolerances listed in Tables 2, 3 and 4. No general rules can be cited to define design details and dimensional tolerances for premium-quality castings.

A limited number of foundries can produce premium-quality castings; they must be able to work with the design engineer from the outset.

Factors Influencing Characteristics. In premium-strength castings, consistently high mechanical properties can be guaranteed within critically stressed areas of the casting. Attainment of the highest mechanical properties feasible with the alloy composition and heat treatment is their principal characteristic.

Controlling three interdependent conditions develops optimum mechanical properties in premium-strength castings: alloy type, foundry technique influencing direction and rate of solidification, and selection and control of heat treatment.

The alloys listed in Table 5 can be classified as premium strength. The alloy grouping in the table is chronological, and represents stages in the development of successively higher levels of mechanical properties. Although the reliability required for premium-strength structural applications renders separately cast test bars virtually useless for design purposes, mechanical properties of such specimens are recorded in Table 5 as an index

Table 5. Typical Mechanical Properties of High-Strength Aluminum Casting Alloys(a)

Alloy(b)	Tensile strength, psi	Yield strength (0.2% offset), psi	Elongation, % in 2 in.
Alloy Group I			
220-T4	48,000	26,000	16.0
355-T6	42,000	27,000	4.0
356-T6	38,000	27,000	5.0
Alloy Group II			
C355-T62	49,000	36,000	6.0
A356-T62	43,000	32,000	7.0
Alloy Group III			
354-T62	57,000	46,000	3.0
A357-T62	53,000	42,000	3.0
359-T62	50,000	42,000	5.0
Tens 50-T6	50,000	44,000	6.0

(a) Properties obtained from standard 0.5-in.-diam tensile test specimens, individually cast, and tested without machining the surface. (b) All are permanent mold cast alloys except 220-T4, which is sand cast.

to the effect of alloy type. (Volume I, Chapter 8 provides information on nominal compositions and properties and discusses the various alloy systems.)

Alloy 220-T4 was among the first developed for high-strength structural castings requiring high resistance to shock loads and to corrosion. Because large risers and generous chilling are needed if mechanical properties are to approach those of separately cast bars, 220-T4 is limited to relatively simple shapes.

In premium casting production, the most important alloys are those in the aluminum-silicon-magnesium and aluminum-silicon-copper-magnesium systems. During the last 35 years, a number of investigators determined the effects of various combinations of silicon, copper, magnesium, and the iron impurity element on mechanical properties. Alloys A356-T62, A357-T62, 359-T62 and Tens 50-T6, in Groups II and III of Table 5, provide a range of combinations of high tensile properties and excellent resistance to corrosion. In the other alloys in these groups, C355-T62 and 354-T62, addition of copper provides higher strength and improved machinability at some sacrifice in resistance to corrosion.

Mechanical properties in premium-strength castings are related directly to the solidification pattern achieved by the foundry. Correlations of cooling curve data, temperature gradients during solidification, and melt quality with mechanical properties show that foundry gate and riser practices are even more important than choice of alloy. Selection and location of mold materials, gates, risers, and pouring temperature are the main factors in obtaining the desired fine microstructure, free of harmful internal discontinuities.

Process Capabilities. Premium-quality castings produced in composite molds are used for structural applications, primarily in aerospace vehicles. Castings of the alloys in Group III, Table 5, made to predetermined strength levels, provide uniform,

Table 6. Design Tensile Values for High-Strength Aluminum Alloy Castings

Alloy	Tensile strength, psi Guaranteed minimum(a)	Tensile strength, psi Adjusted value(b)	Yield strength, psi Guaranteed minimum(a)	Yield strength, psi Adjusted value(b)	Elongation, % in 2 in. Guaranteed minimum(a)	Elongation, % in 2 in. Adjusted value(b)
Sand Castings						
220-T4	42,000	32,000	22,000	17,000	12.0	3.0
Permanent Mold Castings						
355-T6	37,000	28,000	23,000	17,000	1.5	0.4
356-T6	33,000	25,000	22,000	17,000	3.0	0.8

Alloy	Tensile strength, psi	Yield strength, psi	Elongation, % in 2 in.
Premium-Quality (Composite Mold) Castings(c)			
354-T62	50,000	42,000	2.0
C355-T62	44,000	33,000	3.0
A356-T62	40,000	30,000	3.0
A357-T62	50,000	40,000	3.0
359-T62	47,000	38,000	3.0

(a) Minimum guaranteed values for separately cast sand and permanent mold test bars. (b) Suggested design values; equal to 75% of minimum tensile and yield strength and 25% of elongation required of separately cast test bars (a). (c) Minimum properties of specimens cut from designated high-stress areas of castings, and suggested design values.

reliable mechanical properties with two or three times the safe design allowables attainable with commercial castings.

Table 6 shows the differences in static properties between commercial and premium-strength (composite mold) castings for structural applications. When a specific part is designed to tensile yield strength, design values for commercial 220-T4, 355-T6 and 356-T6 sand or permanent mold castings are based on 75% of the minimum yield strength of separately cast test bars, providing tensile-yield-strength design values of 17,000 psi. Among high-strength composite mold alloys, the lowest yield-strength design value is 30,000 psi; the highest, 42,000 psi.

The minimum tensile values for the composite mold group of alloys are based on minimum properties of specimens cut from designated high-stress areas in the castings. The designer can take full advantage of the higher design values without applying the 75% reduction factor required previously to relate separately cast test bar properties to those expected in castings.

In addition to the minimum tensile values, a number of other properties and process capabilities must be considered in selecting alloy and foundry process for a specific application. These additional properties, including shear and fatigue strengths, creep and elevated-temperature characteristics, along with resistance to corrosion, are discussed in Volume I, Chapter 8.

Investment Castings

Although design of investment castings follows the criteria given in Fig. 1, the factors applied to thickness may be reduced considerably when vacuum or pressure is employed. Similarly, blending of metal around bosses and flanges can be reduced.

Although size limitations are not inherent in the investment casting process, its advantages are realized in producing small, precision parts in multiple-cavity molds. Investment molds usually do not exceed 24 in. maximum dimension, but as many as several hundred pieces may be cast in one mold. Generally, sections thicker than 0.500 in. are not cast, because of pattern skrinkage; large cross sections of wax are likely to form skrinkage hollows on solidifying. Thin walls down to 0.030 in. can be cast readily; ribs as thin as 0.015 in. have been cast. The dimensional tolerances for plaster castings given in Table 4 are applicable to investment castings.

The surface on investment castings has a smooth matte

appearance and the roughness ranges from 60 to 90 micro-in. Machining allowance usually is 0.0010 to 0.015 in., and should not exceed 0.025 in. Removing more surface metal exposes fine, internal gas porosity or skrinkage.

Factors Influencing Characteristics. Mechanical and physical properties of investment cast alloys approach those obtained in sand castings. Because of the slow rate of solidification (especially when dehydrated, dense plaster molds are used) investment castings have somewhat larger grain size and coarser microstructure. This can result in lower strength and elongation values.

The most popular alloys for investment casting are 43 and 356. Both provide the required high fluidity, low solidification shrinkage, and good resistance to hot cracking. Selecting an alloy that ages at room temperature — A612, D612, or Tenzaloy — eliminates the distortion and growth that occur during heat treatment. However, because of their hot cracking tendency and lower fluidity, alloys of this type are less suitable than 43 or 356 for producing fine design details.

The inherently slow solidification rate of the gravity investment casting process results in more internal gas and skrinkage porosity than is prevalent in sand castings of comparable section thickness. With respect to unsoundness, the investment castings are similar to die castings, although the causes of unsoundness are different. Extensive machining of investment castings exposes porosity and causes leakage.

Process Capabilities. The investment process is an effective method for producing parts of intricate design that are difficult or impossible to machine. If parts cannot be made by die casting, machining, stamping, or pressing, investment casting should be considered. The very irregular contours desired for jewelry preclude the use of any other casting process. Because investment casting is able to produce parts with very irregular shape, back drafts, and excellent finish, instrument, aerospace, sporting goods, jewelry, and dental supply industries specify it.

Centrifugal Castings

The addition of centrifugal force to the conventional permanent mold, sand or plaster casting processes is an effective method for producing flow into thin sections, increasing strength of castings, and reducing the weight of metal poured. Centrifugal casting is particularly advantageous for cylindrical shapes.

The minimum section thickness that can be produced by the centrifugal process varies from 0.070 in. for surface areas up to 4 sq in. to 0.156 in. for areas over 100 sq in. A dimensional tolerance of ±0.0010 in. is acceptable between two points produced by one part of a mold. An additional tolerance of ±0.0010 in. is required between points that cross a parting plane. Draft angles are determined by the mold material (Tables 2, 3 and 4). The methods of joining walls to the ribs, bosses and flanges of centrifugal castings follow the design rules for all aluminum casting processes (Fig. 1).

Comparison With Competitive Processes and Materials

Differences Between Casting Methods. The characteristics of the end products, production, tooling, and cost factors that affect the choice of aluminum casting process are rated qualitatively in Table 7. Although relative ratings provide a means of comparing the various casting methods when new parts are being reviewed for design and ultimate production, there is no precise way to choose the best method from such a table.

Casting Versus Other Fabricating Methods. A comparison of aircraft-quality aluminum parts made by casting, forging, extruding, and fabricating sheet metals appears in the "Metals Handbook" (3). In comparing castings and forgings, common denominators are established to relate the costs of parts to a size reference: volume in cubic inches for castings, and projected area for forgings. For example, the tooling (patterns, molds or dies) costs for 10-cu-in.-volume castings range from $150 for sand casting to $2000 for die casting. The part costs for the same size of castings vary from $2 per piece for permanent mold and $4 for sand and die to $20 per piece for investment castings. In comparison, the die cost for a small forging, projected area 100 sq in., is approximately $15,000 and may exceed $100,000 for large forgings with projected areas of about 1000 sq in.

Although castings are more economical in most comparisons than aluminum forgings or fabricated assemblies, the design stresses usually dictate the choice of manufacturing method.

Competitive Materials. Aluminum, zinc and magnesium are competitive materials for die casting. From the standpoint of casting characteristics, zinc is the optimum die casting metal; its use in castings is confined to this process. With zinc, the thinnest sections and finest surface detail attainable in die castings are achieved. In comparison with aluminum, the lower melting temperature of zinc results in longer die life and smoother as-cast surfaces. The cost of polishing zinc castings prior to plating generally is lower than for comparable aluminum castings.

In comparison with zinc, aluminum has lower density but comparable strength, resulting in a strength-to-weight ratio that favors aluminum. Because of zinc's low resistance to creep, it generally is not recommended for applications where appre-

Table 7. Comparison of Aluminum Casting Methods(a)

	Die	Permanent mold	Sand	Plaster or investment	Composite(b)
Strength	B	A	B	B	A
Structural density	C	A	B	B	A
Reproducibility	A	B	C	B	A
Pressure tightness	C	A	B	B	A
Cost per piece(c)	A	B	C	D	D
Production rate(c)	A	B	C	D	C
Flexibility as to alloys	C	B	A	B	B
Tolerances	A	B	C	A	A
Design flexibility	C	B	A	A	A
Size limitation	B	B	A	C	B
Surface finish	A	B	C	A	A
Time to obtain tooling	B	B	A	B	C
Pattern or mold cost(d)	C	B	A	B	D

(a) Ratings A, B, C and D indicate relative advantage, A being best. (b) Applicable to specific or critical areas of premium-quality castings in the permanent mold and plaster portions of the molds. (c) Although this rating covers the majority of castings, in the case of multiple patterns or mold cavities, sand or permanent mold may take first place. (d) The cost of die casting dies plus the cost of tooling for machining is frequently less than the same over-all cost for sand or permanent mold castings.

ciable sustained stress is applied. Zinc normally is preferred over aluminum for ornamental and decorative parts, particularly those finished by electroplating. The principal applications for aluminum die castings are functional, being based on fatigue strength, ease of machining, retention of finish without protective coatings, and dimensional stability on temperature cycling.

Although few ferrous alloy castings are made by the high-production permanent mold process, a comparison of their characteristics with those of aluminum permanent mold castings would be similar to that for sand cast parts.

Ferrous alloy sand castings generally provide higher unit strength than aluminum. An increase of up to 50% in section thickness usually provides equal strength in an aluminum sand casting while still retaining the advantage of a lighter weight part. Lower machining costs are advantageous when the total cost of a cast aluminum part is compared to a ferrous part.

Aluminum alloy and magnesium alloy castings are generally equal in several characteristics. They rate approximately the same in castability, as-cast surface quality, and ability to be cast in intricate configurations. Magnesium has lower density (two thirds that of aluminum) and generally lower unit strength than aluminum, although the weight-strength ratios may be similar when optimum designs are developed. Aluminum has a decided advantage over magnesium in environments where corrosive conditions exist. Although both metals may require protective coatings, the systems applicable to aluminum frequently cost less than those required on magnesium.

References

1 "Casting Design Handbook", American Society for Metals, 1962
2 "Engineering Standards—Series E", American Die Casting Institute, New York, 1958
3 Examples of Light Metal Parts for Aeronautical Construction, in "Metals Handbook", Vol 1, 8th Ed, American Society for Metals, 1961, p 901–915

Chapter 6

Design Factors for Extrusions

C. R. ANDERSON and A. L. HURST

THE GROWTH in the use of aluminum extrusions has resulted from the versatility of the extrusion process. Shapes can be produced in virtually unlimited cross-sectional designs that place the metal where needed to meet functional and appearance requirements. Full utilization of this capability of the extrusion process depends principally upon the ingenuity of designers in creating new and useful configurations. The extrusion process is described in Volume III, Chapter 3.

The cross-sectional design of an extruded shape can have an important influence on its producibility, production rate, cost of tooling, surface finish, and ultimate production cost (1). The optimum design of an extruded shape must take into account alloy, shape size, thickness or thicknesses involved, and the complexity of the shape.

In normal preproduction procedure, the designer submits a dimensioned sketch or drawing of the desired shape to the extruder for review. The extruder accepts the design or suggests modifications to permit extrusion of the shape, or to contribute to lower costs, better finish, or improved dimensional control, while retaining the desired functional and appearance characteristics.

Classification of Extruded Shapes

The complexity of a shape producible as an extrusion is a function of metal flow characteristics of the process and the means available to control flow. Control of metal flow places a

C. R. Anderson is production manager, Aluminum Company of America, Cressona, Pa. A. L. Hurst is quality assurance manager, Aluminum Company of America, Lafayette, Ind.

Table 1. Classifications of Extruded Aluminum Shapes

Classification	Description
General	Any shape other than rod, bar or tube
Semihollow	A shape with any part of its cross section partially enclosing a void, the ratio of the area of the void to the square of its width being: Void width, in. — Ratio 0.035 to 0.061 — Over 2 0.062 to 0.124 — Over 3 0.125 to 0.249 — Over 4 0.250 to 0.499 — Over 5 0.500 and greater — Over 6
Hollow	A shape with any part of its cross section completely enclosing a void. Class 1: A hollow shape with a round void 1 in. or more in diameter and with its weight equally distributed on opposite sides of two or more equally spaced axes Class 2: Any hollow shape other than Class 1, not exceeding a 5-in.-diam circle and having a single void of not less than 0.375-in. diam or 0.110-sq-in. area Class 3: Any hollow shape other than Class 1 or 2
Solid	Any shape other than hollow or semihollow
Stepped	A shape having cross-sectional changes in area at intervals along its length
Structural	Any shape commonly used for structural purposes, but limited to those produced by rolling, such as angles, channels, or Z's.
Rod	A solid extrusion with a round cross section of 0.375-in. diameter or greater (smaller sizes classified as wire)
Bar	A solid extrusion with a symmetrical cross section—square or rectangular, with sharp or rounded corners or edges—or a regular hexagon or octagon with width (greater dimension) of 0.375 in. or more (smaller sizes classified as wire)
Tube	A hollow shape with a symmetrical cross section—round, square, rectangular, hexagonal, octagonal or elliptical—and a wall of uniform thickness, except as affected by corner radii

few limitations on the design features of the cross section of an extruded shape. These design features are important to both designer and extruder, because they affect production rate, dimensional and surface quality, and costs. Classification of shapes as solid, hollow and semihollow recognizes differences in shape complexity from an extrusion production viewpoint (Table 1). Hollow shapes are divided into three subgroups of increasing complexity.

The important shape factor of an extrusion is the ratio of its perimeter to its weight per foot. For a single classification, increasing shape factor is a measure of increasing complexity. Designing for minimum shape factor promotes ease of extrusion.

Shape Design Factors

The aluminum alloys differ in inherent extrudability. Alloy selection is important, as it establishes the minimum thickness for a shape and has a basic effect on extrusion cost. In general, the higher the alloy content and the higher its strength (Volume I, Chapter 9), the more difficult it is to extrude and the lower its extrusion rate. The most important commercial extrusion alloys and their relative extrudabilities are given in Table 2.

The size of an extruded shape affects ease of extrusion and dimensional tolerances. As the circumscribing circle size (smallest diameter that completely encloses the shape) increases, extrusion becomes more difficult. In extrusion, the metal flows fastest at the center of the die face. As the circle size of a shape becomes larger, the tendency for differential metal flow increases, and it is more difficult to design and construct extrusion dies with compensating features that provide uniform metal flow rates to all parts of a shape.

Ease of extrusion improves with increasing thickness of a shape; a shape of uniform thickness is most easily extruded. A shape cross section with elements of widely differing thicknesses increases the difficulty of extrusion. The thinner a flange on a shape, the less the length of flange that can be satisfactorily extruded. Thinner elements at the ends of long flanges, or other shape detail, are difficult to fill properly and make it hard to obtain the desired dimensional control and finish. Although it is

Table 2. Relative Extrudability of Aluminum Extrusion Alloys(a)

Alloy	Relative extrudability, %	Alloy	Relative extrudability, %	Alloy	Relative extrudability, %
EC	160	6063	100	5083	20
1060	135	6061	60	2024	15
1100	135	2011	35	7075	9
3003	120	5086	25	7178	8
		2014	20		

(a) Extrudability of 6063 is assigned a value of 100% for base.

desirable to produce the thinnest shape feasible, the increased cost for extrusion resulting from reducing thickness can more than offset the savings in metal cost. Extruded shapes 0.040 in. thick and even less are produced, depending on alloy, shape, size

Table 3. Standard Manufacturing Limits for Aluminum Extrusions

Diameter of circumscribing circle, in.	Minimum wall thickness, in.				
	1060, 1100, 3003	6063	6061	2014, 5086, 5454	2024, 2219, 5083, 7001, 7075, 7079, 7178
Solid and Semihollow Shapes, Rods, and Bar					
0.5 to 2	0.040	0.040	0.040	0.040	0.040
2 to 3	0.045	0.045	0.045	0.050	0.050
3 to 4	0.050	0.050	0.050	0.050	0.062
4 to 5	0.062	0.062	0.062	0.062	0.078
5 to 6	0.062	0.062	0.062	0.078	0.094
6 to 7	0.078	0.078	0.078	0.094	0.109
7 to 8	0.094	0.094	0.094	0.109	0.125
8 to 10	0.109	0.109	0.109	0.125	0.156
10 to 11	0.125	0.125	0.125	0.125	0.156
11 to 12	0.156	0.156	0.156	0.156	0.156
12 to 17	0.188	0.188	0.188	0.188	0.188
17 to 20	0.188	0.188	0.188	0.188	0.250
20 to 24	0.188	0.188	0.188	0.250	0.500
Class 1 Hollow Shapes(a)					
1.25 to 3	0.062	0.050	0.062	...	...
3 to 4	0.094	0.050	0.062	...	...
4 to 5	0.109	0.062	0.062	0.156	0.250
5 to 6	0.125	0.062	0.078	0.188	0.281
6 to 7	0.156	0.078	0.094	0.219	0.312
7 to 8	0.188	0.094	0.125	0.250	0.375
8 to 9	0.219	0.125	0.156	0.281	0.438
9 to 10	0.250	0.156	0.188	0.312	0.500
10 to 12.75	0.312	0.188	0.219	0.375	0.500
12.75 to 14	0.375	0.219	0.250	0.438	0.500
14 to 16	0.438	0.250	0.375	0.438	0.500
16 to 20.25	0.500	0.375	0.438	0.500	0.625
Class 2 and 3 Hollow Shapes(b)					
0.5 to 1	0.062	0.050	0.062	...	...
1 to 2	0.062	0.055	0.062	...	...
2 to 3	0.078	0.062	0.078	...	...
3 to 4	0.094	0.078	0.094	...	...
4 to 5	0.109	0.094	0.109	...	...
5 to 6	0.125	0.109	0.125	...	...
6 to 7	0.156	0.125	0.156	...	...
7 to 8	0.188	0.156	0.188	...	...
8 to 10	0.250	0.188	0.250	...	...

(a) Minimum inside diameter is one half the circumscribing diameter, but never under 1 in. for alloys in first three columns or under 2 in. for alloys in last two columns. (b) Minimum hole size for all alloys is 0.110 sq in. in area or 0.375 in. in diam.

and design. Manufacturing limits showing the minimum thicknesses practicable for extruded shapes are given in Table 3.

Size, thickness, and the relationship of various element combinations can add to the complexity of an extruded shape. Rod, bar and regular shapes of uniform thickness are easily produced. A 0.125-in.-thick bar, a 1-in.-diam rod, and a 0.750-in. by 1.000-in. angle with a 0.0625-in. thickness are readily extruded. However, a 3-in. bar-type shape with a 0.125-in. flange is more difficult.

Each void or gap in an extruded shape requires a tongue in the extrusion die, which must have adequate strength to resist the extrusion force. Channel shapes become increasingly difficult to produce as the depth-to-width ratio increases. Wide, thin shapes are difficult to produce and make it hard to control dimensions. Channel-type shapes and wide, thin shapes may be fabricated if an increase in thickness is permitted. Thin flanges or projections from a thicker element of the shape add to the complexity of an extruded design. On thinner elements at the extremities of high flanges, it is difficult to get adequate fill to obtain desired dimensions. The greater the difference in thickness of individual elements comprising a shape, the more difficult it is to produce. The effect of such thickness differences can be greatly diminished by blending one thickness to the other by tapered or radiused transitions. As far as practicable, sharp corners should be avoided, because they reduce the maximum extrusion speed obtainable. Fillet radii of at least 0.031 in. are desirable, but corners with as little as 0.015-in. radii are feasible.

In general, the more unbalanced and the more unsymmetrical an extruded shape cross section, the more difficult it is to produce. Despite this, the production of grossly unbalanced and unsymmetrical shapes is the basis of the great growth that has occurred in the use of aluminum extrusions, and such designs account for the bulk of extruded shapes produced today.

Dimensional Tolerances

Tolerances on dimensions and contour attainable in extrusions are affected by shape, configuration and complexity. They also are influenced by die-opening size and placement, die bearing design, die deflection, die wear, extrusion temperature, extrusion speed and pressure, and subsequent operations.

To control dimensions and contour requires careful attention to die-opening placement, and balancing and blending of the die

Table 4. Standard Cross-Sectional Dimensional Tolerances for Extruded Rod, Bar and Shapes (a)
(See sketch at the end of this table for the location of the dimensional tolerances given in the various columns.)

Specified dimension, in.	Tolerance(b), ±, in. — Metal dimensions — Allowable deviation where 75% or more of the dimension is metal(c): All except those covered by Column 3		Wall thickness enclosing space 0.11 sq in. and over (eccentricity) (e)		Space dimensions — Allowable deviation where more than 25% of dimension is space(d) — At dimensioned points, from base of leg, in.: 0.250–0.624		0.625–1.249		1.250–2.499		2.500–3.999		4.000–5.999		6.000–8.000	
Column 1	Column 2		Column 3		Column 4		Column 5		Column 6		Column 7		Column 8		Column 9	
	Alloys 5083, 5086	Other alloys	Alloys 5083, 5086	Other alloys	Alloys 5083, 5086	Other alloys	Alloys 5083, 5086	Other alloys	Alloys 5083, 5086	Other alloys	Alloys 5083, 5086	Other alloys	Alloys 5083, 5086	Other alloys	Alloys 5083, 5086	Other alloys
Circumscribing Circle Less Than 10 In. in Diameter																
Up thru 0.124	0.009	0.006	±15% of specified dimension; ±0.090 max, ±0.015 min	±10% of specified dimension; ±0.060 max, ±0.010 min	0.013	0.010	0.015	0.012	...	...	...	...	...	...	...	...
0.125– 0.249	0.011	0.007			0.016	0.012	0.018	0.014	0.020	0.016	...	...	...	...	...	...
0.250– 0.499	0.012	0.008			0.018	0.014	0.020	0.016	0.022	0.018	0.024	0.020	...	...	...	...
0.500– 0.749	0.014	0.009			0.021	0.016	0.023	0.018	0.025	0.020	0.027	0.022	...	...	...	...
0.750– 0.999	0.015	0.010			0.023	0.018	0.025	0.020	0.027	0.022	0.030	0.025	0.035	0.030	...	...
1.000– 1.499	0.018	0.012			0.027	0.021	0.029	0.023	0.032	0.026	0.036	0.030	0.041	0.035	...	...
1.500– 1.999	0.021	0.014			0.031	0.024	0.033	0.026	0.038	0.031	0.043	0.036	0.049	0.042	0.057	0.050
2.000– 3.999	0.036	0.024			0.046	0.034	0.050	0.038	0.060	0.048	0.069	0.057	0.080	0.068	0.092	0.080
4.000– 5.999	0.051	0.034			0.061	0.044	0.067	0.050	0.081	0.064	0.095	0.078	0.111	0.094	0.127	0.110
6.000– 7.999	0.066	0.044			0.076	0.054	0.084	0.062	0.104	0.082	0.121	0.099	0.142	0.120	0.162	0.140
8.000– 9.999	0.081	0.054			0.091	0.064	0.101	0.074	0.127	0.100	0.147	0.120	0.182	0.145	0.197	0.170

Table 4. (Continued)

Circumscribing Circle 10 In. in Diameter and Over																
Up thru 0.124	0.021	0.014	±15% of specified dimension; ±0.090 max, ±0.025 min	±15% of specified dimension; ±0.090 max, ±0.015 min	0.025	0.018	0.027	0.020	...	...	...	...	...	...	...	...
0.125– 0.249	0.022	0.015			0.026	0.019	0.029	0.022	0.035	0.028	...	...	...	...	...	...
0.250– 0.499	0.024	0.016			0.028	0.020	0.032	0.024	0.038	0.030	0.058	0.050	...	...	...	...
0.500– 0.749	0.025	0.017			0.030	0.022	0.035	0.027	0.049	0.040	0.068	0.060	...	...	...	...
0.750– 0.999	0.027	0.018			0.031	0.023	0.039	0.030	0.057	0.050	0.079	0.070	0.099	0.090	...	...
1.000– 1.499	0.028	0.019			0.033	0.024	0.043	0.034	0.069	0.060	0.089	0.080	0.109	0.100	...	...
1.500– 1.999	0.036	0.024			0.046	0.034	0.056	0.044	0.082	0.070	0.102	0.090	0.122	0.110	0.182	0.170
2.000– 3.999	0.051	0.034			0.061	0.044	0.071	0.054	0.097	0.080	0.117	0.100	0.137	0.120	0.197	0.180
4.000– 5.999	0.066	0.044			0.076	0.054	0.086	0.064	0.112	0.090	0.132	0.110	0.152	0.130	0.212	0.190
6.000– 7.999	0.081	0.054			0.091	0.064	0.101	0.074	0.127	0.100	0.147	0.120	0.167	0.140	0.227	0.200
8.000– 9.999	0.096	0.064			0.106	0.074	0.116	0.084	0.142	0.110	0.162	0.130	0.182	0.150	0.242	0.210
10.000–11.999	0.111	0.074			0.121	0.084	0.131	0.094	0.157	0.120	0.177	0.140	0.197	0.160	0.257	0.220
12.000–13.999	0.126	0.084			0.136	0.094	0.146	0.104	0.172	0.130	0.192	0.150	0.212	0.170	0.272	0.230
14.000–15.999	0.141	0.094			0.151	0.104	0.161	0.114	0.187	0.140	0.207	0.160	0.227	0.180	0.287	0.240
16.000–17.999	0.156	0.104			0.166	0.114	0.176	0.124	0.202	0.150	0.222	0.170	0.242	0.190	0.302	0.250
18.000–19.999	0.171	0.114			0.181	0.124	0.191	0.134	0.217	0.160	0.237	0.180	0.257	0.200	0.317	0.260
20.000–21.999	0.186	0.124			0.196	0.134	0.206	0.144	0.232	0.170	0.252	0.190	0.272	0.210	0.332	0.270
22.000–24.000	0.201	0.134			0.211	0.144	0.221	0.154	0.247	0.180	0.267	0.200	0.287	0.220	0.347	0.280

A typical extrusion showing dimensions to which tolerances given above are applicable. Metal dimensions are given in Columns 2 and 3 and space dimensions in Columns 4 through 9.

(*Footnotes are on the next page.*)

Footnotes for Table 4

(a) These standard tolerances are applicable to the average shape; wider tolerances may be required for some shapes and closer tolerances may be possible for others. Tolerances for extruded shapes in T3510, T4510, T6510 and T8510 tempers are subject to special inquiry.

(b) The tolerance applicable to a dimension composed of two or more component dimensions is the sum of the tolerances of the component dimensions if all of the component dimensions are indicated. When a dimension tolerance is specified other than as an equal bilateral tolerance, the value of the standard tolerance is that which would apply to the mean of the maximum and minimum dimensions permissible under the tolerance.

(c) These tolerances do not apply to space dimensions such as dimension X of Example 1 below, even when Y is 75% or more of X. For the tolerance applicable to dimension X, use Columns 4, 5, 6, 7, 8 or 9, dependent on distance A.

(d) At points less than 0.250 in. from base of leg, the tolerances in Column 2 are applicable. The following tolerances apply where the space is completely enclosed (hollow shapes, Example 2): For the width (dimension A), the tolerance is the value shown in Column 4 for the depth (dimension D). For the depth (dimension D), the tolerance is the value shown in Column 4 for the width (dimension A). In no case is the tolerance for either width or depth less than at the corners (Column 2, Metal dimensions).

(e) Where dimensions specified are outside and inside, rather than wall thickness itself, the allowable deviation (eccentricity) given in Column 3 applies to mean wall thickness (the average of two wall thickness measurements taken at opposite sides of the void). For Class 1 hollow shapes, the standard wall thickness tolerance for extruded round tube is applicable. (A Class 1 hollow shape is one whose void is round and 1 in. or more in diameter and whose weight is equally distributed on opposite sides of two or more equally spaced axes.) Tolerance applicable to the wall thickness enclosing the void of hollow and semihollow shapes is subject to special inquiry when the nominal thickness of one wall is three times or greater than that of the opposite wall (Example 3).

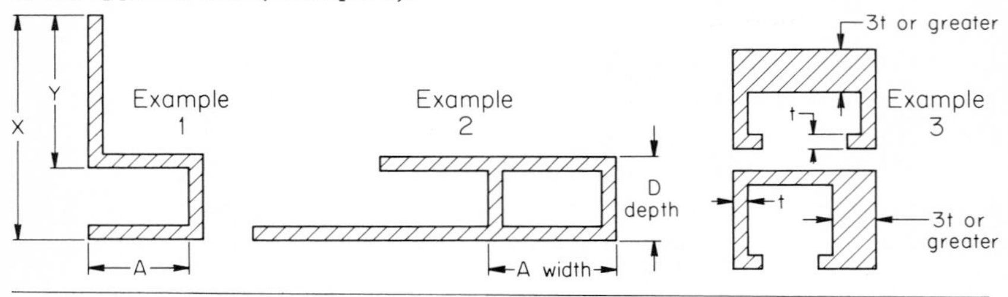

bearing length to obtain uniform metal flow to all elements of a shape. Die-opening dimensions are made oversize to allow for the contraction of the extrusion on cooling from the working temperature. Die deflection and die wear also contribute to dimensional variations. Extrusion conditions, including temperatures of ingot, container and die, as well as extrusion speed, must be controlled within a close range to minimize variations along an extruded length. Decreases in extrusion pressure and increases in extrusion temperature during the press cycle cause inherent dimensional variations.

Standard dimensional tolerances decrease continuously with increasing thickness; for shapes with circumscribing circle sizes less than 10 in. diam, they range from about ±6% for thickness less than 1/8 in. to about ±0.6% for thickness over 6 in. Special half-standard tolerances — and in some extrusions, even closer tolerances — usually can be supplied, provided the number of special tolerances applicable to a single shape is not excessive. Tolerances closer than standard result in additional extrusion costs. Standard cross-sectional dimensional tolerances for extruded rod, bar and shapes are given in Table 4.

Tolerances on dimensions and contour also are influenced by subsequent operations. Variations in mechanical properties along the length of an extrusion cause the lower-property cross sections to reduce more than higher-property portions during stretcher straightening, increasing dimensional variation.

Straightness and flatness tolerances sometimes are difficult to achieve with unbalanced cross sections. In stretching, symmetrical sections respond uniformly, whereas unsymmetrical sections may not be fully corrected, necessitating other supplementary straightening.

Tolerances for shapes that are to be assembled cannot always be detailed, because the type of assembly desired may vary considerably, involving snap fits, loose lateral lay-on assemblies, tight or loose longitudinal slide assemblies, or lateral slide assemblies. When tolerances cannot describe the assembly requirements adequately, extruders usually guarantee assembly but not specific dimensions. Tolerances applicable to extrusions are published by the Aluminum Association (2) and others.

Surface Finish

Surface finish of extrusions depends on the alloy, ingot quality, design and condition of the die and support tooling, extrusion speed and temperature, and subsequent thermal treatment. The degree of surface imperfections generally increases as the total alloy content and extrusion speed or temperature increase. Die lines, pickup, surface roughness, handling marks, and heat discoloration affect surface finish.

The design of an extruded shape can affect appearance or finish. For exposed surfaces of a shape, increasing width and multiplicity of exposed surfaces decrease the uniformity and level of finish attainable. The use of a design incorporating small ribs on an exposed surface to break the continuity of a flat

Table 5. Typical Longitudinal Mechanical Properties of Extrusions at Room Temperature

Alloy	Temper	Thickness, in.(a)	Area, sq in.	Tensile strength, psi	Yield strength, psi	Elongation, % in 2 in. or 4D(b)
EC.....	O	All	All	11,000	5,000	45
	H111	All	All	12,000	6,000	45
1060....	O	All	All	11,000	5,000	50
	H112	All	All	12,000	6,000	50
1100....	O	All	All	13,000	6,000	35
	H112	All	All	14,000	7,000	35
2011....	T6	0.250–1.499	Through 20	55,000	40,000	17
2014....	O	All	All	27,000	15,000	18
	T4, T451*x*	All	Through 32	58,000	43,000	24
	T6, T651*x*	Through 0.499	Through 20	68,000	64,000	12
		0.500–0.749	Through 25	74,000	68,000	12
		0.750 and over	Through 25	75,000	69,000	12
		0.750 and over	25 through 32	75,000	69,000	11
2219....	O	All	Through 32	27,000	14,000	19
	T351*x*	Through 0.499	Through 20	46,000	31,000	30
		0.500–1.499	Through 25	50,000	32,000	26
		1.500–2.999	Through 25	50,000	32,000	26
	T851*x*	Through 2.999	Through 25	65,000	49,000	11
2024....	O	All	All	30,000	15,000	17
	T4, T351*x*	Through 0.249	Through 20	64,000	52,000	18
		0.250–0.749	Through 20	71,000	56,000	17
		0.750–1.499	Through 25	78,000	61,000	15
		1.500 and over	Through 25	80,000	61,000	14
		1.500 and over	25 through 32	80,000	60,000	14
	T81, T851*x*	0.050–0.249	All	70,000	65,000	7
		0.250 and over	Through 32	72,000	66,000	9
3003....	O	All	All	16,000	8,000	40
	H112	All	All	16,000	9,000	40
5083....	O	Through 5.000	Through 32	45,000	23,000	20
	H111	Through 5.000	Through 32	47,000	33,000	18
	H112	Through 5.000	Through 32	46,000	25,000	18
6061....	O	All	All	16,000	8,000	30
	T4, T451*x*	All	Through 32	33,000	21,000	22
	T6, T651*x*	All	Through 32	44,000	41,000	15
6063....	T1	Through 0.500	Through 20	22,000	12,000	24
		0.501–1.000	Through 25	22,000	11,000	24
	T4	Through 0.500	Through 20	24,000	13,000	24
		0.501–1.000	Through 25	23,000	12,000	24
	T5	Through 0.500	Through 20	33,000	29,000	14
		0.501–1.000	Through 25	32,000	27,000	18
	T6	Through 0.124	Through 20	36,000	32,000	12
		0.125–1.000	Through 25	36,000	32,000	14

(*Continued on next page*)

Table 5. (Continued)

Alloy	Temper	Thickness, in.(a)	Area, sq in.	Tensile strength, psi	Yield strength, psi	Elongation, % in 2 in. or 4D(b)
7075....	O	All	All	33,000	19,000	15
	T6, T651x	Through 0.249	Through 20	88,000	82,000	11
		0.250–0.499	Through 20	90,000	84,000	11
		0.500–1.499	Through 25	90,000	84,000	11
		1.500–2.999	Through 25	90,000	84,000	11
		3.000–4.499	Through 20	88,000	80,000	10
		3.000–4.499	Through 32	86,000	77,000	11
		4.500–5.000	Through 32	86,000	76,000	11
7178....	O	All	All	34,000	20,000	15
	T6, T651x	Through 0.249	Through 20	95,000	89,000	10
		0.250–1.499	Through 25	96,000	89,000	10
		1.500–2.999	Through 25	97,000	90,000	10

(a) The thickness of the cross section from which the tension test specimen is taken determines the applicable mechanical properties. For material 1½ in. or less in thickness, when not tested in full section, the tension test specimen is taken from the center of the section; for material over 1½ in. in thickness, the specimen is taken midway between the center and the surface. (b) D is the diameter of specimen.

surface enhances the appearance. Nonuniform appearance or finish can result at sharp corners or abrupt changes in shape thickness. The use of generous radii or blends improves finish and appearance. Some nonuniformity of appearance can occur on surfaces opposite the junction of webs and flanges. In designing an extruded shape, consideration should be given to the additional operations that are required to complete its manufacture. The shape should also be designed as far as possible to facilitate handling and further fabrication and to minimize possible damage and impairment of the surface finish.

Extrusions for architectural, decorative and trim applications, where an attractive appearance is desired, usually are supplied in 6063-type alloys. In such applications, designating which surfaces of the extrusion will be visible in use enables the extruder to concentrate manufacturing effort on producing, at lower cost, optimum surface quality only where essential.

Mechanical Properties

Mechanical properties of extrusions are influenced by extrusion ratio, extrusion temperature, and alloy characteristics.

The amount of working during extrusion increases from front to rear along the length, and can cause a significant variation in structure and properties. Likewise, the amount of working in an extruded cross section increases from center to surface, and can cause corresponding variations in mechanical properties.

Typical longitudinal mechanical properties (given in Table 5) are usually slightly higher than the transverse tensile properties in recrystallized extrusions. In heat treated extrusions with unrecrystallized structures, tensile properties in the transverse direction, including elongation, generally are significantly lower than longitudinal properties (Fig. 1). One exception is in very wide, relatively thin extrusions, where properties are essentially the same in either direction.

In the non-heat-treatable strain-hardened alloys, the properties of extrusions are essentially those of the annealed temper, as extrusion is a hot working process. Relatively thin extrusions of the heat treatable alloys have lower properties than thick extrusions, because they are generally extruded at relatively high extrusion ratios and possess sufficient equivalent cold work to be completely recrystallized after heat treatment.

The thickness and cross-sectional area of an extrusion affect the level of mechanical properties obtainable in high-strength heat treatable alloy extrusions. Depending on the relative quench-sensitivity of the alloy, the strength reaches a maximum at a thickness of about 4 in. and an area of about 16 sq in. Some decrease in strength occurs with further increase in thickness and area, reflecting the resulting decreasing quench rate.

Process Capabilities

The equipment currently in use in the aluminum extrusion industry can produce extrusions:

1 In the complete range of commercial wrought alloys
2 In thicknesses from 0.040 in. and less to 12 in.
3 With circumscribing circle (smallest that encloses the shape completely) diameters of 0.250 in. and less to 40 in.
4 With per-foot weights of 0.05 to 200 lb and over
5 In individual lengths through 110 ft long, and 2500 lb each
6 Tube in diameters of 0.250 to 33 in.
7 Pipe in diameters up through 20-in. pipe size
8 Coils of small-cross-section extrusions and tube in virtually unlimited lengths

Both solid and hollow shapes are regularly extruded with an unlimited variety of internal and external configurations, both symmetrical and nonsymmetrical, that are not producible by any other method of metalworking. Hollow shapes are fabricated with single or multiple cavities. Seamless hollow shapes of nonsymmetrical configurations are produced, even in the high-strength alloys.

Despite the diverse size of shapes produced by extrusion, some limiting factors should be considered in designing commercial extrusions. Deep, narrow channels, either as individual shapes or as elements of a shape, often are the most severely limiting design feature; they frequently are extruded open and then contour rolled to the final configuration.

The extrusion press size generally is the limiting equipment factor that determines the producibility of an extrusion. However, the strength of steel available for tooling or the strength of the tool assembly may limit the producibility of an extrusion.

Application Considerations

Occasionally certain quality characteristics of some extrusions do not completely meet the end use requirements. For example, high-strength aluminum alloy extrusions cannot be supplied with the same surface quality as the intermediate-strength and lower-strength alloys, and thus are not always suitable where appearance or surface smoothness is also a prime requirement, unless they can be mechanically finished. In some intermediate-

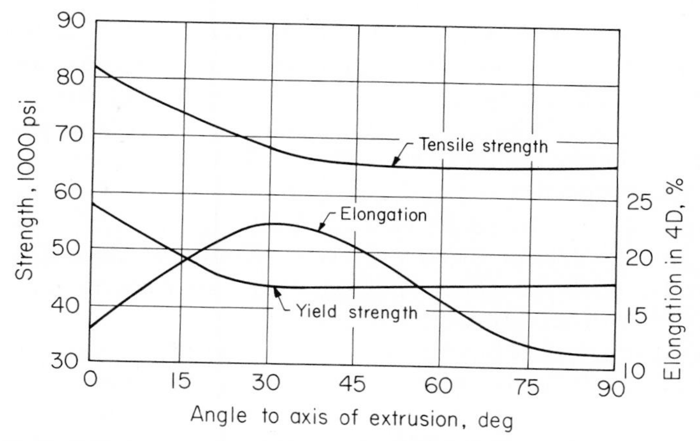

Fig. 1. Relation of tensile properties of 2024-T4 extrusion, 3 in. thick, with angle of tensile specimen to axis of extrusion (3)

Fig. 2. Complex aluminum extrusions for specialized applications

strength and lower-strength alloys, attractive surfaces of 60 micro-in. and less are produced regularly. In these alloys, however, minute surface imperfections and handling marks do appear on the extrusions, and the individual user may have to perform a polishing operation to achieve the finish desired.

Extruded tube is inexpensive compared to cold drawn tube, and is used where somewhat greater tolerances are acceptable.

The mechanical properties of extrusions are among the highest obtainable in aluminum alloy products. These high properties apply primarily to the longitudinal direction. Transverse mechanical properties generally are slightly lower than for other wrought aluminum products. Formability in the transverse direction for extrusions usually is somewhat less than for rolled products, such as sheet. Nevertheless, extrusions have good formability in all directions.

Extrusions are economical and are generally competitive with products produced by other manufacturing methods, particularly when the item to be produced is of nonuniform thickness or complex cross section. Die costs are low; in most instances, extrusions compete favorably with weldments and castings.

Machining or other surface finishing of extrusions usually is not necessary. Dimensional tolerances generally permit a manufacturer to fabricate end products by simple operations such as cutoff, drilling, punching, or minor machining. Even in small quantities, extrusions are almost always more economical than parts machined from bar stock.

The virtually unlimited variety of cross-sectional designs possible in aluminum extrusions permits significant simplification and economy in the manufacture of many end products. Extrusions are produced in integral cross sections that provide in a single shape a combination of elements or simple shapes, thereby eliminating mechanical joining, welding or other assembly operations. Shapes are provided with tongue and groove, snap, press, or sliding fit, self-tapping machine screw slots, and other cost saving features. Designs are shown in Fig. 2, 3 and 4.

Comparison With Competitive Processes and Materials

The extrusion process can distribute metal in a cross-sectional configuration in lengths that cannot be approached by most other metalworking processes. For thin shapes of uniform thickness in sufficient volume to offset high roll cost, however, roll forming of sheet stock generally will be more economical than extruding. Nonsymmetrical, intricate, cross-sectional shapes now account for a major portion of production volume. The use of the extrusion process for aluminum exceeds by far its use for any other metal. The addition of very large extrusion presses in

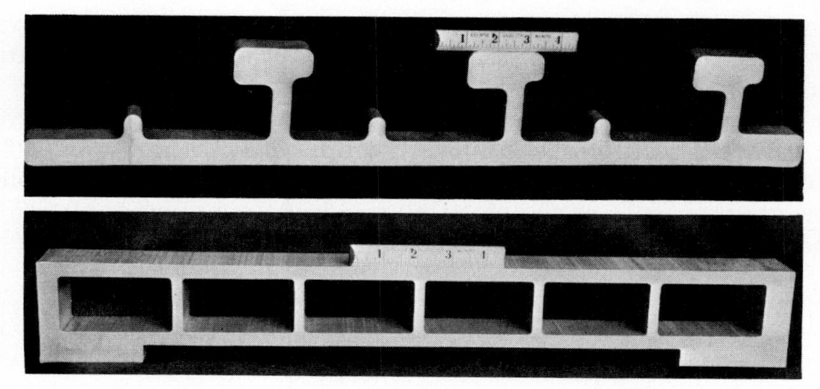

Fig. 3. Extruded section of high-strength 7075-T6511 alloy (top) that functions as an integrally stiffened aircraft wing panel after machining. Large, six-void, hollow 6061-T6 extruded shape (bottom) provides integral cooling ducts for an instrument housing.

Fig. 4. Multivoid hollow extrusion in 6063 alloy is 18.5 in. wide and contains 24 internal passages. This shape is used to make air-cooled, pressurized cabinets to house electronic equipment in high-altitude aircraft. This type of extrusion solves heating and cooling problems in a variety of applications.

the aluminum industry over the past decade has extended greatly the size range of extrusions available. Aluminum extrusions have little competition from extrusions of other metals, except where inherent characteristics not available in aluminum alloys are essential.

Through improvements in technology in recent years, extruded shapes, tube, and pipe of various plastics now compete with aluminum extruded products in some fields of application where properties of the plastics are adequate and other characteristics afford some special advantage.

References

1 How to Cut Costs in Extrusion Design, Modern Metals, **20**, No. 11, 58–62 (Dec 1964)
2 "Standards for Aluminum Mill Products, 1966", The Aluminum Assoc.
3 E. H. Dix, Jr., "Physical Metallurgy of Aluminum Alloys", American Society for Metals, 1949, p 220

Chapter 7

Design Factors for Impact Extrusions

R. A. KLENK and A. M. MILLER

IMPACT EXTRUSIONS combine a forged section and one or more extruded sections in a single part. The forged section can be a base, flange or hub of any approximately symmetrical shape and may contain bosses, lugs and other projections or recesses. The extruded sections can be of any essentially symmetrical, hollow or solid shape and can extend upward, downward or sideways from the forged section. They may have round, oval, square or rectangular cross sections and contain ribs or flutes on the inner or outer sidewalls, or both. From the direction of the metal flow come the names of the basic types of impacts: reverse, forward, lateral, and combination. (Volume III, Chapter 4 describes the procedures used in producing impacts of these four types.)

A wide variety of sizes and shapes are impact extruded in alloys that range from low-strength and intermediate-strength work-hardening compositions to the highest-strength heat treatable alloys. Part size is limited only by available press equipment and the strength of existing tool materials.

Among the important characteristics of the impact extrusion process are: (*a*) close dimensional tolerances; (*b*) smooth surface finish; (*c*) freedom from draft and flash; (*d*) product strength and toughness; (*e*) good control of grain structure; (*f*) desirable grain flow; and (*g*) ability to incorporate integral ribs, bosses, flanges and other design features without requiring extensive subsequent machining or assembly operations.

R. A. Klenk is a senior development engineer, Manufactured Products Div., Aluminum Company of America, New Kensington. A. M. Miller is quality assurance manager, Aluminum Company of America, Vernon, Calif.

Fig. 1. Multiple-wall aluminum impacts of varied cross section. Part at top is assembly of two double-wall impacts, the inner of which is shown at lower left.

Factors Affecting Choice of Process

Six general rules can be used to determine when a product can be made by impact extrusion:

1 When base thickness is to be greater than sidewall thickness
2 When the base must include bosses, lugs, projections or recesses
3 When the wall thickness must be increased at the open end of the shell
4 When tube is required with a heavy flange or heavy wall section at one end
5 When sidewalls have internal or external longitudinal ribs, or both
6 When length of shell exceeds 1½ to 2 times the diameter

Parts having any or all of these design features can be produced readily by impact extrusion. Many parts designed for drawing, spinning, stamping or turning may be altered to utilize the impact extrusion process.

The impact process is an economical, reliable method for producing housings and cylinders for applications requiring

Fig. 2. Flanged tubular aluminum impacts (sectioned and as subsequently fabricated). Capability of the process to incorporate an integral flange eliminates expensive subsequent assembly and provides parts with higher properties. Large part in center has integrally fabricated stepdown in tube.

pressure tightness. The capacity of the process to provide integral bosses and tubular extensions offers savings in manufacturing cost by eliminating expensive welding or brazing operations. It is often desirable to provide material for threading or tapping the open end of a pressure cylinder to obtain a proper closure. The impact extrusion technique can provide a part with extra wall thickness at the open end.

Single impacts with multiple walls (Fig. 1) can frequently be substituted for complex welded, brazed or mechanically assembled composites. Strength and reliability are improved.

Figure 2 illustrates a variety of one-piece, flanged tubular sections. By use of the impact process, light-wall tubing and heavy-flange ends can be combined in one piece. Other methods

Fig. 3. Aluminum impacts employed as machining blanks (with part as subsequently machined). Use of impacts permits major savings in machining, compared with fabricating such components from conventional wrought stock.

of fabrication generally require complicated assembly or involve higher costs.

A considerable amount of turning, deep drilling, milling and broaching can frequently be avoided by impact extruding a "machining blank" such as those shown in Fig. 3. Savings in material are substantial compared to machining the parts from rod or closed-die forgings. Draft-free chucking surfaces and close tolerances are provided. A parting line is avoided, and excellent grain-flow pattern achieved.

No general statement can be made regarding the minimum number of parts required to justify the use of the impact process. If the principal considerations are tooling and development cost and price per piece, 5000 parts or more may be required to justify impact extrusion. However, if alternate methods are expensive or result in inferior quality, 50 parts may constitute an economical impact run. A few parts produced as impacts cannot be made by any other method; for such designs, tooling expense can sometimes be justified to make a single piece.

Metallurgical Characteristics

Typical impacts have a completely wrought structure and a grain flow that favors strength and toughness. Because ribs, bosses and flanges, and other design features are integral and there is no flash to be trimmed or draft angle to be machined off, grain flow is continuous and exposed end-grain is absent or at a minimum. When impacts are used as machining blanks, metal removal requirements are minimized by the close tolerances provided and by the amount of detail that can be achieved. Thus, the machined parts retain more of the favorable grain flow than when parts less precisely formed are machined. Grain direction in the final impact extrusion is determined by the grain direction in the slug and grain flow during impact extrusion.

Because impact extrusion is normally completed at a temperature appreciably below that required for recrystallization to occur, good control of as-extruded grain structure can be achieved by controlling the grain structure of the slug. The slug grains are elongated and fragmented during impact extrusion to a greater or lesser extent, depending on slug temperature, section thickness, and part shape. However, except for very low extrusion ratios, the degree of work hardening of slugs extruded at room temperature is relatively consistent over a considerable range of section thicknesses, because thin sections generate more heat during extrusion and this compensates for the greater reduction in area.

The highly cold worked and essentially full-hard as-extruded structure recrystallizes readily into fine, slightly elongated grains during subsequent annealing or solution heat treating operations. The structure obtained when aluminum alloys are impact extruded at an elevated temperature, due to the lesser amount of equivalent cold work, is more typical of a die forging, particularly after solution heat treatment.

Table 1. Relative Pressure Requirements for Cold Impact Extruding Annealed Slugs of Representative Alloys (Alloy 1100 = 1.0)

Alloy	Relative extrusion pressure
1100	1.0
3003	1.2
6061	1.6
2014	1.8
7075	2.3

Impact extrusions can be produced in all the commercial aluminum alloys discussed in Volume I, Chapter 9, but certain compositions are more widely used than others because of their fabrication characteristics or their properties in the finished product. From the fabricating standpoint, those alloys that extrude at the lowest pressure provide definite advantages in cheaper dies, longer die life, and smaller equipment requirements. The relative pressure requirements for cold impact extruding annealed slugs of several representative alloys are given in Table 1. Although these values are applicable to simple impacts of moderate size and wall thickness, they provide a reasonable guide for most impacts in these alloys.

Factors Affecting Design

Wide latitude is permissible in the design of the sidewall or the extruded section of an impact. Cylindrical shapes usually are easily adaptable to simple production methods. However, shapes having oval, square or rectangular cross section, and many special shapes, are readily produced. Symmetry of cross section

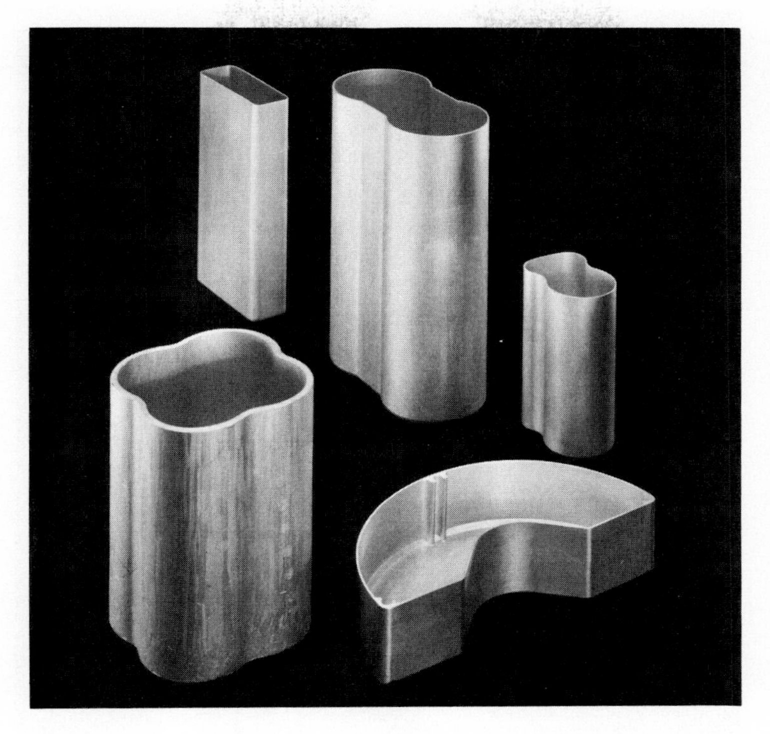

Fig. 4. Aluminum impacts with noncylindrical or unsymmetrical cross sections (see Fig. 1 for multiple-wall impacts)

simplifies the fabrication of impacts, but it is not essential. Figure 4 illustrates several impacts with special cross sections, some of which depart from symmetry.

Longitudinal ribs can be incorporated in the sidewall of impacts by modifying the tooling to provide an appropriate extrusion orifice. Ribbing can be on either the inside or the outside of the part; it has, on occasion, even covered the bottom of impacts. Figure 5 shows various decorative and functional ribs that are common with the process.

Design detail such as lugs, bosses, grooves and depressions can be incorporated on both surfaces of the pressure section of an impact. Again, symmetry of design helps fabrication and is desirable. If unsymmetrical designs cannot be avoided, methods to minimize their effect often can be devised. Figure 6 depicts a group of typical closed-end design details that are simple and readily produced.

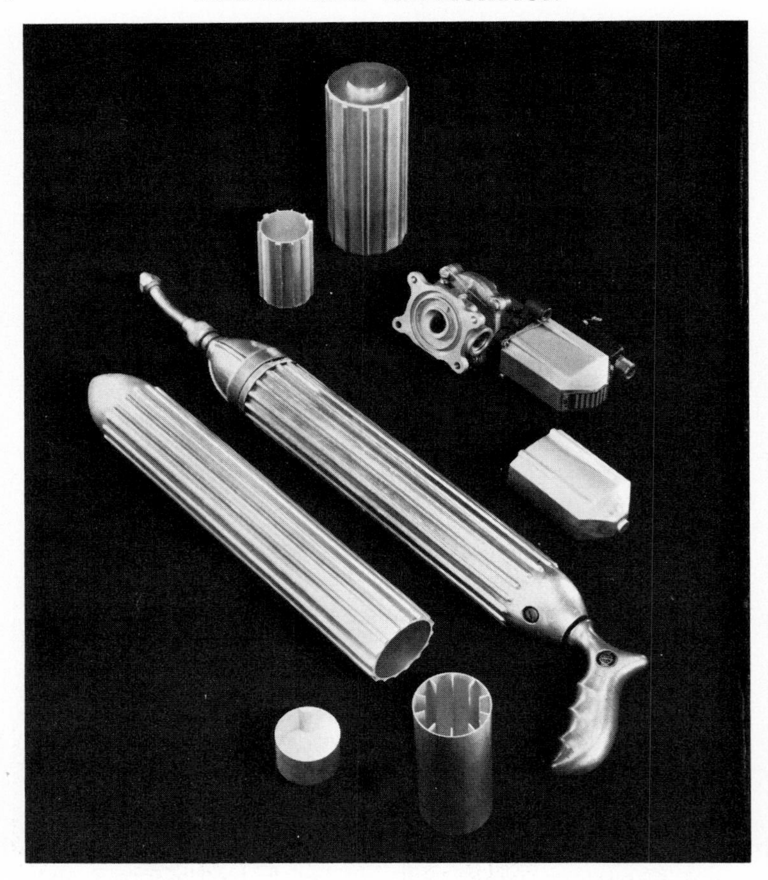

Fig. 5. Aluminum impacts incorporating longitudinal external or internal ribs (two shown in complete final assembly). Ribs are employed decoratively or functionally, as for tapping holes, grip surfaces, or heat transfer vanes.

Assuming sufficient stroke length to remove the part from the press, the maximum length of reverse impacts depends largely on the ability of the punch to withstand the impact load without bending. In terms of diameter of the extruded section, the maximum length is generally about 10 to 12 diameters. However, lengths up to 18 diameters in some parts are produced successfully, and improvements in tool design and materials, and in press equipment, should extend this ratio further.

The largest presses designed for impact extrusion that are operating in the United States are capable of producing reverse and forward impacts up to 16 in. in diameter. Reverse impacts may be up to 60 in. long; with forward impacts, length is limited only by the cross section of the part and the capacity of the press, unless a flange necessitates backing the part out of the die, when the maximum length is about 60 in.

Hydraulic extrusion and forging presses, with suitable modifications, are also employed for making very large impacts. Impacts up to 33 in. in diameter have been produced by reverse extrusion from high-strength aluminum alloys on a 14,000-ton extrusion press. Similar impacts up to 40 in. in diameter have been produced on large forging presses. It is estimated that reverse impacts up to 50 in. in diameter and forward impacts up to 100 in. in diameter could be fabricated on suitably equipped 35,000 and 50,000-ton forging presses, such as are available in the United States. The lengths of these impacts would be limited by the press clearance, but could be up to about 100 in.

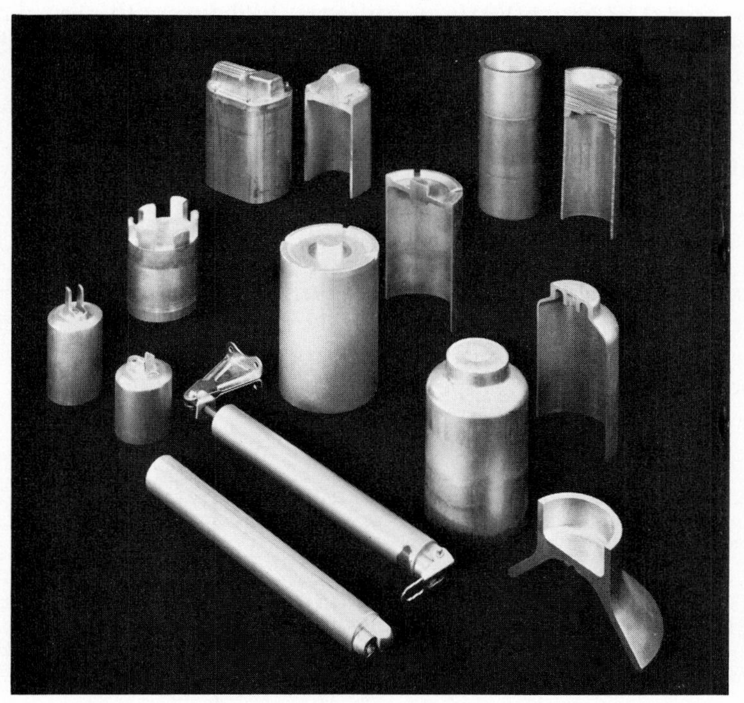

Fig. 6. Web section detail in aluminum impacts (most shown in cross section, but two as subsequently fabricated). Ability of the process to permit this type of detail eliminates weldments and other assemblies, permits strong, pressure-tight components, and minimizes secondary machining costs.

Tolerances

Because impacts are produced by the flow of metal through an orifice, they are inherently free of draft. In general, impacts are manufactured to close tolerances. The degree depends on size, shape, alloy, wall thickness, type of tooling required, and press equipment. On the basis of these factors, the minimum wall thicknesses for various diameter impacts have been established. Table 2 provides a guide for design purposes.

Wall thickness tolerances are from ±0.001 to ±0.005 in. for relatively thin-wall, low-strength alloy, cylindrical shapes of moderate size, but they may be as large as ±0.010 to ±0.015 in. for large parts of high-strength alloys (Table 3). Wall thickness tolerances for rectangular shells range from ±0.005 to ±0.015 in., depending on size, alloy and nominal wall thickness (Table 4). Diameter tolerances typically range from ±0.001 in. for small parts to ±0.010 to ±0.015 in. for large, high-strength alloy parts. Closer control of diameter can be achieved on small, heavy-walled parts by centerless grinding the impacts. Dimensional tolerances in the forged part of the impact are highly influenced by many variables, but ±0.005 to ±0.015 in. is typical. Variations in extruded length usually require a separate trimming operation.

Surface Finish

Impact surface finishes typically range from 20 to 70 micro-in. Smoother surfaces can sometimes be attained by using special lubricants and techniques. Large, strong-alloy impacts and parts produced at elevated temperature may have rougher surfaces.

Table 2. Approximate Minimum Wall Thickness for Aluminum Alloy Impact Extrusions

Diameter of shell, in.	Minimum wall thickness(a), in.		
	Alloys 1100, 3003	Alloys 6061, 6151	Alloys 2014, 7075
¾ through 1½	0.010	0.015	Subject to special inquiry
2 through 2½	0.015	0.020	
3	0.020	0.025	
3½	0.025	0.030	
4	0.030	0.035	
4½	0.035	0.040	
5	0.060	0.070	
6	Subject to special inquiry		

(a) Minimum thicknesses shown are intended to serve as a guide for design purposes. There are conditions under which walls of less thickness can be produced.

Table 3. Dimensions and Tolerances of Round Impact Extruded Aluminum Alloy Shells(a)

Diameter, in.	Outside diam, in.	Inside diam, in.	Nominal wall, in.	Bottom, in.	Corner radius, in.	Max (b) length, in.	Tolerances: Outside diam, ± in.	Tolerances: Inside diam, ± in.	Tolerances: Min wall, in.	Tolerances: Bottom, ± in.	Tolerances: Length outside, ± in.
3/4	0.750	0.730	0.010	0.020	1/32	4 1/2	0.005	0.006	0.005	0.007	1/32
3/4	0.750	0.720	0.015	0.025	1/32	4 1/2	0.005	0.006	0.010	0.007	1/32
3/4	0.750	0.710	0.020	0.030	1/32	3 1/8	0.005	0.006	0.015	0.007	1/32
7/8	0.875	0.855	0.010	0.020	1/32	5 1/4	0.005	0.006	0.005	0.007	1/32
7/8	0.875	0.845	0.015	0.025	1/32	5 1/4	0.005	0.006	0.010	0.007	1/32
7/8	0.875	0.835	0.020	0.030	1/32	3 3/4	0.005	0.006	0.015	0.007	1/32
1	1.000	0.970	0.015	0.025	1/16	6	0.005	0.006	0.010	0.010	1/32
1	1.000	0.960	0.020	0.030	1/16	4 1/4	0.005	0.006	0.015	0.010	1/32
1	1.000	0.950	0.025	0.035	1/16	3 3/8	0.005	0.006	0.020	0.010	1/32
1 1/8	1.125	1.095	0.015	0.025	1/16	6 3/4	0.005	0.006	0.010	0.010	1/32
1 1/8	1.125	1.085	0.020	0.030	1/16	4 7/8	0.005	0.006	0.015	0.010	1/32
1 1/8	1.125	1.075	0.025	0.035	1/16	3 5/8	0.005	0.006	0.020	0.010	1/32
1 1/4	1.250	1.220	0.015	0.025	1/16	7 1/2	0.005	0.006	0.010	0.010	1/32
1 1/4	1.250	1.210	0.020	0.030	1/16	5 1/4	0.005	0.006	0.015	0.010	1/32
1 1/4	1.250	1.200	0.025	0.035	1/16	4	0.005	0.006	0.020	0.010	1/32
1 3/8	1.375	1.345	0.015	0.025	1/16	8 1/4	0.005	0.006	0.010	0.010	1/32
1 3/8	1.375	1.335	0.020	0.030	1/16	6 1/8	0.005	0.006	0.015	0.010	1/32
1 3/8	1.375	1.325	0.025	0.035	1/16	4 1/2	0.005	0.006	0.020	0.010	1/32
1 1/2	1.500	1.470	0.015	0.025	1/16	9	0.005	0.006	0.010	0.010	1/32
1 1/2	1.500	1.460	0.020	0.030	1/16	6 3/4	0.005	0.006	0.015	0.010	1/32
1 1/2	1.500	1.450	0.025	0.035	1/16	5	0.005	0.006	0.020	0.010	1/32
1 3/4	1.750	1.710	0.020	0.032	1/16	8 1/4	0.006	0.007	0.015	0.012	1/32
1 3/4	1.750	1.700	0.025	0.037	1/16	6 1/4	0.006	0.007	0.020	0.012	1/32
1 3/4	1.750	1.690	0.030	0.042	1/16	4 1/2	0.006	0.007	0.025	0.012	1/32
2	2.000	1.960	0.020	0.032	3/32	10	0.007	0.008	0.015	0.012	1/32
2	2.000	1.950	0.025	0.037	3/32	10	0.007	0.008	0.020	0.012	1/32
2	2.000	1.940	0.030	0.042	3/32	8	0.007	0.008	0.025	0.012	1/32
2 1/4	2.250	2.210	0.020	0.032	3/32	10	0.007	0.008	0.015	0.012	1/32
2 1/4	2.250	2.200	0.025	0.037	3/32	10	0.007	0.008	0.020	0.012	1/32
2 1/4	2.250	2.190	0.030	0.042	3/32	9 3/8	0.007	0.008	0.025	0.012	1/32
2 1/2	2.500	2.460	0.020	0.032	3/32	10	0.007	0.008	0.015	0.012	1/32
2 1/2	2.500	2.450	0.025	0.037	3/32	10	0.007	0.008	0.020	0.012	1/32
2 1/2	2.500	2.440	0.030	0.042	3/32	10	0.007	0.008	0.025	0.012	1/32
3	3.000	2.950	0.025	0.040	1/8	10	0.009	0.010	0.015	0.015	1/32
3	3.000	2.930	0.035	0.050	1/8	10	0.009	0.010	0.025	0.015	1/32
3	3.000	2.900	0.050	0.065	1/8	7 3/4	0.009	0.010	0.040	0.015	1/32
3 1/2	3.500	3.450	0.025	0.040	1/8	10	0.009	0.010	0.015	0.015	1/32
3 1/2	3.500	3.430	0.035	0.050	1/8	10	0.009	0.010	0.025	0.015	1/32
3 1/2	3.500	3.400	0.050	0.065	1/8	9	0.009	0.010	0.040	0.015	1/32
4	4.000	3.900	0.050	0.065	1/8	10	0.011	0.012	0.035	0.015	1/32
4	4.000	3.880	0.060	0.075	1/8	8 1/2	0.011	0.012	0.045	0.015	1/32
4 1/4	4.250	4.150	0.050	0.075	1/8	11	0.011	0.012	0.035	0.015	1/32
5	5.000	4.860	0.070	0.085	3/16	11	0.014	0.015	0.055	0.015	1/32
6	6.000	5.800	0.100	0.125	3/16	12	0.020	0.020	0.085	0.015	1/32

(a) Data apply only to round, flat-bottomed shells. Tolerances for any variation in design depend on other design considerations. (b) Lengths exceeding indicated maximums are available under certain conditions.

Table 4. Dimensions and Tolerances of Square and Rectangular Impact Extruded Aluminum Alloy Shells

							Tolerances				
							Cross section(a)				
Outside dimensions, in.	Inside dimensions, in.	Nominal wall, in.	Bottom, in.	Side radius, in.	Bottom radius(b), in.	Max(c) length, in.	Outside dimensions, ± in.	Inside dimensions, ± in.	Min wall, in.	Bottom, ± in.	Length outside, ± in.
Rectangular Impact											
1.571 by 1.133	1.521 by 1.083	0.025	0.035	1/16	1/32	3 1/2	0.008	0.010	0.015	0.015	1/32
1.783 by 1.408	1.733 by 1.358	0.025	0.035	3/32	1/16	4 3/4	0.008	0.010	0.015	0.015	1/32
1.884 by 1.446	1.834 by 1.396	0.025	0.035	1/8	1/16	6	0.008	0.010	0.015	0.015	1/32
2.000 by 1.000	1.950 by 0.950	0.025	0.035	7/32	1/16	3 1/2	0.008	0.010	0.015	0.015	1/32
2.381 by 1.818	2.281 by 1.718	0.050	0.065	1/4	1/8	4 23/32	0.008	0.010	0.040	0.015	1/32
2.375 by 1.938	2.325 by 1.888	0.025	0.035	1/4	3/32	5 5/16	0.008	0.010	0.015	0.015	1/32
2.375 by 1.938	2.275 by 1.838	0.050	0.065	1/4	3/32	3 7/16	0.008	0.010	0.040	0.015	1/32
2.500 by 1.188	2.438 by 1.126	0.031	0.050	1/4	1/16	4 1/4	0.008	0.010	0.020	0.015	1/32
2.500 by 1.891	2.438 by 1.829	0.031	0.050	3/32	3/32	6	0.008	0.010	0.020	0.015	1/32
2.500 by 2.250	2.437 by 2.188	0.031	0.050	1/4	1/16	6	0.008	0.010	0.020	0.015	1/32
2.750 by 3.250	...	0.051	0.070	1/4	3/32	6	0.015	0.015	0.051	0.015	1/32
Square Impact											
1.425 by 1.425	1.375 by 1.375	0.025	0.035	5/32	1/16	6	0.008	0.010	0.015	0.015	1/32
1.750 by 1.750	1.700 by 1.700	0.025	0.035	3/16	1/16	6	0.008	0.010	0.015	0.015	1/32
2.000 by 2.000	1.950 by 1.950	0.025	0.035	1/4	3/32	6	0.008	0.010	0.015	0.015	1/32
2.250 by 2.250	2.125 by 2.125	0.062	0.075	1/4	3/32	6	0.008	0.010	0.050	0.015	1/32

(a) Cross-sectional tolerances apply at the tangent points of the corner radii only and are exclusive of the "bow" in sidewalls, which is indeterminate. (b) A fillet, used between sidewall and base of shells, should have a height equal to the radius incorporated on the outside bottom of the shell. (c) Lengths exceeding indicated maximums are available under certain conditions.

Mechanical Properties of Impacts

Mechanical properties attainable in impact extrusions cover virtually the entire range that can be achieved with available wrought alloy compositions, cold work or heat treatment, or by combinations of the three. Although a large number of different tempers could be produced, this has not been necessary. The as-extruded, F, temper serves adequately for most applications where a work-hardening alloy is specified; then the desired strength is obtained by choice of alloy. However, no entirely satisfactory alloy has been found that combines high as-extruded strength with excellent extrusion characteristics. The added cost of subsequent heat treating and artificial aging is, therefore, required for most applications demanding high mechanical properties. Heat treated impacts have mechanical properties similar to those of forgings of the same alloy and temper (Table 5).

When mechanical property testing is required, the largest standard, or subsize, round specimen that can be machined from the part is used. Unless otherwise specified, or prevented by the size and shape of the part, an area with grain flow substantially parallel to the axis of the specimen is selected. Testing in one or more specific locations in the part is sometimes specified. A flat specimen is employed when section thickness does not permit cutting out a round sample. Parts too small to provide a tensile test specimen are controlled by Brinell hardness.

Table 5. Typical Mechanical Properties of Impact Extrusions at Room Temperature(a)

Alloy and temper	Tensile strength, psi	Yield strength, psi	Elongation, % in 2 in. or in 4*D*	Brinell hardness number(b)
1100-H152	27,000	24,000	4.0	40
1100-F	27,000	24,000	4.0	40
2014-T4	64,000	37,000	24.0	105
2014-T6	70,000	62,000	11.0	135
3003-F	33,000	29,000	6.0	60
6151-T6	49,000	43,000	18.0	105
6061-T4	35,000	17,000	28.0	60
6061-T6	47,000	42,000	16.0	100
6061-T84(c)	45,000	42,000	12.0	90
7075-T6	81,000	72,000	14.0	160

(a) ASTM standard or subsize round specimens with axes substantially parallel to grain direction. (b) 500-kg load, 10-mm ball. (c) Properties apply only to parts 0.040 in. or more in thickness.

Certain critical impacts are pressure tested either on a 100% or sample basis, to ensure adequate strength and freedom from defects. Also, certain parts may require 100% or sample hardness testing; this is usually done on direct-reading equipment.

Comparison With Competitive Processes and Materials

Various processes compete with different types of impacts:

1 Certain forgings and castings and many screw-machine products compete with solid or relatively short, heavy-wall impacts.
2 Drawn parts compete with short, relatively thin-wall impacts.
3 Welded, brazed or mechanically joined composites, customarily assembled from tubing, castings and screw-machine parts compete with most types of impacts.

When a part is of a configuration especially adapted to the impact process and is required in quantity, the other processes are usually at an economic or quality disadvantage, or both.

Forgings and screw-machine products generally require considerably more stock and have less favorable grain flow patterns. However, a screw-machine product may save time and money for a relatively small number of parts.

Forgings and castings are seldom produced to as close dimensional tolerances as are impacts. Most castings are less sound and have lower mechanical properties.

Drawing of sheet may have a competitive cost advantage for cans with length-to-diameter ratios up to about 2-to-1, if a bottom thickness equal to or only slightly heavier than the wall thickness is satisfactory. However, ribs, bosses and other design details cannot be produced in drawn cans, and drawing tools are generally more expensive than impact tools.

Composite assemblies can save time and money in fabricating a relatively small number of parts. However, they are usually not as strong and reliable as impacts.

Materials. Lead and tin, the only metals as readily impact extruded as aluminum, are more expensive and lower in strength than aluminum. Their use is confined to applications requiring their special characteristics. All other metals are more difficult to impact extrude than aluminum, and all but steel are more expensive. Aluminum impacts sometimes find it difficult to compete with assemblies of steel tubing, stampings, and drawn cans on a strictly cost basis. Similarly, molded and extruded plastics offer increasing competition for certain applications.

Chapter 8

Design Factors for Forgings

R. F. BELL and A. E. FAVRE

GOOD DESIGN for forgings, as for other types of fabricated products, is influenced significantly by manufacturing requirements and by the equipment available. A knowledge of forging processes and equipment should aid an engineer to develop sound basic designs that can be produced at a minimum cost, and to utilize a forging to the greatest advantage (Volume III, Chapter 5). Choice of alloy and temper, type and location of stresses, and service environment also contribute to the design problem, and must be carefully considered to obtain the maximum potential of an aluminum forging.

General information for designing aluminum forgings is given in this chapter. Also, specific relationships and limits on rib and web thickness, radii, fillets, and tolerances are provided. Although these do not answer all possible design questions, they should solve a majority of problems. For other problems, consultation with a qualified forging design expert is recommended.

Types of Forgings

The basic types of aluminum alloy forgings are: (*a*) open-die forgings (flat-die, smith, or hand forging), with variations known as standard (or regular) shape, contour (or special) shape, and mandrel-forged rings; (*b*) closed-die forgings (blocker, conventional, precision and cored); (*c*) rolled rings.

R. F. Bell was formerly quality assurance manager, Aluminum Company of America, Cleveland. A. E. Favre is forging project manager, Aluminum Company of America, Cleveland.

H. J. Rowe, secretary, Research and Development Committee, Aluminum Company of America, Pittsburgh, assisted in preparing this chapter.

Open-die forgings are usually made on flat dies in hydraulic presses or hammers. Round or V-impression dies may be used to produce round or circular cross sections. "Hand forgings" is the descriptive term most commonly used; open-die forgings of square, rectangular or round cross section are known as "standard" or "regular-shape" hand forgings. "Biscuits", which are also standard-shape hand forgings, are made in various diameters and thicknesses.

Contour or special-shape hand forgings include mandrel-forged rings and rings machined from biscuits. Contour hand forgings usually are made on flat dies, and may be forged, sawed

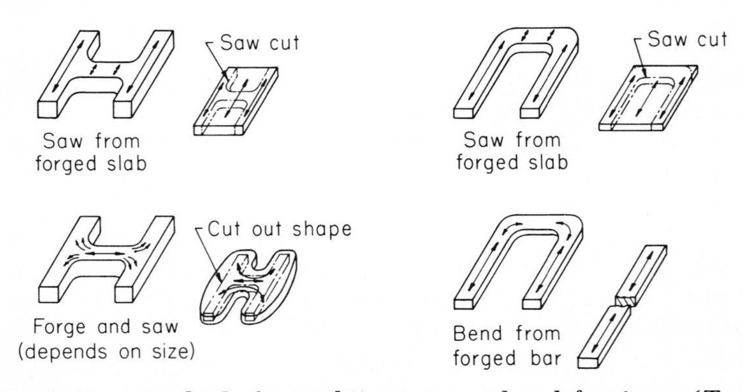

Fig. 1. Two methods for making contour hand forgings. (Top) Grain flow when shapes are sawed from forged slab. (Bottom) Grain flow obtained with use of simple forging and bending tools.

or rough machined to final shape. Occasionally, simple dies or hand tools may be used to provide varying contours. In more complicated shapes, combinations of procedures may be employed. Figure 1 shows how two simple contour hand forgings could be made by different methods. Choice of method depends on the mechanical properties and grain flow required.

Special or contour hand forgings more closely resemble the finished part than do standard hand forgings, and may have grain-flow patterns comparable to their closed-die counterparts (Fig. 2, left). Contour hand forgings are more costly than standard hand forgings because of the additional forging and finishing operations required. However, they usually provide a more desirable combination of mechanical properties, and superior grain flow. Contour hand forgings are recommended where the number of pieces required does not warrant costly die investment and for interim production while dies for conventional die forgings are being built.

Ring forgings that are produced in hammers or hydraulic presses by the mandrel method may be classified as open-die forgings. A hollow aluminum alloy billet is placed on a mandrel or arbor of suitable size. As the billet is rotated slowly under repeated blows or squeezes, its wall thickness is reduced and its diameter increased. This method is suitable for ring forgings of any diameter and width within equipment limitations.

Closed-die forgings have many forms. Cross sections of three types commonly used in forging aluminum alloys are illustrated in Fig. 3. Blocker-type die forgings have generous design factors, including large fillet and corner radii, thick webs and wide ribs, and normally require subsequent machining on all surfaces (Fig. 2, center). Generally, only one set of die cavities is necessary to fabricate a blocker-type forging.

Conventional forgings, the most common type, are designed with more detail, less finish allowance, and to closer tolerances than blocker forgings. More than one set of die cavities may be necessary to produce them.

Precision die forgings have small fillet and corner radii, thin

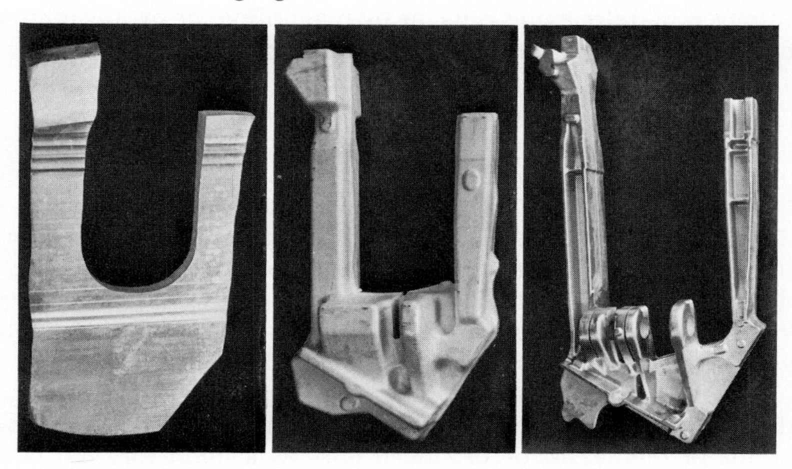

(Left) Special or contoured hand forging, weighing 1400 lb, for fast, low-cost prototype development. (Center) Blocker forging, weighing 875 lb, produced with minimum die expense. (Right) Precision forging for quantity production with minimum finish machining; weight of forging, 306 lb, and length, 65 in.

Fig. 2. Three forging methods may be used to create a part for the same end use.

webs and narrow ribs, with low or zero draft angles, and are forged to such dimensions and tolerances that little finish machining is required (Fig. 2, right). Tooling for precision forgings is more costly than for other types. Not only are the dies built to closer tolerances, but also many must be made of segments or inserts locked and held together in a special holder. Precision forgings represent the ultimate in shaping a part by forging. In the ideal part, the grain flow conforms exactly to the contour of the final part, affording maximum strength in all sections with little or no intersecting of grain flow by subsequent machining operations.

Cored forgings, another type of closed-die forging, are made on mechanical upsetters or presses employing side rams in conjunction with a vertical ram. The side rams produce one or more impressions, usually at right angles to those produced by the action of the vertical ram. Typical parts produced as cored forgings are large T and cross pipe fittings.

Rolled ring forgings are produced on ring-rolling machines from a hollow billet that is rotated between a mandrel and a pressure roll to reduce the thickness of the billet and increase the diameter. Rings with other than flat faces are produced with contoured mandrels and rolls, or by machining, or by a combination of the rolling and machining fabrication techniques.

Choice of Type of Forging

Cost of tooling, possible development work required, and availability of parts by alternate methods influence the choice of a forging process. For some parts, tooling costs are inconsequential; for others, no alternate method of production is available; a relatively few pieces would justify selecting an aluminum alloy closed-die forging in either situation. In general, where quantities are large, tool costs per unit are negligible.

For low quantities, it may be uneconomical to produce a part other than as a hand forging. A part requiring several thousand pounds of metal can be produced only as a hand forging; with smaller parts, there may be a choice between a hand forging and a relatively simple closed-die forging. Repetitive parts ordered in large quantities can usually justify the tooling cost of conventional or precision forging.

Design variables affect tooling and forging costs regardless of the type of forging selected. Generally, the closer the forging is to the finished part, the higher are the forging and tooling costs. A contour or even a standard-shape hand forging may be adequate functionally; it will cost less than a closed-die forging.

Aluminum Forging Alloys

A wide selection of aluminum alloys is available for forging. The mechanical properties and characteristics of the wrought aluminum alloys (Volume I, Chapter 9) are inherent in the chemical composition and therefore persist in the forging.

For applications requiring maximum mechanical properties, alloys 2014, 2024, 7075, 7079 and X7080 are the most frequently used. Alloy 2014 and 2024 forgings are extensively used for airframe components, truck wheel hubs, and ordnance and missile parts. Alloys 7075, 7079 and X7080 are used primarily

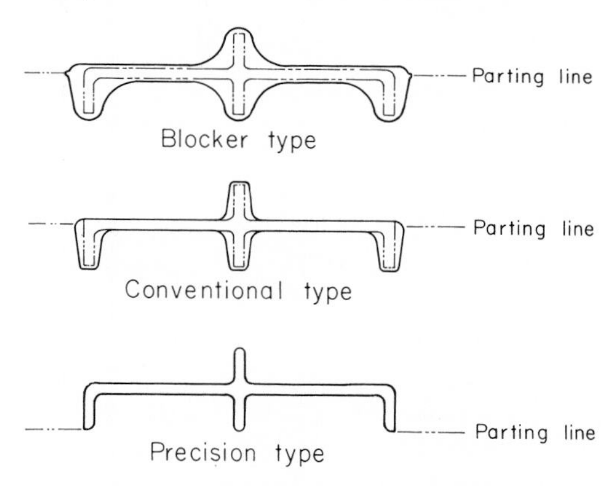

Fig. 3. Comparable cross sections of typical blocker, conventional, and precision aluminum alloy closed-die forgings

for airframe applications requiring the highest mechanical properties. Alloy X7080 is particularly useful for heavy-section airframe and landing gear parts involving sections over 3 in. thick and requiring low residual stress, because of its ability to be quenched in boiling water and still retain high mechanical properties.

Alloys 2024, 2218, 2219, 2618 and 4032 have good mechanical properties at elevated temperatures. With proper heat treatment they provide maximum dimensional stability, and are employed for aircraft engine pistons, cylinder heads, and other elevated-temperature applications. Alloy 4032 has the lowest coefficient of thermal expansion of the common forging alloys; it is widely used for truck, locomotive and marine diesel engine pistons.

For applications requiring superior resistance to corrosion along with moderate mechanical properties, 6061 and 6151 alloys are used. Both have excellent forgeability and are readily machined; they are used for automotive, hardware, and machinery parts such as spool heads and spinning buckets for the textile

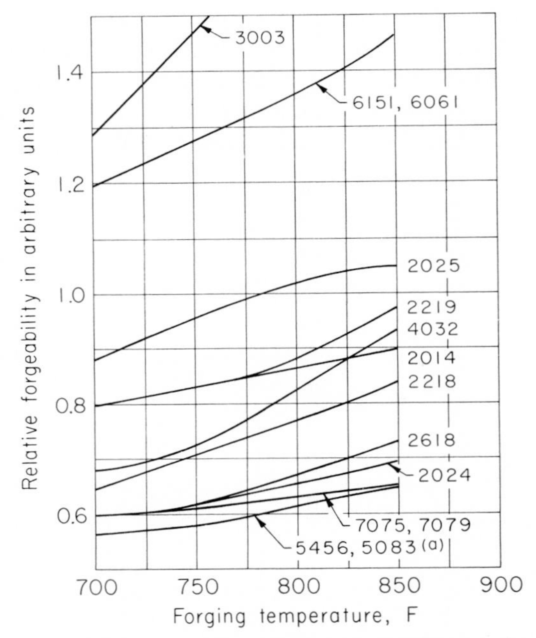

Fig. 4. Effect of temperature on relative forgeability of various aluminum alloys. Vertical scale is based on deformation per unit of energy absorbed. (a) Estimated from production experience.

industry, and plaster and cement workers' trowel handles. Although limited in forgings, non-heat-treatable alloys 1100 and 3003 have excellent resistance to corrosion and are the most readily forged. Alloys for applications requiring good weldability include 2219, 5083, 5456 and 6061.

Although all commercial alloys can be shaped by at least one forging process, 5083, 5456, 7075, 7079 and X7080 alloys require the highest pressures. All flow much less readily than do 6061 and 6151.

Wherever a choice is possible, lower costs through longer die life, cheaper dies, better forgeability, and less process scrap can be achieved by selecting one of the alloys more easily forged. Alloys 6061 and 6151 forge readily in hammers or presses. Alloys 2024, 5083, 5456, 7075, 7079 and X7080 forge less readily on hammers; they are better suited for hydraulic press forgings, particularly for large, complex forgings. Figure 4 illustrates the relative forgeability of some common forging alloys. The forgeability relationships shown are based on the deformation per unit of energy absorbed at various temperatures in the range most frequently used in forging aluminum alloys.

Metallurgical Characteristics

The grain structure obtained in forgings reflects the combined effect of grain flow in stock and direction of metal flow during forging. The final pattern establishes the uniformity of mechanical properties. The highest strength and ductility are obtained in a direction parallel to maximum grain flow during forging. This is called the longitudinal direction. Minimum strength and ductility occur perpendicular to the longitudinal direction and parallel to the axis of the forging hammer or press ram; this is the short transverse direction. Intermediate properties are found in the third, "long transverse", direction.

Part complexity and the design and number of dies employed are important in establishing the grain flow pattern in die forgings. Controlling these factors will provide optimum metal flow for each part, avoiding transverse flow in areas that are highly stressed in service normal (90°) to the grain flow. Such condition is usually most pronounced at the parting line, where flash develops and where a strongly defined grain flow results. The strength of a forging is generally lower across this plane than in any other area, and this factor should be considered in the design of each part. For forgings subject to heavy loads or impact, tooling should be designed to develop the desired grain flow in critically stressed areas. A smooth, uninterrupted flow parallel to the service stresses to be sustained is desirable.

In sections thicker than 3 in., it is not always possible to obtain clearly defined grain-flow patterns at the center, even though the structure is completely hot worked. The working

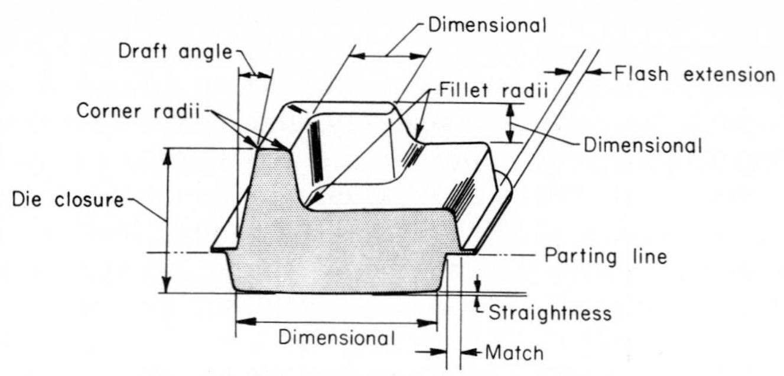

Fig. 5. Conventional terms applied to aluminum alloy closed-die forgings

force of the hammer or the press is such that mechanical deformation takes place throughout the entire cross section. For an equivalent amount of reduction, heavy sections produced by forging will have more thoroughly worked structures and more uniform mechanical properties throughout than similar sections that have been produced by rolling or extrusion.

Factors Affecting Design

Many design factors that affect choice of process also have a direct influence on cost and quality. The parting line of a forging is an important factor. (This is shown in Fig. 5, together with other design nomenclature used in subsequent discussion.)

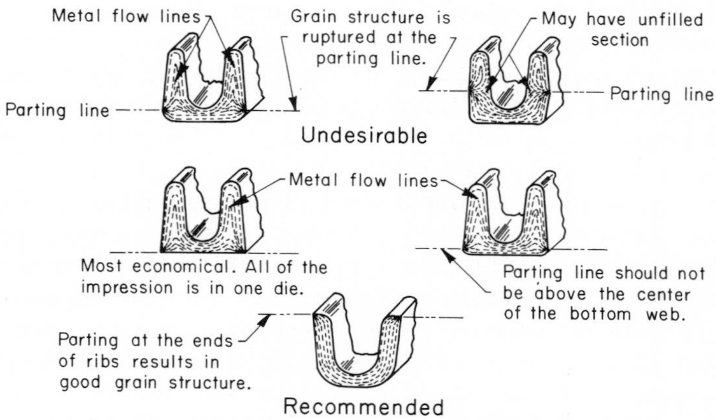

Fig. 6. Effect of location of parting line on metal-flow pattern of aluminum alloy closed-die forgings

Because it is easier to move metal laterally in a spreading action than to fill deep, narrow die impressions, the choice of the parting line is an important consideration; parting line location can have important effects on metal flow pattern and on quality (Fig. 6), as well as on cost. Placing the impression entirely in one die (Fig. 7) results in an economical forging, but the forged sections would normally be heavier than with other impression placement. Locating the parting line at an angle to the forging plane is undesirable, because excessive side thrusts would re-

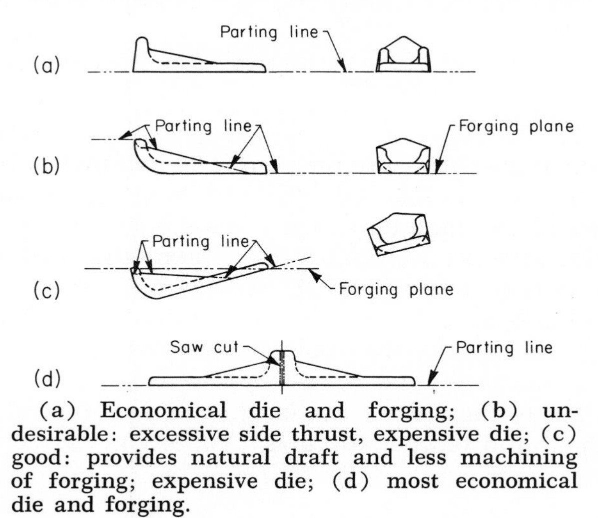

(a) Economical die and forging; (b) undesirable: excessive side thrust, expensive die; (c) good: provides natural draft and less machining of forging; expensive die; (d) most economical die and forging.

Fig. 7. How choice of parting line can affect forging design and ultimate costs

quire expensive die counterlocks. Inclining the forging in the die is good, because square-end surfaces with natural draft are possible. Most economical is the double forging that is symmetrical about a centerline (Fig. 7).

The taper given to the internal and external sides of a closed-die forging to facilitate its removal from the die cavity is termed draft. The angle between the taper and the plane parallel to the direction of ram travel is the draft angle (Fig. 5). Common die-sinking draft angles are 3, 5 and 7°. Forgings of many parts can be produced with no draft or very small draft angle if the higher production cost is justified.

Thin web and rib requirements in a forging impose a strain on both die and equipment. A greater number of blows on a

Table 1. Suggested Web Thickness for Conventional and Precision Aluminum Closed-Die Forgings

Average width, in.	Total plan area, sq in.(a)	Minimum web thickness, in.(b)	Average width, in.	Total plan area, sq in.(a)	Minimum web thickness, in.(b)
3	10	0.09	22	850	0.44
4	30	0.12	26	1200	0.50
6	60	0.16	34	2000	0.62
8	100	0.19	41	3000	0.75
11	200	0.25	47	4000	1.25
14	350	0.31	52	5000	2.00
18	550	0.37			

(a) Punchout holes not included in plan area. (b) Use larger web thickness when width and area are not on same line.

hammer or higher pressure on a press is required to forge such parts to size. Die life is reduced, and close tolerances become more difficult to maintain. Thin webs and ribs adjacent to heavier sections act as cooling fins, promoting distortion and warpage during heat treating, which necessitate expensive straightening operations. Frequently, straightening dies also are necessary, adding to the tooling cost and price per piece.

Web thicknesses from approximately 3/32 in. for precision forgings to as high as 1 in. or greater are typical in large conventional and blocker forgings (Table 1). Piercing holes in

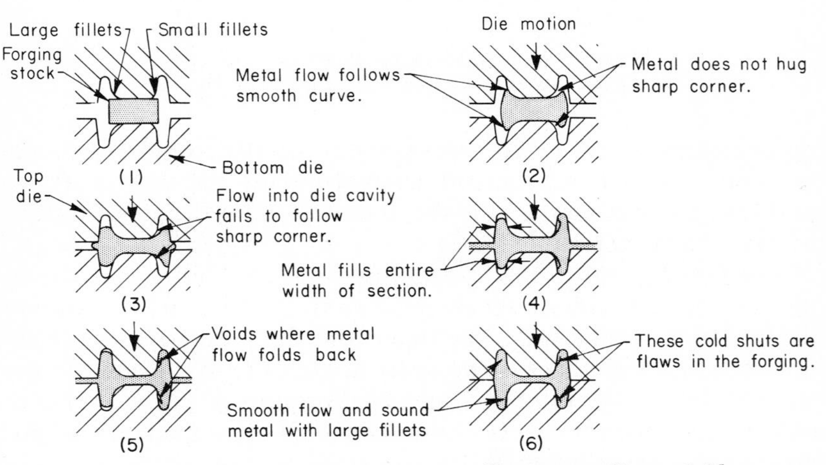

Fig. 8. Progressive forging steps illustrate effect of fillet radius on metal flow. Small fillets in right side of die contribute to unfilled sections, laps, and cold shuts.

web areas to permit the reduction of web thicknesses is especially useful where web area is completely surrounded by ribs.

Liberal fillet radii on forgings permit the metal to follow die contours more readily and provide uninterrupted flow of metal, so that the smoothest possible grain flow is obtained (Fig. 8). This assures improved forging soundness. Fillet radii in precision forgings are generally about one half those in conventional forgings (Fig. 9). Fillet radii in blocker forgings should be as large as the design permits.

Corner radii (Fig. 5) are usually smaller than fillet radii. Generally, corner radii of precision forgings are one half to one quarter those of conventional or blocker forgings (Fig. 10). Blending different sizes of corner or fillet radii in a specific

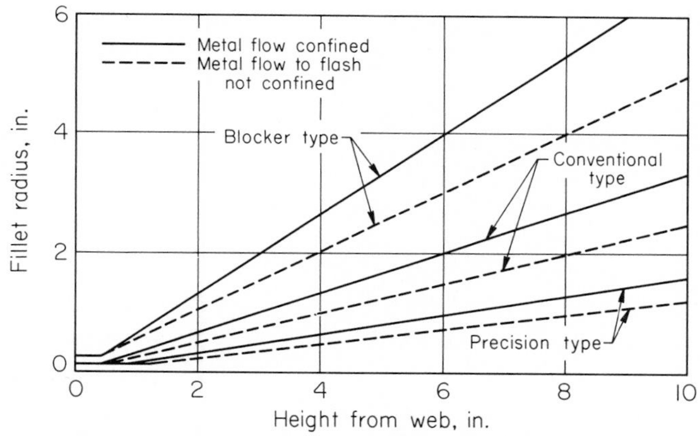

Fig. 9. Minimum fillet radii for aluminum closed-die forgings

forging increases die cost; forgings thus should be designed with constant fillet and corner radii, where possible. Generous corner radii increase die life, which contributes to lower forging costs.

Tolerances

The major tolerances applicable to aluminum forgings are given in Tables 2, 3 and 4 (1). Dimensional (length and width) tolerances take into account shrinkage and die allowance factors. Other tolerances are provided for die closure, match, straightness, flash extension and machining; these consider the normal variations in forging practice that have an effect on such dimensions.

Shrinkage is the dimensional contraction of the forging removed hot from the die and cooled to room temperature (Table 2). How much a section shrinks depends on the temperature of the die and of the forging as it comes from the die, and on their coefficients of thermal expansion. For aluminum alloys, these values range from 11 to 14 micro-in. per in. per °F. The die cavity is made larger than the desired forging by this factor, corrected to compensate for the wider temperature range involved with forgings of heavy sections. Where shrinkage cannot

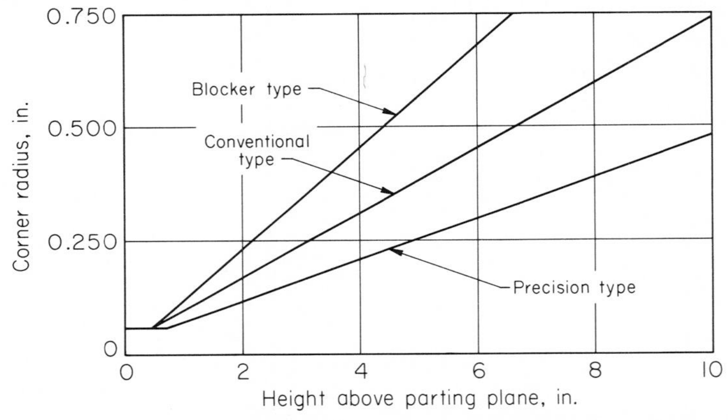

Fig. 10. Minimum corner radii for aluminum closed-die forgings

be predicted accurately, extra metal can be added to assure ample stock on the finished part.

Die allowance includes die-sinking tolerance and allowance for anticipated die wear and normal die repair (Table 2). Die-sinking tolerance is based on the accuracy of the diemaking machine and of the final hand polishing workmanship. Allowance for die wear and repair is not the same on all die surfaces because of variations in the amount of wear. The areas of maximum wear are usually those requiring maximum repair and polishing; these lead to die cavity and final forging larger than the original design.

Not to be confused with dimensions between surfaces within the upper or lower die (Table 2) are the dimensions measured between surfaces formed by the opposing dies and in the direction parallel to ram travel. Tolerances for these latter dimensions are known as die-closure tolerances (Table 3). Such

Table 2. Length and Width Tolerances Applicable to Aluminum Alloy Closed-Die Forgings(a)

Forging type	Shrinkage tolerance, A, in. per in.	Die allowances, B	
		For each surface up to 60-in. length	For each surface over 60-in. length
Blocker	±0.002	+0.062	+0.093
Conventional	±0.002	+0.031	+0.062
Precision	±0.0015	+0.016	+0.031

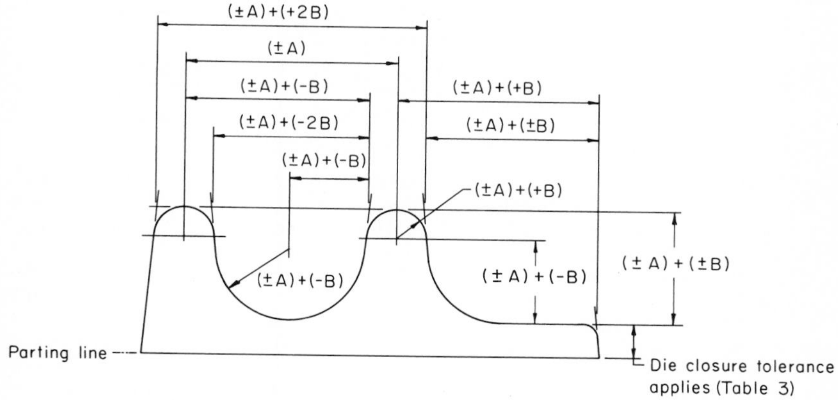

(a) See sketch for application of tolerances. Tolerances apply to all dimensions other than those affected by die closure, including dimensions perpendicular to parting line.

tolerances are necessary because of die-sinking limits and other process variations, such as stock volume, die and stock temperature, lubrication, and die deflection.

Match (Fig. 5) tolerance is the maximum shift or misalignment variation allowed between the two die halves at and parallel to the parting plane (Table 3). Imperfect alignment can be caused by component forces exerted parallel to the forging plane. Guided holders, guide pins, and counterlocks are employed to counteract these forces and maintain match.

A straightness tolerance (Table 3) is necessary, particularly on large forgings, because differential cooling takes place in the various sections both after forging and during quenching from solution heat treating. Such distortion cannot be removed completely by straightening processes. Straightness tolerance is the permissible deviation of the forged surface from a theoretical true plane or line in contact with the forging (Fig. 5).

Flash extension tolerances for forgings are necessary, regardless of the trimming method (Fig. 5). When trimming dies are employed, closer tolerances can be met than when forgings are trimmed with a saw (Table 3).

Chiefly because of the nonscaling characteristic of aluminum, forgings can be produced to closer tolerances than in steel. Each design tolerance is independently established. Machining allowances, which take into account the closer tolerances of the forging, include the extremes of the design tolerance and the normal machine finish allowance. The procedure for establishing machining allowances in relation to the other forging tolerances is shown in Table 4.

Table 3. Typical Dimensional Tolerances for Conventional Aluminum Alloy Closed-Die Forgings(a)

Die closure			Match		
Weight, lb	Plan area, sq in.	Tolerance, in.(b)	Weight, lb	Maximum dimension, in.	Tolerance, in.(b)
0 to 0.5	Less than 10	+0.020, −0.010	0 to 1	0 to 10	0.015
0.5 to 1	10 to 30	+0.031, −0.016	1 to 5	10 to 17	0.020
1 to 5	30 to 100	+0.047, −0.016	5 to 20	17 to 25	0.030
5 to 20	100 to 400	+0.062, −0.031	20 to 50	25 to 50	0.045
20 to 50	400 to 750	+0.093, −0.031	50 to 100	50 to 75	0.060
50 to 100	750 to 1000	+0.125, −0.031	100 to 200	75 to 100	0.080
100 to 200	1000 to 2000	+0.187, −0.031	200 to 500	100 to 150	0.100
200 to 500	2000 to 3500	+0.250, −0.031	Over 500	150 to 250	0.120

Straightness		Flash extension		
Length, in.	Straightness TIR, in.(c)	Weight, lb	Length, in.	Flash, in.(b)
0 to 10	0.015	0 to 0.5	0 to 5	0.015(d)
10 to 20	0.030	0.5 to 5	5 to 15	0.030(d)
20 to 30	0.045	5 to 25	15 to 30	0.060(d)
30 to 40	0.060	25 to 50	30 to 60	0.120
40 to 50	0.075	50 to 100	60 to 120	0.120
50 to 60	0.090	Over 100	Over 120	0.250
60 to 90	0.120			
90 to 150	0.180			
Over 150	0.250			

(a) For blocker forgings, tolerances are usually 25 to 50% larger than shown. For precision forgings, tolerances are usually considered for each individual design, but are approximately 75% of values shown. (b) Use the larger tolerance when weight and dimensional requirements do not appear on the same line in die-closure, match, and flash-extension columns. (c) Total indicator reading, maximum. (d) Tolerances apply for die trimming, and values should be doubled for saw trimming. All other values shown apply for saw trimming.

Table 4. Manner in Which Machining Allowances Affect Various Forging Dimensions

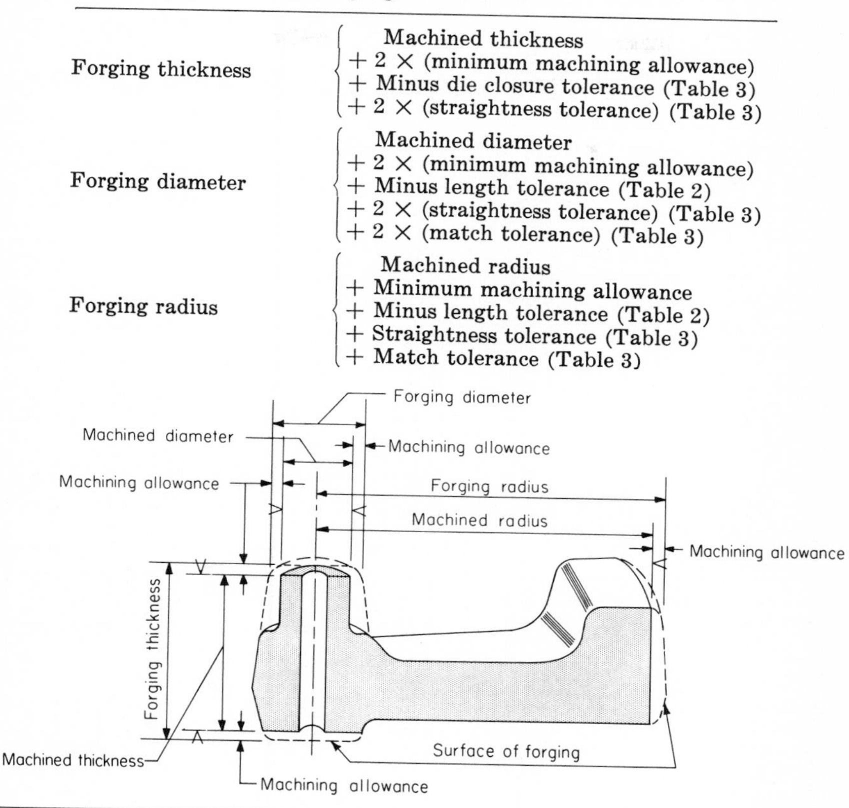

Forging thickness	Machined thickness + 2 × (minimum machining allowance) + Minus die closure tolerance (Table 3) + 2 × (straightness tolerance) (Table 3)
Forging diameter	Machined diameter + 2 × (minimum machining allowance) + Minus length tolerance (Table 2) + 2 × (straightness tolerance) (Table 3) + 2 × (match tolerance) (Table 3)
Forging radius	Machined radius + Minimum machining allowance + Minus length tolerance (Table 2) + Straightness tolerance (Table 3) + Match tolerance (Table 3)

Mechanical Properties

Typical mechanical properties developed in hand and die forgings in the more commonly used alloys are listed in Tables 5 and 6, respectively. These are properties expected under the normal conditions of forging and heat treating discussed in Volume III, Chapter 5. In certain forgings, these properties can be improved in any one direction or in any given area, by specifically selected tool design and forging practices. Such forgings are subject to special negotiation between customer and producer. The alloys for which data are given are the common forging alloys, which are described as to forgeability on pages 165 to 167 of this chapter.

Table 5. Typical Mechanical Properties for Standard-Shape Aluminum Alloy Hand Forgings at Room Temperature

Thickness, in.	Tensile strength, psi			Yield strength, psi			Elongation, % in 2 in. or $4D$		
	Longitudinal	Long transverse	Short transverse	Longitudinal	Long transverse	Short transverse	Longitudinal	Long transverse	Short transverse
Alloy 2014-T6									
Up through 2.000	71,000	70,000	...	62,000	62,000	...	12	7	..
2.001 to 3.000	70,000	69,000	67,000	62,000	61,000	61,000	12	7	6
3.001 to 4.000	69,000	68,000	66,000	61,000	61,000	60,000	12	7	6
4.001 to 5.000	68,000	67,000	65,000	60,000	60,000	59,000	11	6	5
5.001 to 6.000	67,000	66,000	64,000	59,000	59,000	59,000	11	6	5
6.001 to 7.000	66,000	65,000	63,000	58,000	58,000	58,000	10	6	5
7.001 to 8.000	65,000	64,000	62,000	57,000	57,000	57,000	10	6	5
Alloy 6061-T6									
Up through 4.000	42,000	42,000	41,000	40,000	40,000	38,000	14	12	9
4.001 to 8.000	41,000	41,000	39,000	39,000	39,000	37,000	12	10	8
Alloy 7075-T6									
Up through 2.000	82,000	79,000	...	73,000	69,000	...	14	10	..
2.001 to 3.000	81,000	77,000	76,000	71,000	67,000	66,000	14	10	9
3.001 to 4.000	79,000	76,000	75,000	70,000	66,000	65,000	13	9	8
4.001 to 5.000	77,000	74,000	73,000	68,000	64,000	64,000	12	9	8
5.001 to 6.000	76,000	72,000	72,000	66,000	63,000	63,000	11	9	8
Alloy 7079-T6									
Up through 2.000	78,000	75,000	...	69,000	66,000	...	13	9	..
2.001 to 3.000	78,000	74,000	71,000	67,000	64,000	62,000	13	9	8
3.001 to 4.000	77,000	74,000	71,000	67,000	64,000	62,000	13	9	8
4.001 to 5.000	76,000	73,000	70,000	66,000	63,000	61,000	13	8	8
5.001 to 6.000	75,000	72,000	70,000	65,000	61,000	60,000	13	8	8
6.001 to 7.000	74,000	71,000	69,000	64,000	59,000	59,000	13	8	8
7.001 to 8.000	73,000	70,000	68,000	63,000	58,000	58,000	13	8	8

Process Capabilities

The capabilities of the forging process are established by the size of forging equipment available, ability to produce accurate dies in all sizes required, and the ingenuity of the designer. With existing equipment, closed-die forgings ranging in length up to 23 ft (Fig. 11) and in weight from a fraction of a pound to over 3000 lb, and open-die forgings up to 15,000 lb have been produced. Small, simple parts requiring only one die impression

Table 6. Typical Mechanical Properties of Die Forgings at Room Temperature(a)

Alloy and temper	Tensile strength, psi	Yield strength, psi	Elongation, % in 2 in.	Brinell hardness(b)
1100-F	13,000	5,000	40	25
2014-T6	72,000	65,000	12	140
2024-T6	66,000	57,000	10	125
2025-T6	58,000	37,000	20	110
2218-T72	43,000	32,000	8	90
2219-T6	62,000	42,000	12	115
2618-T61	64,000	52,000	10	125
3003-F	16,000	6,000	30	30
4032-T6	54,000	47,000	6	125
5052-H112	28,000	13,000	25	50
5083-H131	49,000	37,000	14	85
5456-H112	47,000	24,000	24	75
6061-T6	46,000	42,000	18	100
6151-T6	47,000	44,000	18	105
7039-T6	65,000	55,000	12	120
7075-T6	83,000	73,000	12	150
7075-T73	73,000	63,000	16	140
7079-T6	80,000	70,000	12	150
X7080-T7	71,000	64,000	16	140

(a) Values apply to standard 0.5-in.-diam test specimens machined from separately forged coupons. For test specimens machined from forgings up to 4-in. thickness or diameter (3 in. for 7075 and 6 in. for 7079) with the axis of the specimen substantially parallel to the direction of grain flow, the properties of the table apply, except that the typical elongation is approximately 70% of the values in the table. (b) 500-kg load, 10-mm ball.

can be made at the rate of several hundred pieces per hour; larger, more intricate parts requiring numerous separate forging operations net only a few pieces per hour.

Application Considerations. When relatively few parts are needed, selection of a precision forging is usually impractical, because of the high die and production costs. Design requirements must then be met with a conventional or blocker forging. This is usually accompanied by some increase in weight and higher or additional machining costs for the final part. However, even with a conventional forging, proper die design and the use of suitable equipment assure finished parts with reasonably thin webs and ribs, and acceptable machining costs.

Perhaps to a greater degree than any other metal, aluminum

Fig. 11. Aircraft wing spar, forged from an alloy 7079 billet, is about 23 ft long, weighs approximately 320 lb, and is one of the longest closed-die forgings ever produced. The part was shaped in a die by the pressure of a 50,000-ton press, operated under the Air Force Heavy Press Program.

permits the manufacture of precision parts. These are produced under carefully controlled conditions and in dies made to a high degree of accuracy. Although die and part costs are high, lower machining cost, minimum assembly time and cost, and highest possible strength-to-weight ratios in all sections may make the investment economically sound. The time required to produce dies and fabricate precision forgings usually is longer than for conventional forgings. This extends delivery time, which must be recognized when precision forgings are ordered.

Relationship of weight, cost per pound, die cost, unit pressure required, and delivery time for the various types of forgings is shown in Table 7. These are only approximate. Any specific

Table 7. Approximate Relationship Between Weight, Forging Cost, Die Cost, Pressure Requirements for Various Types of Aluminum Alloy Forgings

Item	Open-die hand forgings	Closed-die forgings: Blocker	Closed-die forgings: Conventional	Closed-die forgings: Precision
Weight	10X+	5 to 10X	2 to 5X	X(a)
Cost per pound	X	2 to 3X	3 to 5X	5 to 25X+
Die cost	None	X	2 to 4X	4 to 10X+
Setup cost	None	X	2 to 3X	3 to 10X+
Delivery time	X	3 to 5X	5 to 8X	Over 8X
Unit pressure required	X	2 to 3X	3 to 5X	5 to 10X+

(a) X represents the base unit.

design concessions over those considered standard for these types of forgings could make a significant change in this comparison. For example, slight increases in corner and fillet radii, thickening of a web or elimination of sharp changes in section thickness would affect several of these factors and hence their relative comparison. The Metals Handbook (2) provides specific data on parts produced as various types of forgings.

Comparison With Competitive Processes and Materials

Where characteristics of aluminum alloys other than high strength are required, premium engineered castings may be satisfactory (Chapter 5, this volume and Volume III, Chapter 2). Rarely does an aluminum forging compete favorably in cost with cast parts. Initial investment in tools and dies, even for large production quantities, frequently precludes the use of a forging. However, for some parts, a forging may be chosen over a casting because of superior surface finish and freedom from voids and irregularities. A forged surface permits a variety of attractive surface finishes, such as polishing and anodizing, with minimum preparation.

Selection of aluminum over some other metal for a forging usually is based on specific physical and mechanical property requirements and cost. Where a forging is indicated by design criteria and the specific properties of steel are not required, aluminum forgings are often competitive. In some applications, such as airframe structural parts, properly designed aluminum forgings often compete favorably with alloy steel parts.

A composite assembly of plate, extrusions and tubing may save time and money for a small quantity of parts. A forging, however, generally is stronger, more reliable, lighter in weight, and more economical when produced in large quantities. With presses of 35,000 and 50,000 tons capacity available, parts formerly made by joining several smaller forgings or other components can be made as a single unit, thus saving machining and assembling costs and reducing the weight of the finished assembly. This capability has been utilized to the greatest extent in the manufacture of large airframes (3).

As a general rule, forgings are at an economic disadvantage if the part is of a configuration that can be produced as an impact extrusion or by drawing, spinning, forming, or some combination of these processes. Where configuration would dictate one of these except for integral bosses, ribs or other attachments, forging may be both economically feasible and desirable.

References

1 "Tolerances for Impression Die Forgings", Forging Industries Association, Cleveland, 1963

2 Examples of Light Metal Parts for Aeronautical Construction, in "Metals Handbook", Vol 1, 8th Ed, American Society for Metals, 1961, p 910–915

3 The Selection and Application of Aluminum and Aluminum Alloys, in "Metals Handbook", Vol 1, 8th Ed, American Society for Metals, 1961, p 869–871

Chapter 9

Design Factors for Structural Engineering

J. W. Clark and E. C. Hartmann

STRUCTURAL DESIGN, as the term is used in this chapter, refers to the proportioning of strength members to withstand the applied loads with a margin of safety appropriate to the specific applications. The principles involved are those that would apply to any metal. With aluminum alloys, however, the designer will usually emphasize minimum weight, and hence he will refine his analysis to a higher degree than he might with another metal. Although structural designers are often required to follow established codes and specifications, these should never become a substitute for sound judgment in arriving at the optimum configuration that will provide the necessary strength at minimum cost without needless extra weight.

Factors of Safety

A margin of safety may be obtained either by designing for loads higher than expected, or by scaling down to allowable or design-stress values the stresses representing the strength of a member. In either case, the object is to reduce the probability of failure of the structure to a value that is small enough to be acceptable without making the resulting structure too costly.

Determination of allowable working stresses usually involves consideration of at least two different factors of safety. One is

The authors are with Alcoa Research Laboratories, New Kensington. J. W. Clark is assistant chief, Engineering Design Div. E. C. Hartmann is director of research.

the ratio of the ultimate load to the working load (or the ratio of the ultimate strength to the design stress); the other is the ratio of the load that will cause excessive deformation or permanent set to the design load (or the ratio of yield strength to design stress). The latter is sometimes known as the factor of serviceability.

Depending on the type of structure, other factors of safety may be introduced. The purpose of these is to provide adequate margins against other types of failure, such as fatigue failure, local buckling of thin-gage elements (where local buckling does not precipitate collapse but is undesirable at working loads), stress rupture, or excessive creep deformation. The latter two need be considered only for structures subjected to elevated temperature.

Since this chapter is concerned with the strength of aluminum members, no attempt is made to specify allowable design stresses. Appropriate factors of safety should be applied in relating the strength data to design problems. The magnitude of the factors of safety chosen is influenced by the following:

1 The precision with which the assumed loadings (including impact and repeated loads, as well as static loads) represent the actual service loading, both present and future
2 The precision with which the strength of the structure can be calculated for the various types of loading
3 The importance of the structure being designed, and the consequences of failure
4 Precedent established by generally accepted specifications applying to the type of structure being designed

Some examples of factors of safety used in various specifications for aluminum structures are listed in Table 1. These factors of safety are applied to expected minimum strength values, except for creep-rupture and creep strength in the ASME Boiler Code. These are based on "conservative average" values.

Tension Members

For a member loaded in static axial tension, two important strength considerations are of interest to the designer: the load at which the member begins to yield or take appreciable permanent set, and the load at which fracture occurs. Appreciable yielding may be expected when the average stress on the minimum net section reaches the tensile yield strength of the material.

Fracture may be expected when the stress on the minimum net section is equal to the tensile strength of the material. A suitable factor of safety must be provided against both yielding and fracture. If a member is designed according to some code or specification, this factor of safety is provided simply by proportioning the member so that the stress on the minimum net section is equal to or less than the allowable design stress. The minimum net section is determined in the same way as for structural steel.

Where bending as well as direct tension is introduced in a member, the stress due to the combined loading should be calculated and maintained within allowable limits. For single angles fastened by one leg, an approximate way to take account

Table 1. Factors of Safety Used in Specifications for Aluminum Structures

Type of structure	Factors of safety applied to;					
	Ultimate strength(a)	Yield strength	Local buckling(b)	Fatigue strength	Stress rupture	Creep
Buildings(c)	1.95	1.65	1.2	1.2	..	..
Bridges(c)	2.2	1.85	1.35	1.35	..	..
Structural supports for highway signs (d)	2.2	1.85	...	...	..	..
Unfired pressure vessels(e)	4.0	1.5	...	...	1.0(f)	1.0(g)

(a) Applies to ultimate strength of columns as well as to tensile strength. (b) Applies where local buckling does not precipitate collapse, but is undesirable at working loads. (c) Specifications published by ASCE Task Committee on Lightweight Alloys, 1962. (d) Specifications of American Association of State Highway Officials, 1961. (e) Specifications of Subcommittee of ASME Boiler Code Committee, 1962. (f) Applies to stress producing rupture in 100,000 hr. (g) Applies to stress producing a secondary creep rate of 0.1% in 10,000 hr.

of bending due to eccentricity is to consider the effective area as the net section of the connected leg plus one half of the section of the outstanding leg. The stress on the member is then considered to be the tensile load divided by the effective area.

Although holes and other discontinuities produce localized concentrations of stress, this can generally be ignored in calculating the static strengths of tension members for the structural aluminum alloys. These alloys have sufficient ductility so that the stress concentrations encountered in most structures are alleviated by local yielding with little if any reduction in static strength. Stress concentration is more important, however, in members that are expected to undergo large plastic deformations

Table 2. Buckling Formulas for Aluminum(a)

Case No.	Type of member	Type of buckling	Buckling stress for slenderness less than λ_1, 1000 psi	Slenderness limit, λ_1	Buckling stress for slenderness greater than λ_1, 1000 psi
			Direct Compression Loading, Compressive Stress		
1....	Columns (12)	Over-all bending	$B_c - D_c \frac{KL}{r}$	$\frac{KL}{r} = C_c$	$\frac{\pi^2 E}{(KL/r)^2}$
2....	Flat plates (b)	Local	$B_p - D_p k_p \frac{b}{t}$	$\frac{b}{t} = \frac{C_p}{k_p}$	$\frac{\pi^2 E}{(k_p b/t)^2}$
3....	Round tubes (13)	Local	$B_{tc} - D_{tc}\sqrt{\frac{R}{t}}$	$\frac{R}{t} = C_{tc}$	$\frac{\pi^2 E}{16(R/t)(1 + \sqrt{R/t}/35}$
			Bending Loading, Compressive Stress		
4....	Single-web beams	Over-all lateral buckling	$B_c - \frac{D_c}{1.2}\left(\frac{L_b}{r_y}\right)$	$\frac{L_b}{r_y} = 1.2C_c$	$\frac{1.44\pi^2 E}{(L_b/r_y)^2}$
5....	Box beams	Over-all lateral buckling	$B_c - 1.6D_c\sqrt{\frac{L_b S_c}{I_y}}$	$\frac{L_b S_c}{I_y} = \left(\frac{C_c}{1.6}\right)^2$	$\frac{\pi^2 E}{2.56 L_b S_c/I_y}$
6....	Solid, rectangular beams	Over-all lateral buckling	$B_b - 2.3D_b \frac{d}{t}\sqrt{\frac{L_b}{d}}$	$\frac{d}{t}\sqrt{\frac{L_b}{d}} = \frac{C_b}{2.3}$	$\frac{\pi^2 E}{5.29(d/t)^2 L_b/d}$
7....	Flat plates	Local	$B_b - D_b k_p \frac{b}{t}$	$\frac{b}{t} = \frac{C_b}{k_p}$	$\frac{\pi^2 E}{(k_p b/t)^2}$
8....	Round tubes (13)	Local	$B_{tb} - D_{tb}\sqrt{\frac{R}{t}}$	$\frac{R}{t} = C_{tb}$	Same as Case 3
			Shear Loading, Shear Stress		
9....	Flat plates	Local	$B_s - 1.25D_s \frac{a_e}{t}$	$\frac{a_e}{t} = \frac{C_s}{1.25}$	$\frac{\pi^2 E}{(1.25a_e/t)^2}$

The terms appearing in the formulas are defined as follows:

a_e = equivalent span of rectangular shear panel, in.

$$a_e = \frac{a_1}{\sqrt{1 + 0.7(a_1/a_2)^2}}$$

a_1 = shorter span of rectangular shear panel, in.
a_2 = longer span of rectangular shear panel, in.
b = clear width of outstanding flange or flat plate supported on both unloaded edges, in.
d = depth of beam, in.
E = compressive modulus of elasticity, 1000 psi
I_y = moment of inertia of beam (about axis parallel to web), in.^{4}
K = end-fixity factor for columns
k_p = factor representing effect of edge restraint on local buckling strength of plates

(*Continued at bottom of facing page*)

in order to absorb impact loads, or in members that are loaded repeatedly for a large number of cycles so that fatigue failure is a possibility. Fatigue failure is treated more fully subsequently.

Columns

All members subjected to axial compressive loads may be considered as columns, but the procedures for design will differ depending on the length and general proportions of the cross section.

In calculating the effective cross-sectional area of compression members, allowance should be made for any open holes. Holes well filled with rivets or tightly fitted bolts may be ignored in calculating the effective cross-sectional area of compression members.

Compression members that are long enough to fail by bending or twisting must be designed differently than short, compact members. Bending failure of columns is the type usually understood when the expression "column strength" is used without qualification. The column strength of aluminum alloys, as with other metals, is a function not only of the properties of the alloy but also of the effective slenderness ratio of the member. The effective slenderness ratio is the ratio KL/r, in which L is the length of the column, r is the corresponding radius of gyration, and K is the factor that represents the effect of the end conditions of the column.

(Continued from facing page)

L = length of compression member between points of lateral support, in.
L_b = length of beam between points at which the compression flange is supported against lateral movement or length of cantilever beam from free end to point at which the compression flange is supported against lateral movement, in.
R = outside radius of round tube, in.
r = least radius of gyration of a column, in.
r_y = radius of gyration of a beam about axis parallel to web, in. (For beams that are unsymmetrical about the horizontal axis, r_y should be calculated as though both flanges were the same as the compression flange.)
S_c = section modulus of a beam (compression side), in.^{3}
t = thickness of flange, plate, web, or tube, in. (For tapered flanges, t is the average thickness.)

(a) See Tables 3 and 4 for equations giving values of constants B, D, and C for various types buckling. (b) These formulas also apply to plate elements of beams where the plate itself is der uniform compression, for example, flanges of I-beams bent in the strong direction.

A typical relationship between column strength and effective slenderness ratio is illustrated in Fig. 1. For relatively long, axially loaded columns, the ultimate strength, F_c, in psi, is:

$$F_c = \frac{\pi^2 E}{(KL/r)^2} \tag{1}$$

where E is the compressive modulus of elasticity in psi. An average value of $\pi^2 E$ for aluminum alloys is 102,000,000 psi.

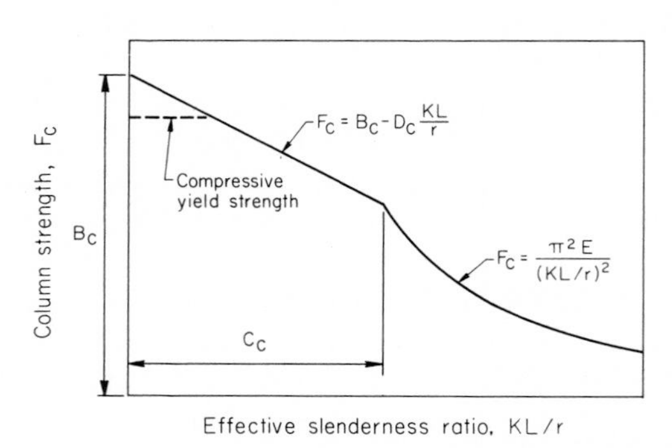

Fig. 1. Typical column strength curve for aluminum alloys

Equation 1 applies when KL/r is greater than the value C_c, as shown in Fig. 1. When KL/r is less than C_c, the relationship between column strength and effective slenderness ratio is:

$$F_c = B_c - D_c \frac{KL}{r} \tag{2}$$

Equations 1 and 2 are listed in the first line of Table 2, which also gives buckling equations for a number of other types of members. The formulas in Table 2, and also those in Tables 3 and 4, are expressed in 1000 psi.

The constants B_c, D_c, and C_c depend upon the mechanical properties of the material. For all products except those that are artifically aged (see list of tempers in Table 3), the straight line represented by Eq 2 is tangent to the elastic buckling curve, Eq 1. Formulas for B_c, D_c, and C_c in this case are listed in Table 3 (first line). For artificially aged products, values of B_c, D_c, and C_c are given by the formulas in the first line of Table 4; the corresponding straight line is not tangent to the elastic curve.

Specific values of E, B_c, D_c, and C_c for various products are tabulated in literature published by manufacturers of structural aluminum alloy plates and shapes (1).

Table 3. Formulas for Coefficients in Equations for Inelastic Buckling Strength

(All aluminum alloys in the O temper, H tempers, and tempers in which the designation begins with T3 or T4, such as T3, T31, T351, T4 or T42)

Case No. in Table 2	Intercept, 1000 psi	Slope, 1000 psi	Slenderness limit
1, 4, 5	$B_c = F_{cy}\left(1 + \sqrt{\frac{F_{cy}}{1000}}\right)$	$D_c = \frac{B_c}{20}\sqrt{\frac{6B_c}{E}}$	$C_c = \frac{2}{3}\left(\frac{B_c}{D_c}\right)$
2	$B_p = F_{cy}\left(1 + \frac{\sqrt[3]{F_{cy}}}{7.6}\right)$	$D_p = \frac{B_p}{20}\sqrt{\frac{6B_p}{E}}$	$C_p = \frac{2}{3}\left(\frac{B_p}{D_p}\right)$
3	$B_{tc} = F_{cy}\left(1 + \frac{\sqrt[5]{F_{cy}}}{5.8}\right)$	$D_{tc} = \frac{B_{tc}}{3.7}\sqrt[3]{\frac{B_{tc}}{E}}$	(a)
6, 7	$B_b = 1.3F_{cy}\left(1 + \frac{\sqrt[3]{F_{cy}}}{7}\right)$	$D_b = \frac{B_b}{20}\sqrt{\frac{6B_b}{E}}$	$C_b = \frac{2}{3}\left(\frac{B_b}{D_b}\right)$
8	$B_{tb} = 1.5F_y\left(1 + \frac{\sqrt[5]{F_y}}{5.8}\right)$	$D_{tb} = \frac{B_{tb}}{2.7}\sqrt[3]{\frac{B_{tb}}{E}}$	$C_{tb} = \left(\frac{B_{tb} - B_{tc}}{D_{tb} - D_{tc}}\right)^2$
9	$B_s = F_{sy}\left(1 + \frac{\sqrt[3]{F_{sy}}}{6.2}\right)$	$D_s = \frac{B_s}{20}\sqrt{\frac{6B_s}{E}}$	$C_s = \frac{2}{3}\left(\frac{B_s}{D_s}\right)$

F_{cy} = compressive yield strength, 1000 psi
F_y = tensile or compressive yield strength, whichever is lower, 1000 psi
F_{sy} = shear yield strength, 1000 psi

(a) The intersection between the curves representing elastic and inelastic buckling in this case can be found by iteration or by a graphical solution.

The effective length factor K depends upon whether or not the ends of the column are free to tip or rotate as the column deflects, and values of K are selected in the same manner as for structural steel columns (2). An adequate factor of safety should be used with the column formulas and care should be taken not to use too low a value of the factor K.

Sometimes a column is made up of relatively thin plates and shapes that will buckle locally before the column as a whole reaches its limiting load. This type of local buckling failure must be guarded against, by increasing the thickness of the parts, by providing additional stiffening elements, or by lowering the stress. The buckling of such thin, flat parts is treated in a separate section.

Twisting failure need not be considered for most columns, because they are so stiff in torsion. This is true of box-section columns, closed tubes of any shape, and solid shapes such as rounds and rectangles. Flanged columns whose cross sections are symmetrical about a point, such as I, H, and Z-section columns, are not likely to fail by twisting unless they are supported in such a manner that the effective length for twisting failure is much greater than that for failure by bending.

Twisting-type failures are most likely to occur in torsionally weak sections that are unsymmetrical or have only one axis of symmetry, such as angles and tees. These members tend to fail by combined twisting and bending. For channels of conventional cross section, however, this type of buckling will generally not reduce the load-carrying capacity appreciably below the critical load for bending failure in the weak direction. For angles having equal legs, the critical load for twisting failure approximates the load that causes local buckling of the outstanding legs.

The heat of welding reduces the strength of heat treated or work-hardened alloys in a narrow zone surrounding the weld. The maximum extent of this zone in aluminum alloys measured from the center of a butt weld or the root of a fillet weld can be considered as 1.0 in. This reduction in strength can have an effect on column strength if there are large areas of heat-affected

Table 4. Formulas for Coefficients in Equations for Inelastic Buckling Strength

(All aluminum alloys in which the temper designation begins with T5, T6, T7, T8 or T9, such as T5, T6, T62, T651, T73, T81 or T87)

Case No. in Table 2	Intercept, 1000 psi	Slope, 1000 psi	Slenderness limit
1, 4, 5	$B_c = F_{cy}\left(1 + \sqrt{\frac{F_{cy}}{2250}}\right)$	$D_c = \frac{B_c}{10}\sqrt{\frac{B_c}{E}}$	$C_c = 0.409\left(\frac{B_c}{D_c}\right)$
2	$B_p = F_{cy}\left(1 + \frac{\sqrt[3]{F_{cy}}}{11.4}\right)$	$D_p = \frac{B_p}{10}\sqrt{\frac{B_p}{E}}$	$C_p = 0.409\left(\frac{B_p}{D_p}\right)$
3	$B_{tc} = F_{cy}\left(1 + \frac{\sqrt[5]{F_{cy}}}{8.7}\right)$	$D_{tc} = \frac{B_{tc}}{4.5}\sqrt[3]{\frac{B_{tc}}{E}}$	(a)
6, 7	$B_b = 1.3F_{cy}\left(1 + \frac{\sqrt[3]{F_{cy}}}{7}\right)$	$D_b = \frac{B_b}{20}\sqrt{\frac{6B_b}{E}}$	$C_b = \frac{2}{3}\left(\frac{B_b}{D_b}\right)$
8	$B_{tb} = 1.5F_y\left(1 + \frac{\sqrt[5]{F_y}}{8.7}\right)$	$D_{tb} = \frac{B_{tb}}{2.7}\sqrt[3]{\frac{B_{tb}}{E}}$	$C_{tb} = \left(\frac{B_{tb} - B_{tc}}{D_{tb} - D_{tc}}\right)^2$
9	$B_s = F_{sy}\left(1 + \frac{\sqrt[3]{F_{sy}}}{9.3}\right)$	$D_s = \frac{B_s}{10}\sqrt{\frac{B_s}{E}}$	$C_s = 0.409\left(\frac{B_s}{D_s}\right)$

F_{cy} = compressive yield strength, 1000 psi
F_y = tensile or compressive yield strength, whichever is lower, 1000 psi
F_{sy} = shear yield strength, 1000 psi

(a) The intersection between the curves representing elastic and inelastic buckling can be found by iteration or by a graphical solution.

material at locations remote from the supports. However, transverse welds usually are located at points of lateral support, and the effect of such welds on column strength can be ignored — provided that the effective length factor, K, is considered to be 1.0. The effect of longitudinal welds on column strength can also be neglected if the heat-affected area is less than 15% of the total area. For columns with a larger percentage of the area affected by longitudinal welds, the effect of the welds should be taken into account. Likewise, it must be considered for columns with transverse welds at locations other than the supports and also for cantilever columns with a weld at the support (since such a weld has the same effect as a weld at the center of a column supported at both ends). Methods of calculating the strength of such columns are given by Brungraber and Clark (3).

Beams and Girders

Elastic and Inelastic Action. Elastic stress and deflection in aluminum alloy beams are computed by conventional formulas where the maximum stresses do not exceed the yield strength. When the extreme fiber stresses in an aluminum beam reach the yield strength, yielding of the most highly stressed material is restrained by the material closer to the neutral axis, which is still in the elastic stress range. As a result, the apparent stress (bending moment divided by section modulus) at the extreme fiber can exceed the yield strength by a considerable margin before yielding becomes apparent. This can be accounted for by inserting a "shape factor" in the beam formula, as follows:

$$M_y = k_y F_y S \tag{3}$$

where M_y = yield moment (bending moment corresponding to 0.2% offset on the curve of apparent stress, M/S, versus extreme fiber strain), in.-lb
k_y = shape factor for yielding
F_y = yield strength (tensile or compressive yield strength, whichever is lower), psi
S = section modulus, $in.^3$

Values of the shape factor, k_y, for various structural shapes are listed in Table 5.

Aluminum beams generally can undergo large plastic deformations, with the corresponding apparent stresses (bending moment divided by section modulus) well above the tensile strength of the material, before fracture of the tension flange will occur. Tension-flange failure is not usually a critical factor in design.

Lateral buckling, involving lateral bending and twisting, generally limits the strength of single-web beams and girders that do not have continuous lateral support. The compressive bending stress that will cause buckling may be estimated from the formulas in Table 2. Equations for the buckling formula coefficients are shown in Tables 3 and 4. The formulas given for single-web shapes are approximations that become conservative

Table 5. Shape Factors for Yielding of Aluminum Beams

Shape	Shape factor for yielding, k_y
Solid round	1.40
Round tube	1.17
Solid rectangle	1.30
Rectangular tube	1.09
WF, I, and channel shapes bent about weak axis	1.30
WF, I, and channel shapes bent about strong axis	1.07

for values of L_b/r_y exceeding about 50. More precise values of buckling strength are determined by substituting an "effective r_y" for r_y in the formulas in line 4 of Table 2 (4). Values of effective r_y are given in the following formulas:

For beams subjected to end moment only or to transverse loads applied at the neutral axis of the beam:

$$\text{Effective } r_y = \frac{k_b}{1.7}\sqrt{\frac{I_y d}{S_c}}\sqrt{1 + 0.152\frac{J}{I_y}\left(\frac{L_b}{d}\right)^2}$$

For beams subjected to transverse loads applied on the top or bottom flange (where the load is free to move laterally with the beam if the beam should buckle),

$$\text{Effective } r_y = \frac{k_b}{1.7}\sqrt{\frac{I_y d}{S_c}}\left[\pm 0.5 + \sqrt{1.25 + 0.152\frac{J}{I_y}\left(\frac{L_b}{d}\right)^2}\right]$$

where d = depth of beam, in.
I_y = moment of inertia of beam about axis parallel to web, in.^4
J = torsion constant of beam, in.^4
k_b = coefficient depending on type of loading on beam
L_b = length of beam between points at which the compression flange is supported against lateral movement, or length of cantilever beam from free end to point at which the compression flange is supported against lateral movement, in.
S_c = section modulus of beam, compression side, in.^3

Table 6. Values for k_b to Be Used in Calculating Effective r_y

Description of loading	Coefficient, k_b
Beams Restrained Against Lateral Displacement at Both Ends of Span	
Uniform bending moment, uniform transverse load, or two equal concentrated loads equidistant from the center of the span	1.00
Bending moment varying uniformly from a value of M_1 at one end to M_2 at the other end	
$M_1/M_2 = 0.5$	1.14
$M_1/M_2 = 0$	1.33
$M_1/M_2 = -0.5$	1.53
$M_1/M_2 = -1.0$	1.60
Concentrated load at center of span	1.16
Cantilever Beams	
Concentrated load at end of span	1.13
Uniform transverse load	1.43

Values of the coefficient k_b in the above formulas are given in Table 6. The plus sign in front of the term "0.5" in the second equation applies if the load is on the bottom flange; the minus sign, if the load is on the top flange.

To establish allowable stresses for beams, the stress that causes lateral buckling is divided by the factor of safety for ultimate strength. The resulting allowable stress should be checked to insure an adequate factor of safety against yielding, taking into account the shape factor as discussed in preceding paragraphs.

The effect of welding on lateral buckling strength of beams is similar to its effect on columns. That is, welds located at points of support have a negligible effect on buckling strength, as do longitudinal welds, provided that only a small percentage of the cross section is affected.

Local buckling of thin-gage elements such as flanges, webs, or the walls of tubes influences the strength of beams as it does the strength of columns. The possibility of local buckling should be checked by methods outlined subsequently in this chapter.

Beam Columns

The strengths of members loaded in combined compression and bending are predicted with the aid of the interaction formulas in Table 7. These formulas apply to bending resulting from eccentricity of axial load as well as to bending resulting from lateral load.

Combinations of stress such that the left sides of the equations in Table 7 are less than unity should not cause failure. As the definitions of terms in Table 7 indicate, the equations in the table are applicable either to ultimate strength or to yield strength. Working stresses may be used for terms f_c and f_b, if F_c, F_b, and F_{ec} are divided by an appropriate factor of safety.

Buckling of Flat Plates

Local buckling strength of thin elements, such as webs and outstanding flanges of compression members and compression flanges of beams, should be checked in addition to the over-all column buckling strength. Such elements may buckle in the form of local waves or wrinkles. The local buckling strength of flat plates in edge compression can be calculated from the expressions in Table 2, line 2, with the coefficients in the inelastic buckling formulas being determined from the equations

Table 7. Strength of Members Subjected to Combined End Load and Bending

Loading condition		
Description	Examples of bending moment diagrams	Combinations of stress to cause failure
Bending moment at center ≥ 0.9 of max bending moment in span		$\frac{f_c}{F_c} + \frac{f_b}{F_b(1 - f_c/F_{ec})} = 1$
Bending moment at center ≤ 0.5 of max bending moment in span		$\frac{f_c}{F_c} + \frac{f_b}{F_b} = 1$
Bending moment at center between 0.5 and 0.9 of max bending moment in span		$\frac{f_c}{F_c} + \frac{f_b}{F_b[1 - (2M_c/M_m - 1)f_c/F_{ec}]} = 1$

f_c = stress caused by axial compressive load, psi
F_c = ultimate strength (or yield strength) of member subjected to axial compression only, psi
f_b = maximum compressive stress caused by applied bending loads only, psi
F_b = compressive stress that will cause failure (or yielding) for member acting as a beam only, psi
F_{ec} = $\pi^2E/(KL/r)^2$
KL/r = effective slenderness ratio for member considered as a column tending to fail in the plane of the applied bending forces
E = compressive modulus of elasticity, psi
M_c = bending moment at center of span resulting from applied bending loads, in.-lb
M_m = maximum bending moment in span resulting from applied bending loads, in.-lb

Table 8. Recommended Values of k_p in Formulas for Buckling of Plates

Type of edge support	Sketches defining width of plate, b, and showing axis of bending, x-x	Recommended value of k_p
	Column in Uniform Compression	
One edge (simple support)		5.13
Two edges (simple support)	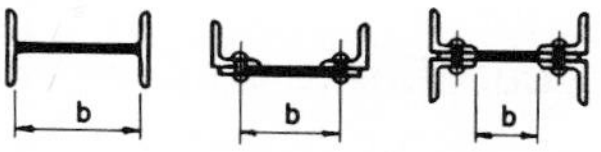	1.63
	Beam in Uniform Compression	
One edge (partial restraint)	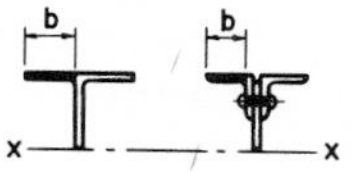	4.5
Two edges (simple support)	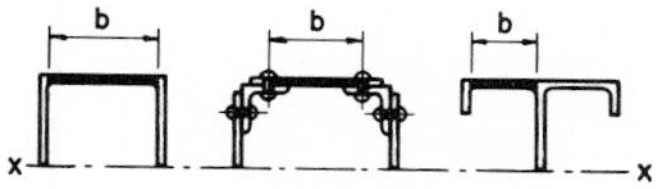	1.63
	Beam in Bending	
One edge (partial restraint)	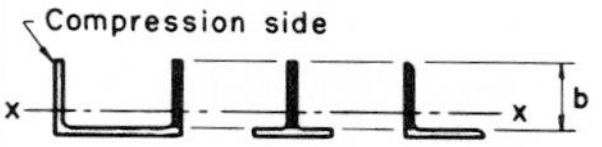 Compression side	3.5
Two edges (partial restraint)	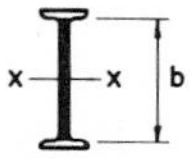	0.6

in Tables 3 and 4. The coefficient k_p depends on the conditions of restraint at the edges of the plate. Values of k_p recommended for various typical structural members are listed in Table 8.

The importance of buckling of flat plates depends upon the proportions of the member of which the flat plate is a part. When one or both unloaded edges are fastened to parts much stiffer than the plate itself, the plate can buckle without precipitating collapse of the member as a whole. This phenomenon is discussed further in the section on postbuckling. When the plate is one leg of an angle or T-section — and is, therefore, a major portion of the total cross-section area — buckling of the flat plate is very likely to bring about collapse of the member as a whole. In this case, the factor of safety to be used against buckling should be the same as that applied to ultimate strength.

Flat plates under bending in the plane of the plate, such as the webs of beams or girders, are subjected to stress that varies from tension at one edge to compression at the other. Thin webs may buckle under the influence of the compressive stresses, similar to the buckling of flat plates in edge compression. Line 7 of Table 2 gives formulas for the buckling stress in this case. Tables 3 and 4 show how to calculate B_b, D_b, and C_b.

It is customary to apply a low factor of safety to the buckling strength of webs under bending in the plane of the web, because the contribution of the web to the bending strength of the beam is minor.

Shear buckling of flat plates is a factor in the design of thin-web girders. Elastic buckling of this kind is often visible in the sides of heavily loaded highway trailers. Shear buckling stresses are calculated from the formulas in Table 2, line 9. These equations are based on the assumption that the edges of the plate are about halfway between the fixed and simply supported conditions, which is a reasonable assumption for many common types of construction.

Shear buckling of unstiffened beam webs can cause collapse of the beam, and the factor of safety used with ultimate strength should be applied. Stiffened panels, however, can usually sustain loads much higher than the buckling load, and the principal reason for guarding against shear buckling of such panels is to avoid the unsightly appearance of a wrinkled sheet at operating loads. This can be avoided by keeping the shear stress at operating load below the critical value. No question of collapse of the structure is involved, and therefore the factor of safety used may be small.

The influence of welding on the local buckling strength of flat plates can be ignored, if the effect of welding is taken into account in establishing the yield strength, which generally governs the allowable stress for thick sections.

Buckling of Curved Plates and Tubes

Round tubes make attractive structural members because of their efficiency and trim appearance. A few examples of aluminum structures in which round tubes are used are highway sign support trusses, transmission towers, lighting standards, and structural domes. Thin curved panels are also frequently used as structural members. In addition to the familiar example of aircraft construction, curved panels are encountered in such structures as tank trailers, railroad cars, and storage vessels.

Thin, curved sheets loaded in edge compression sometimes fail by local buckling. Critical stresses for curved plates in edge compression are considerably affected by variations in curvature and straightness. The formulas in Table 2, line 3, give critical stresses that are conservative in comparison with the results of most tests on curved plates and cylinders in edge compression. The critical stress is divided by the factor of safety on ultimate strength to determine allowable stresses.

Sometimes stiffeners are added to curved sheets or plates to divide the surface into panels. The buckling equations in Table 2 that apply to round tubes are applicable to curved panels. If the resulting buckling stress is less than that for a flat plate of the same dimensions as the curved panel, however, the buckling stress for the flat plate should be used.

The bending strength of round tubes is generally controlled either by local buckling of the wall on the compression side, or, in the case of relatively thick tubes, by distortion of the cross section. Round tubes are not subject to failure by lateral buckling and twisting.

For thin tubes ($R/t > C_{tb}$), the compressive stress that will cause local buckling in bending is approximately the same as that which will cause failure in direct compression. For thicker tubes, the redistribution of stress that accompanies plastic bending results in apparent buckling stresses (bending moment divided by section modulus) that may be appreciably higher than those developed in direct compression. The buckling stresses here are given by the expression in line 8 of Table 2, with the constants B_{tb}, D_{tb}, and C_{tb} being determined as indicated in Tables 3 and 4. As with direct compression, the factor of safety to be applied to the local buckling strength to establish allowable stresses for round tubes in bending is the factor of safety on ultimate strength.

Circumferential welds may reduce the compressive or bending strength of round tubes of heat treated or work-hardened material. This may be taken into account by using the formulas of Table 2, Cases 3 or 8, the coefficients in the formulas being given by the equations in Table 3, with the yield strength (measured on a 10-in. gage length across a weld) substituted for F_{cy}. In this case, Table 3 is used for all tempers of material, even the artificially aged tempers. Longitudinal welds usually have little effect on local buckling strength, because the heat-affected area is a small percentage of the total.

Stiffened Plates

Flat plates loaded in edge compression, such as the compression flange of a box beam or a plate element of a column, may be effectively strengthened by the use of stiffeners. Longitudinal stiffeners (that is, stiffeners with axes parallel to the direction of the main compressive stress in the plate) can be treated as columns, and the compressive stresses that will cause them to buckle can be determined from the column formulas.

In computing the radius of gyration of a longitudinal stiffener for use in the column formulas, the stiffener should be considered to consist of the stiffening member itself, plus a width of attached sheet equal to the spacing between the stiffeners. The effective length of the stiffener may generally be taken to be the distance between points at which the stiffener is supported against movement in the direction normal to the plane of the plate.

For long panels with relatively few stiffeners, the effective slenderness ratio may be less than that described in the preceding paragraph, because of the restraining effect of the plate. The reduced effective slenderness ratio for such stiffeners is given by Eq 4. This ratio should be used whenever its value is less than the actual value of L/r for the stiffener.

$$\lambda_s = \frac{4N}{3}\left(\frac{b}{t}\right)\sqrt{\frac{1 + A_s/bt}{1 + \sqrt{\frac{32I_e}{3t^3b} + 1}}} \qquad (4)$$

where λ_s = equivalent slenderness ratio for stiffener
N = total number of panels into which the longitudinal stiffeners divide the plate
b = stiffener spacing, in.
t = thickness of plate, in.
I_e = moment of inertia of plate-stiffener combination (using an effective width of plate equal to b), in.^{4}
A_s = area of stiffener (not including any of the plate), sq in.

Equation 4 is used in the design of intermediate stiffeners on plates that are supported by other parts of the structure along both unloaded edges.

Lips and bulbs for free edges on outstanding flanges are often used to increase the resistance to buckling. The extrusion process permits such stiffening devices to be incorporated readily into extruded shapes; it also is common to stiffen the free edges of formed sheet products by bending the edge to form a lip.

It is usually advantageous to make the stiffening lip large enough so that the compressive buckling stress of the stiffened flange is equal to that of a plate simply supported on both unloaded edges. If the thickness of the stiffening lip is the same as that of the supported flange, as in formed sheet construction, the clear width of stiffening lip required for this purpose is given by the formula:

$$b_L = \frac{b}{3} \text{ or } 8t \text{ (whichever is smaller)} \tag{5}$$

where b_L = clear width of lip, in.
b = clear width of flange, in.
t = thickness of flange, in.

A more general formula, which does not require that the thickness of the stiffening lip be the same as that of the flange, is the following:

$$r_L = \frac{b}{5.2} \text{ or } 4.6t \text{ (whichever is smaller)} \tag{6}$$

where r_L = radius of gyration of lip or bulb about face of flange from which lip projects, in.

If Eq 6 is used, the local buckling strength of the lip itself should also be checked.

Thin shear webs, in contrast to the relatively thicker webs of structural shapes, are generally stiffened to increase the shear buckling resistance of the web. Vertical stiffeners designed to resist shear buckling of girder webs should have a moment of inertia not less than that shown by the following formulas:

$$\frac{s}{h} \leq 0.4, \qquad I_s = \frac{Vh^2}{22{,}400{,}000}\left(\frac{s}{h}\right) \tag{7a}$$

$$\frac{s}{h} > 0.4, \qquad I_s = \frac{Vh^2}{140{,}000{,}000}\left(\frac{h}{s}\right) \tag{7b}$$

where s = spacing of vertical stiffeners (clear distance between stiffeners for stiffeners composed of a pair of members on each side of the web, and center-to-center distance between stiffeners composed of a member on one side of the web only), in.
h = clear height of shear web, in.
I_s = moment of inertia of stiffener (about face of web in contact with stiffener for a member on one side only, and about midthickness of web for stiffener composed of members of equal size on both sides of web), in.^{4}
V = shear force on web at stiffener location, lb

The moment of inertia of vertical stiffeners at points of

bearing should not be less than that given by the formula:

$$I_b = I_s + \frac{Ph^2}{\pi^2 E} \quad (8)$$

where I_b = moment of inertia of bearing stiffener, $in.^4$
P = local load concentration on stiffener, lb
E = compressive modulus of elasticity, psi

To increase the resistance of the web to buckling under the influence of longitudinal compressive bending stresses, it may be advantageous to introduce a horizontal stiffener. The most efficient location for such a stiffener is at a point 0.4 of the distance from the toe of the compression flange to the neutral axis of the girder. For such a stiffener, the required moment of inertia is

$$I_h = 2\alpha f t h^3 \left[\left(1 + 6\frac{A_h}{ht}\right)\left(\frac{s}{h}\right)^2 + 0.4 \right] \times 10^{-6} \quad (9)$$

where I_h = moment of inertia of horizontal stiffener, $in.^4$
α = a factor equal to unity for a stiffener consisting of equal members on both sides of the web, and equal to 3.5 for a stiffener consisting of a member on one side only
f = compressive stress at toe of girder flange, 1000 psi
t = thickness of web, in.
A_h = gross area of cross section of horizontal stiffener, sq in.
h and s are as defined for Eq 7a and 7b.

Corrugated sheet can be used effectively in shear webs, and the shear buckling strength can be calculated from the formulas in Table 2, Case 9, with the equivalent slenderness ratio for plate buckling, $1.25a_e/t$, replaced by an equivalent slenderness ratio shown by the following formula:

$$\lambda_{cs} = 0.63h\left(\frac{p}{sr^3t}\right)^{1/4} \quad (10)$$

where λ_{cs} = equivalent slenderness ratio for shear buckling of corrugated sheet
h = depth of panel parallel to the direction of the corrugations, in.
p = pitch of corrugations, in.
s = developed length of section in width p, in.
r = radius of gyration of cross section of corrugated sheet, in.
t = thickness of sheet, in.

For greatest effectiveness, a corrugated shear web should be fastened to the beam flanges through both planes of the corrugations. Corrugated shear webs fastened through one plane have appreciable strength, however, and may be used where tests have demonstrated that this method of attachment is adequate for the application.

Postbuckling of Flat Plates

Local buckling of thin sheet elements of load-carrying members does not necessarily bring about the collapse of the member. Thin sheets used as stiffened shear webs or as compression elements can usually carry appreciable load after local buckling has taken place, and this postbuckling strength is often used advantageously in design.

In columns, the importance of local buckling depends on the type of member. The ultimate strength of single-angle or T-section struts often does not exceed greatly the local buckling strength of the individual elements, but most other types of compression members can develop appreciable postbuckling strength. This is taken into account in design by the effective area method, in which a portion of a plate along the attached edges is considered fully effective in carrying load after the local buckling strength of the plate is exceeded. The remainder of the plate is assumed to carry no load. The width of the portion of the plate that is considered to be effective after local buckling is called the "effective width". The sum of the portions of the plate areas considered effective, plus areas of other elements of the member that are not affected by local buckling, is called the "effective area" of the member. The effective width of a plate loaded in compression can be estimated conservatively by:

$$b_e = b\frac{f_{cr}}{f_c} \tag{11}$$

where b_e = that part of the unsupported width of plate considered effective, in.
b = unsupported width of plate, in.
f_c = compressive stress on gross area, psi
f_{cr} = local buckling stress for plate, psi

The column can be expected to fail when the stress on the effective area reaches the compressive stress determined from the column formula. In using the column formula, it is satisfactory to use the radius of gyration determined from the gross section of the column.

For a beam or girder, the same effective width formula is used and the stress on the effective area of the compression flange may be found by multiplying the stress on the gross section of the flange by the ratio of the gross area to the effective area. This stress must be within acceptable limits established on the basis of yielding or lateral buckling of the beam. In determining the buckling stress, section properties based on the gross section may be used.

After local buckling, stiffened shear webs continue to carry shear forces by diagonal tension or "tension-field" action. The ultimate strength of the panel will then be limited by the tensile strength of the plate, by the strength of the connections between the plate and the edge stiffeners, or by the strength of the stiffener members themselves. For calculating the reserve strength of a rectangular flat panel after shear buckling, further data can be found in references on diagonal tension webs (5).

Sandwich Construction

Sandwich construction offers one of the strongest, stiffest, and lightest types of construction available. The American Society for Testing and Materials defines structural sandwich construction as "a laminar construction comprising a combination of alternating dissimilar simple or composite materials assembled and intimately fixed in relation to each other so as to use the properties of each to attain specific structural advantages for the whole assembly" (6). The most common type of structural sandwich involving aluminum is two parallel sheets of aluminum alloy separated by and intimately bonded to a lightweight core material such as foamed plastic or aluminum honeycomb. Sometimes the core material provides thermal insulating characteristics to the finished panel in addition to its structural function, as in the case of foamed plastic. The core material provides the shear resistance for the panel, and continuous or near-continuous structural support for the thin face sheets, to prevent buckling under the influence of edgewise compression stresses. The bonding medium is usually an adhesive, although brazing can be used under some circumstances. For added dent resistance, a suitable backup material is sometimes interposed between the thin facing sheets and the core material.

Sandwich panels are usually designed to resist bending forces, in which case one facing sheet becomes the compression flange and the other the tension flange, with the core material serving as a shear web between the two flanges. The core material is usually assumed to have no bending resistance. The shear stress in the core is considered to be equal to the shear load divided by the area of the core cross section. The faces should be checked for both yielding and local buckling. The compressive stress that will cause local buckling of a sandwich panel face can be found approximately from the column formulas, Case 1, Table 2, with the following equivalent slenderness ratio substituted for KL/r:

$$\text{Equivalent slenderness ratio} = 4.4\left[\left(\frac{E}{E_c}\right)\left(\frac{E}{G_c}\right)\right]^{1/6} \tag{12}$$

where E = compressive modulus of elasticity of face, psi
E_c = modulus of elasticity of core in direction perpendicular to face, psi
G_c = shear modulus of core, psi

To develop a given local buckling stress in the face, f_{cr}, the tensile strength of the bond between the face and the core, and also the tensile and compressive yield strength of the core itself, should not be less than

$$T = 0.001(f_{cr})^{2/3} \tag{13}$$

where T = tensile strength of bond between facing and core, tensile yield strength of core, or compressive yield strength of core, 1000 psi
f_{cr} = compressive local buckling strength of panel face, 1000 psi

Where a sandwich panel is expected to resist edge compression loading, the facing sheets are assumed to carry the full load, with the core again serving merely to stabilize the facing sheets against buckling. In calculating the slenderness ratio of the panels, it may be necessary to make some allowance for the fact that the core material has rather low resistance to shear deformation; thus, the effective radius of gyration will be somewhat less than the square root of the ratio of the moment of inertia to the cross-sectional area. This same influence of shear deformations of the core must be considered in calculating the deflections of sandwich panels under lateral bending loads (7). Local buckling strength of the faces of sandwich panels loaded in edge compression can be considered the same as for panels in bending.

Plastic Design

Aluminum frames can be designed by the principles of plastic design, in which "plastic hinges" are assumed to be formed at locations of high bending moment, provided that the proportions of the members are restricted so as to prevent loss in strength due to buckling, and provided that account is taken of the effect of any welding on the mechanical properties of the alloy.

Because aluminum does not have a well-defined yield point, the bending moment corresponding to the development of a plastic hinge cannot be precisely defined; the bending moment continues to increase as the angle of rotation increases. However, it is convenient and conservative to compute the plastic hinge moment in the same way as for structural steel beams, using the conventional yield strength for aluminum (defined at 0.2% offset from the initial modulus line) in place of the yield point for steel.

The limiting proportions of aluminum alloy members required to prevent the onset of instability before a plastic hinge is developed can be estimated from the corresponding limits for steel structures. For this purpose, the limiting slenderness ratio or width-to-thickness ratio for structural carbon steel (ASTM A36) is multiplied by the quantity $\sqrt{12/F_y}$, in which F_y is the yield strength of the aluminum alloy, in 1000 psi.

Where the members are butt welded at the point of maximum bending moment, the yield strength used should be the value defined at 0.2% offset on a 10-in. gage length across a butt weld. If only part of the cross section is welded, the yield strength can be considered to be the weighted average of the 10-in. gage length yield strength across a butt weld on the part of the cross section that lies within 1 in. of the weld, and the yield strength of the parent metal for the remainder of the cross section.

Torsion

Torsion or twisting of a member subjects it to shearing stresses; the allowable stress levels must be related to the shear yield strength and shear strength of the alloy. Unless the elements of the member are relatively thick or well supported, shear buckling may be involved, and must be guarded against by providing an adequate factor of safety against the shear buckling stresses.

The most efficient members for resisting or transmitting torsional forces are those with tubular (particularly circular) cross sections. The formulas for calculating the maximum shear stresses for such sections are well known; designing such sections becomes merely a matter of providing an adequate factor of safety against the shear yield strength and the shear strength. However, torsional loadings sometimes are applied to more complicated shapes, such as I-beams or channels, and the calculation of the shearing and bending stresses becomes more complicated and beyond the scope of this treatment of the subject (8).

Effect of Joining Methods on Structural Design

The design of connections to provide adequate strength for transmitting loads from one member to another is treated in Volume III, Chapters 11, 12, and 15. For riveted and bolted joints, it should be remembered that the rivet and bolt holes reduce the cross-sectional areas so that the net area, rather than the gross area, is the part available for transmitting the tensile forces. For compression stresses, this difference between net area and gross area can be ignored where the hole is filled with a rivet or with a tightly fitted bolt.

For welded members, unless the parent metal is in the annealed condition, the effect of the heat of welding on the properties of the parent metal must be considered. Some weldments can be heat treated after welding to restore the full strength of the parent metal, but a narrow band of metal on each side of the weld will usually exhibit lower properties than the remainder of the parent metal. For design purposes, this heat-affected zone can generally be considered as extending for a distance of not more than 1 in. in any direction from the center line of a butt weld, or from the root of a fillet weld. If the weld is transverse to the direction of stressing, the heat-affected zone becomes the weakest part of the member, and probably controls the stress level in the member as a whole. If the weld is parallel to the direction of stressing, the surrounding unaffected parent metal supports the heat-affected zone, so that the weld has little effect on the strength. Where the heat-affected zone comprises more than about 15% of the total area, the strength of a cross section containing a longitudinal weld should be estimated by assuming that the material within 1 in. of the weld has the same strength as the weld itself, and that the remainder of the cross section has the strength of unaffected parent metal. The sum of the strengths of the heat-affected area and the remaining area is the strength of the cross section. This procedure is applied to either yield strength or ultimate strength.

Table 9 gives data on the strength of welded joints for some of the more commonly used weldable aluminum alloys. The values of tensile strength in Table 9 represent ASME weld-qualification test requirements for butt welds. The minimum strength for design purposes is sometimes considered to be 90% of this value (4). The values of yield strength across butt welds and shear strength of fillet welds in Table 9 are expected minimum values, and are used as a basis for selection of allowable design stresses. Yield strength across a butt weld is defined on the basis of 0.2% offset on a gage length of 10 in. The amount of yielding that occurs in a welded joint at this stress level has been found to be roughly equivalent to that which occurs in riveted or bolted joints when the stress on the net section reaches the minimum yield strength of the alloy.

The effect of welding on buckling of columns and other parts is discussed in other sections of this chapter.

With adhesive-bonded joints, there is no problem of net section or of heat-affected zones. The joint itself may introduce some eccentricity locally at the joint, since most adhesive joints are of the lap type, but otherwise it does not weaken the surrounding parent metal. The successful use of adhesive bond-

Table 9. Minimum Strength Data for Welded Joints(a)
(TIG or MIG welding with no postweld heat treatment)

		Across butt weld		
Parent material(b)	Filler wire(c)	Tensile strength, psi	Yield strength, psi(d)	Shear strength of fillet welds, psi(e)
3003	1100	14,000	7,000	7,500(f)
3004	4043	22,000	11,000	11,500(f)
5052	5052	25,000	13,000	7,500(f)
5154	5154	30,000	15,000	12,000(f)
5454	5554	31,000	16,000	17,000(f)
5086	5356	35,000	19,000	17,000(f)
5083(g)	5556	40,000	24,000	20,000
5456(g)	5556	42,000	26,000	20,000
6061-T6	5556	24,000	20,000	20,000
6061-T6	5356	24,000	20,000	17,000
6061-T6	4043	24,000	15,000(h)	12,000(f)
6063-T5, T6, T83, T831, T832	4043	17,000	11,000	12,000(f)

(a) These are minimum expected strength values to be used as basis for design. Typical or average strength values are appreciably higher. (b) Strength values apply to all tempers of non-heat-treatable alloys except as noted under note (d).

(c) Filler wires are those commonly used. They do not necessarily represent recommended filler wires for all applications. (d) Yield strength across a butt weld corresponds to 0.2% set on a 10-in. gage length. Values listed for non-heat-treatable alloys are for tempers quarter hard or harder. For annealed temper, this value will be the same as yield strength of parent metal.

(e) Applicable to throat area of fillet. (f) Greater strengths can be obtained with higher-strength filler alloys. (g) Tensile and yield strengths given for these alloys apply to sheet and plate up to 1½ in. thick. (h) Material more than ⅜ in. thick. For thinner material, yield strength is 20,000 psi.

ing requires care in the design of the joint, in the selection of adhesive, and in the fabrication procedure, to insure that a good bond will be effected (see Volume III, Chapter 15).

Fatigue

When a member is subjected to many cycles of repeated loading, it may fail eventually even though the maximum stress in any cycle is considerably below the static strength of the material. This is called fatigue failure. The failure occurs by the formation of a minute crack that gradually extends until the area of the part is so reduced that the part ruptures.

Fatigue life is governed by the peak stresses at points of stress concentration, rather than by the nominal stresses used in ordinary design. When a fatigue failure occurs in a structure, it is almost always traceable to some "stress raiser", such as a notch, hole or sharp re-entrant corner. Concentrations of stress at such points can frequently be alleviated by proper design, fabrication or maintenance, or a combination of these, resulting in greatly improved fatigue life. Unfortunately, present knowledge of fatigue is not sufficiently advanced to permit precise design for a specified life, even in simple parts. Furthermore, it is almost never possible to predict accurately the stress conditions that a part will encounter in service.

The number of repetitions of load, or cycles of stress, required to produce failure depends both upon the stress level and the range of stress. In many instances, it is not possible to predict accurately the maximum values of these quantities. Another difficulty is that the load cycles are often not repeated exactly, but actually are combinations of many different load cycles. Additional complications are introduced by the effects of the magnitude of residual stress, the surface condition of the part, and plastic yielding.

The fact that it is not presently possible to predict fatigue life within close limits should not discourage the engineer from trying to obtain satisfactory resistance to fatigue action. Information on the actual fatigue strength of typical construction is available in the literature and provides a guide to the designer (9). Fatigue failures almost always occur at points of stress concentration caused by discontinuities in the member. Rivet holes, bolt holes, re-entrant corners, weld beads, and other abrupt changes in cross section are the most likely sources of the initiation of fatigue cracks. At first thought, it would seem that the engineer would merely calculate the magnitude of the stress concentration at the most severe of these, and apply this calculated stress to the smooth-specimen fatigue strength of the alloy to establish the probable life. Experience has shown, however, that this approach to the problem does not produce realistic results. The only safe procedure is to establish the fatigue strength of typical construction details, simulating those used in the actual structure, and to keep the working stresses in the structure below those that have been found to produce failure in tests. In ordinary structural design, if adequate fatigue strength is provided in the joints, it is almost certain that the remainder of the structure will be free of fatigue failures.

The fatigue strength of welded joints can usually be improved by: machining the weld flush with the surface; avoiding spatter; avoiding integral backup strips; reducing secondary stresses due to flexing of a joint, by designing symmetrical joints or applying stiffeners; using continuous rather than intermittent fillet welds;

Table 10. Maximum Shear Stress

f_s = shear stress, 1000 psi
f_1 and f_2 = normal stresses, 1000 psi
$(f_s)_{max}$ = maximum shear stress in plane of sketch, 1000 psi

Condition	Sketch	Maximum shear stress
Pure shear, f_s	f_s	$(f_s)_{max} = f_s$
Simple tension or compression, f_1	f_1	$(f_s)_{max} = \frac{f_1}{2}$
Two normal stresses, f_1 and f_2 at right angles to each other. (Stresses f_1 and f_2 are either tension or compression, tension being considered positive and compression negative.)	f_2, f_1	$(f_s)_{max} = \frac{f_1 - f_2}{2}$
One normal stress, f_1, and shear stress, f_s, on planes parallel and perpendicular to f_1.	f_s, f_1	$(f_s)_{max} = \sqrt{\left(\frac{f_1}{2}\right)^2 + f_s^2}$
Two normal stresses, f_1 and f_2, and shear stress, f_s, on planes parallel and perpendicular to f_1 and f_2.	f_2, f_s, f_1	$(f_s)_{max} = \sqrt{\left(\frac{f_1 - f_2}{2}\right)^2 + f_s^2}$

and, where possible, employing butt welds rather than fillet welds. Fatigue strengths of butt-welded joints generally equal or exceed those of well-designed riveted joints having equal static strength. Welding may cause residual stresses that approach the tensile yield strength of the heat-affected material. Fatigue tests have shown that these residual stresses can reduce fatigue strength significantly for large numbers of cycles. In the non-heat-treatable alloys, these residual stresses can be largely removed by a thermal treatment (Volume III, Chapter 10), with a resulting improvement in fatigue strength.

Combined Stresses

Yielding and fracture of parts of machines and structures under a system of "combined stresses" can occur at different loads than would be predicted by the mechanical properties of the alloy as determined on test specimens in simple tension, compression, or shear. The effect of these combined stresses on the performance of the part may be predicted approximately by means of the "maximum shear stress" rule. According to this rule, yielding occurs under any system of stresses when the maximum shear stress reaches a value equal to half the tensile yield strength as determined in axial tension. Similarly, the rule predicts ultimate failure under combined stresses when the maximum shear stress reaches a value that is equal to half the tensile strength.

The maximum shear stress in any plane can be determined by the formulas in Table 10. In using these formulas, it should be remembered that any actual stress condition involves all three principal dimensions. It may, therefore, be necessary to examine the shear stress in more than one plane, to assure that the largest value has been found.

Local buckling of flat plates subjected to combined stresses in the plane of the plate is a problem encountered in members such as a beam or girder web, which must resist simultaneously shear and bending in the plane of the web. If the member must also carry axial forces, then a uniform edge compressive stress is superimposed on the shear and bending stresses.

Combinations of stress that cause buckling of flat plate panels can be determined from the formula

$$\frac{f_c}{F_c} + \left(\frac{f_b}{F_b}\right)^2 + \left(\frac{f_s}{F_s}\right)^2 = 1 \qquad (14)$$

where f_c = uniform edge compressive stress in plate, psi
F_c = critical stress for plate under only edge compression, psi
f_b = maximum compressive stress in clear height caused by bending in plane of plate, psi
F_b = critical stress for plate under only bending, psi
f_s = average shear stress in plate, psi
F_s = critical stress for plate under only uniform shear, psi

In the above formula, the stresses are assumed to be combined in the same way as in the web of a beam-column under axial load and bending. That is, the direct stress at one edge of the panel, parallel to the edge, is $(f_c + f_b)$, and at the opposite edge the direct stress is $(f_c - f_b)$. The shear stress f_s occurs on planes parallel and perpendicular to the direction of f_c and f_b.

Equation 14 can be used to determine permissible combinations of stress in the working range, if f_c, f_b, and f_s are the stresses caused by the working loads and F_c, F_b, and F_s are allowable design stresses for compression, bending, and shear.

Stiffness Considerations

The deflections of aluminum alloy members and assemblies can be calculated using conventional deflection formulas. Since the modulus of elasticity of aluminum alloys averages about 10,000,000 psi, the deflection of an aluminum member will be about three times that of a steel member of the same configuration, for the same total loading. This does not mean, however, that aluminum members must have three times the moment of inertia of steel members, because in many instances the steel member is far stiffer than necessary. The designer should always consider carefully the stiffness requirements on the basis of the proper functioning of the part, rather than on the basis of some arbitrary deflection requirement for other materials.

Where deflection becomes a controlling item in the design, care should be taken to use the available metal as effectively as possible, in the interest of both economy and elimination of needless dead weight. For members under axial tension or compression, unit lengthening or shortening can be decreased only by increasing the cross-sectional area and thus reducing the stress. For members or assemblies in flexure, the deflection can be reduced in two ways: by adding cross-sectional area, suitably distributed, while holding the depth of the member constant; or by increasing the depth with or without additional area. The second method is preferable, because it requires less metal.

Impact

Impact loadings in engineering design problems are often handled by applying a suitable impact factor to the moving loads to take account of the dynamic effects. Problems involving dynamic loadings are thus translated into terms of equivalent static loadings. This procedure is satisfactory only where sufficient experience has been accumulated to guide selection of the impact factors to be used. In other cases, it may be necessary to calculate the amount of energy involved in the impact loading, and to estimate the stresses that will result as the structure absorbs this amount of energy. However, it is difficult to make this calculation accurately, because the energy-absorbing capacity of a structural member is often limited by the deformation characteristics of the connections, or by local buckling, so that the full energy-absorbing capability of the alloy itself is seldom used. The best method to determine energy-absorbing capacity of a structural assembly is by full-scale dynamic tests.

Properly designed and fabricated welded assemblies generally resist shock loading about as well as comparable riveted assemblies. Welded assemblies of softer alloys usually carry shock loadings more satisfactorily than those of harder alloys, because yielding in the softer alloys is likely to be more general throughout the structure. In the harder alloys, yielding tends to be concentrated in the heat-affected zones near the welds.

Properties of aluminum alloys are substantially constant for speeds of loading generally encountered in engineering design.

Vibration

It is sometimes necessary to consider possible harmful effects of vibration on members or assemblies. The natural frequencies of the parts, and of the assembly as a whole, should lie outside a range from half to twice the frequency of any regularly repeated impulses; if not, the deflections of the part or assembly can build up dangerously, and the stresses can be far above those calculated for static loading conditions.

The natural frequency of a member or assembly can be estimated by the formulas shown in Table 11. For horizontal structural members, the deflection D is calculated in the ordinary manner, but for members whose position is other than horizontal, the deflection is calculated as though the member were in a

Table 11. Natural Frequency of Vibration

Concentrated load on relatively light beam or spring	Uniform load on simple beam	Uniform load on cantilever beam
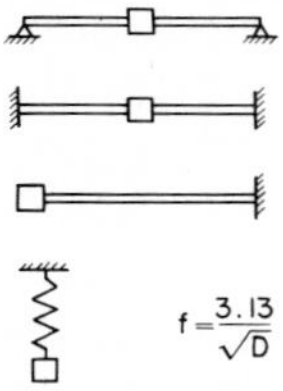	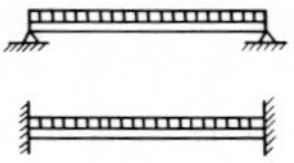	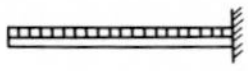
$f = \frac{3.13}{\sqrt{D}}$	$f = \frac{3.55}{\sqrt{D}}$	$f = \frac{3.89}{\sqrt{D}}$

f = natural frequency of vibration, cycles per second
D = maximum static deflection of member under its own weight plus any weights that vibrate with it, in.

horizontal position. This use of the deflection is simply a convenient method of taking into account the stiffness and span length of the member, and the magnitude and distribution of the mass that is in motion when the member is vibrating.

Designing With Castings

Because virtually all of the published properties for cast materials are based on separately cast test bars, the published values must be adjusted on the basis of stress analysis, proof testing, and experience, to provide allowable stresses for structural design. Some specifications for castings state that for test specimens cut from the actual casting, the average tensile strength shall not be less than 75%, and the elongation not less than 25% of the values obtained from separately cast test bars. Other specifications require specific minimum tensile properties for specimens cut from the castings. Experimental stress analysis or destructive testing is often used to establish the design requirements and to provide guidance for redistribution of metal to improve serviceability. There may be considerable scatter in test results, and several destructive tests may be needed to attain safe design.

Experience has shown that fatigue is an important factor in the serviceability of many castings; where repeated loadings are involved, particular attention should be paid to the effects of fatigue. Here again, simulated service testing is probably the safest procedure; in any event, the designer should avoid sharp re-entrant corners and other stress raisers.

Most castings are likely to exhibit lower ductility in service than would be expected of an equivalent part made from a wrought alloy. However, high ductility can be obtained with some casting alloys, such as A356 and 220. Where shock loadings are to be expected, or where for any other reason low ductility may contribute to early failure, destructive testing of sample castings is the best guide to adequate design.

Temperature Considerations

For service at atmospheric temperatures, aluminum alloy parts may be designed using the published room-temperature properties. When structures are to operate at elevated temperatures, it is important that the designer consider the decrease in strength that can occur at such temperatures. Some alloys and tempers are not recommended for elevated-temperature use. The factors that are important in design are the maximum temperatures reached in the metal parts and the length of time the metal is subjected to these temperatures.

In addition to elevated temperatures during service, the designer sometimes must take into account the possible effects of temperature applied to the metal during hot bending or other hot fabricating. For welded parts, the effects of the heat of welding must be taken into account, as described previously in this chapter.

Low temperatures, even down to the cryogenic range, do not pose any problem in the design of aluminum alloy structures. The metal becomes stronger and retains its ductility. The aluminum alloys undergo no transition to brittle behavior at low temperature as do carbon steels and many other ferrous alloys.

The amount of movement involved in thermal expansion or contraction of aluminum is about twice that for an equivalent steel structure. Where adequate provision can be made for the necessary relative movement of parts by expansion joints, these thermal effects can be ignored in the design. When the designer can arrange for the expansion and contraction to be dissipated in elastic deformation of the parts, the relatively low modulus of elasticity of aluminum is a distinct advantage. Difficulty from expansion and contraction usually occurs only where the designer has ignored its effects and has failed to provide for the necessary movement or for the stresses induced when movement is prevented.

Structural Efficiency

Light weight is essential in many products that employ aluminum. Aircraft and missiles are obvious examples. Minimization of weight is also important in the marine, automotive, railroad, and military equipment fields. Even in stationary structures, such as bridges and towers, the use of a lightweight structural material is advantageous, because it reduces dead load and simplifies erection.

To simplify the problem of selection for applications requiring light weight, materials are often compared on the basis of the ratio of strength to density, the material with the highest ratio being the most efficient. The strength value that should be used in such a comparison is the one that controls the design of the specific part. For a part loaded in tension, this might be the tensile strength, tensile yield strength, notch strength, fatigue

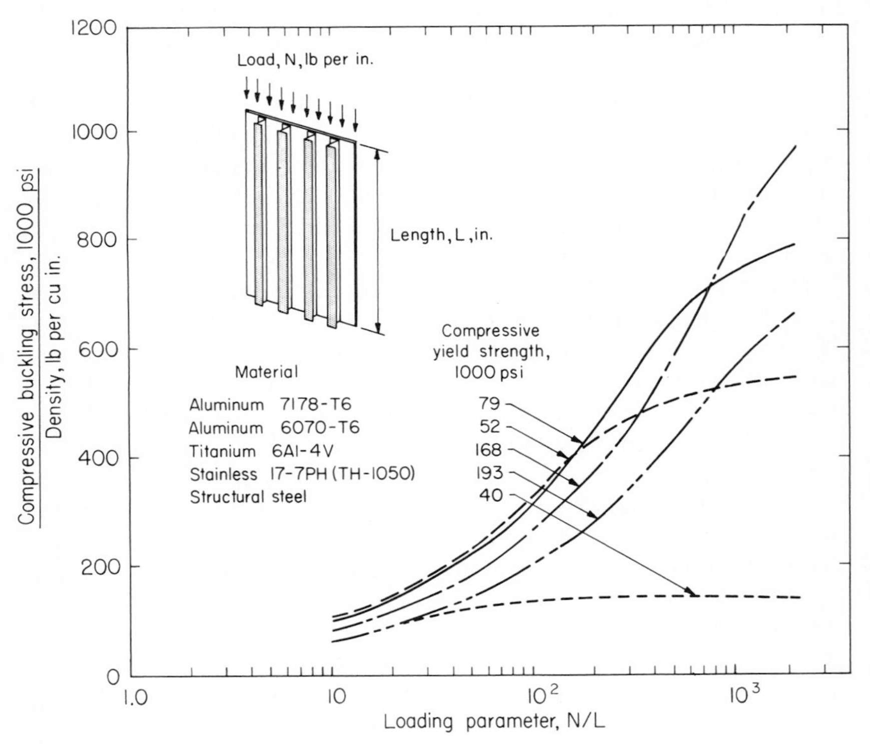

Fig. 2. Ratios of compressive strength to density for stiffened sheet panels

strength, or creep strength. The relative efficiency of compressively loaded parts, whose strength is limited by buckling, depends on the intensity of loading. The buckling strength of a lightly loaded member is controlled by the modulus of elasticity, whereas the yield strength governs the strength of heavily loaded members. Thus, no single ratio or index covers all cases.

As an example of the use of strength-to-density ratios, Fig. 2 compares the ratios of compressive buckling strength to density for two aluminum alloys and some other structural materials, based on typical compressive stress-strain relationships. The type of structural element considered in Fig. 2 is a stiffened sheet panel of optimum proportions to carry a compressive load of intensity *N*, expressed in pounds per inch of width, over a length of *L* inches (10). Such a panel might be part of an airplane wing, a ship structure, or a box girder. Similar, but not identical, comparisons would be obtained if corresponding curves were drawn for columns or unstiffened flat plate panels.

Considerable caution must be used in interpreting simplified comparisons of materials such as shown in Fig. 2. For example, an assumption made in constructing these curves is that the plate and stiffener elements selected are the thinnest ones that can carry the given load without local buckling. Some materials may not be available in the required size and thickness because of fabrication problems; other considerations, such as resistance to corrosion or local indentation, may limit thickness.

Despite their limitations, comparisons of the type shown give a useful first approximation to the relative efficiency of materials. Figure 2 illustrates the high efficiency of aluminum in compressively loaded structural elements. The loading intensities for most practical applications are in the range where the curves for aluminum are uppermost.

Table 12. Allowable Stresses for 6061-T6, 6063-T5, and 6063-T6

	Allowable tensile stress in members subjected to axial load, psi			
	Locations farther than 1.0 in. from a weld		Locations within 1.0 in. of a weld	
Alloy and temper	Bridge structures	Building structures	Bridge structures	Building structures
6061-T6	17,000	19,000	10,000	11,000
6063-T5	8,500	9,500	6,000	6,500
6063-T6	13,500	15,000	6,000	6,500

SOURCE: Proc ASCE, Papers 3341 and 3342

Design Specifications and Codes

The principal American specifications for aluminum alloys in structures are those published by the Task Committee on Lightweight Alloys of the American Society of Civil Engineers (Papers 3341 and 3342). Allowable tensile stresses from these specifications are given in Table 12. See Table 1, page 183, and Ref 11 for additional specifications and codes.

References

1 "Alcoa Handbook of Design Stresses for Aluminum", Aluminum Company of America, Pittsburgh, 1966

2 Column Research Council, "Guide to Design Criteria for Metal Compression Members", John Wiley and Sons, Inc., New York, 1966, Chap 2

3 R. J. Brungraber and J. W. Clark, Strength of Welded Aluminum Columns, Trans ASCE, **127**, Part II, 202–226 (1962)

4 Task Committee on Lightweight Alloys, Suggested Specifications for Structures of Aluminum Alloys 6061-T6 and 6062-T6, Paper 3341, J Structural Div, Proc ASCE, **88**, ST6, 1–45 (1962)

5 P. Kuhn, J. P. Peterson, and L. R. Levin, A Summary of Diagonal Tension — Part I, Methods of Analysis, NASA Tech Note 2661 (1952)

6 Standard Definition of Terms Relating to Structural Sandwich Constructions, C274-53, ASTM Std, Part 16, 11 (1966)

7 E. W. Kuenzi, Structural Design Criteria, Sandwich Panel Design Criteria, Nat Res Council Publ 798, 9–18 (1960)

8 S. P. Timoshenko, Theory of Bending, Torsion, and Buckling of Thin-Walled Members of Open Cross Section, Part II, J Franklin Inst, **239**, no. 4, 249–268 (1945)

9 G. E. Nordmark and J. W. Clark, Fatigue of Joints in Aluminum Alloy 6061-T6, Paper 4156, J Structural Div, Proc ASCE, **90**, ST6, 35–50 (1964); H. Mindlin, Fatigue of Aluminum-Magnesium Alloys, Welding J, **42**, No. 6, 276s–281s (1963); G. E. Nordmark, Peening Increases Fatigue Strength of Welded Aluminum, Metal Progress, **84**, 101–103 (Nov 1963); E. C. Hartmann, M. Holt and I. D. Eaton, Fatigue Strength of Welded Butt Joints in Aluminum Alloy Plates, Prod Eng, Annual Handbook, B6–B18 (1955); M. Holt, I. D. Eaton and R. B. Matthiesen, Fatigue Tests of Riveted or Bolted Aluminum Alloy Joints, Paper 1148, J Structural Div, Proc ASCE, **83**, ST1 (1957)

10 G. Gerard, "Minimum Weight Analysis of Compression Structures", New York University Press, New York, 1956, p 43

11 "Structural Aluminum Design", Reynolds Metals Co., Richmond, Va., 1966

12 H. N. Hill and J. W. Clark, Straight Line Column Formulas for Aluminum Alloys, Alcoa Research Lab Tech Paper 12, Aluminum Company of America, Pittsburgh, 1955

13 J. W. Clark and R. L. Rolf, Design of Aluminum Tubular Members, Paper 4184, J Structural Div, Proc ASCE, **90**, ST6, 259–289 (1964)

Chapter 10

Building Construction

L. M. Dunn and W. R. Tyler

ONLY 40 years ago, the first major effort was made to establish aluminum as a building material. Less than three decades later, construction required more aluminum annually than any other field of application. In 1965, an estimated 905,000 tons of aluminum was used in building construction in the United States. Table 1 lists tonnages for residential and nonresidential uses and for a number of specific building products for 1960 and 1964.

The characteristics of aluminum that have been primarily responsible for its use in building construction are appearance, resistance to weathering, ease of forming, finishing potential, and light weight with high strength.

In most building construction applications, a consideration of primary importance is surface — from the standpoint of decoration, weatherability, or maintenance. All of the natural and colored finishes available on aluminum have been employed on one or more building construction products. These finishes are classed broadly as mechanical, chemical, electrochemical, organic, plastic, and porcelain enamel, and are described in Volume III, Chapters 16 to 22. The maintenance of these finishes is discussed in Volume III, Chapter 23.

In building construction applications, aluminum is often complemented by — or complements — other building materials. In employing aluminum with these other materials, it may

L. M. Dunn was formerly manager for building products and structures, Sales Development Div., Aluminum Company of America. W. R. Tyler is manager for building and highway products, Application Engineering Div., Aluminum Company of America, New Kensington.

Table 1. Tonnages of Some Aluminum Building Construction Products Sold in the United States

Application	Tons in 1960	Tons in 1964
Residential		
Siding	118,500	172,500
Gutters and downspouts	12,200	18,000
Awnings, patio covers and carports	20,900	32,300
Windows and doors	247,700	315,500
Total(a)	431,300	587,600
Nonresidential		
Windows, doors and storefronts	36,500	71,400
Curtain walls	26,000	44,300
Solar shading and decorative screens	1,800	3,100
Decorative handrails	1,800	3,360
Hardware	7,400	10,400
Copings and gravel stops	1,300	2,400
Industrial roofing and siding	13,000	21,400
Farm roofing and siding	28,000	30,000
Total(a)	130,200	217,300
Total, all building construction	591,500	841,000

(a) Because only selected items are listed, their weights do not add to the totals given.

be necessary to follow certain procedures to avoid galvanic or poultice corrosion (Volume I, Chapter 7). Also, judgment may be required in selecting one aluminum alloy for use with another; this is generally of greatest importance in obtaining an acceptable color match, after anodizing, between sheet, extrusion, and casting alloys, and at welded joints.

Table 2 lists the aluminum sheet and extrusion alloys generally employed in building construction, and the yield strengths associated with the common tempers.

Among aluminum alloys in general, all alloys in Table 2 have outstanding resistance to corrosion and excellent finishing characteristics. Variation among them in these respects is minor and less than the differences among service environments. In most atmospheres, paint, anodic finishes, or other coatings are not required for protection but are frequently used for decorative effects. Where high-strength alloys with lower resistance to corrosion are required, or in applications where extra precaution is desired against excessive depth of pitting, alclad alloys are sometimes used.

The alloys vary in appearance after anodizing, because of the effects of various added or impurity elements in the alloy. For example 6063, containing no copper, is preferred for extrusions where a minimum change in the original appearance of the extrusion is desired.

All of the alloys commonly used in building construction have good weldability; variation is minor, the alloys without magnesium being somewhat superior. Price differentials for extrusions generally favor 6063, but there is little difference in prices for the various sheet alloys used in building construction.

Residential Construction

Residential construction has two important market divisions: new-house construction and house improvement. Most residential aluminum building products are used in both categories.

In most new-house construction, the principal influence on the design and construction of products to be incorporated is the house builder, who is generally guided by the Minimum Property Standards of the Federal Housing Administration. As these standards specify minimum requirements for a wide range of building products, they are a valuable reference for the designer.

It is possible to virtually enclose a house in aluminum building products (Fig. 1). In fact, aluminum prefabricated houses are being mass produced. Many mobile homes also are virtually enclosed in aluminum (Volume II, Chapter 15).

Siding of aluminum has emerged as the leading sheet product for residential construction, requiring 172,500 tons in 1964. The

Table 2. Typical Yield Strengths at Room Temperature of Some Aluminum Sheet and Extrusion Alloys Commonly Used in Building Construction

Sheet alloys	Yield strength, psi — Temper: O	H14	H16	H18	H34	H38
1100	5,000	17,000	20,000	22,000	...	...
3003	6,000	21,000	25,000	27,000	...	...
3105	...	24,000	28,000	...	...	...
5005	6,000	22,000	25,000	28,000	20,000	27,000
5050	8,000	...	...	...	24,000	29,000
5052	13,000	...	...	...	31,000	37,000

Extrusion alloys	Temper: O	T4	T5	T6	T42
6061	8,000	21,000	...	40,000	...
6063	7,000	13,000	21,000	31,000	13,000

greater portion is for renovation. Aluminum siding is available in two basic styles — horizontal and vertical. After installation, horizontal siding resembles conventional clapboard siding. Vertical siding provides the effect of traditional 12-in. board-and-batten or 8-in. V-groove.

A typical siding product is roll formed from prepainted coiled sheet. As installation of the siding progresses, nails and joint details are concealed. It is important that the nails not be driven too tightly in the slotted holes, so that each piece of siding can expand and contract with temperature change. Accessories such as starter strips, outside and inside corner trim, and window and door trim are available. For new construction, the installed cost of aluminum siding is approximately the same as the cost of properly painted wood siding.

Aluminum siding products are available in a range of colors, although white is by far the most common selection. A uniform acrylic, alkyd, or vinyl paint film, applied on automated paint lines under carefully controlled mill conditions, provides a

Available products make it possible to sheath a house in aluminum from the ground up. Standard products of aluminum include plain and prepainted windows, prepainted siding, shutters, soffit (under eaves), fascia (eave facing), gutters, downspouts and trim.

Fig. 1. Aluminum residential building products

durable surface that can last many years without repainting, because aluminum is a good substrate for paint and has advantages for paint application.

Alloy 3003, 3105, or 5005 sheet is commonly employed for siding, as well as for soffits (under eaves), fascia (eave facing), gutters and downspouts, ventilators and louvers, awnings, patios, and carports, which are to be discussed subsequently. The hardest formable temper is chosen for each application; tempers usually range from quarter hard to three-quarters hard. Sheet thickness is commonly 0.019 to 0.032 in., but can range up to 0.050 in., depending on strength requirements. Extrusions used with these sheet products are generally of 6063-T5, but can be 6063-T6 or 6061-T6, if higher strength is required.

Soffits. The exposure most damaging to any building material is generally the underside of overhanging projections, such as the soffit area under the eaves of a house. Aluminum soffit systems are being produced and installed in increasing quantities. Accessories include roll-formed fascia "boards" and trim moldings. Soffit sheets that are perforated or louvered, either completely or partly, offer a simple means of providing attic ventilation. For insect control, louvered soffits are normally backed with screening; the holes in perforated soffits are limited to a maximum diameter of ⅛ in. The same sheet alloys and gages are employed as for siding. Aluminum soffits are typically formed from prepainted sheet, usually ribbed or corrugated for extra strength and stiffness.

Gutters and downspouts of aluminum are gaining recognition. Gutters are available in the popular styles, including ogee, half-round and box. Sizes range from 3 to 6 in. Size selection is based more on style and custom than on technical considerations. Accessories include miters, end caps, expansion joints, drop tubes (outlets), elbows, leaf strainers, and hangers. Joints between lengths of aluminum gutters should not be soldered, because of the corrosion problem associated with flux residues. Instead, such joints are made by various combinations of mechanical devices, such as blind rivets and proprietary organic sealing compounds, often pigmented with aluminum powder.

Gutters and downspouts are roll formed from coiled sheet. The alloys and gages used are the same as for siding. Often the sheet is prepainted with a baked enamel finish, usually white.

Ventilator and louver products for houses are available in aluminum. In addition to perforated or louvered soffits, available items include triangular or rectangular louvers for gable ends, individual roof ventilators, and continuous ridge ventilators to serve attics. These products utilize the same alloys and sheet thicknesses as siding. Aluminum screening is incorporated where needed for insect control.

Roofing. To date, the use of aluminum in residential roofing is insignificant compared with competing materials, because of its appreciably higher cost. Condensation on aluminum, or any metal roofing product, can be a problem unless careful attention is given to design.

Aluminum shingles were produced in the late 1920's, and after 40 years, installations are still in service. Since the second World War, several similar products have been marketed. Aluminum shingles provide a fireproof, low-maintenance roof that, because of the light weight, requires minimum truss or rafter support.

Aluminum sheet alloys such as 1100, 3003, and 3105, in the hardest formable temper, are used for residential roofing products; alclad material provides additional protection at little increase in cost. The minimum nominal gage allowed by FHA Minimum Property Standards is 0.019 in.

Awnings, patio covers, and carports are other residential products made from aluminum sheet. Aluminum awnings — fixed or adjustable — are available in several styles, featuring vertical or horizontal lines. Similar choices are available in patio covers. All these products are subject to code requirements covering wind and snow loads in some localities. Parts are ordinarily roll formed from coiled sheet of the same alloys and gages utilized for siding, and are prepainted in a range of colors.

This material offers longer life than canvas awnings, even though aluminum awnings are left in place, exposed to the weather, throughout the year. This application of aluminum is relatively new, but installations made 10 years ago show no evidence of deterioration. An added advantage of aluminum over canvas is the high reflectivity and low emissivity of radiant heat from the painted aluminum surfaces.

Residential windows and doors are the largest single application for aluminum extrusions, accounting for 315,500 tons in 1964. Although only the window frames are aluminum, and the same is true for most doors, the products are termed aluminum windows and doors in accordance with commercial practice. The extruded members are almost exclusively alloy 6063-T5, normally with a wall thickness of about 0.062 in. Extrusions are used extensively, because the wide latitude afforded by the process enables the designer to shape each member to fit his individual needs and preferences. They are supplied in the as-extruded condition, or are etched to provide greater uniformity of surface appearance. They are also available with anodic coatings, which produce a more uniform appearance and afford increased resistance to weathering, easier maintenance of appearance, and a hard [illegible] wear.

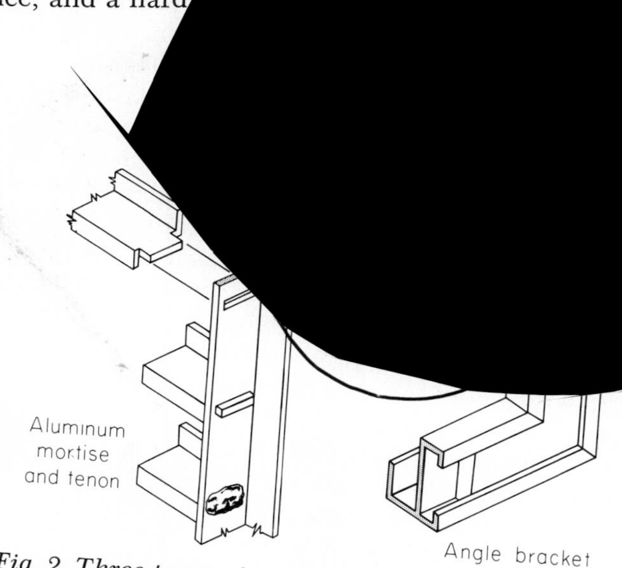

Fig. 2. Three types of mechanical joints commonly used in assembly of aluminum building products

Because the surfaces of aluminum windows, doors, and other aluminum building products may be marred during the construction period by contact with alkaline concrete, mortar or plaster, the metal should be protected by a factory-applied coating such as a tested and approved clear methacrylate lacquer. Some aluminum windows and doors are available in a factory-applied baked enamel finish

mortise and tenon. For joining mitered corners, angle brackets (also called corner inserts, locks, or keys) are used; such brackets are attached by self-tapping screws or rivets, or by staking. These mechanical methods of fastening are illustrated in Fig. 2.

Residential windows and doors are classed either as prime or storm. Prime aluminum windows are made in a number of styles; these include, in decreasing order of use, horizontal sliding [illegible] awning, double-hung, [illegible] n 4% of the prime [illegible] teadily and rapidly [illegible] tributed largely to [illegible] wood. Both are [illegible] ion are about the [illegible] able have aluminum [illegible] minum is used almost [illegible] ause of its light weight, [illegible] bility of complex extruded [illegible] ndow design and construction [illegible] is toward the use of concealed [illegible] have [illegible] thermal breaks to eliminate cold window frames and minimize condensation.

The most popular type of aluminum prime door used in houses is the large sliding glass door. These are offered in a number of variations of fixed and sliding panels. Joints are commonly made using screw grooves. Specifications of minimum construction and performance requirements for residential aluminum prime windows and sliding glass doors are part of the FHA Minimum Property Standards.

A product complementary to aluminum prime windows is aluminum screens. Frame members for screens are roll formed from coiled sheet, usually 3003-H14 or 3105-H14, or extruded in 6063-T5. Government specifications for aluminum tubular frame screens cover aluminum screens made from roll-formed tubular shapes, and are a valuable guide to the designer. Typical [illegible] 0.011-in.-diam alclad

three-track, self-storing type, with screens and glass storm panels interchangeable. Framing members in combination storm-and-screen windows are typically made from 6063-T5 extrusions for minimum cost and good finishing characteristics. While the majority of doors are fabricated from extrusions, roll-formed sheet sections are also used as framing members. Both extruded and sheet members usually are mitered and joined together with corner inserts. Available finishes include mill, anodized, and baked enamel.

Although aluminum locksets and other hardware products are available for residential use in numerous finishes and sizes, most aluminum hardware is used in nonresidential construction.

Weatherstripping is made from aluminum sheet, commonly 0.008 or 0.010 in. thick. A finish available on some aluminum weatherstrip is a continuously applied, clear anodic coating followed by a sealing treatment that imbeds wax in the pores of the coating, providing lubrication.

Large quantities of aluminum weatherstrip are consumed annually as window track in wooden double-hung windows. Aluminum weatherstrip should not be used, however, in conjunction with other aluminum products where there is to be rubbing or sliding, because galling and seizing commonly occur in aluminum-to-aluminum contacts of this type. Weatherstrip is roll formed from coils of 3003, 5005, 5050, or 5052 strip in tempers ranging from H12 (or H32) through H18 (or H38).

Reflective insulation is an important use for aluminum. Because of its low emissivity and high reflectivity of radiant heat, aluminum is the most economical material for this application. There are five basic types of reflective insulation products in which aluminum is utilized: (*a*) paper surfaced with a reflective coating of flaked aluminum pigment; (*b*) aluminum foil in an expansible form, which provides multiple reflective air spaces when installed; (*c*) aluminum foil laminated to one surface of insulating board or plasterboard; (*d*) fibrous insulation faced or enclosed with foil, or with paper coated with flaked aluminum pigment, or with a combination of both; and (*e*) aluminum foil "sheet" (foil backed by paper).

In addition to low emissivity and high reflectivity, foil provides an excellent vapor barrier. Thus, a single product serves both as reflective insulation and vapor barrier. In addition, foil is available in "breather" products — perforated to permit passage of vapor while retaining the reflective qualities.

Another important application of foil in this general field is on thin, rigid paperboard used as reflective sheathing in wood frame construction. The paramount fact in utilization of these aluminum products as insulation is that, to be functional, an aluminum surface must be bounded by air (1).

Foil for insulation is usually of an alloy in the 11*xx* series in the O temper, in thicknesses of 0.00025 to 0.004 in.

Nonresidential Construction

Nonresidential construction, which preceded residential as an application for aluminum, includes commercial, industrial, monumental, institutional, and agricultural buildings.

Licensed architects and engineers design most buildings in this field, except in the agricultural class. Architects are, therefore, a powerful influence on the selection of building materials and the design of building products. They usually are guided and directed by local building codes. Every major city has its own building code, each differing from the others. The so-called standard or model codes, however, offer a degree of standardization to guide the designer of nonresidential building products. The best known of these standard codes are:

1 Basic Building Code, Building Officials Conference of America, Inc., Chicago
2 Midwest Building Code, Midwest Conference of Building Officials, Waterloo, Iowa
3 National Building Code, The National Board of Fire Underwriters, New York
4 Southern Standard Building Code, Southern Building Code Congress, Birmingham, Ala.
5 Uniform Building Code, International Conference of Building Officials, Los Angeles

Windows, doors, and store fronts of aluminum consume more of the metal annually than any other product in nonresidential construction. More than 60% of such windows are aluminum. The types of windows used in the nonresidential field, in decreasing order of use, are projecting, double-hung, single-hung, horizontal-sliding, and awning. Other types are vertically pivoted, top-hinged, and casement.

Virtually all of the frames are in the form of 6063-T5 extruded shapes, with a wall thickness range of 0.062 to 0.125 in., depending on window type.

Window frames normally are finished by sanding, buffing, and etching, sometimes followed by a clear anodic coating. Color-anodized finishes (either integral or applied) are also used, although some require alloys other than 6063. As recommended for residential windows, a clear, temporary organic coating should be applied over these finishes when they may be subject to staining by alkaline materials such as mortar, plaster, or concrete during construction. Joining procedures generally follow those described for residential windows.

The use of sliding glass doors is also growing in nonresidential construction. Standards and performance requirements for most types and classes of window frames and sliding glass doors used in this field are published by the Architectural Aluminum Manufacturers Association.

Extruded store fronts and entrance doors, a natural complement to aluminum windows, are typically supplied in 6063-T5 with a clear anodic coating over a buffed surface. Store front systems normally employ mitered mechanical joints made in the field and concealed with small cover caps stamped from aluminum sheet, typically alloy 5005 or 1100, finished to match. Horizontal rail members in doors usually are butted into vertical stile members at 90°; joining methods include through bolts, corner inserts, welding, or a combination of these.

Hardware products available in aluminum include locksets, hinges, door closers, panic exit devices, push and pull bars, and kick plates. Sheet, extrusions, and castings are used for these products. Alloy and temper selection depends on fabrication and finishing requirements.

Curtain walls of aluminum closely followed the rapid acceptance of nonresidential aluminum window frames. In the form of sand castings, curtain wall units can include considerable ornamental detail (Fig. 3). Larger aluminum curtain wall units can be produced and handled than with heavier materials, increasing the speed of erection. The fewer joints resulting from the larger units, in combination with the excellent weatherability of the panels, minimizes maintenance.

Aluminum curtain walls are typically about 4 in. thick. Because they are much thinner than other types of external wall construction, they result in more floor area in a building having the same outside dimensions. Also, the light weight of aluminum curtain walls reduces the total weight of a building, permitting a less costly foundation and a lighter structural frame.

A curtain wall does not support vertical loads and is not part of a building's structural frame. Its primary function is to enclose the building and keep the weather out. The curtain wall must transmit live loads, primarily wind, to the building frame.

Approximately 9000 aluminum spandrels were installed in the initial building phase of Rockefeller Center, representing the largest early architectural use of aluminum. After 32 years of exposure (when photo was taken), there was no evidence of deterioration. Spandrels were cast in alloy 43 (5% Si) and received a ball-burnished finish. Other aluminum applications included copings, sills, and grills.

Fig. 3. Cast aluminum spandrels on RCA Building, New York

Because of differences in thermal expansion and contraction of different construction materials, provision must be made for the curtain wall to move with respect to the building frame. To accomplish this, some joint and anchorage designs employ split mullions for horizontal movement and clips or slotted holes for vertical movement (2). Capillary breaks and caulking or gaskets are used with concealed flashing to exclude the weather.

Aluminum curtain wall systems can impart to a building an effect of vertical lines, horizontal lines, a grid, or an over-all "texture" (3). In the common grid type of curtain wall, large aluminum extrusions are used to form an exposed grid spanning each exterior bay of the building framework. Aluminum facing panels (including spandrels) and window frames, and fixed glass are inserted into the grid. Joints are normally made mechanically with bolts and nuts, or self-tapping threaded fasteners, concealed with snap-fit members. Insulation is achieved either by a backup or by prefabricated insulated panel inserts, with fire ratings granted accordingly.

Frames and panels are supplied in a wide choice of finishes. Extruded framing members are usually given a clear anodic coating. Plain or patterned sheet for panels is usually either color anodized or porcelain enameled. Castings can also be finished by these processes, but a more uniform appearance can be obtained with mechanical finishes.

Frames and panel inserts are provided in various degrees of preassembly. Much standardization has made this type of curtain wall economical for small commercial and institutional buildings as well as for multistoried structures. Frames are sometimes sheet but are usually extrusions; panels are sheet or castings. Unless special finishes are required, extrusions are 6063-T5, sheet is typically 3003, 3004, or 5005, in the H16 temper, and castings are 43 alloy. Proprietary alloys are employed for all forms where special finishes are to be applied.

The thickness of sheet or extruded frames is dictated by strength and stiffness requirements. Typically about 0.125 in., the thickness varies with spans and loads. Sheet panels are 0.0625 to 0.156 in. thick; cast panels, 0.188 to 0.250 in. Minimum thickness in a cast panel is controlled by the casting practice required to produce the specific design.

Solar Shading Devices. Since air conditioning has become more prevalent, the use of solar shading devices is growing. These generally are in the form of long fins running vertically

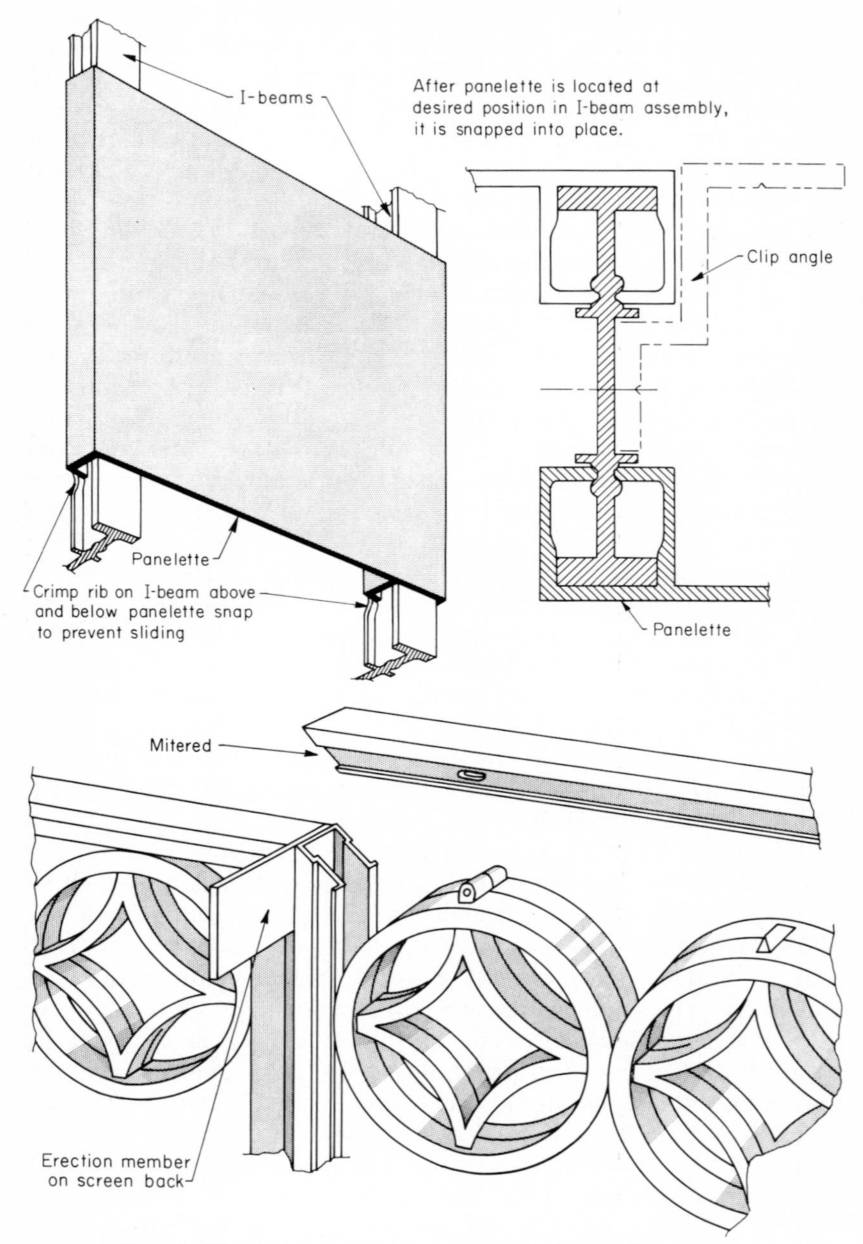

Fig. 4. Mounting details for extruded panelettes and circular-shape die castings for exterior screens

Fig. 4 (continued). Exterior screens for decorative purposes and for solar shading. Sheet, extrusions and castings are used.

between windows up the side of a building or in the form of long, continuous, open louvers across the tops of windows in horizontal bands. They are used to shade glass areas from direct sun rays, and can contribute sizable savings in the cost of air conditioning equipment and its operation. Aluminum is preferred for solar shading devices because of its high reflectivity of radiant heat.

Another line of solar shading products, called decorative screens, is employed principally for aesthetic purposes, with functional shading secondary in importance. Sheet, extrusions and castings combine with the many finishes for aluminum to provide numerous designs and effects. These products are especially useful for remodeling, as shown in Fig. 4.

Ornamental Metalwork and Trim. Aluminum is popular for many types of ornamental metalwork and trim, both interior and exterior. Examples of such products include decorative railings, grills, chair rails, picture molds, baseboards, window sills, door frames, thresholds, and directory frames. Some products of a related nature are office partitions and ceiling systems. Ease of cutting, drilling, and joining is an advantage for field installation of these products. The infinite variety of profiles available in extrusions makes them of special interest for ornamental applications. The alloy used is typically 6063-T5. Patterned sheet is also popular in this field. Aluminum sand castings are used for ornate parts of a sculptured nature (Fig. 5) and for statuary. The casting alloy is generally 43, but if a natural aluminum color is desired after anodizing, alloy 214 is used.

Industrial Railings, Copings, and Gravel Stops. Aluminum is used for utility and industrial railings, especially in environments such as chemical and salt-air atmospheres. The railings are usually made of extruded 6063-T6 1¼, 1½, or 2 in. Schedule 40 IPS pipe, with mechanical or welded joints (Fig. 6). Accessories, such as wall brackets, floor flanges, and fittings, generally are made as castings or forgings.

Copings and gravel stops, used for capping walls or finishing roof edges, are available in aluminum as complete systems in 6063-T42 extrusions. They are produced in a range of sizes and in various styles. Accessories include inside and outside mitered corners and joint covers, fascia extensions, soffit trim, fasteners, and anchors.

Installation should provide for thermal expansion and contraction. This generally is accomplished by limiting section

Fig. 5. One of the earliest major architectural aluminum installations — the 80-ft spire of castings on the Smithfield Congregational Church, Pittsburgh, installed in 1926 — is framed by the entrance of the Alcoa Building, the world's first aluminum-skinned skyscraper, completed in 1953.

lengths to 8 to 12 ft, and fastening them to the building at midpoints or third points. A gap of 3/8 to 1/2 in. is usually left between section ends, and joint covers installed using a flexible sealant. Where joint covers are not used, the section ends are lapped 4 to 6 in. and sealed. With neither technique should fasteners tie the sections together.

Industrial roofing and siding is supplied in a variety of corrugated or ribbed forms and in a thickness range of 0.024 to 0.050 in., depending on aesthetic and strength requirements. The forms include the traditional sinusoidal profile, as well as various trapezoidal configurations. Figure 7 illustrates a special design of siding sheet. Complete lines of accessories are available. They include closure strips, ridge roll, endwall flashing, sidewall flashing, flat and roll flashing (for custom fabrication of field-formed flashings), and fasteners. Typically, the sheet is alclad 3004-H16, although other alloys and tempers are suitable.

Industrial corrugated roofing and siding products also are used in field erection of thermally insulating "sandwich" walls. In this case, a layer of aluminum corrugated sheet is applied to the steel framework of the building. Fiber glass insulation is then placed against the sheet. Finally, a second layer of corrugated sheet is applied over the fiber glass. Through-fasteners retain both aluminum skins and impale the insulation.

Fig. 6. Utility railing of extruded pipe, and detail of rail-to-post connection of railing system, showing fittings used to permit rail to bypass post

A special deep V-beam sheet is used as siding. The sheet was designed to resist hurricane-force winds in excess of 90 psf. This building is the world's largest, with approximately 50% more volume than the Pentagon.

Fig. 7. Vehicle Assembly Building, Cape Kennedy, Fla.

Factory-fabricated sandwich panels are available, comprising insulating structural cores and aluminum sheet for one or both of the skins. These panels are commonly produced in sizes as large as 5 by 18 ft and in thicknesses up to 8 in. Thickness is determined by insulation and structural needs. The panels are assembled with mechanical joints or are glazed into frames.

Roofing for monumental and institutional buildings employs aluminum sheet and battens (Fig. 8). The sheet for these long-life roofs is typically 3003-H14, 0.032 to 0.040 in. thick. The battens are brake-formed sheet, commonly alloy 3003-H14, or extruded 6063-T5. The first aluminum roof, installed in 1897 on St. Joachim's Church in Rome, is still in sound condition.

Farm roofing and siding also is produced in the form of corrugated sheet, in sinusoidal, trapezoidal, and V-crimp configurations. Some of these products are marketed with mill-applied paints of excellent durability. Available accessories include ridge roll and ridge caps, endwall flashing, sidewall and gambrel flashing, end closures, roll-valley sheet, and fasteners.

Farm roofing and siding is nailed in place. The preferred nail for roofing is an aluminum fine-thread, screw-shank roofing nail, with a soft, flat neoprene washer under the head. These nails are also used for siding. Alloys are 5056-H19 and 6061-T913.

Overly Mfg. Co.

Fig. 8. Aluminum provides roof covering, arch covers, cornices, skylights, and interior for the Sacred Heart Church, Waltham, Mass., Aldo A. Minotti, architect.

Sheets used for farm roofing and siding range from 0.0175 to 0.021 in. thick, and are available in sizes up to 4 ft wide by 24 ft long. The sheet is typically made from aluminum-manganese alloys such as 3005-H18. Selection of corrugation and thickness is based on loading conditions.

During the metal shortage immediately after the second World War, a strong demand for rural roofing was met by alclad sheet utilizing wartime-generated scrap metal in the core. Much was of aluminum-copper alloys of lower resistance to corrosion than aluminum alloys normally used where weatherability is important. Roofing and siding fabricated from this scrap-base material did not perform as expected; approximately 5% of it corroded and was replaced. Since that time, alloys of high resistance to corrosion have been employed for these products.

Advantages of aluminum include easy application, high reflectivity and low emissivity for radiant heat from the sun, and appreciable reduction in radiant heat emitted by the roof interior.

References

1 Design Heat Transmission Coefficients, "ASHRAE Guide and Data Book for 1965 and 1966", American Society of Heating, Refrigeration and Air-Conditioning Engineers, Inc., New York, 1965, p 417–454

2 H. W. Johnson, Aluminum Curtain Walling, "Symposium on Aluminum in Building", Aluminium Development Association, London, England, July 9 and 10, 1959, p 47–88

3 Curtain Walls Revisited, Progressive Architecture, 47, No. 2, 178–179 (Feb 1966)

Chapter 11

Structures for Highway, Electrical, Petroleum and Other Engineering Applications

R. C. KASSER, J. R. STEMLER and
E. T. WANDERER

ALL CONSTRUCTION activity not directly related to buildings will be considered in this section, under the following headings: highway products, electrical structures, petroleum production equipment, construction equipment, and other structural uses. Table 1 lists the tonnages of aluminum consumed in the United States for some of the applications that are discussed here. Because of the considerable variation in the properties of interest, and consequently in the alloys utilized, the applicable alloys and tempers will be discussed in each section. Design stresses in Ref 1 should be used unless other codes are known to apply.

Highway Products

Aluminum products are contributing to the solution of two of the most important problems of highway engineers: maintenance and motorist safety. As a result, the use of aluminum in highway products is increasing rapidly.

Bridges. Typical of contemporary highway bridge design is the roadway separation structure shown in Fig. 1. The bridge,

R. C. Kasser is construction manager, Alcoa Technical Center, Pittsburgh. J. R. Stemler is a development engineer, Product Development Div., Aluminum Company of America, New Kensington. E. T. Wanderer is manager for machinery and equipment, Application Engineering Div., Aluminum Company of America, New Kensington.

220 ft long, was erected by the Iowa Highway Department in 1958. Welded plate girders are fabricated of alloy 5083, and field connections are bolted. Composite action with the reinforced concrete deck is established through short lengths of aluminum structural channels welded on the top flanges, perpendicular to the girders. The light weight of aluminum permitted the shipment and placement of large one-piece shop assemblies of girders and diaphragms, in contrast to the individual installation required for steel girders.

Initial costs of this type of structure are 25 to 50% higher than for conventional steel construction, and the steel-to-aluminum weight ratio is about 2-to-1. A ratio of about 3-to-1, expected in long-span bridges because of the higher ratio of dead load to live load, makes aluminum bridges close to steel in initial cost, and in addition aluminum offers near freedom from maintenance.

Table 1. Aluminum Used in the United States for Various Structural Applications (1964)

Category	Tons used
Bridge, street and highway products	32,000(a)
Bridge railings	8,000
Highway signs	7,500
Lighting standards	4,700
Chain link fence	2,150
Electrical structures	4,500
Concrete forms	1,000

(a) Some of the other items in the table are part of this total.

Bridge drainage systems are constructed of aluminum pipe in alloys 6061-T6 and 6063-T6, and occasionally of formed sheet. This application is most popular in seacoast areas where salt-water spray requires frequent maintenance of ferrous materials.

Aluminum pedestrian overpasses consist of through trusses of 6061-T6 tubes or structural shapes that support a walkway of raised-pattern tread plate, abrasive-clad tread plate, or industrial open grating. The structures may be enclosed in aluminum chain link fencing to prevent pedestrians from falling off and to restrict the throwing of objects onto the highway below.

Bridge Railings. In 1963, the aluminum industry sponsored a series of dynamic tests on simulated field installations of bridge railing at the Lehigh University Institute of Research.

Fig. 1. Erection of large, shop-fabricated section of highway bridge near Des Moines, Iowa. Shop assembly of girders and diaphragms was shipped and placed in one piece.

Parapet railings, with a post height of 12 in., up to three-rail systems 36 in. high were erected on reinforced concrete pads for testing. Passenger cars directed by radio control were driven into the railing installations at 60 mph and 25° to the railing. The tests helped to establish a new high-elongation casting alloy, A344-T4. They also proved that properly designed aluminum railings can retain vehicles under the test conditions and absorb enough kinetic energy to limit "bounce-back" into the traffic.

To perform effectively, aluminum bridge railings must conform to the following criteria: (*a*) The alloy must have satisfactory ductility; (*b*) riveted or bolted connections are preferable; (*c*) rails should be erected in continuous lengths spanning four or five posts and attached to the front flanges of the posts to act as rub rails; (*d*) rail splices must have a moment capacity equal to that of the rails, and (*e*) moderate deflection in the elastic stress range of the alloy is desirable.

The aluminum industry has prepared a group of bridge railing designs that incorporate these criteria. The designs use round, rectangular, oval and semi-oval extruded rails supplied in single lengths up to 39.5 ft. Wall thickness varies from ⅛ to ⅜ in. Moment-carrying splices develop continuous-beam action in the rails. The posts are of wide flange or T cross section, cast or extruded, with a section thickness of ¼ to ¾ in. Extruded rails and posts are made from alloy 6061-T6 and cast structural posts are made from alloy A344-T4.

One of several designs subjected to dynamic tests with a vehicle, simulating actual service. The rail retained the vehicle and limited "bounce-back" into the traffic lane.

Fig. 2. Experimental aluminum highway guardrail

Guardrail. Beam-type aluminum guardrail for roadside or medial strip protection is produced in the universal beam corrugated cross section. Figure 2 shows an experimental guardrail that was tested by simulated service at Lehigh University Institute of Research. A test car was directed by radio control into the railing at 15° and 60 mph. This car moved 250 ft nearly parallel to the rail and then turned out 20 ft to the left and rear of the rail line before stopping. The rail allowed only limited bounce-back into the traffic lanes.

Aluminum guardrail costs about 15% more than steel rail as installed, but two paintings eliminate the initial cost advantage of the steel rail.

Three thicknesses of rail are available in alclad 2024-T3 sheet: 0.105, 0.125, and 0.156-in. The two thicker sheets are designed to develop the joint tensile strengths established by the American Association of State Highway Officials for 12 and 10-gage steel rail, respectively. Although normally punched at 12.5-ft centers for post bolts, on request the rails are punched at 6.25-ft centers, to accommodate the reduced post spacing now popular for critical roadside installations and for median rails. The rails are usually installed on steel or timber posts.

Signs and Sign Structures. Highway sign blanks are usually made of flat 6061-T6 sheet that is 0.063 to 0.125 in. thick. The aluminum industry supplies blanks in the many standard sizes and shapes established by the U. S. Department of Commerce, Bureau of Public Roads. Aluminum blanks have up to 70% more bending strength before yielding than the steel blanks that are normal alternates. It has also been demonstrated that the paint and other organic finishes employed are more durable on an aluminum substrate than on steel, primarily because of the superior resistance to corrosion of aluminum.

An aluminum street-name sign is a completely maintenance-free assembly when the sign plate is combined with cast or stamped aluminum hardware, aluminum fasteners, and aluminum tube or pipe. These signs are made from flat 6061-T6 sheet or embossed 3105-H25 or 5052-H32 sheet, 0.063 to 0.125 in. thick, and extruded 6063-T6 bar-bell-shape sections having a minimum thickness of 0.091 in. The signs are compatible with the background surface finishes normally used.

Most large informational signs are fabricated from special 12-in.-deep, channel-shaped 6063-T6 extrusions, bolted together after finishing to form a broad face for message mounting.

Figure 3 shows the rear of a sign in this category. It is fabricated of the most popular series of extruded sections, which incorporate special erection features. Wide sheets of 3003-H18, 0.080 in. thick, are also used for these signs. The sheets, ranging in width from 12 to 48 in., are longitudinally stiffened with spot

Sign panels have integrally extruded T-slots along their edges to receive square-head bolts, eliminating the necessity for drilling or punching holes in panels and post flanges and obtaining accurate alignment between them.

Fig. 3. Aluminum sign panels

Fig. 4. Stocked parts assembled into sign structure that meets AASHO specifications

welded 6063-T6 extrusions. Another system consists of large sheets of 6061-T6, 0.125 in. thick and normally 4 ft wide, supported by longitudinally placed extruded stringers bolted to the post flanges.

Aluminum overhead sign structures were introduced in 1950 when a welded tubular structure with cast aluminum hardware, bolting flanges, truss seats, post bases, and tube-end caps was erected. This type of structure is still the most popular, because tubes combine high structural integrity, easy truss fabrication, and good appearance. The tubes are of alloy 6061-T6 or 6063-T6, with 1.5 to 12-in. OD and 0.125 to 0.375-in. wall thickness. The aluminum industry bases complete sets of suggested standard designs on specifications developed by the American Association of State Highway Officials (2).

Roadside sign structures normally have posts fabricated of wide-flange beams of 6061-T6, 4 to 12 in. in depth, extruded tubes of 6061-T6, 4 to 12 in. in OD with 3/16 to 3/8-in. wall, or tapered extruded tubes of 6063-T6. The tapered tubes range from 6 to 12 in. in OD at the base and from 4 to 9 in. at the top. Wall thickness ranges from 3/16 to 1/4 in. The posts are usually supported by cast alloy 356-T6 bases bolted to reinforced concrete footings, but some designers embed the post ends in concrete. The cast bases have the advantage of easy replacement of the post in case of damage.

A recent development is a series of lightweight tubular structural frames that support large informational highway signs (Fig. 4). These structures offer little resistance to colliding vehicles and reduce highway accident fatalities. The posts consist of tubes of 3-in. OD by 1/8-in. wall and 4-in. OD by 1/8-in. wall, 3 and 4-in. structural tees, and cast fittings. They are shop or field assembled to provide structures meeting AASHO specifications.

Street lighting standards and bracket arms of aluminum have been a rapidly growing application of aluminum since the 1940's. Savings in freight charges and in handling and erection costs are significant. Whereas the weight of a 25-ft steel pole would be 400 lb and that of a similar concrete pole 1000 lb, the weight of the corresponding aluminum pole is 150 lb.

A less recognized benefit is that, if an aluminum pole is knocked down, as standards of all materials occasionally are, it is less likely to drop onto the vehicle. This fortunate reaction to impact results from the relatively low inertia of the aluminum pole, which gives it a tendency to fall away from the vehicle. With similar design, a heavier pole would be more likely to fall toward the vehicle.

Aluminum standards are commonly fabricated by spin tapering 6063-T4 extruded tubes about 1/8 in. per ft; cast alloy 356 bases, handhole frames, and bracket-supporting devices are attached by welding; and the entire assembly is artificially aged. The section sizes are similar to those used for tapered tubular roadside signposts. However, some manufacturers form lighting standard shafts from 5052 or 6061 sheet.

Fencing and Glare Screen. High-speed weaving machines make chain link fence fabric from 0.120, 0.148, and 0.192-in.-diam wire of alloy 6061-T89 or 6061-T94 having a tensile strength of 54,000 psi. The normal mesh size is 2 in. The fabric is attached by wire clips to top and bottom rails or to tension wires supported by sturdy 6063-T6 line and end posts. Complete materials specifications are established.

Aluminum glare screen, introduced in 1960, has served effectively in shielding drivers' eyes from the glare of approaching vehicle headlights. The screen can be mounted on top of guard railing, or it can be erected separately in sheets of required height. Because of the orientation of expanded sheet strands, oncoming headlight glare is eliminated, although the mesh is virtually transparent when viewed from a 90° angle to the fence.

Culvert pipe of aluminum has achieved good acceptance within the past few years. Because aluminum culvert can be installed faster and more economically than steel culvert, many contractors quote aluminum at a lower price than steel on an installed basis. Culvert pipe is fabricated from alclad 3004-H34 corrugated sheet in a thickness range of 0.060 to 0.164 in.

Electrical Structures

Electrical structures support power distribution conductors, or the equipment necessary to control the current flow, from the point of generation to the consumer. The components from which electrical structures are fabricated have a higher metal cost in aluminum than in steel, and therefore, based on comparable design and loading conditions, it is to be expected that shop-fabricated cost would be higher for aluminum. Costs for field erection of the lighter-weight parts usually offset only a portion of the first-cost differential; therefore, credit from reduced maintenance over a portion of the life of the structure is normally required to establish economic feasibility for aluminum. In some situations, however, interruptions for maintenance cannot be tolerated, and aluminum electrical structures are immediately justified.

Self-Supporting Towers. Pilot installations of self-supporting aluminum towers for electrical conductors were made more than 20 years ago. A result of this experience was the introduction of the composite aluminum-steel tower in a complete transmission line in 1950. The first all-aluminum transmission tower lines in this country were erected in 1959 by Commonwealth Edison Co., Chicago; Philadelphia Electric Co., Philadelphia; and Public Service Electric and Gas Co., Newark. Subsequently, other power companies in industrial areas have made similar installations.

The first tower lines employed self-supporting structures similar in design to those in steel that existed in the vicinity. Structural angular shapes, ranging in section size from 3 by 3 by 3/16 in. to 10 by 10 by 1¼ in., and plate, ¼ to ¾ in. thick, were

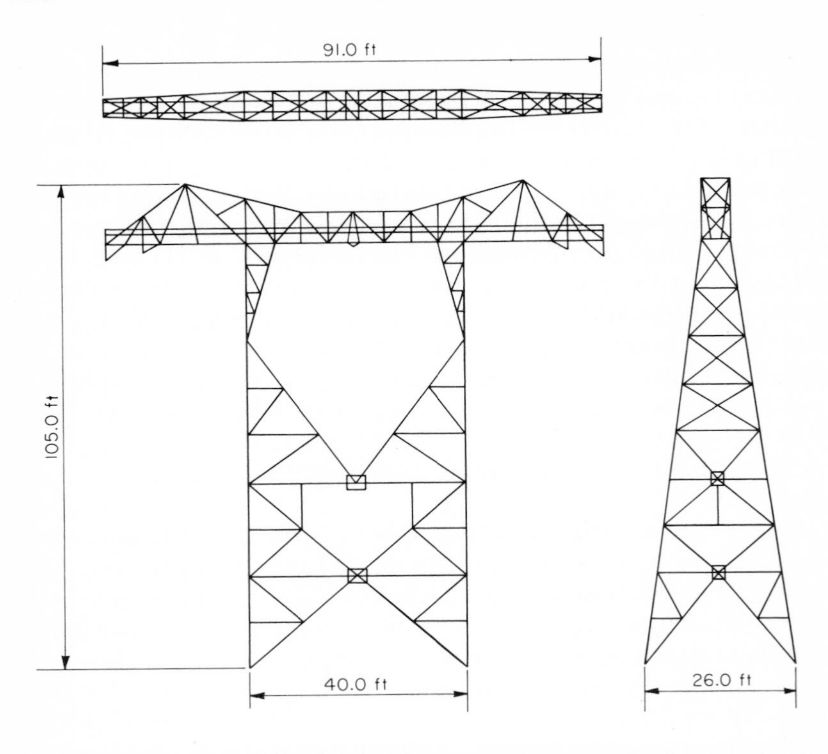

The extrusion process permits the design of members with metal precisely where needed—for example, the Y-shaped members illustrated.

Fig. 5. Standard aluminum structural shapes, tubes and special extrusions used in electrical transmission structures

of 6061-T6, an alloy that combines good resistance to weathering with mechanical properties in the structural range. As designers, fabricators, and utilities gained experience with aluminum towers, special extruded shapes became accepted as superior alternates to the long-established structural shapes (Fig. 5). Aluminum towers are built for transmission of energy throughout the presently established voltage range up to 500 kv, and have been employed experimentally at higher voltages.

Many high-voltage single-circuit connection lines are being constructed, including one that employs self-supporting aluminum H-frame structures (3). Similar in general outline to X-braced wood-pole structures, this line has columns and crossarm assemblies that make maximum use of extruded shapes designed specifically for this application. Also, where advantage can be taken of the higher mechanical properties of alloy 6070-T6, it replaces 6061-T6.

Guyed Towers. Since 1960, extensive research, design investigation, testing, and experimental fabrication have led to the construction of several transmission lines employing guyed towers. Structures forming a V, in that the two struts supporting a single-circuit crossarm meet at a common foundation, were built in greater number than any other single type of aluminum tower. Variations of the V design, and also guyed H-frame towers, were constructed, but in smaller numbers. In contrast to the self-supporting towers, substantially all guyed aluminum tower lines are located in rural areas.

Under most conditions, guyed towers weigh less than self-supporting structures of similar capacity and thus permit reduced field erecting costs. Helicopters are successfully employed to set fully assembled guyed towers. These structures, having a single foundation, eliminate the problem of leg extensions that are required with self-supporting towers to accommodate side-hill locations. The factors to be considered in evaluating the feasibility of guyed towers in comparison with the self-supporting type are the installation of the guys and the placing of the associated anchors.

In further comparison of the types of towers discussed, the conventional self-supporting variety consists of relatively large members. For example, framing members range from 4 by 4-in. to 10 by 10-in. angles. These members are framed together to form substantial open spaces with chords up to 30 ft apart. By contrast, the self-supporting H-frames and the guyed towers are almost invariably composed of smaller members, such as alloy 6061-T6 angles 2½ by 2½ by 3/16 in. to 4 by 4 by 3/8 in. Struts for these types are built with triangular or rectangular cross sections with chords placed approximately 2 ft apart. These configurations result in many similar small parts assembled into uniform struts that permit mass-production techniques in fabrication and erection. Since painting of these latticed struts is impractical, aluminum alloys are especially well suited.

Towers are usually designed on the basis of stipulated loading conditions, including wind and ice, with appropriate overload factors applied. Code loading requirements are augmented by many utilities to suit local conditions.

Crossarms of aluminum for wood-pole transmission structures offer long-term savings in many cases. In numerous geographical areas, wood-pole, H-frame structures are preferred. Transmission at higher voltage has led to the investigation and use of strong metal crossarms as an alternate to wood, because the higher voltage requires a larger, heavier conductor that applies a greater load on the crossarms. Alloy 6061-T6 tubes in the range of 8 to 10 in. in diameter with a 3/16 to 3/8-in. wall are employed advantageously as crossarms where no shield wire is used. However, braced crossarms of tubes and structural shapes of 6061-T6 are installed on wood structures equipped with shield wires.

Outdoor substation and switchyard structures built of aluminum alloys have gained in acceptance annually since 1946, and presently aluminum is used on both large and small units as an alternate to galvanized steel. These structures support equipment that is constantly energized; hence there is little opportunity for maintenance painting.

Components for substation and switchyard structures are often latticed columns and trusses. Recent trends are toward low-profile structures utilizing tubular sections of 6 to 12-in. OD with 1/8 to 1/4-in. walls in alloy 6061-T6. Wide-flange sections 4 to 12 in. deep replace conventional latticed members. Although many elements are assembled by bolting, welding is rapidly becoming a common joining technique.

Substation and switchyard structures often are designed in accordance with standard codes. Member sizes are usually determined with a factor of safety similar to that employed for building frames. Users of structures in this classification generally specify that design and fabrication conform to ASCE Specifications for Structures of Aluminum Alloy 6061-T6.

Petroleum Production Equipment

Drilling Rigs. The use of aluminum alloys in drilling structures is based on their combination of light weight and mechanical strength. The weight saving is particularly valuable for portable rigs, such as those employed in work-over operations, and those designed to be flown into otherwise inaccessible locations.

Aluminum alloys have been used in portable rigs since 1954 for numerous applications, including masts, bed and winch frames, racking and crown safety platforms, ladders, stairways, walkways, catwalks, dog houses, jack-bearing sills, substructures, mud ditches and tanks, skids, handrails, finger boards, and miscellaneous piping. Two fly-in rigs were built in 1964. In all cases reported, equipment has performed satisfactorily.

Reynolds Metals Co.

Fig. 6. First aluminum platform installed in Lake Maracaibo, Venezuela, is lowered into position.

The light weight of aluminum offers advantages for portable piping, such as drilling-rig supply pipe. This product is handled manually, often under difficult conditions; a length of pipe normally is moved many times during its life. The weight of alloy 6063-T6 Schedule 5 pipe is only about 15% that of Schedule 40 steel pipe and 33% that of lightweight steel pipe. As the pipelines frequently must be laid over irregular terrain, aluminum's modulus of elasticity of 10 million psi is advantageous in permitting easier conformity to land contour. Quick-acting couplers of the grooved or flared type, some made of aluminum, generally are employed. The use of aluminum pipe allows crew reduction and lowers transportation costs between job locations. The initial cost premium for aluminum usually is offset during the first two moves; subsequent moves result in cost saving.

Offshore Structures. Aluminum platform structures gained popularity in 1957 during drilling activity in the brackish waters of Lake Maracaibo, Venezuela (Fig. 6). A typical aluminum structure extends as much as 120 ft from the lake bottom and weighs about 40 tons. It consists of a center conductor pipe and four corner legs, all 34-in. OD by 0.375-in. wall, laced together with tubular members in sizes to 12-in. Schedule 40 pipe. Alloys used were 6061-T6 and 6063-T6. The structures were built on shore, barged to the site, and lowered onto the lake bottom. Installation was completed by driving tubular steel piling through each leg and the conductor pipe. Procedures were introduced to separate the steel and aluminum electrically to prevent galvanic corrosion.

Along the Louisiana and Texas Gulf Coast, many offshore wells are drilled in marshy or shallow water. Tubular "well-guards" protect the well head from floating debris and provide a work deck for servicing the well. To provide adequate life, conventional steel well-guards require costly corrosion protection measures, including coatings and anodes. Well-guards made of alloys 6061-T6 and 6063-T6 are performing satisfactorily without exterior coatings.

Drill Pipe and Drilling Accessory Components. Drilling rigs normally are classified by drilling-depth capability, determined by capacities of the mast and of hoisting, rotating and pumping machinery. By using aluminum drill pipe, a rig can be upgraded to drill deeper than its classification based on steel drill pipe, provided mud pumping capacity is adequate and casing loads can be handled. For example, a 10,000-ft string of 4⅝-in.-OD

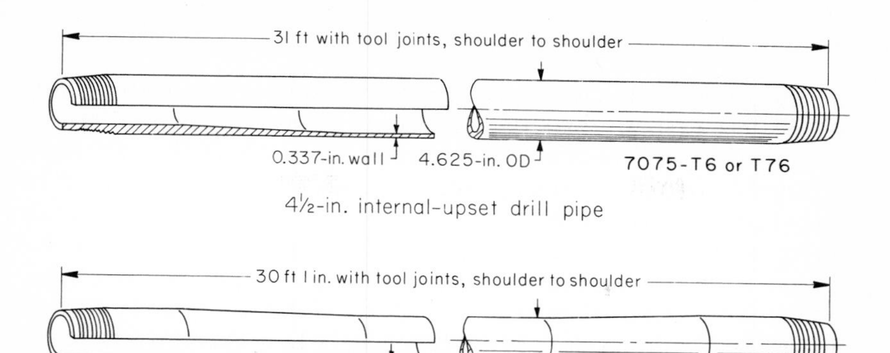

(Top) Typical 4½-in. drill pipe, as fabricated by two manufacturers. Choice between internal-upset and external-upset pipe depends on field conditions and user preference.

(Bottom) Lightweight aluminum drill pipe, complete with standard steel tool joints, can upgrade the capacity of a drilling rig 50%.

Fig. 7. Aluminum drill pipe

aluminum drill pipe with tool joints and 50,000 lb of drill collars weighs less than an identically equipped 6500-ft string of 4½-in.-OD steel pipe. Thus, the rig can drill 3500 ft deeper with aluminum drill pipe, an upgrading of over 50% (Fig. 7, bottom).

Aluminum drill pipe, used increasingly since 1960, reduces transportation, handling, fuel, and wire line (steel cable) costs. Round trips (removing the drill string and replacing it in the hole) require less time because of handling ease and quicker shifting of equipment into higher gear when the shift is regulated by load.

Two types of 4½-in.-OD aluminum drill pipe are in use, both produced in lengths of about 30 ft by special extrusion processes (Fig. 7, top). One, with uniform outside diameter, is similar to internal-upset steel drill pipe; the other, of uniform inside diameter, is comparable to external-upset steel drill pipe. High-strength alloys, such as 2014 and 7075 in special tempers, are employed. A steel tool joint is attached to each end of an aluminum pipe length by a combination of threading and shrink fitting, providing a joint at least as strong as the drill pipe.

Because aluminum is nonmagnetic, directional survey records can be made from within the pipe, eliminating the need for nonmagnetic drill collars.

Other aluminum applications in petroleum drilling operations are: nonmagnetic drill collars, which cost less than those made of conventional cupro-nickel alloys; drill-collar lifting subs (lengths of pipe that engage a drill collar at one end and rig elevators at the other) that are light enough for one man to handle; drill-pipe protectors and stabilizers, plugs, and well-survey instruments. Forged or cast aluminum alloys are used in a variety of machinery components, including power-end and pump-frame castings for cementing pumps, cross-head hand-hole covers and safety guards, connecting rods, clutch housings, torque converter parts, pistons, bearings, and cat heads (friction drums). Aluminum cast parts in tongs for power casing, drill pipe, and rod reduce equipment weight and facilitate handling.

Storage Tanks. Aluminum alloys are often selected for oil-field surface equipment because of their resistance to hydrogen sulfide contained in "sour" gas and crude oil. Aluminum roofs have been in continuous service since the 1930's on steel sour-crude tanks in West Texas, where steel roofs failed in less than five years.

Because the vapor space in such tanks is the most corrosive

Sour-crude storage tanks utilize roofs and top rings of aluminum, because of its high resistance to sulfur compounds in the tank vapor space.

Fig. 8. Crude-oil storage tanks

zone, aluminum top rings and decks frequently are employed, so that only aluminum is contacted by the vapor (Fig. 8). For the same reason, thin-wall Schedule 5 aluminum pipe replaces Schedule 40 steel pipe for vent lines from these sour-crude tanks.

Aluminum coiled tube is used widely for air instrument lines in and around field, storage and processing equipment. Alclad (outside) 5050-O alloy tube is now used.

Pipelines of aluminum in sea and fresh waters and in various soils handle a wide variety of petroleum industry fluids, including sour and sweet crude oil, natural gas, gasoline, jet fuel, and petrochemicals.

Aluminum has five primary advantages for pipelines:

1 Light weight, which results in substantial reduction in handling and shipping costs
2 High resistance to corrosion in most environments, including hydrocarbon fluids containing hydrogen sulfide and carbon dioxide

Aluminum conforms to rugged mountain terrain with a minimum of bends. Its light weight allows sections to be carried to inaccessible locations by helicopter.

Fig. 9. Mountain pipeline

3 Smooth surface with a low friction factor, which minimizes pressure drop and can reduce paraffin buildup
4 Relatively low modulus of elasticity, which provides more flexibility than steel
5 Rapid welding, by either manual or portable machine technique

For pipelines in mountainous terrain, light weight simplifies handling and permits long lengths of line to be pulled from the welding station, reducing costs substantially; favorable modulus of elasticity allows conformity to terrain with a minimum of field-fabricated bends (Fig. 9). A procedure for "hot tapping" aluminum lines has been developed, permitting the addition of branch connections while a line is under pressure.

Pipelines to wells completed on the ocean floor are an interesting application for aluminum pipe. Because of their relative inaccessibility, these wells must be controlled from shore, a procedure requiring three pipelines: one for flow, one for control, and a multipurpose line. Where aluminum is used, a ballast-containing (anchor) pipe is added to overcome buoyancy during periods when the pipelines may be empty. (This fourth pipe can be made of an alloy anodic to the other three, to protect them cathodically.) The four aluminum lines are bundled into a cluster and strapped together (Fig. 10). The bundle of empty lines is floated into position, then progressively sunk by flooding the anchor-anode line with water. Subsequently, cement grout is pumped into the anchor line for a permanent installation.

Fig. 10. Ocean pipeline. Tug pulls a mile of aluminum pipe bundle through the surf to an ocean floor oil well.

A typical bundle consists of three 2-in. Schedule 80 alloy 5456-H112 pipes and one 3-in. Schedule 10 7*xxx* series anchor-anode pipe, held together with 6061-T6 straps. Alloys of the 5*xxx* series are selected for flow and service lines because of their weldability and high strength, as welded.

Construction Equipment

Concrete forms of aluminum are generally more expensive than steel or wood forms, but they are easier to handle and do not need a protective coating during storage. Sheets of alloys 3003, 5052, and 6061, with welded 6063 extruded stiffeners, are used successfully for the placement of residential concrete basement walls. Cast aluminum forms that produce a decorative pattern on cured walls are also employed. Some forms are built up from a series of special extruded shapes of 6063-T6 having stiffening ribs integral with the flat facing.

Shoring, Pallets, and Racks. Aluminum adjustable horizontal and vertical shoring is used because of handling savings. The adjustable beam expands up to 15 ft in length and offers significant economy to the contractor because of rapid erection and stripping. The beam is constructed of special extrusions of 6061-T6 alloy with sections 0.105 to 0.375 in. thick.

Aluminum is gaining acceptance for the pallets and racks used for concrete block casting and curing. Investigations by block producers showed that plate pallets ¼ in. thick and welded racks of 6061-T6 have a substantially longer life than steel units and also eliminate staining of the blocks.

Mobile crane booms and jibs employ riveted or bolted 2014-T6 extruded structural shapes to obtain maximum weight reduction. The lower weight increases the reach of the booms and maintains the weight of the cranes under the legal weight limits of the highways. Counterweight sizes are decreased, and less power is required to swing the booms.

Many aluminum buckets of the dipper and clamshell varieties are fabricated of aluminum alloy plate ¼ to ¾ in. thick. Since welded construction is normally used, high-strength alloys of the 5*xxx* series, such as 5456, are generally employed. Steel wear strips and cutting edges usually are riveted to the welded aluminum bodies. Aluminum buckets have about 25% more capacity than steel units of equal weight.

Ladders and scaffolding of aluminum are important to the

Fig. 11. Semigantry crane fabricated of alloy 5456-H321 plate. Span, 166 ft; capacity, 240 tons; welded box beam construction.

construction industry because their easier handling, compared to wood or steel, means large dollar savings to the contractor. Many manufacturers offer complete lines of ladders and scaffolding meeting the structural specifications established by the American Standards Association. The units are normally fabricated from 6061-T6 or 6063-T6 extruded tubes and shapes, and 6063-T832 drawn tubes.

Gin Poles. Aluminum gin poles are useful in the erection of electrical transmission towers and similar structures. A complete series of welded 6061-T6 tubular poles is produced, ranging in height up to 96 ft. The poles are usually sectionalized to permit the contractor to assemble the units required for a specific job.

Other Structural Uses

Applications reviewed in this section are associated with specific industries; they are discussed separately because the most critical criterion of design is strength (4).

Large overhead and gantry cranes of welded box-beam construction, using 0.25 to 3.0-in. plate in alloys 5456 and sometimes 5083, have produced significant savings in weight and total cost compared to steel. The structural aluminum portions of these cranes weigh about 50% less than comparable steel units. Although an aluminum crane costs about 10% more than a similar steel crane, cost reductions permitted in the supporting structure, driving motors, and wheel capacities make aluminum and steel directly competitive in over-all initial cost. Aluminum has cost advantages during service, in that the reduced weight increases acceleration rates and thus productivity, and painting maintenance is eliminated. Figure 11 shows a 166-ft-span, 5456-

Fig. 12. One of five tainter gates with facings of alclad 5456 plate on steel radial arms and crossbeams, for the Suriname River hydroelectric development

H321 semigantry with a 240-ton capacity. Construction of this crane required 140 tons of aluminum.

Aluminum was used for the framework for a 300-ft-diam by 100-ft-high bauxite storage structure in Jamaica. The 6061-T6 tubular struts are 10 in. in diameter, with walls 0.25, 0.50, and 0.75 in. thick. The struts have 5456-H321 plate weldments at each end for field attachment by steel bolts to 6061-T6 plate hubs. After the framework was completed, ⅛-in.-thick alclad 6061-T6 triangular-shaped sheets were bolted to the tubular structure for the roof, or cover. Although this structure had a higher material cost than a similar steel building, significant savings were realized in the overseas shipment of the prefabricated struts and the field erection of the lightweight units.

The Westinghouse Telecomputer Center in Pittsburgh demonstrates the advantages offered by the extrusion process in a specially designed structure. In contrast to curtain-wall construction, special extruded shapes function as both the load-bearing columns and the window mullions. Because of the low handling costs of the one-piece unit and the lower glazing costs, the architects estimated a saving of $13,650, compared to conventional construction.

The Rocky Reach Dam on the Columbia River near Wenatchee, Wash., used over 500 tons of aluminum alloys for structural, architectural, and electrical applications. Of this total, 205 tons was employed for wing gates, diffusion gratings and supports, orifice gates, regulating gates, walkway gratings and supports, and stop logs. These parts were fabricated from 6061-T6 plate and structural shapes and from 5083-H113 plate. The unpainted aluminum assemblies weighed about 35% as much as comparable steel units. Had these been steel assemblies, it would have been necessary to apply two shop coats of vinyl paint and two coats of paint in the field, increasing their cost to that of the aluminum units.

Five aluminum-faced tainter gates were installed in 1963 on the Suriname River in Suriname, South America. Each was approximately 42 ft high and 35 ft wide. Special extruded 6061-T6 stiffener T's were welded with 5556 filler wire to the rear of alclad 5456-H321 plate faces 0.375 to 0.625 in. thick. Type 304 stainless steel bolts were used to attach these assemblies (Fig. 12) to the A7 steel radial arms and crossbeams. The aluminum tainter gate facings cost only 8% more than adequately painted steel faces. Cost studies indicated that this premium approxi-

North American Aviation, Inc.

Fig. 13. Alloy 6061 tube, 12 in. in diameter, is welded by the consumable-electrode metal inert-gas process to form a section of a 60-ft-diam backup structure for the U. S. Air Force Project Haystack's 120-ft-diam radio telescope.

mated the cost of the first necessary routine maintenance program for steel.

Many movable radio telescopes are constructed of aluminum, primarily because the low density reduces over-all costs and upgrades operating characteristics. A notable example is the Project Haystack structure (Fig. 13).

References

1 Alcoa Handbook of Design Stresses for Aluminum, Aluminum Company of America, Pittsburgh, 1966

2 The Handbook of Aluminum Overhead Sign Structures, Aluminum Company of America, Pittsburgh, 1964

3 T. N. Cofer, Aluminum 345-Kv H-Frames Lower Cost Per Mile, Electrical World, **163**, No. 2, 78–81 (Jan. 11, 1965)

4 Proceedings of a Symposium on Aluminium in Structural Engineering, London, June 11 and 12, 1963, Aluminium Federation, London, 1964

Chapter 12

Structures and Equipment for Chemical, Food, Drug, Beverage and Atomic Industries

R. L. HORST, JR.

THE CHEMICAL PROCESS industries considered here include those that process specific chemical compounds and mixtures, plus those that require prolonged exposure of equipment and structures to unusually corrosive environments. Within these categories are industries producing such major commodities as paper, fertilizers, petroleum products, and foods. Also discussed are applications in the nuclear field. Details of the corrosion mechanisms encountered in many types of environments are given in Volume I, Chapter 7.

The characteristics of aluminum most advantageous for applications in the chemical process industries are:

1 Resistance to corrosion by a variety of chemicals, waters and atmospheres
2 White or color-free salt formation, permitting processing and storage of color-sensitive products without discoloration
3 Ability to be fabricated into equipment at costs generally lower than for equipment made of stainless steels or copper alloys

Typical applications of aluminum in chemical process industries are listed in Table 1. Aluminum mill products widely employed are given in Table 2. For details on the corrosion

The author is a research engineer, Chemical Metallurgy Div., Alcoa Research Laboratories, New Kensington.

E. T. Wanderer, manager for machinery and equipment, Application Engineering Div., Aluminum Company of America, New Kensington, assisted in the preparation of this chapter.

Table 1. Some Aluminum Applications in Chemical Process Industries Classified by Industry(a)

Industry	Applications
Brewing	Yeast equipment, wort coolers, crown liners, brew kettles, storage tanks, fermenters, filters, coils, coolers, pasteurizing equipment, beer barrels, carbonating tanks
Chemical:	
Alcohols	Drums, tanks, piping
Aldehydes	Drums, piping, storage tanks, tank cars
Ammonium nitrate	Ammonia tanks, nitrogen chilling exchangers, prilling towers, tank cars, piping, floor grating, drums, solution storage tanks, structural members, housings, smoke stacks, drainage trench lining, electrical fittings and devices, electrical conduit, instrument lines
Ammonium hydroxide	Condensers, dephlegmators, stills, piping
Cellulose acetate	Tanks, acetylators, precipitators, washing equipment, driers, dephlegmators, stills, condensers, evaporators, piping
Essential oils	Flasks, containers, drums
Fatty acids	Condensers, storage tanks, filters, melting tanks, trays, piping, tank cars
Formaldehyde	Distillation towers, scrubbers, heat exchangers, receivers, storage tanks, tank cars, piping, shipping drums
Glycerin	Stills, heat exchangers, condensers, receivers, storage tanks, piping, tank cars
Hydrogen peroxide	Stills, storage tanks, piping, drums, tank cars, pumps, heat exchangers
Lower aliphatic acids	Condensers, receivers, storage tanks, tank cars, piping, oxidizing kettles, crystallizers, filters, melting vessels, pumps
Nitric acid (82% or over by weight)	Storage tanks, drums, piping, ducts, hoods, tank cars, heat exchangers (tube bundles)
Nitroglycerin, gun cotton, dynamite	Hoods, ducts, packaging, filters, blenders, storage tanks, piping, wash tanks, extractors, solvent recovery tanks
Oxygen and other cryogenic liquids	Heat exchangers, towers, piping, truck tanks
Paints, varnishes, naval stores	Stills, condensers, storage tanks, piping, drums, tank cars, kettles, filters, solidification trays, screens, centrifuges, heating coils, heat exchangers, emulsifiers, extractors
Soda ash	Piping, vapor ducts, absorbers, ammonia condensers, heat exchangers
Sulfur	Piping, pumps, tanks, solidification forms, recovery and purification equipment
Water, distilled or deionized	Storage tanks, piping, condensers, receivers, valves, fittings, degasifiers
Dairy	Pasteurizers, heat exchangers, milking machines, storage tanks, truck tanks, piping, valves, cheese vats, butter churns, packaging

(*Continued on the next page*)

Table 1. (Continued)

Industry	Applications
Food	Kettles, conveyors, truck tanks, stock pots, pans, piping, packaging, refrigeration equipment, cookers, storage tanks, drying trays, evaporators, cooling coils, chutes, screens
Edible gelatin	Evaporators, tanks, piping, cookers, drying tanks, chutes
Edible oils and fats	Deodorizers, condensers, tanks, piping
Microbiological	Fermenting tanks, solution tanks, medium tanks, adsorption tanks, solvent storage, piping
Paper	Table rolls, suction boxes, couch and suction rolls, draping poles, drier hoods, economizers, air lines, core-winder shafts, festoon-type driers, tall-oil tankage and piping
Plastics: synthetic resins	Storage tanks, stills, condensers, receivers, piping, heating coils, weighing tanks, reaction vessels
Petroleum	Condensers, storage tanks, heat exchangers, instrument tubing, piping, towers, tower internals, covering for thermal insulation, truck tanks, flame arrestors, tank roofs, gratings
Refrigeration: ammonia, salt brines, carbon dioxide, Freons (11, 12, 21, 22, 113, 114), methyl formate, sulfur dioxide	Compressors, heat exchangers, evaporators, receivers, tubing, cooling pans, piping, brine tanks, lockers, trays, shelves, grills, insulation
Rubber	Latex cups, hand carts, storage tanks, acid mixers, coagulation vats, bulker tanks, vulcanization molds, curing equipment, pans, trays, containers, mandrels
Textiles, natural and synthetic:	
Acrylics	Storage tanks, heat exchangers, distillation towers, reactors, piping, textile machine parts
Acrylonitrile	Storage tanks, heat exchangers, distillation towers, piping
Polyamides (nylon)	Storage tanks, tank cars, piping, textile machine parts
Rayon	Hoods, ducts, desulfurizing equipment, piping, tubing, extractors, pallets, conveyors, precipitators, traverse bars, guide holders, gear covers, separator blades, reel frames, emulsion rolls, spinning compartment covers, spools, buckets
Wool, silk	Bleaching equipment, dyeing equipment, textile machine parts

(a) These industries also make substantial use of aluminum building products.

behavior of aluminum with a large number of commercial chemicals, the reader may consult References 1 to 6.

This chapter is concerned with processing and handling applications. Most process industry plants also use aluminum alloys for architectural applications such as roofing, siding, door and window frames, and trim (Chapter 10, this volume) and conduit (Chapter 21, this volume).

Table 2. Some Aluminum Applications in Chemical Process Industries, Classified by Mill Product

Aluminum product	Applications
Anodes	Cathodic protection
Bus conductor	Power transmission in electrochemical plants
Cable	Power distribution
Cans	Packaging citrus concentrates, beer, foods
Castings	Pipe fittings, blower housings
Closures	Packaging foods and drugs
Collapsible tubes	Packaging cosmetics and adhesives
Drums	Shipping beverages and liquid chemicals
Extrusions	Architectural and structural shapes, pipe, conduit
Foil	Reflective insulation, packaging food
Forgings	Pipe fittings, blower housings
Ingot	Deoxidizing steel, producing catalysts
Plate	Process and storage tanks and vessels, heat-exchanger tube sheets
Powder	Production of metallo-organic catalysts
Roofing and siding	Plant construction
Sheet	Process equipment, jacketing for thermal insulation
Tube	Fluid transport, heat exchange

Fabrication Methods and Alloy Selection

Most process equipment is of welded construction, built according to applicable codes and specifications. Sound welded joints are essential to code approval. Since World War II, fabricators have become adept at welding aluminum. An experienced steel welder, employing equipment designed for inert-gas arc welding of steel, can become proficient in aluminum welding within a short time. The acceptance and growth of the use of aluminum in the process industries have resulted from development of effective, economical welding techniques that permit full use of an increasing variety of alloys and products available in warehouse stocks.

Most process vessels and horizontal storage tanks are cylindrical and less than 50 ft long; the choice between shop fabrication and field erection usually is based on diameter. Vessels up to 11 ft in diameter (including protruding fittings) can be shipped by rail without special arrangements. Vessels 11 to 12.5 ft in diameter may require special attention by the railroad, depending on points of origin and destination. Vessels larger than 12.5 ft in diameter require exclusive use of road, because of insufficient clearance between tracks; also, overpass and tunnel clearances often require devious routing. Since exclusive road use is very expensive, large tanks are shipped by a water route if available, or are field erected.

Smaller storage tanks for service at ambient temperature and pressure usually are shop fabricated in alloy 1100-H112 or 3003-H112, or other tempers meeting forming requirements. Pressure vessels fabricated in the shop and large field-erected storage tanks usually are built in 5*xxx* or 6*xxx* series alloys having high strength as welded.

Vessel design is based on the properties of alloys in the annealed condition or as welded. Exceptions are heat treatable alloy bottles and containers that are small enough to be heat treated after assembly.

Almost every commercial cast or wrought aluminum alloy is employed in the chemical process industries. Alloy selection normally involves a compromise among desired characteristics, with resistance to corrosion usually being the most important. Resistance to corrosion for some applications is evaluated from general performance; for other applications, test results or experience related to the individual application are used to determine the suitability of the alloy.

For wrought alloy applications needing only low mechanical properties and requiring high resistance to general corrosion or to specific chemical environments, the 1*xxx* and 3*xxx* series alloys are popular and economical. For higher strength and similar corrosion characteristics, the generally higher-cost 5*xxx* and 6*xxx* series alloys often are chosen. Highest strength is provided by the heat treatable 2*xxx* and 7*xxx* series, but usually at a sacrifice in corrosion resistance. Their as-welded strength can be increased by heat treating after assembly. These alloys have limited use in corrosive environments.

Among cast alloys, 13 and 360 are preferred for die castings; 43, 214, and 356 for sand castings; and A214, 356, A356, and 359 for permanent mold castings. All are corrosion resistant.

Virtually all aluminum process equipment operates within the range of −452 to +400 F, using conventional alloys. At the present time, equipment construction codes provide design stresses for aluminum at temperatures as high as 400 F. Aluminum is used at higher temperatures; for example, special-purpose 8001 alloy handles high-purity water at about 600 F in the nuclear energy field.

Codes and Standards. Aluminum is recognized in the following design codes and standards for chemical process equipment, piping, and transportation equipment:

Process and Storage Equipment
- ASME Boiler and Pressure Vessel Code, Sections II, VIII, and IX (unfired pressure vessels)
- Standards of Tubular Exchanger Manufacturers Association, Inc. (heat exchangers)
- Heat Exchange Institute Standards (surface condenser tubes)
- Standards of Feedwater Heater Manufacturers Association, Inc. (heat exchangers)

American Standards Association
- Code for Pressure Piping (petroleum refinery piping, power piping, and refrigeration piping)
- Flanges
- Welded aluminum alloy storage tanks

Interstate Commerce Commission
- Barrels and drums; carboys; cargo tanks, motor vehicle; drums, single trip; railroad tank cars; steel drums, aluminum-lined; tanks, portable; and welded cylinders.

Organic Compound Production

Acids. Aluminum storage tanks, piping, tank cars, and drums are used to store and ship many concentrated organic acids and acid-anhydride mixtures. Product clarity is maintained; corrosion is negligible at ambient temperature.

Acetic acid is the most widely used organic acid. Non-copper-bearing aluminum alloys and certain stainless steels are the only practical alloys for storage tanks that must resist corrosion by acetic acid. Aluminum tanks (Fig. 1) cost considerably less than those of stainless steel and have proved entirely satisfactory.

In producing acetic acid, air oxidation of acetaldehyde originally was a batch process, carried out in 1000-gal steel reactors lined with alloy 3003 sheet and equipped with stainless steel cooling coils for temperature control. Currently, the oxidation is a continuous process. Acetaldehyde is transferred from alloy 3003-F tanks to oxidizers made of the same alloy by a 356-T6 centrifugal pump. The oxidizers are equipped with aluminum cooling coils. Vapors, usually containing 80% acetic acid, 20% acetaldehyde, and traces of water, are recovered in an aluminum condenser. The acetic acid is purified by redistillation and stored in aluminum tanks.

Aluminum reaction vessels are used for esterification of glycerol with glacial acetic acid to produce triacetin, a solvent employed in cosmetics. Triacetin is purified in aluminum stills.

Aspirin and its raw materials (acetic acid or anhydride, and salicylic acid) are prepared, piped, stored, and packaged in aluminum equipment, to maintain product purity and color. Aluminum ventilators and ducts resist the organic acid vapors at ambient temperatures.

Aluminum equipment employed in producing acetanilide by

Fig. 1. Standard aluminum storage tanks. Shell course and head being prepared for assembly. The 10-ft-diam tanks are made from 0.250-in. 3003-H112 plate welded with 4043 filler metal.

reaction of glacial acetic acid with aniline includes storage tanks, piping, reaction vessels, vapor lines, heating coils, evaporators, and reflux condensers.

Aluminum tankage and equipment also handle other low-molecular-weight aliphatic acids, such as propionic and butyric, which are similar to acetic in corrosion characteristics.

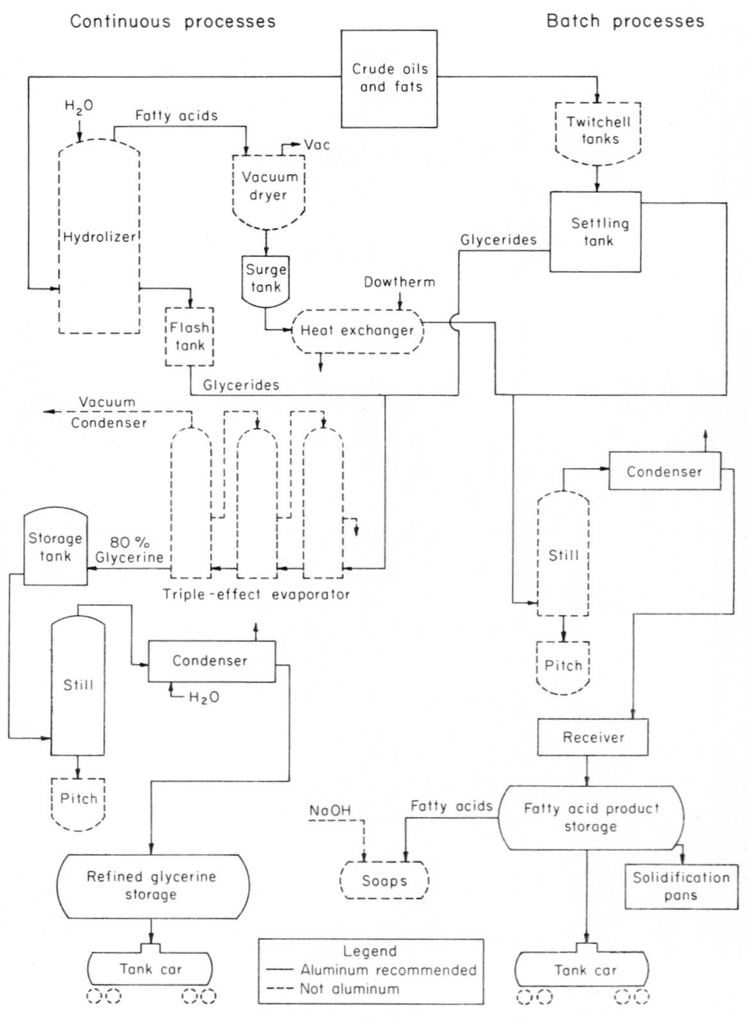

Fig. 2. Aluminum applications in the production of refined fatty acids and glycerin from crude oils and fats

High-molecular-weight fatty acids are stored and transported in aluminum tanks and steam-traced piping to avoid product deterioration or discoloration (Fig. 2). Alloy 6063-T5 double-passage extruded aluminum pipe, especially designed for steam tracing, provides installation economies and uniform pipe-wall temperatures (Fig. 3).

Because of good resistance to attack by hydrocyanic acid as gas or in water solution, aluminum equipment is used for measuring and feed tanks, distillation and absorption columns, heat exchangers, piping, storage tanks, tank cars, and drums. Associated architectural applications include jacketing over thermal insulation.

Alcohols. To maintain product purity, a variety of commercial alcohols are processed and handled with aluminum stills, heat

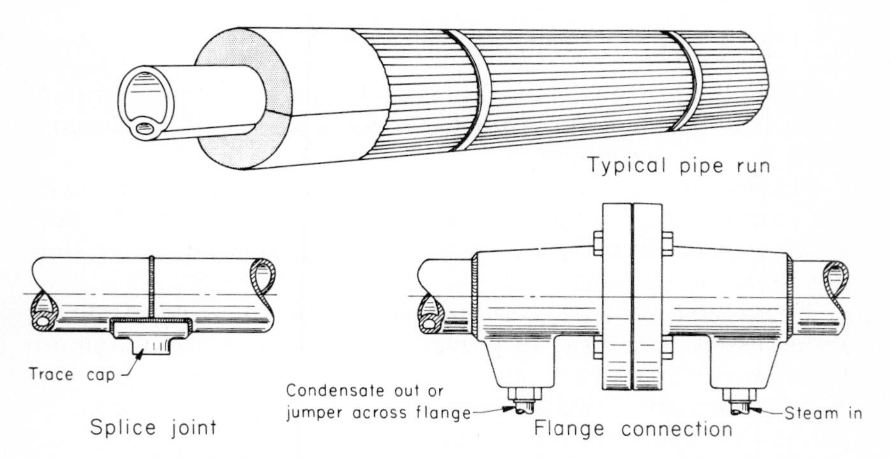

The trace tube is an integral part of the extrusion, providing efficient control of product temperature. Standard pipe insulation can be used. The special flanges required mate with all standard 150-lb ASA pipe flanges, valves, and pumps.

Fig. 3. Extruded pipe for steam-traced systems

exchangers, piping, tankage, and drums. These include sorbitol, isopropanol, glycerol, and various glycols. Schedule 40 3003-H112 alloy pipe, welded with 4043 filler metal, has been in service for over 10 years conveying denatured 95% ethanol at a naval stores plant in Louisiana.

At room temperature, commercial alcohols generally have no significant corrosive action on aluminum. At elevated temperatures, aluminum resists attack if a trace of water is present (see Chapter 7, Volume I). An aluminum reflux condenser built of alloy 1100 served more than 16 years for condensing a 90% methanol – 10% formaldehyde mixture at 122 F.

Aldehydes are produced and transported using aluminum stills, heat exchangers, scrubbers, storage tanks, piping, drums, tank cars, and tank trailers. Aluminum does not catalyze polymerization of aldehydes, and thus product quality is maintained.

Some commercial formaldehyde solutions cause an initial self-stopping attack on aluminum; others of the same concentration cause no corrosion. The difference has been ascribed to the presence of trace amounts of copper or mercury in the solution. A corrosion allowance up to 0.125 in. in wall thickness or the use of alclad alloys are practical solutions to this problem.

Plastic and Synthetic Fiber Industry

The dominant reason for the extensive use of aluminum equipment with plastics and synthetic fibers is assurance of freedom from product discoloration.

Plastics. In production of polyethylene, aluminum is employed for storage bins, hoppers, blending tanks, cooling vats, dilution-water coolers, driers, conveying systems, high-purity-water storage tanks, and piping.

To preserve product clarity, styrene is polymerized in aluminum vessels. Also used in producing polystyrene are aluminum high-purity-water storage tanks and piping. The purity and color of ethyl benzene, used in styrene production, are protected by aluminum vaporizers and condensers.

Aluminum silos, driers, and pneumatic conveying systems handle polyethylene, polypropylene and polystyrene (Fig. 4).

Polymethyl methacrylate resin is cast as rod or tube in aluminum molds.

Water-white alkyd resins are produced in alloy 3003-H112 reaction vessels at temperatures up to 450 F. Raw materials for producing these resins, such as phthalic anhydride and glycerol, are handled and stored in aluminum. Double-passage extruded piping, in 2 and 3-in. Schedule 40 pipe size, transports and steam-traces molten phthalic anhydride.

The desired degree of cellulose acetate transparency for film and wrapping-material production is maintained by aluminum acetylators, aging tanks, hoods, ducts, precipitators, water-extraction tanks, conveyors, and rotary driers, as well as storage facilities for the raw materials.

The production of ester gum resin utilizes aluminum stills, condensers, and receivers.

Fig. 4. Storage bins and piping for handling polyethylene. Use of aluminum prevents staining or smudging of plastic.

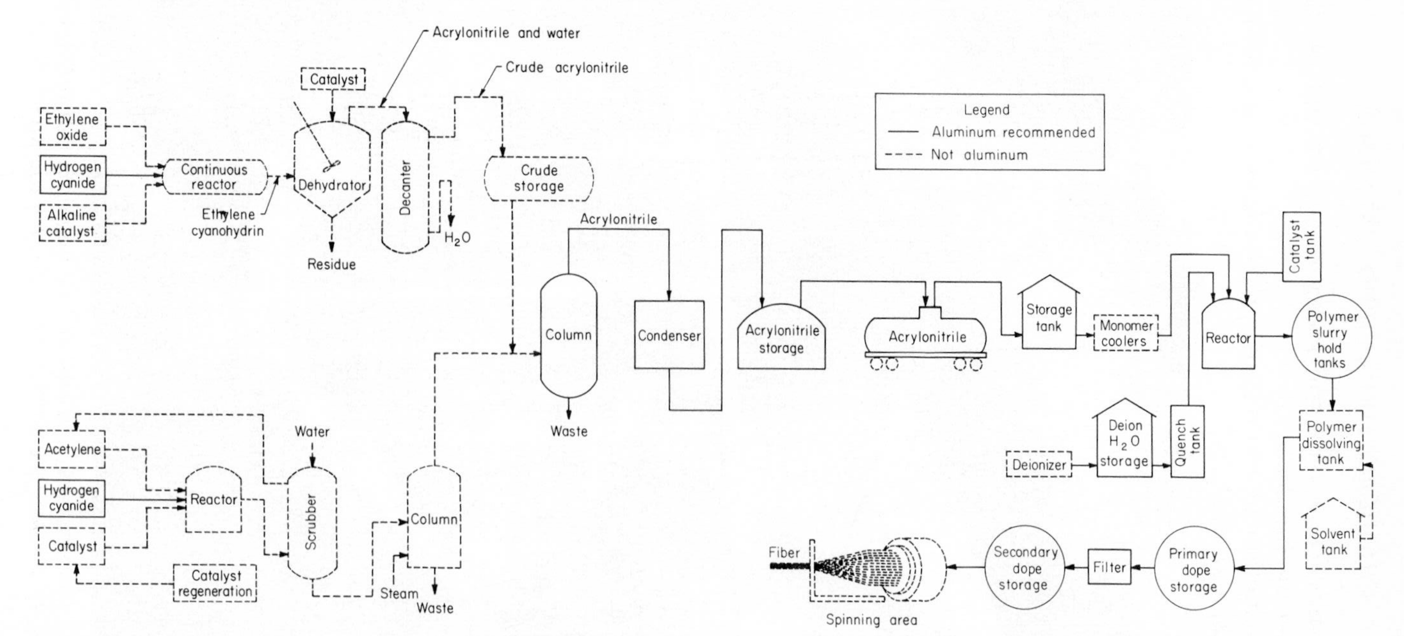

Fig. 5. Aluminum applications in the production of acrylonitrile and acrylic fibers

Phenol-formaldehyde and urea-formaldehyde plastics are made in alloy 3003-H112 reaction kettles.

High-purity isothiocyanates (raw materials for polyurethanes) are processed in aluminum distilling pots and condensers.

Vinyl chloride and vinyl acetate slurries are handled in alloy 3003-H112, 6061-T6, and 6063-T6 piping without product discoloration. Alloy 3003-H14 condensers and storage tanks serve in preparing polyvinyl acetate, which is shipped in 3003-H112 drums and 6061-T4 bulk-storage containers.

Rayon. Components of machines used in spinning viscose rayon are made of aluminum, including traverse bars, guide holders, gear covers, spinning spools, and compartment covers. Forged resin-coated spinning buckets withstand the centrifugal stresses of spinning. Wash water is piped in aluminum; anodized skein holders are 3003-H112 cylinders, often cut from Schedule 40 pipe. Desulfurizing tanks, twisting-machine separator blades, reel frames, and emulsion rolls generally are aluminum. High resistance to attack by hydrogen sulfide makes aluminum especially suitable for ventilating and heating ducts and blowers.

Nylon. The major aluminum applications in nylon production are 3003-H112 and 6063-T6 piping and 3003-H112 and 5052-H112 tankage for nylon salt solutions. In addition, cylindrical chip hoppers over spinning machines, and mineral oil and adipic acid tankage and piping, commonly are aluminum. Cyclohexanol, a raw material for adipic acid, is handled in 3003-H112 drums and tank cars.

Nylon-filament shipping bobbins are anodized aluminum, usually 6063-T832 drawn tube, 2.336-in. ID with 0.084-in. wall. Tube size is based on inside diameter because tubes must fit closely on high-speed spindles.

Acrylics. Aluminum equipment is employed in redistillation, storage, and shipment of acrylonitrile (an intermediate in producing acrylic fibers), and for producing, handling, and shipping hydrocyanic acid, an acrylonitrile ingredient. Glacial acrylic acid is shipped in aluminum tanks and alloy 3003-H112 drums.

In the production of acrylic fibers, aluminum is used for piping, monomer coolers, and tanks for catalyst, quench water, deionized water, polymer slurry, and polymer dissolving. Polyvinyl-chloride-lined 3003-H112 storage tanks handle primary and secondary dope storage.

The flow chart in Fig. 5 illustrates many of these applications.

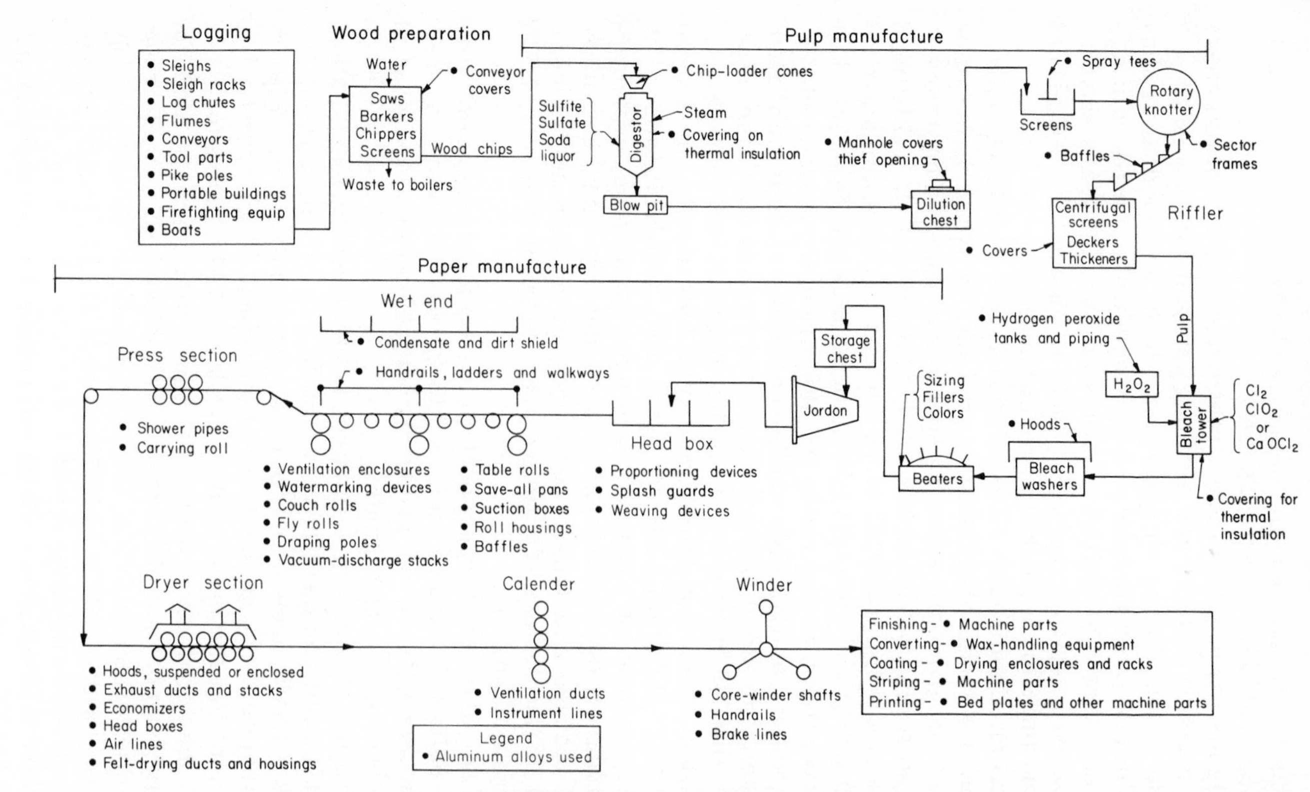

Fig. 6. Aluminum applications in the production of pulp and paper

Pulp and Paper Industry

In the pulp and paper industry, aluminum is employed primarily for architectural and structural applications where its resistance to paper mill atmospheres permits significant reduction in plant maintenance costs (Fig. 6).

Aluminum encloses specific areas within buildings, such as sulfur-burning rooms in sulfite mills, rooms for festoon drying of coated paper, and partitions in kraft digester areas. Aluminum sheet is utilized for general ductwork in many paper mills.

Pulp Mills. Although aluminum is not suitable for direct contact with acidic sulfite or alkaline kraft and soda liquors, it is relatively unaffected by their fumes and vapors in concentrations normally encountered in pulp-mill atmospheres. Aluminum spray T's and baffles prevent contamination of the stock with highly colored corrosion products of many other materials.

Other applications of aluminum in pulp mills are conveyor covers, chip-loader cones, coverings for thermal insulation on digesters and steam lines, hatch covers, sector frames and rotary knotters, riffler baffles, and centrifuge, fine-screen, and decker covers.

Applications in bleach plants include tanks, piping, and shipping containers for hydrogen peroxide; jacketing for thermal insulation on chlorine and chlorine dioxide bleach towers; hoods and exhaust ducts, pulp and rough flumes, pulp skids, and equipment covers.

A major chemical byproduct derived from pulp digestion is tall oil. Some metals react with the fatty acids in tall oil to form compounds that discolor the oil. Aluminum does not, and it is used widely for tanks, tank cars, piping, fittings, steam-tracing, and shipping containers to handle refined tall oil, as well as fatty acids and rosins extracted from the oil.

Paper mills typically employ aluminum for fly rolls, air lines, carrying rolls, catwalks, core-winder shafts, couch and suction rolls, dandy roll housings, doctor blade frames and housings, draping poles, economizers, exhaust ducts, felt-drying system ductwork, gratings, guardrails, hoods, ladders, meter housings, pit ventilator enclosures, proportioning devices, shower pipes, splash guards, stacks, starch-head boxes, suction boxes, table rolls, table-roll housings and baffles, vacuum-pump discharge stacks, watermarking devices, weaving-device components, and wire shields.

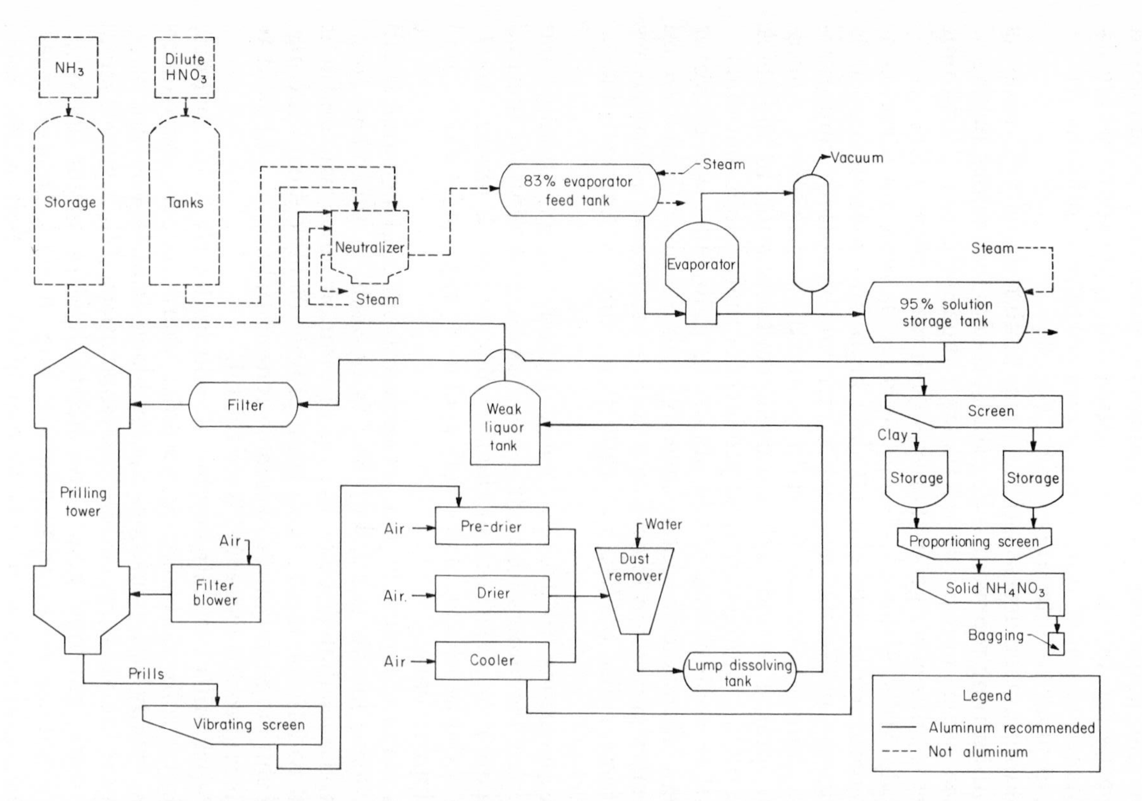

Fig. 7. Aluminum applications in the production of ammonium nitrate

Advantages of aluminum alloys in paper-mill machinery are resistance to corrosion, low maintenance cost, and minimum stock contamination. Light weight is especially desirable in draping poles on the wet end of a Fourdrinier machine, because they must be handled or removed for wire-belt changes.

Aluminum's light weight also is utilized in finishing and converting machinery where reduction in inertia of high-speed reciprocating parts reduces power costs and machine wear. Because aluminum does not discolor wax, it is used in wax melting, storing, and handling equipment. Molten waxes are carried in double-passage extruded pipe. Aluminum sheet is employed to enclose drying rooms and for ventilation ducts. Festoon-type driers are made from aluminum tubular products.

Fertilizer Industry

Ammonium Nitrate. Aluminum's high resistance to ammonium nitrate solutions has made it an economical material for process equipment (Fig. 7) and plant construction. Aluminum is utilized for prilling towers (Fig. 8), storage tanks, hoods, conveyors, electrical conduit, pipe and vessel jacketing, and railroad tank cars.

There are two types of all-aluminum ammonium nitrate prilling towers. The skin-and-framework type generally is rectangular in cross section, and uses 3004-H14 or 6061-T6 sheets bolted to external 6061-T6 structural members. A first-cost premium of 50% over steel construction is common, but this difference is offset by elimination of painting, downtime during painting, and other maintenance costs. The second, the self-supporting silo-type tower, preferably cylindrical in cross section, uses 6061-T6 plate throughout. It costs about 15% less than the skin-and-framework type; its use should increase as it becomes better known by designers.

For nitrogen fertilizer solutions, aluminum is used for storage tanks, tank cars, and farm storage and spreading tanks. With large field-erected bulk storage tanks, savings in sidewall metal and welding labor costs can be realized with tapered aluminum plate. Vertically tapered panels are thicker at the bottom, where hydrostatic pressure is greater. Alloys used for bulk storage tank walls are 3004, 5052, and 5454, in any available temper.

Excessive acidity in hot 83% ammonium nitrate solution can cause corrosion of 5*xxx* series alloy tanks, particularly in heat-affected weld zones. This can be avoided by (*a*) maintaining solution temperature at a minimum to reduce ammonia loss; (*b*) controlling the solution at or above pH 6 as measured in the 83% solution at 180 F; and (*c*) providing adequate circulation during

Fig. 8. Ammonium nitrate prilling towers. The two towers at the right are all-aluminum construction; tower on left, constructed earlier, is aluminum skin with external steel supporting structure.

storage. If these recommendations are followed, 83% ammonium nitrate solution can be handled by tanks constructed of any of a number of aluminum alloys, including 1100, 3003, 3004, 5050, 5052, 5454, 6061, 6063, and their recommended welding filler metals (Volume III, Chapter 12).

Aluminum should not be used for steam coils in 83% ammonium nitrate storage tanks, because ammonia may be released at the hot metal surface, creating localized excessive acidity.

Pipe employed for ammonium nitrate service should be alloy 3003 welded with 1100, because this combination exhibits good resistance to corrosion with no localized attack under acid conditions.

Also, aluminum is used for grating, handrails, and stair tread in plant buildings, and for electrical line and motor components.

Urea. Aluminum equipment is commonly used in all major urea processes. Many applications parallel those in ammonium nitrate plants, such as aluminum or aluminum-lined prilling towers. In the separation, recycle, and finishing sections, aluminum or stainless steel is used for most of the process, conveying and handling equipment, and piping and fittings.

Aluminum applications in urea service also include storage tanks and bins, pipe, heat exchangers, distillation columns and concentrators, vacuum crystallizers, cyclones and driers, pumps and valves, raschig rings, ducts, pipe jacketing, conveying equipment and covers, tank trailers, and tank cars.

Phosphate mining atmosphere contains varying concentrations of phosphate-rock dust. Both bare and alclad aluminum building products have good resistance to corrosion in this environment, and they are used for conveyor housings and office buildings. After 11 years' service at one plant, these products were found to be in good condition, showing only normal weathering.

Mixed liquid fertilizers, containing various amounts of nitrogen, phosphorus, and potassium, vary in their effect on aluminum. Corrosivity generally increases with phosphate content. Solutions containing urea are more aggressive than similar compositions formulated with ammonium nitrate. Solutions containing low amounts of phosphate and formulated with ammonium nitrate are handled successfully in aluminum tanks and piping. Other compositions may require the addition of a corrosion inhibitor such as ammonium fluoride or ammonium dichromate before aluminum could be used.

Explosives and Rocket-Propellant Production

Aluminum is used extensively to produce and handle raw materials for explosives. It is employed similarly with rocket fuels and oxidizing agents, such as phenol, sulfur, liquid oxygen, hydrogen peroxide, fuming nitric acid, alcohols, hydrazine, and nitrogen tetroxide.

Nitroglycerin is stored in aluminum tanks. Aluminum is used for flooring in nitroglycerin drying sheds. Hoods, ducts, wash tanks, and centrifugal extractors made of aluminum are employed in the manufacture of gun cotton. Gelatin dynamite is packaged by aluminum equipment. Aluminum is used in dynamite driers and mixers.

Pentaerythritol, a raw material for one high explosive, is filtered in an aluminum press. The explosive also is handled in aluminum equipment. Lead azide initiator forms a supersensitive explosive in contact with copper and, therefore, is packed in aluminum detonators. Alloy 3003-H14 melting and collecting pans are employed in the manufacture of TNT. Smokeless powder is processed in alloy 3003-H112 tanks.

Corrosion investigations by industry and government agencies have established aluminum's compatibility for storing space-age liquid propellants such as nitrogen tetroxide, unsymmetrical dimethylhydrazine (UDMH), and hydrazine. For most fuels and fuel blends, aluminum alloys are approved for unrestricted use in applications such as storage containers and valves. Ground-support equipment, and many missile components in contact with fuels and oxidizers, are made of aluminum (Chapter 18, this volume). The fuel and oxidizer tanks of the Saturn and Titan missiles, comprising the bulk of the airframe, are constructed of 2014-T6 plate with milled ribs for stiffness.

Mineral Acid Production

The resistance of aluminum to attack by mineral acids is discussed in detail in Volume I, Chapter 7.

Nitric Acid. The high resistance of aluminum alloys to attack by fuming nitric acid solutions is well established. Aluminum piping, tanks, condensers, coolers, drums, and tank cars are used extensively to handle, store, and ship both red and white fuming nitric acids (82% or over by weight). Nitrating tanks containing 70% nitric acid in the production of nitrofuran have aluminum covers. Aluminum hoods and ducts are satisfactory for handling fumes and vapors containing nitrogen oxides. In one plant, 2-in. Schedule 40 3003-H112 pipe, welded with 1100 filler, carries 98% acid at 180 F from an acid concentrator to a nitric-sulfuric acid mixing tank.

Red fuming nitric acid inhibited with 0.5% hydrofluoric acid has been demonstrated to be compatible with all aluminum alloys including the 2*xxx* and 7*xxx* series up to at least 160 F.

Sulfuric Acid. Aluminum has good resistance to highly concentrated and very dilute solutions of sulfuric acid. Aluminum pipe handles sulfuric acid solutions of over 98% concentration. In one plant, alloy 1100 pipe carries 99.5% acid at 113 F; in another, 98% acid is transported in alloy 1100-H112 pipe at 392 F. An aluminum reactor is employed in the catalytic conversion of sulfur dioxide to sulfur trioxide at 450 F. A sulfur trioxide absorption tower used in the production of oleum has cast aluminum covers. In unpublished experiments, small additions of hydrofluoric acid were found to inhibit corrosion in 75 to 100% sulfuric acid at ambient temperatures.

In dilute solutions, aluminum is employed to process a thin aqueous slurry containing 1% sulfuric acid at room temperature. An aluminum condenser cools sludge vapors from coking pots. Although the dilute sulfuric acid condensate causes some corrosion, aluminum has proven economical.

Phosphoric Acid. At room temperature, the corrosion rate of alloy 1100 increases linearly with phosphoric acid concentrations of 5 to 90%. Chromate ion is a good inhibitor; a mixture of 5% phosphoric acid plus 2% chromic acid at 185 F is used widely as a chemical cleaning solution and prepaint treatment for aluminum (Volume III, Chapters 17, 21 and 23).

A 2% phosphoric acid solution is employed at room temperature in several steam power plants to clean the cooling water side of aluminum steam condenser tubes. The solution, circulated through the tubes for several hours, has only a superficial etching action.

Aluminum can be used selectively for building applications in phosphoric acid plants. Successful applications are pipe and tank jacketing, grating, and covers for conveyors.

Halide acids, the most corrosive to aluminum of the mineral acids, generally are not employed in contact with aluminum. However, small concentrations of hydrofluoric acid function effectively as inhibitors in strong nitric or sulfuric acids.

Mixed Acids. In Europe, many alloy 1100 tanks handle mixed mineral acids. The most frequently encountered mixture is 86% nitric acid – 12% sulfuric acid – 2% water. Alloy 1100 has shown corrosion rates less than 0.001 ipy (in. per year) in 85% nitric acid – 13.5% sulfuric acid – 1.5% water at room temperature. The alloy is highly resistant when the water content is below 5%, in both the liquid and vapor phases. Aluminum storage tanks in service handle the mixture containing 1.5% water and a similar mixture containing 3% water.

Soda Ash Production

In soda ash plants, carbon dioxide gas is scrubbed with water to remove dust as it leaves the limestone kilns. Because it is high in resistance to moisture-laden carbon dioxide, aluminum is utilized in many parts of the scrubbers and, in one plant, for a 42-in.-diam, 3003-H14 kiln-gas outlet pipe.

Gaseous mixtures of carbon dioxide, ammonia, and water vapor are handled in alloy 3003-H14 heat-exchanger tube and 3003-H112 pipe. Tube bundles of bare or alclad 3003-H14 tubes are employed in carbon dioxide gas coolers, and in similar heat exchangers where water is removed from ammonia–carbon dioxide mixtures.

In carbonating towers, the resistance of aluminum tubing to waterside scaling improves over-all heat transfer and increases tower capacity as much as 20%, compared to towers containing cast iron tubes. Aluminum alloys have been tested successfully as a construction material for carbonating tower shells.

Other aluminum applications in soda ash production include ammoniated brine coolers, ammoniated liquor storage tanks and 3003-H112 piping in sizes up to 8 in., raschig rings in carbon dioxide absorption towers, calciner condensers, ammonium carbonate scrubbers, distilled-water lines, and driers for ammonium chloride and calcium carbonate fines. Aluminum EC-H112 bus bar is used in electrolytic cell rooms. Many of these applications are illustrated in Fig. 9.

In raw-materials operations, aluminum applications include skips in limestone mines, raw-brine storage equipment, and 3003-H112 pipe for brine wells, raw-brine handling, and coke-oven gas.

Byproduct sodium chlorate is shipped in aluminum freight cars to prevent product contamination.

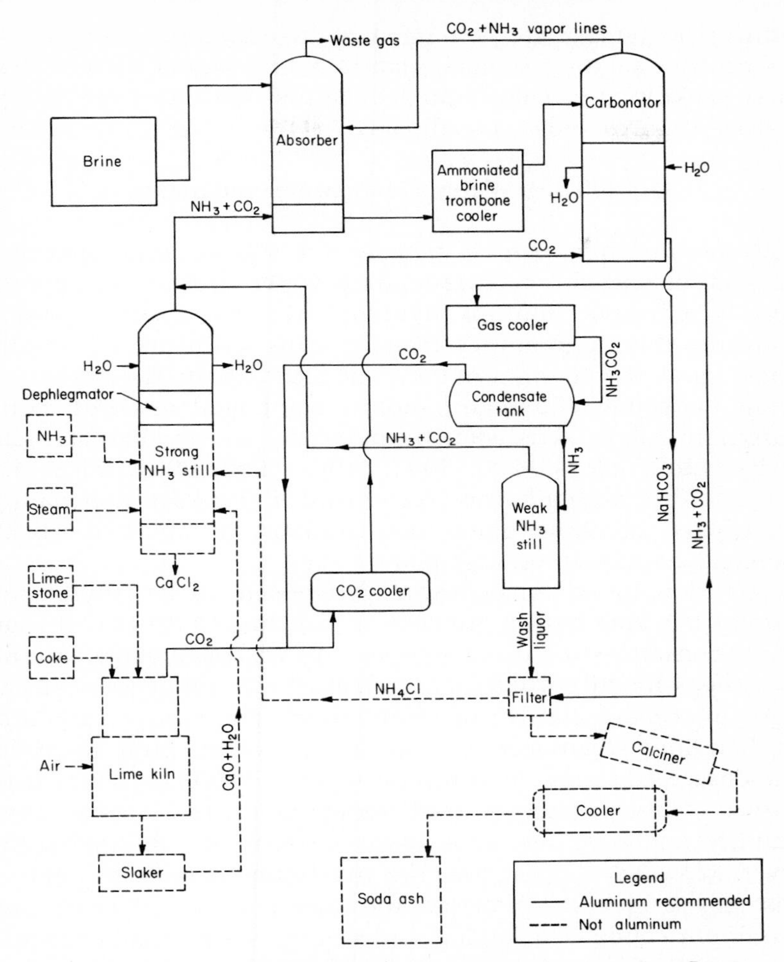

Fig. 9. Aluminum applications in the production of soda ash

Sulfur Production

Aluminum alloys are not attacked by elemental sulfur. Forms and panels employed to build sulfur vats in producer storage areas are 3003 alloy. Aluminum conveyor structures, chutes, and crane cabs and buckets on power shovels handle lump and powdered sulfur. Molten sulfur is carried in extruded aluminum steam-traced piping, and transported in aluminum hopper cars and barge tanks.

Various aqueous-amine and glycol-amine solutions used to

desulfurize natural gas are handled in aluminum equipment. Gas coolers, solution coolers, lean-rich exchangers, towers, and tower packing utilize aluminum's high resistance to corrosion by hydrogen sulfide and carbon dioxide.

High-Purity Water, Condensate, and Steam

Aluminum equipment is popular for storing and conveying distilled, deionized, or demineralized water. During initial contact, a protective film of hydrated aluminum oxide forms. Following this, aluminum's reaction with the water essentially ceases, and the aluminum-ion concentration in the water remains negligible. Although handling equipment made of many aluminum alloys satisfactorily maintains the quality of high-purity water, alloys 1100, 3003, 5050, 5052, 6061, 6063, 43, 214, and 356 normally are recommended. Tankage and piping constructed of these alloys are common in pharmaceutical, chemical, and atomic energy plants.

Corrosion by steam or steam condensate in non-aluminum systems has long been a problem. A principal cause of corrosion by condensate is dissolved oxygen and carbon dioxide. Aluminum alloys are not corroded by condensate containing these gases.

An increasing number of steam power plants use aluminum for handling steam condensate. In one plant, built in 1953, condensate is stored in three 8-ft-diam, 30-ft-high 3003-H112 vertical cylindrical field-erected storage tanks. In 20 consecutive monthly analyses, the total solids content of the condensate never exceeded 4 ppm, and the maximum aluminum content was only 0.04 ppm. A major Midwestern utility reported that aluminum condensate piping and storage substantially reduced the amount of iron oxide carried into the boilers.

Aluminum surface-condenser tubes are used in several steam power plants where their good resistance to corrosion by a variety of cooling waters permits taking advantage of their low initial cost — only half that per foot of brass or stainless steel. The relatively low resistance of aluminum tubes to wet-steam erosion is countered by placing type 304 stainless steel tubes or clips in locations subject to direct steam impingement.

Aluminum alloys employed for surface-condenser tubes include 3003-H14, alclad 3003-H14, 5052-H34, 6061-T4 and 6063-T831. Prevalent sizes are 0.75 to 1.00-in. OD, 0.058-in. wall, 30 to 35 ft long. Where fresh water is used for cooling, the aluminum tubes are expanded into carbon steel tube sheets, effecting an additional cost saving in comparison with the Muntz metal tube sheets usually specified when brass tubes are used. Where sea water or brackish water is the coolant, alclad 6061-T651 tube sheets with alclad (inside) 3003-H14 tubes are preferred; steel water boxes are painted to minimize galvanic effects.

Salt Water Conversion Processes

In salt water conversion, which promises to be a major utility within two decades, aluminum has many potential applications.

Aluminum equipment is utilized in the three major current conversion processes: distillation, freezing, and electrodialysis.

In the distillation process, alclad 3003-H14 condenser tubes, costing about half as much per foot as aluminum-brass or cupronickel tubes, are giving good service handling sea water up to 212 F; experimental work indicates that aluminum can be used at higher temperatures. Alclad alloys are preferred for the process equipment exposed to aerated sea water. However, all these conversion processes employ deaerated sea water to reduce corrosion of the various construction metals. In deaerated sea water, nonclad aluminum alloys also are proving successful.

A triple effect all-aluminum brine concentrator at an East Coast test facility has been handling deaerated sea water and salt brines for almost three years at temperatures up to 130 F. Except for the condenser tubes, which handle incoming aerated sea water, all components are made from nonclad alloys and show insignificant corrosion. An all-aluminum sea water deaerator, also made from nonclad alloys, has been in service on another pilot plant at this same test facility for three years, and shows negligible corrosion.

In one government-sponsored study, alloy 5454 was described as the most resistant aluminum alloy to deaerated 1*M* NaCl, pH 6 to 10.5, at 302 F.

A portable, all-aluminum vapor compression converter has been developed by the United States Army Corps of Engineers.

In the freezing process, one manufacturer uses an aluminum heat exchanger of unique construction.

In the electrodialysis process, aluminum's light weight is desirable for membrane frames; aluminum bus conductor offers high corrosion resistance and low cost.

Electrochemical Industries

Because of the large quantities of direct-current electric power consumed by the electrochemical industries, bus conductor is a major application for aluminum. In 1895, flat bar was employed for 600-volt, 20,000-amp bus for the Niagara Falls aluminum smelter of the Pittsburgh Reduction Company. This bus was in service until the plant was retired in 1949. Today, all aluminum smelters utilize aluminum bus systems (Fig. 10).

Nearly all producers of electrolytic sodium hydroxide and chlorine use EC-grade aluminum bus from the direct-current power source to the first cell and for the return bus from the last cell. Corrosion is negligible; protective coatings are not required. While aluminum could also be employed for the short jumpers between adjacent cells, these usually are located close to the floor

Fig. 10. Aluminum bus used in aluminum primary smelters

and occasional caustic splash during anode renewal would require a coating at these points. At all bolted joints between aluminum and copper bus, spring-loaded washers and electrical joint compounds are recommended (Chapter 21, this volume).

The maximum depth of attack on an EC aluminum bus installation after 10 years on the roof of a plant producing sodium at Baton Rouge, La., measured 22 mils. The attack probably occurred during the first 2 to 4 years of operation, and was of the self-stopping type (Volume I, Chapter 7). The thickened oxide layer on the surface had increased thermal emissivity, allowing the bus to operate at higher currents (or to run cooler).

In production of electrolytic manganese, bus and cathode bars are aluminum.

Aluminum bus was specified for all locations in a lithium plant, except for connecting closely spaced copper switches located under the cells.

In the electrowinning of zinc and cadmium, aluminum sheet cathodes are employed. Stripping zinc from aluminum sheet is easy, if the sheets are maintained in good condition. Because the deposited zinc does not bond metallurgically to the aluminum, a smooth sheet permits the zinc to drop off when jarred slightly. Use roughens the aluminum, making it necessary to pry off the zinc deposit with a knife, but polishing restores the aluminum surface. Removal also can be improved by applying stripping compounds to the aluminum sheet. In one plant, the electrodes were conditioned by immersion in spent electrolyte.

Many electroplating and anodizing installations use aluminum bus. In one strip-galvanizing plant, aluminum bus installed in 1930 was still in operation when inspected in 1956. A crust of zinc sulfate had formed over the bus where it passed under a leaky recirculating trough. The warm bus quickly dried the acidified sulfate solution. Under this crust, the bars had maintained original dimensions.

Hydrogen Peroxide. Water solutions of this major electrochemical are produced, piped, stored and shipped in aluminum equipment (Fig. 11). Aluminum is the only common metal that does not catalyze decomposition of hydrogen peroxide.

Extensive use is made of 1060-H112 for storage tanks, piping, drums, and process equipment. Where stronger alloys are required, as for tank cars, trailers, or large field-erected storage tanks, 5254-H112 and 5652-H112 are selected.

Fig. 11. Hydrogen peroxide storage tanks. Aluminum is the only common metal suitable for long-time storage of hydrogen peroxide.

Alloys 5254 and 5652 differ from their standard counterparts 5154 and 5052 by having lower copper and manganese contents. These higher-purity versions are accepted by ASME and ICC as equal to the standard alloys for code design and approval. The requirement of high-purity-base aluminum alloys for hydrogen peroxide service reflects the tendency of many metals to decompose this compound, especially copper and manganese.

Before use, all new aluminum equipment is passivated to improve its compatibility with hydrogen peroxide solutions. This treatment essentially is exposure to a dilute nitric or sulfuric acid solution to remove surface contaminants, such as iron particles, that are known to accelerate hydrogen peroxide decomposition. The passivation treatment also is applied to tank cars that previously carried another product. Normally, however, hydrogen peroxide tank cars transport this product exclusively.

Silicon-containing alloys, such as 356 and 4043, darken during passivation with acid solutions; other aluminum alloys assume a frosty white appearance. Although the dark color of the passivated aluminum-silicon alloys has no effect on peroxide decomposition, these alloys are held under some suspicion because of their discoloration. However, alloy B356, a higher-purity modification of 356, is approved for long-time contact with hydrogen peroxide; several manufacturers offer valves with B356 bodies. Alloy 4043 filler metal was used on at least one producer's 6063-T6 peroxide transfer line.

Although hydrogen peroxide solutions have no corrosive action on aluminum, the presence of chloride ion promotes pitting. Alloy 1060 is relatively resistant to this effect; nitrate ion in the solution is reported to act as an inhibitor. Chlorides are not involved in hydrogen peroxide production, but atmospheric contaminants can be drawn into the vented tanks during unloading. Tanks located along a seacoast or in any chloride-containing atmosphere should have a vent filter.

Petroleum Refining

In refinery distillation towers, aluminum has given good performance as bubble caps, raschig rings, and expanded mesh. Bubble caps have served 10 to 15 years in debutanizer columns handling gasoline distillates from West Texas sour crudes at temperatures of 200 to 425 F. Similar service has been obtained from bubble caps in cracking-unit fractionating columns for sour-crude gas oils at 400 to 625 F.

Aluminum raschig rings are used advantageously in carbon dioxide and hydrogen sulfide scrubbing and absorption towers. They cost less than in competitive materials, and light weight permits savings in tower construction.

Aluminum heat exchanger tubes and tube bundles are employed in catalytic-cracking overhead condensers, and compressor intercoolers and aftercoolers. In natural-gasoline plants, lean-oil, rich-oil heat exchangers with aluminum tubes serve at temperatures as high as 475 F.

Aluminum heat exchanger tubes do not catalyze polymerizations, which can cause degradation and sludging of petroleum products (Fig. 12). The tubes thus are accepted widely for lubricating oil and furfural coolers. Common sizes are 0.750 to 1-in. OD with 0.049 to 0.083-in. wall. If cooling water is recirculated through a multimetallic system, suitable water treatment is employed. Organic algaecides should be used, rather than copper or mercury salts, which can introduce corrosion problems.

Aluminum heat exchanger tubes in common sizes cost significantly less per foot than either seamless carbon steel or brass

Shell-side vapors include hydrogen sulfide, carbon dioxide, moisture, and hydrocarbons. Inspection after 18 months showed no corrosion or fouling in this service; brass bundle had to be replaced in this length of time.

Fig. 12. Heat exchanger bundle

tubes. They are competitive in cost with welded carbon steel tubes, and provide superior resistance to hydrogen sulfide, ammonia, carbon dioxide, hydrocarbons, and cooling waters.

Tank Trucks and Trailers. Aluminum alloys are used extensively in tank trucks and trailers that transport petroleum products, to obtain increased payload. Refined products are the most widely carried, although aluminum trailers have been built for transporting hot asphalt. A discussion of tank trucks and trailers is contained in Chapter 15 of this volume.

Petroleum Production Structures. The use of aluminum for these structures is discussed in Chapter 11 in this volume.

Reaction Applications

A catalyst prepared by action of aqueous sodium hydroxide solution on an aluminum-nickel alloy is known as a Raney catalyst. The alkali dissolves out almost all of the aluminum, leaving a porous, highly surface-active nickel matrix. This catalyst is used commonly for virtually all types of hydrogenation, desulfurization, dehalogenation, and other reduction reactions.

Aluminum powders or granulated ingot are employed to make trimethyl and triethyl aluminum catalysts, for production of such chemicals as polyethylene, polypropylene, and lauryl alcohol, by the Ziegler process. The organo-aluminum compounds are not true catalysts, because they are consumed in the process.

Alkyl halides or olefins react with benzene in the presence of anhydrous aluminum chloride catalyst to yield alkyl benzenes. The catalyst is made by reaction of chlorine with molten aluminum. Because the catalyst must be of high purity, it is usually made from primary ingot, or from primary and secondary ingot with controlled impurity limits on the mixture. Iron, magnesium, silicon, and zinc produce chlorides that contaminate aluminum chloride. Other metal impurities, such as chromium, copper, and manganese, form chlorides that accumulate in the molten metal, requiring periodic shutdown to clean and recharge. Aluminum ingot of 99.0% purity is satisfactory both to produce pure aluminum chloride and to prevent contamination of the molten metal. In recent installations, anhydrous aluminum chloride was made from granulated ingot, foil scrap, or powder.

Catalytic grades of alumina serve as catalyst or catalyst support in numerous reactions, including re-forming, hydrorefining, oxidation, dehydrogenation, hydrogenation, halogenation, destructive dehydration, dehydrocyclization, and petroleum cracking. They are used at temperatures to 2000 F.

Food, Drug, and Beverage Industries

Aluminum is not affected adversely by steam sterilizing and cleaning; it is nonabsorptive and does not harbor insects or bacteria. The nontoxicity of aluminum and its compounds is particularly beneficial for handling yeasts and other microbiologicals. Its high thermal conductivity is important where containers are heated or refrigerated.

Because aluminum equipment in these industries is frequently subjected to chemical cleaning, alloy selection is based not only on mechanical properties, but also on freedom from discoloration after cleaning. Alloys commonly selected include 214, 3003, and the 5*xxx* series.

Edible Oils, Fats, and Gelatin. Aluminum alloys are suitable for processing and handling edible oils and fats, such as lard, margarine, and palm, cottonseed, and peanut oils. Aluminum equipment has been used for over 30 years in batch deodorizing of coconut oil at 400 F. Oil of peppermint containing 1% water is shipped in aluminum drums to avoid discoloration or sludging. In the margarine industry, aluminum is employed for kneading machines, cooling and dropping vats, and pails.

Production of edible gelatin requires processing equipment that can be cleaned easily and does not affect product purity or color; aluminum is used extensively. Typical applications are extraction kettles, multiple-effect evaporators to concentrate dilute liquor, piping, drying trays or wire nets, and filter presses for gelatin clarification (Fig. 13).

Sugar. Aluminum dry-bulk containers are used widely for in-plant and interplant shipment of granular sugar; it also is conveyed pneumatically in aluminum pipe. Liquid bulk containers with built-in filling and discharging equipment handle syrups and molten chocolate. Alloy 3003-H14 jacketing sheet is em-

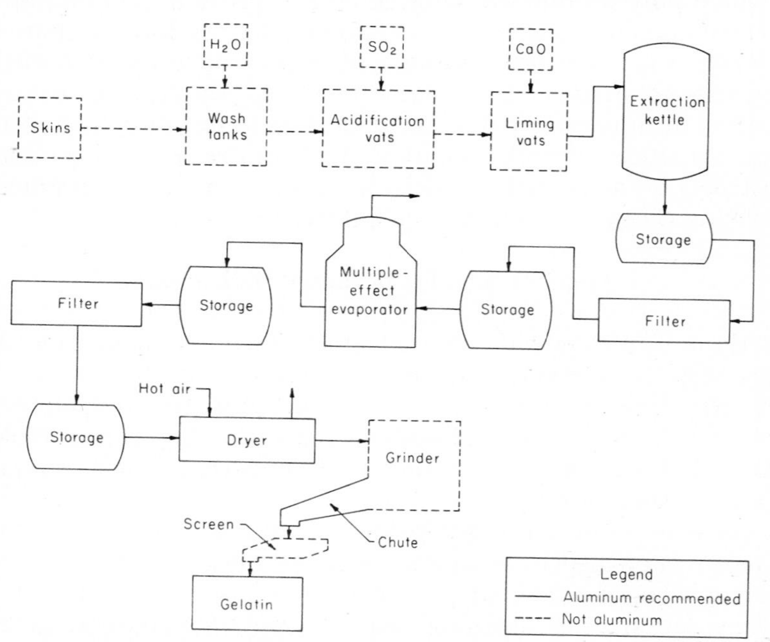

Fig. 13. Aluminum applications in the production of edible gelatin

ployed to weatherproof insulated tanks and piping. Refined and semirefined syrups are stored and transported in aluminum tanks and tank trailers.

Aluminum pipe satisfactorily handles refined invert sugar solutions. Although inverting is accomplished by acidifying the solution, the sugar acts as a corrosion inhibitor, preventing aluminum pickup in the liquor.

Dairy Products. Aluminum is extensively used in Europe, and to a lesser extent in the United States, for processing and handling fresh milk and milk products. Equipment includes pasteurizers, coolers, butter churns, cottage cheese vats, storage tanks and smaller containers, strainers, stirrers, and tank trucks, and also driers and flash tanks for powdered milk production.

Aluminum milk-bottle hoods are common, and butter is packaged in decorated aluminum foil wrappers. Aluminum is utilized for ice cream molds, scoops, freezers, paddles, and packaging.

Dairy equipment of aluminum is cleaned easily with acid or silicate-inhibited alkaline cleaners (Volume III, Chapter 23).

Meat Products. Aluminum applications for processing meat include kettles to prepare various meat products, cans for blood storage prior to dehydration, sticks for smoking meat, a variety of pans, trimming buckets, bulk containers for in-plant handling, and consumer packaging.

Structurally, aluminum is popular for truck and cold-room liners, floors, hanger rails, and meat truck exteriors. Smudging caused by dressed meat rubbing against aluminum linings can be prevented by anodizing or applying methacrylate lacquer to the metal.

Drugs. Because aluminum does not interfere with the action of micro-organisms, or enzymes and their products, it is suitable for equipment and appliances employed in industrial fermentation and other mold-growth processes.

Three 3000-gal 1060-H112 alloy absorbers are used in a pharmaceutical plant to prepare chloramphenicol and streptomycin. Aluminum also is employed for tanks containing mediums, pre-seed mediums, and slurry, and for storing and distributing deionized water and acetone. Aluminum equipment is nontoxic to penicillin molds, and it is employed in penicillin production.

Aluminum filling and packing devices and closures are common for handling serums, vaccines and vitamins. Aluminum storage tanks and piping are used in the manufacture of aspirin.

In commercial nitration of furfural to nitrofurans, aluminum equipment is used in a number of steps. Acetic anhydride, stored in 16,000-gal aluminum tanks, is transferred by vacuum to 200-gal aluminum measuring tanks. Nitration takes place in aluminum nitrators. Aluminum feed tanks handle the furfural.

Beer. Although aluminum is accepted widely for brewery process equipment in Europe, its application in the United States is limited by the wide use of caustic soda to clean brewery equipment. Despite this limitation, aluminum equipment is utilized for yeast tubs, culture tanks, wort coolers, settling and starting tubs, fermenters, brew kettles, filters, skimmers, piping, tubing, beer barrels, and carbonating and storage tanks.

Most breweries have converted to using aluminum in beer cans, either for ends or the entire can (see Chapter 23, this volume). Aluminum crown liners are employed widely in bottle caps because contact with aluminum does not affect flavor or color of chilled beer.

Aluminum beer barrels, manufactured in this country since the early 1930's, cost about one fourth less than stainless steel barrels. They are made of alclad (inside) 6053-T6 and have a forged alclad 6053-T6 side bung welded in place. Aluminum barrel halves are drawn from sheet circles 0.156 in. thick and welded together. The product has demonstrated a service life exceeding 15 years.

The interior surface of the barrels offers high resistance to corrosion; a sanitary condition and clean appearance can be maintained readily with proper cleaning procedures (Volume III, Chapter 23). A five-year service inspection indicated that recommended acid cleaners, used regularly, maintain a smooth, pit-free interior. Acid cleaners are effective in removing trace amounts of copper, which can accumulate on the aluminum surface and cause galvanic corrosion. Alkaline cleaners are satisfactory for aluminum barrels in locations where copper contamination is not a significant problem, but are less effective than acid cleaners for copper removal.

Wines. Aluminum pipe has a service record of over 20 years in the wine-making industry. It is used extensively to transfer the mixture of grape juice, pulp, seeds, and skin from crusher to fermenter. Juice is carried from fermenter to fortifier in aluminum pipe; the final product often flows through aluminum pipe during bottling.

Aluminum alloys are suitable for handling wines where exposure times are relatively short. For exposures of more than a few days, the effect of wine on aluminum — and of aluminum on wine flavor, color, and aroma — depends on the type and source of wine, the temperature, and the alloy selected. Generally, heavy wines, and white wines bleached with sulfurous acid, are affected more than light wines, or those low in pectic acid. Organic-coated aluminum tanks, however, have proven satisfactory in handling wines for extended periods of time.

Spirits. Mixtures of ethyl alcohol and water do not attack aluminum. An aluminum still has produced gin for at least 14 years. Whiskies are processed and transferred in aluminum blending tanks and piping.

Whiskies, brandies, gin, and rum can be handled in aluminum for short-time exposure, but undergo slight changes in flavor and clarity if stored or left in prolonged contact with aluminum. As with wine, this can be attributed to the acidity of those liquors and their slight contamination with heavy metals. Because reaction between aluminum and a liquor varies, tests should precede selection of aluminum for a specific application.

Atomic Energy Industry

Fuel Cladding. Cooling uranium fuel in atomic reactors was a major technical problem solved by the concept of fuel "cladding". The fuel is sealed in a protective jacket, or can, to protect it from corrosion by the coolant, and to prevent fission products from entering the coolant (Fig. 14). Aluminum is employed as nuclear-fuel cladding because of its low neutron-capture cross section (see Volume I, Chapter 1), good resistance to corrosion, and low cost compared to other possible materials. Claddings that do not absorb neutrons are selected because unnecessary removal of neutrons from a functioning fuel element reduces efficiency.

Alloy 1100 is almost universally used as fuel cladding in low-power, water-cooled reactors operating below 212 F, and has been shown suitable up to 400 F. Development of alloy 8001 increased this temperature limit to over 600 F.

In high-power, water-cooled reactors, a trend to higher coolant pressures and temperatures, for greater thermal efficiency, has led to claddings of more expensive metals, such as stainless steel and zirconium alloys. With stainless steel claddings, enriched nuclear fuel is used to compensate for greater neutron absorption.

Aluminum claddings are satisfactory in organic-moderated reactors where pressures are low, even though coolant temperatures are 700 to 800 F. In the organic-moderated reactor at Piqua, Ohio, for example, aluminum powder metallurgy alloy XAP005 was specified for fuel claddings and fuel boxes. These alloys combine outstanding mechanical properties at elevated temperatures with good resistance to the terphenyls used as the organic coolant.

Boral sheet or plate, employed in reactors, is a sandwich product consisting of a core of granular boron carbide dispersed in commercially pure aluminum, clad on both sides with alloy 1100 sheet. The content of boron carbide (B_4C) is nominally 23% by weight of the composite. It is an excellent shielding material for absorption of thermal neutrons, and can be cut, formed, and joined by standard techniques.

Most shielding materials absorb neutrons readily, but in so doing produce one or more high-energy secondary gamma rays,

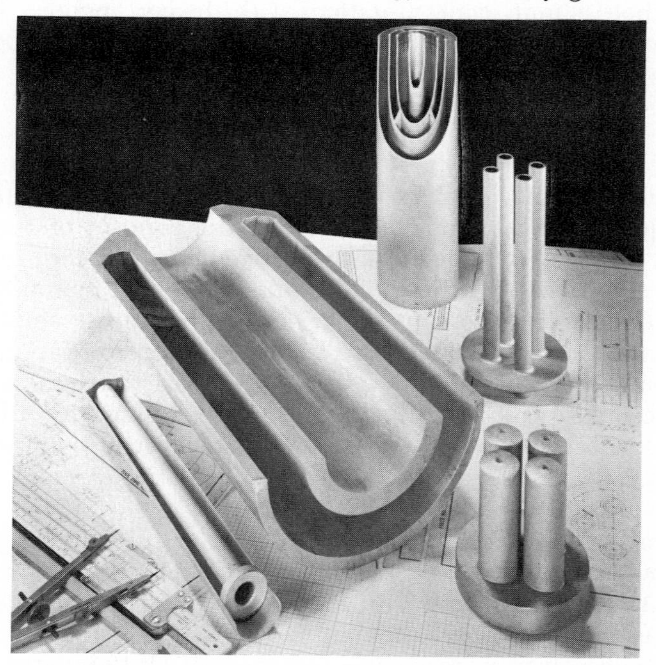

A typical "cap and can" fuel-element cladding assembly of two impacts at lower left. Large impact in center and part at rear (two double-walled impacts, telescoped) are special designs. Components at right are further fabricated and assembled with conventional extrusions.

Fig. 14. Impact extrusions for plutonium production

which require further shielding. Boron absorbs neutrons without emitting high-energy secondary radiation. Therefore, the use of Boral sheet eliminates part of the secondary gamma radiation through a reactor shield. Boral sheet is most effective when located close to the reactor core, so that the neutrons do not encounter gamma-emitting absorbents first, but not so close that it absorbs neutrons that could contribute to the chain reaction. Principal factors that led to the selection of aluminum as the boron carbide binder and cladding were its low cost, high thermal conductivity, and low cross section for the emanation of gamma rays.

Other applications for aluminum in nuclear reactors include linings for reactor and storage pools, storage tanks and piping for high-purity water and deuterium, extrusions for spacer bars, and master-slave manipulator parts.

Aluminum foil honeycomb is used as an energy absorber in reactor domes. The foil honeycomb structure's property of failing at constant load minimizes rebound in case of explosion. In one installation, the honeycomb is designed to absorb kinetic energy as high as 41.5 million ft-lb.

In nuclear power plants, applications include aluminum surface condenser tubes, turbine lubricating oil coolers, hydrogen coolers, low-pressure feedwater heaters, condensate piping and storage tanks, bus bar, jacketing for thermal insulation, and a variety of architectural and structural applications. Radioactive waste holdup tanks often are made of aluminum, because the short half-life of aluminum reduces the waiting time for the tanks to become sufficiently inactive to be safely cleaned for re-use.

Effect of Radiation on Aluminum. The effects of radiation on the mechanical properties of some aluminum alloys maintained

Table 3. Effects of Fast-Neutron Irradiation at 86 F on Tensile Properties of High-Purity Aluminum With Various Degrees of Cold Work (7)

Exposure, neutrons per sq cm having energies of 0.5 mev	Initial sample condition	Property change, %		
		Yield strength	Tensile strength	Elongation
$\sim 7.5 \times 10^{19}$	Annealed(O)	+100	+60	−67
	Half-hard(H14)	+ 10	+ 6	0
	Full-hard(H18)	Very small	Very small	Very small
$\sim 15 \times 10^{19}$	Annealed(O)	+100	+70	−67
	Half-hard(H14)	+ 10	+ 6	0
	Full-hard(H18)	Very small	Very small	Very small

Table 4. Effects of Fast-Neutron Irradiation at 150 F on Tensile Properties of Some Aluminum Alloys (7)

Alloy	Condition	No. of tests	Yield strength, psi	Tensile strength, psi	Elongation, % in 2 in.
1100-O	Control	8	6,800	13,600	38.2
	Irradiated(a)	25	17,100	26,000	21.2
1100-H14	Control	8	16,600	17,300	6.0
	Irradiated	22	24,000	26,000	5.5
5052-O	Control	7	14,700	29,200	34.0
	Irradiated	22	22,900	37,400	30.6
5052-H34	Control	7	29,500	36,000	11.2
	Irradiated	21	36,400	44,700	14.0
6061-O	Control	8	9,400	18,000	28.8
	Irradiated	25	25,600	37,300	22.4
6061-T6	Control	8	38,500	45,000	17.5
	Irradiated	23	44,400	50,600	16.2

(a) Sheet tensile specimens 0.064 in. thick were irradiated for a total neutron irradiation of 1.26×10^{21} n per sq cm, with an estimated fast-neutron exposure of 1×10^{20} n per sq cm. Samples were water cooled to maintain a temperature of about 150 F.

at 86 and 150 F are shown in Tables 3 and 4 (7). Marked increases in tensile and yield strength accompanied by reductions in ductility are shown. The losses in ductility are less than normally produced by cold working. Changes in properties of alloys previously hardened by heat treatment or cold working are much smaller than with annealed material. Table 3 indicates saturation of the changes induced by irradiation.

References

1 "Aluminium in the Chemical and Food Industries", British Aluminium Co., Ltd., London, England, 1959

2 "Aluminum with Food and Chemicals", Aluminum Company of Canada, Ltd., Montreal, Canada, 1966

3 "Process Industries Applications of Alcoa Aluminum", Aluminum Company of America, Pittsburgh, 1960

4 P. Juniére and M. Sigwalt, "Aluminium, Its Applications in the Chemical and Food Industries", English translation, Chemical Publishing Co., New York, 1964

5 "The Encyclopedia of Chemical Process Equipment", edited by Wm. J. Mead, Reinhold Publishing Co., New York, 1964

6 "Metals Handbook", 8th Ed, vol 1, American Society for Metals, 1961, p 928

7 R. V. Steele and W. P. Wallace, "The Effect of Neutron Flow on the Mechanical Properties of Aluminum Alloys", U. S. Atomic Energy Commission Report LRL-145, 1954

Chapter 13

Structures and Equipment for Service at Cryogenic Temperatures

J. G. KAUFMAN and E. T. WANDERER

BECAUSE aluminum and aluminum alloys have no ductile-to-brittle transition and thus no appreciable loss in toughness at low temperatures, they are widely used in the production, storage, transportation and utilization of cryogens.

As indicated in Chapter 4 of this volume, the strengths of aluminum and its alloys and of aluminum welds are higher at subzero temperatures than at room temperature. The differences are negligible down to −50 or −100 F, but at lower temperatures become increasingly significant. At −320 F, the tensile strengths and yield strengths of most alloys average 30% and 20%, respectively, higher than at room temperature; at −423 F, they average about 50% and 35% higher. Data for −452 F suggest that tensile strengths and yield strengths level at about −423 F. Typical tensile properties of some aluminum alloys and welds, which illustrate these differences, are shown in Table 1.

Other static strengths — shear, compressive and bearing strengths—and fatigue strengths also are higher at subzero temperatures. Data (1) showing the higher fatigue strengths of some 5*xxx* alloys and welds are shown in Table 2; fatigue strengths ($R = 0.0$) of parent plate and welds at −320 F averaged 16% and 28%, respectively, higher than at room temperature.

Moduli of elasticity under tensile, compressive and shear loading are higher at subzero temperatures than at room temperature;

J. G. Kaufman is an assistant chief, Mechanical Testing Div., Alcoa Research Laboratories, New Kensington. E. T. Wanderer is manager for machinery and equipment, Application Engineering Div., Aluminum Company of America, New Kensington.

the moduli at −320 and −423 F are about 12 and 16%, respectively, higher than at room temperature (Chapter 4, this volume). The uniformity of increase in moduli under axial and shear loading indicates that Poisson's ratio is the same at cryogenic temperatures as at room temperature.

The ductility of most aluminum alloys at cryogenic temperatures is as high as or higher than at room temperature. For some alloys and tempers, elongations and, to an even greater extent, reductions of area reach a maximum at some subzero temperature, and decrease at lower temperatures; only for a few alloys

Table 1. Typical Tensile Properties of Some Aluminum Alloys (Welded and Unwelded) at Cryogenic Temperatures(a)

Alloy and temper	Tensile strength, 1000 psi			Yield strength(b), 1000 psi			Elongation in 4*D*, %		
	RT	−320 F	−423 F	RT	−320 F	−423 F	RT	−320 F	−423 F
1100-O	13	25	35	5	6	9.5	40	55	55
1100-H14	18	30	48	17	20	23	20	45	50
2014-T6	70	84	103	60	72	81	13	14	12
2024-T3	70	85	112	50	62	75	17	18	17
2219-T81	66	83	99	50	61	68	12	15	18
2219-T81(c)	42	57	59	25	30	33	5	4	4
2219-T81(d)	59	75	79	40	44	55	5	7	6
2219-T87	68	85	99	56	67	73	12	14	17
3003-O	16	33	55	6	8.5	10	40	46	48
3003-H14	22	35	58	21	25	28	16	30	41
5083-O	42	59	80	21	24	26	25	36	32
5083-H321(e)	46	64	88	33	39	41	16	27	29
5454-O	36	54	79	17	19	22	25	39	39
5454-H34	44	63	89	35	41	43	16	30	32
5456-O	45	62	80	23	26	28	20	32	25
5456-H321	51	68	89	37	43	48	16	27	22
6061-T6(f)	45	59	76	40	47	54	17	22	27
6061-T6(g)	27	39	53	15	18	21	12	8	7
6061-T6(h)	43	53	73	39	47	52	2	3	2
X7005-T53	60	82	97	53	64	69	15	16	18
7039-T61	60	77	92	50	60	66	14	14	14
7075-T6	83	102	116	73	92	98	11	9	8
7075-T73	73	92	106	63	72	78	13	14	14
7079-T6	78	92	108	68	80	90	14	12	9
7178-T6	88	106	122	78	94	108	11	5	4

(a) Typical tensile strengths of welds in non-heat-treatable alloys are the same as those of the annealed parent metal; yield strength and elongations vary with temper of parent metal. (b) Offset is 0.2% in 2-in. gage length. (c) As-welded; weld alloy, 2319. (d) Reheat treated and artificially aged after welding to T62 temper; weld alloy, 2319. (e) At −452 F, 83,000 psi tensile strength, 40,000 psi yield strength, 31% elongation in 4*D*. (f) At −452 F, 78,000 psi tensile strength, 54,000 psi yield strength, 27% elongation in 4*D*. (g) As-welded; weld alloy, 4043. (h) Reheat treated and artificially aged after welding; weld alloy 4043.

Table 2. Axial-Stress Fatigue Strength of Some Aluminum Alloys (Welded and Unwelded) at Room Temperature and −320 F

Condition	Type of specimen	Fatigue strength(a), psi — Room temperature — 10^5 cycles	Room temperature — 10^6 cycles	−320 F — 10^5 cycles	−320 F — 10^6 cycles
		5083-H321			
Unwelded	Smooth	39,000	34,000	45,000	40,000
Welded	Smooth	28,000	20,000	32,000	26,000
		5454-H32			
Unwelded	Smooth	39,000	32,000	45,000	40,000
Welded	Smooth	29,000	20,000	36,000	30,000
Welded	Notched(b)	10,000	.....	18,000	.....
		5456-H321			
Unwelded	Smooth	42,000	36,000	47,000	41,000
Welded	Smooth	30,000	23,000	35,000	30,000
Welded	Notched(b)	11,000	.....	17,000	.....

(a) Stress ratio (minimum stress in cycle divided by maximum stress in cycle) = 0.0. (b) Theoretical stress concentration factor $\gtrsim$ 12.

and tempers do they fall significantly below the room-temperature values. For the very-high-strength heat treatable alloys, the ductility at cryogenic temperatures is lower than at room temperature, and decreases gradually with decrease in temperature.

Toughness. The toughness (notch toughness, tear resistance, and fracture toughness, Chapter 4 of this volume) of most aluminum alloys at cryogenic temperatures is very high, as at room temperature (2). The notch toughness of these alloys, as measured by notch-yield ratio, remains about the same over the range of temperatures, as shown by Fig. 1. Even at very low temperatures, these alloys are able to deform plastically (yield) in localized regions of severe stress raisers and thus avoid cracking. Also, the ability to resist the growth of cracks is very high at cryogenic temperatures, even higher in some alloys than at room temperature, as illustrated by Fig. 2. For many of the alloys used in cryogenic applications, the ability to deform plastically and resist crack growth is so great that unstable crack growth in elastically stressed material (brittle fracture) is impossible. Also, there is no indication, even for those alloys with relatively low toughness, of any abrupt change in fracture behavior suggestive of the ductile-to-brittle transition of some ferrous alloys. This is equally true of welds in aluminum alloys; in fact, as the data for welded 5083-H321 in Fig. 1 illustrate, welds usually have even greater notch toughness and tear resistance over the entire temperature range than tempered parent alloys.

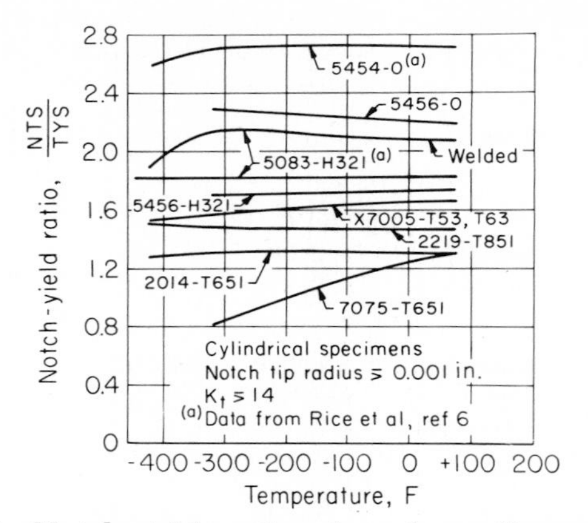

Fig. 1. Notch-yield ratios (notch-tensile strength divided by tensile yield strength) for several aluminum alloys at various temperatures. Data from tests on 0.75 to 1.25-in. plate in the longitudinal direction.

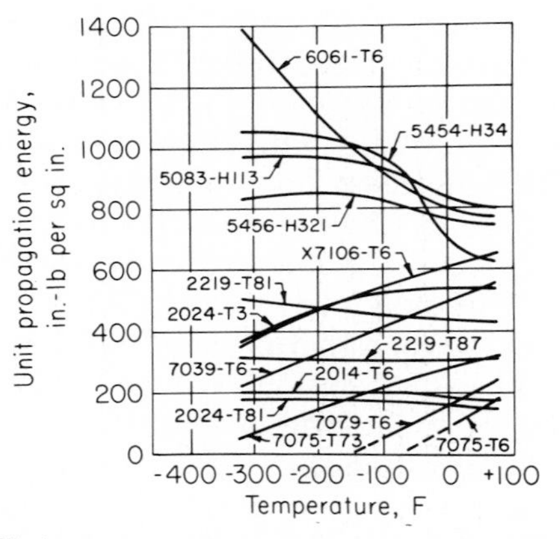

Fig. 2. Unit propagation energies of several aluminum alloys at various temperatures. Data from tear tests on 0.063-in. sheet in the transverse direction.

Physical Properties. Certain physical properties of aluminum and its alloys (in addition to low density) are helpful in cryogenic applications. The low outgassing characteristics of aluminum, its limited hydrogen solubility, and its low rate of hydrogen diffusion compared to other cryogenic metals, minimize contamination of evacuated systems.

Aluminum alloys have low emissivity of radiant energy, relatively independent of alloy composition and temper. The emissivity of clean, mill-finish aluminum alloys at 100 F is 3 to 6%; emissivity is reported to decrease as temperatures approach absolute zero. Mechanically polishing the mill-finish surface has little effect on emissivity.

An advantage of aluminum over alternate cryogenic metals is the additional insulation provided by its higher reflectance. Because aluminum has inherently high reflectance for heat radiation, there is no need to polish or apply reflective coatings. For highest reflectance, the mill-finish surface must be kept clean.

Other physical properties of aluminum alloys that may be important at cryogenic temperatures include (*a*) high thermal conductivity, (*b*) high electrical conductivity, (*c*) relatively high coefficient of thermal expansion, (*d*) low magnetic susceptibility.

Resistance to Corrosion. Aluminum and its alloys are compatible with all known cryogens (3), including fluorine, helium, hydrogen, neon and oxygen. Because direct contact with these materials for prolonged periods produces no adverse effects, there is no need for protective coatings, such as high-purity aluminum, stainless steel cladding, or organics.

Joining. Welding is the most common method of joining aluminum alloys for cryogenic applications, although large fin-type heat exchangers are joined by brazing. Both techniques result in reproducible, sound, strong, leak-tight joints, providing the reliability needed for assemblies for vacuum applications.

Alloy Selection

Most of the alloy systems, in both cast and wrought form, are suited for cryogenic applications:

1xxx Series (Unalloyed, Non-Heat-Treatable). Commercially pure aluminum (1100) with 99.0% min aluminum, and special variations of higher purity, are readily weldable and very ductile. They have greater toughness at cryogenic temperatures than at room temperature. Because these alloys have relatively low strength, they are used in applications where formability, ductility, weldability and certain chemical properties are more important than strength.

2xxx Series (Aluminum-Copper, Heat Treatable). Alloy 2014 has high strength and a useful level of toughness at cryogenic temperatures. As do most 2*xxx* alloys, it retains the same level of toughness at low temperatures that it possesses at room temperature. It is less readily weldable by the standard techniques suitable for many other alloys; however, specialized procedures produce reliable, ductile joints with strengths in excess of 50,000 psi in the as-welded condition. Weld strength usually decreases with increase in section thickness. Postweld heat treatment can produce weld strengths approaching parent metal strengths, but it reduces weld ductility.

Alloy 2219 has slightly lower strengths than 2014, but is much more readily weldable and has substantially greater cryogenic toughness. Therefore, 2219 is used where good strength, weldability and toughness are paramount (4). Welded 2219 is about 75% as strong as the parent metal; postweld heat treatment and aging raises the ratio nearly to 100%. Alloy 2219 is especially useful for applications where thick sections are necessary, because the properties do not vary appreciably with thickness of the heat treated part.

Alloy 2024-T4 bolts are used for low-temperature applications; this alloy and temper has high strength and excellent toughness.

3xxx Series (Aluminum-Manganese, Non-Heat-Treatable). Alloy 3003 has been widely used for cryogenic applications. It has higher strength than alloy 1100, good formability and weldability, and very high toughness. Because it is unexcelled where brazing is to be employed, alloy 3003 is used widely for brazed heat exchangers in cryogenic installations. The alloy can be strengthened by strain hardening, but welding leaves a heat-affected zone that usually governs design. As a result, alloy 3003 is not selected for applications where high strength-to-density ratio is important.

5xxx Series (Aluminum-Magnesium, Non-Heat-Treatable). The 5*xxx* series of aluminum alloys, notably 5083 and 5456, are among those most widely used for cryogenic tankage, and their properties are among the most completely documented (5, 6). As a group, these alloys have excellent toughness and their toughness increases with decrease in temperature, with some leveling of properties at temperatures below −320 F. The 5*xxx* series alloys are readily weldable by inert-gas arc methods, with proper choice of filler alloys. Because the alloys are strengthened by cold work, welding leaves a heat-affected zone, and most designs where the principal stress is transverse to the weld are based on the properties of the annealed temper. Alloy 5456 provides a minimum weld strength of 42,000 psi (the specified minimum tensile strength of 5456 after an annealing treatment), which is one of the highest of any aluminum alloy in the as-welded condition.

6xxx Series (Aluminum-Magnesium-Silicon, Heat Treatable). The toughness of the 6*xxx* series alloys is higher at low temperatures than at room temperature. As a result, these easily welded and extruded alloys have long been used in cryogenic applications, mainly as extrusions, pipe and pipe fittings. Alloy 6061, oldest of this group, has been one of the most widely used; alloy 6063 is lower in cost and strength. In the as-welded condition, the strengths of the 6*xxx* series alloys are less than those of the higher-strength 5*xxx* series alloys (17,000 to 28,000 psi versus 38,000 to 42,000 psi). However, postweld heat treatment increases the strengths of the 6*xxx* series alloys to the upper limits of the weld-strength range, comparable with strengths available with the 5*xxx* series alloys (7).

7xxx Series (Aluminum-Zinc, Heat Treatable). Familiar aircraft alloys 7075, 7079 and 7178, and the newer alloy 7001, in the T6-type temper are the highest-strength aluminum alloys. Because these alloys are not considered weldable by usual practices, and have inherently lower toughness, their use in cryogenic applications is limited. In the special T73 temper, which improves both toughness and resistance to corrosion at some sacrifice in strength compared to the T6 temper, 7075 has been used as high-strength bolts for low-temperature service.

The copper-free Al-Zn-Mg alloys, notably X7005, 7039 and X7106, are relatively insensitive to rate of quenching from solution heat treatment, so that their properties vary little with thickness. They are weldable and have the highest as-welded strengths of the aluminum alloys (after 30-day room-temperature aging). Despite a decrease in toughness with decreasing temperature, they have a very high level of toughness at cryogenic temperatures (8). Stress-corrosion cracking of these alloys can occur even in mild environments, as a result of comparatively low short-transverse tensile stresses — and also long-transverse stresses if the material has been severely cold worked by forming. This type of cracking can be minimized by appropriate design details and fabricating procedures.

Casting Alloys. Most aluminum casting alloys are satisfactory for low-temperature applications. Those with low alloy content or with silicon or magnesium-silicide as the primary alloying addition are particularly well suited for low-temperature applications, because no loss in toughness occurs as the temperature decreases.

Design Considerations

Designing aluminum alloy structures and equipment for cryogenic applications is generally much like designing for room temperature. In many instances, the structure or component must operate satisfactorily at near-maximum stresses at or near room temperature before cool-down. Because the strengths of aluminum alloys are higher at low temperatures than at room temperature, the room-temperature properties govern the design, and the higher properties at the lower temperatures represent an added safety factor.

In contrast, there are applications where the higher strengths at low temperatures can or must be considered. For instance, a shear pin to operate effectively at −423 F must be designed using the higher shear strength that exists at the low temperature.

A primary objective is assurance that the structure is highly resistant to rapid crack growth at the low temperature. The suitability of the alloy and temper in this respect may be judged from the notch toughness and tear resistance: the level of notch-yield ratios and unit propagation energies at the low temperature, and comparison with room-temperature values. Once configuration and alloy and temper are determined, the maximum size of flaw that might be undetected in the structure between inspections should be established; this should then be checked against the critical size for the alloy and temper, based on its fracture toughness at the low temperature and the design stress, as described in Chapter 4 in this volume. A widely accepted guideline is to design the structure so that it will not fail catastrophically at a gross stress equal to the yield strength if a crack exists equal in length to twice the metal thickness. This guards against the possibility of a part-through crack (assumed to be of hemispherical shape) on the inside surface of a structure causing fracture before it extends through the thickness, where it would be visible or cause leakage.

Time under stress is not a factor at normal working stresses at low temperatures. Creep is virtually nonexistent and is not commonly considered in cryogenic design. Fatigue may be important, but because fatigue strength, like static strength, is higher at subzero temperatures than at room temperature, no new or unusual problems are present.

There are few practical corrosion problems for aluminum and its alloys at cryogenic temperatures, because most cryogenic en-

Fig. 3. Aluminum air-separation tower 126 ft high and 11 ft in diameter. The unit contains 60 miles of aluminum tube in the reboiler section and employs 200,000 lb of aluminum. It can produce 800 tons of vapor oxygen and 500 tons of vapor nitrogen daily.

vironments are noncorrosive to aluminum. One possible problem sometimes considered with aluminum-magnesium alloys containing more than 3% Mg is sensitization as a result of occasional deriming operations at 150 to 300 F. This could lead to stress-corrosion cracking, although no service failures have been reported. If necessary, sensitization may be removed by a heat treatment or avoided by the selection of alloy 5454.

Applications

Aluminum alloys are widely used in low-temperature liquefaction and gas-separation process plants (9). For equipment such as distillation columns and pressure vessels, alloy 5083 or 5456 in the H321 temper is employed for shells and heads, and the internals, if any, are of 3003-O or H14 (Fig. 3).

Aluminum alloys are used in heat exchangers, especially in two types that are well suited for low-temperature process plants.

Fig. 4. Brazed sheet-and-fin heat exchanger for air-separation plant. Fabrication of aluminum cryogenic equipment is facilitated by good welding and brazing characteristics of alloys used.

Dip-brazed aluminum heat exchangers (Fig. 4) provide a large heat transfer area in a relatively small, economical package. These units consist of alternate layers of corrugated fins and separator sheets, employing brazing sheet having a 3003 alloy core. Heat exchanger cores are assembled, connected to headers, and incorporated in the cold box of air-separation plants. Similar units are used at other cryogenic facilities, including methane liquefaction plants.

Aluminum has been used in wound exchangers (Fig. 5) for helium plants and more recently for methane liquefaction plants. These employ hundreds of miles of small diameter 3003-O tube wound in layers around a core. Assemblies are placed in cylindrical shells of 5083-O or 5083-H321 alloy.

Piping and fittings can be of the more standard alloy 3003-H112 or 6061-T6. The pipe is extruded, and the fittings and

Air Products and Chemicals, Inc.

g. 5. Coiled tube bundle for helium-processing heat exchanger containing 200 iles of aluminum tube is covered with a shroud and telescopes into a shell that is ½ ft in diameter and 80 ft long and is fabricated from 2-in.-thick aluminum plate.

flanges are forged. Alloy 5083-H113 extruded pipe or 5083-H321 pipe made from rolled and welded plate is employed where higher strength is required.

Process piping and instrument lines must penetrate the insulated space between the two walls of cold boxes and other double-wall units. To minimize heat absorption from the surrounding air, the section of pipe that passes through that space is often made of type 304 stainless steel, because of its relatively low thermal conductivity. The stainless steel pipe is joined to aluminum pipe by special transition joints, generally involving an aluminum alloy pipe or sleeve metallurgically bonded to a length of stainless steel pipe. Some designs employ an interlayer of a third metal, such as silver. Others employ composite plate in which stainless steel is metallurgically bonded to aluminum.

Cryogenic handling and storage units of aluminum alloys

Light weight of aluminum enabled construction of the entire inner sphere before positioning the outside steel shell. Alloy 5083 vessel holds 90,000 gal of liquid hydrogen at −423 F. Space between 29-ft-diam aluminum sphere and 35-ft-diam steel shell is filled with perlite particulate and evacuated. Design is based on an evaporation rate of only 0.13% per day.

Fig. 6. Storage tank for liquid hydrogen

range in size from a few gallons to hundreds of thousands of gallons. They invariably involve double-wall units, the inner container aluminum and the outer aluminum or carbon steel. Insulation is provided by a vacuum in the annular space, by particulate thermal insulation, or a combination of the two. The configuration usually is cylindrical; sometimes spherical containers are used to take advantage of the low surface-to-volume ratio, which minimizes the effect of heat penetration from the environment (Fig. 6). In small units, alloy 3003 is employed in a temper suitable for the forming operation. For larger spherical or flat-bottom cylindrical tanks, the high-strength, weldable 5*xxx* series alloys are used for the inner tank and often for the outer tank. In the larger field-erected, vertical cylindrical storage tanks, tapered plate in 5083-H111 alloy provides maximum economy. Tapered design makes it possible to eliminate unneeded material, because the thickness at any level is that required only by loading and stress considerations. Welding costs are also reduced, because the average thickness welded is less.

Tapered 5083-O plate was recently used in constructing the inner shell of a large double-wall tank for liquefied natural gas. This 72,000-barrel tank was 71.5 ft in diameter and 101 ft high. Two courses of tapered plate were employed for maximum economy. Liquid oxygen, nitrogen, and hydrogen are also stored in aluminum tanks.

For dewar transport vessels, such as portable cryogenic tanks, aluminum is used for both inner and outer shells, to reduce weight. Another advantage of aluminum outer shells compared to steel is the additional insulation provided by aluminum's higher reflectance outside and lower emissivity inside. The low outgassing rate of aluminum contributes to the vacuum integrity of dewar installations.

Double-wall aluminum semitrailers have been in service for several years transporting liquid oxygen and liquid nitrogen. One 4000-gal unit for liquid oxygen, built primarily of alloy 5083-H321, is 11,000 lb lighter and has 40% more load capacity than similar units built of steel. For the inner vessels of railroad tank cars employed to transport cryogenic liquids, 5*xxx* alloys are preferred. These alloys should also be considered for the insulated tanks installed in vessels for marine transport of cryogenic fluids. Aluminum tanks in a steel hull would reduce draft; to attain minimum draft, an aluminum hull also should be employed.

The "Methane Pioneer" demonstrated that ocean transport of

liquid methane is economically feasible. The vessel, carrying 2000 tons of liquid methane in five aluminum tanks, made regular trips from the Gulf Coast of the United States to England. Two sister ships, "Methane Princess" and "Methane Progress", transport liquid methane from Algeria to England. The two ships, each equipped with nine alloy 5083-H321 tanks, can carry about 13,000 tons of liquid methane, enough to provide a year's supply of gas to a quarter million people. Aluminum tanks and piping serve in the dockside liquefaction and receiving plants.

Cryogenic uses of aluminum in the aerospace industry are discussed in Chapter 18 in this volume.

References

1 J. G. Kaufman and F. G. Nelson, Cryogenic Temperatures Up Fatigue Strengths of Al-Mg Alloys, Space/Aeronautics, 38, 1, 91–96 (1962)
2 J. G. Kaufman and Marshall Holt, Fracture Characteristics of Aluminum Alloys, Alcoa Research Laboratories Technical Paper No. 18, 1965
3 J. D. Jackson, W. K. Boyd and P. D. Miller, Reactivity of Metals with Liquid and Gaseous Oxygen, DMIC Memorandum 163, 1965; A. H. Singleton, et al, Corrosion of Metals by Liquid Fluorine, Industrial and Engineering Chemistry, 57, 3, 47–53 (1965)
4 J. G. Kaufman, F. G. Nelson and E. W. Johnson, The Properties of Aluminum Alloy 2219 Sheet, Plate and Welded Joints at Low Temperatures, Advances in Cryogenic Engineering, 8, 661–670 (1963)
5 Marshall Holt, J. G. Kaufman and E. T. Wanderer, Aluminum and Aluminum Alloys for Pressure Vessels, Welding Research Council Bulletin 75, 1962
6 J. E. Campbell, Aluminum Alloys for Cryogenic Service, Materials Research & Standards, 4, 540–548 (1964); L. P. Rice, J. E. Campbell and W. F. Simmons, Tensile Behavior of Parent Metal and Welded 5000-Series Aluminum-Alloy Plate at Room and Cryogenic Temperatures, Advances in Cryogenic Engineering, 7, 478–489 (1962); L. P. Rice, J. E. Campbell and W. F. Simmons, The Tensile Property Evaluation of One 5000-Series Aluminum Alloy at the Temperature of Liquid Helium, Advances in Cryogenic Engineering, 8, 671–677 (1963)
7 F. G. Nelson and F. M. Howell, Strength and Ductility of Butt Welds in Aluminum Alloy Plate, Welding Journal, Research Supplement, 31, 397s–402s (1952)
8 W. A. Anderson, J. G. Kaufman and J. E. Kane, Notch Sensitivity of Aluminum-Zinc-Magnesium Alloys at Cryogenic Temperatures, Advances in Cryogenic Engineering, 9, 107–111 (1964)
9 J. G. Kaufman and E. T. Wanderer, Aluminum for Cryogenic Applications, Machine Design, 37, 30, 199–205 (1965)
10 "Cryogenic Materials Data Handbook", ML-TDR-64-280, Air Force Materials Laboratory, August 1964. Contains low-temperature property data for 12 aluminum alloys, plotted against temperature in 163 graphs.

Chapter 14

Internal Combustion Engines

W. C. KEITH, R. F. SCHAEFER and J. M. SMITH

THE FIRST application of aluminum in an internal combustion engine was in the crankcase of the 1897 Clark three-wheel automobile. In the early 1900's, aluminum castings were first used for engine parts. Application of aluminum to automotive engines after the first World War was stimulated by experience gained in military equipment. In the early 1920's, cast crankcases, cylinder heads, and split-skirt pistons for passenger cars consumed many millions of pounds of aluminum. Forged connecting rods alone required over a million pounds per year. Late in the decade, trucks and buses started to utilize aluminum for engine parts, to increase payload.

The low density of aluminum is of particular importance in the reciprocating parts of engines; the lower inertia permits increased engine speed and efficiency. High thermal conductivity is advantageous for thermally loaded parts such as pistons, cylinder blocks and heads.

This chapter deals with the various current types of internal combustion engines for automotive, marine and railroad motive power and for many types of stationary applications. The principal discussion here is on engines for passenger cars and commercial automotive vehicles. For additional information on motive power for other applications, the reader may refer to Chapters 16, 17, 18, and 19 in this volume.

W. C. Keith is manager, Application Engineering Div., Aluminum Company of America, New Kensington. R. F. Schaefer is an application engineer for cast and forged products — transportation and engines, Application Engineering Div., Aluminum Company of America, Cleveland. Before his retirement in January 1965, J. M. Smith was manager for transportation, Sales Development Div., Aluminum Company of America, Cleveland.

Gasoline engines are discussed separately from diesel and multifuel engines, because design considerations are quite different for many components. Since many other components are similar in both engine types, a reading of the appropriate paragraphs in both sections is necessary for coverage of all details.

GASOLINE ENGINES

Aluminum now is used for many gasoline engine parts. The "all-aluminum" engine has been adopted for several applications, utilizing aluminum for substantially all components except the crankshaft, camshaft, piston rings, and cylinder liners (1).

Cast aluminum engine and accessory parts can, with a few design changes, be produced in sand molds similar to those employed for iron parts. For most aluminum parts, however, high-production permanent mold or die casting (2) is used (Volume II, Chapter 5 and Volume III, Chapter 2).

Cylinder Blocks for Gasoline Engines

Cylinder blocks are one-piece castings that contain the cylinders and support the crankshaft, camshaft, and other engine components. Only in the die cast design has the aluminum cylinder block become economically competitive with cast iron. In order to accomplish this, several design departures are required. Practicability of the die cast cylinder block was shown in the early 1960's when two passenger-car engine designs were produced in considerable quantity. Coated or plated aluminum pistons successfully operate directly on specially finished aluminum cylinder bores. A hypereutectic alloy with 17% Si and 4.5% Cu has given good performance. Practical casting problems, involving the need for very close tolerances and high-quality die castings, have required iron liner inserts for the cylinder walls of commercial multicylinder aluminum engines. Three accepted methods (Fig. 1) are (*a*) the cast-in-place dry liner, (*b*) a dry liner inserted after machining, and (*c*) a wet liner (7).

The cast-in dry liner is provided with a cast surface with suitable projections, or a rough-machined surface with grooves or coarse threads, to mechanically bond the iron liner to the aluminum cast around it.

The dry liner, inserted after machining, requires close-tolerance machining of the aluminum bores and the outside of the

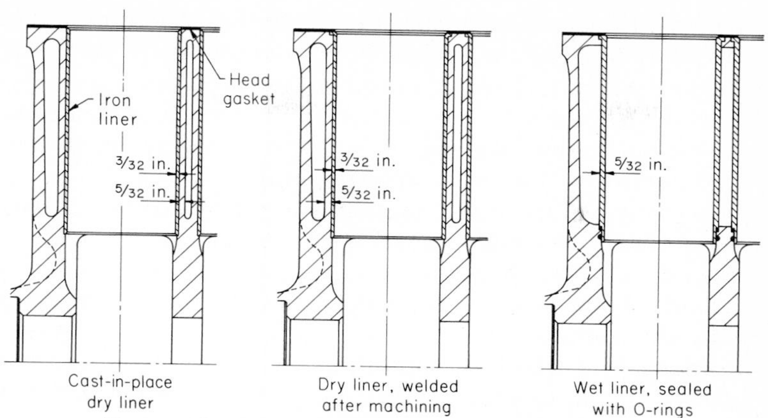

Fig. 1. Three production methods of assembling iron liners in a cast aluminum cylinder block

liner. Counteracting this more costly operation is the less expensive block casting; multiple inserts are not needed.

The wet liner, as the name implies, contacts the cooling liquid and must be provided with O-ring neoprene sealing gaskets at the bottom; the head gasket seals the top. Although the wet liner completely assembled in an engine is the most costly of the three types, its use permits a greatly simplified aluminum casting. The water jacket becomes a rectangular box in which the wet liners are inserted, in contrast to the more complicated cored casting in a dry-liner engine block. Handling and reclaiming dry liners, and the time required to set inserts in the die during the casting cycle also are avoided.

Conventional die cast alloys, such as 13, 380, and 384, are satisfactory for cylinder blocks (Volume III, Chapter 2). Where openings resulting from the casting operation are to be closed permanently, cup plugs of either terne plate or hot dip galvanized steel are recommended over aluminum, because its low modulus of elasticity provides a lower-pressure seal. For equal pressure of an aluminum cup against the hole wall, a heavier gage would be required, making installation difficult and more costly.

For heavy-duty engines, alloys 355-T7, 356-T5, or 356-T6 are generally used as permanent mold or semipermanent mold cylinder blocks; they provide good casting and machining characteristics and dimensional stability. Designing for high strength in the structure of a heavy-duty engine usually results in wall sections too thick to be die cast. Furthermore, production quantities are now insufficient to justify consideration of die casting, and seldom warrant the full permanent mold process.

Holes for threaded fasteners that must be disassembled many times during engine life should be provided with steel screw-thread inserts to reduce wear and stripping.

The cylinder block must support the crankshaft in accurate alignment from bearing to bearing under fluctuating loads and must accurately locate and support the cylinder bores. Cylinder-head loads, both assembly and operational, must be sustained through the cylinder-block walls and bosses. In one wet-liner engine design, in which the liner bottoms against a flange at the lower end, an additional load that results from the preload of the cylinder-head gasket is sustained by the jacket walls.

In the die cast aluminum cylinder block (Fig. 2), the main-bearing bridges are characterized by smooth, flat sides extending upward to the cylinders and water jacket (3). Coring from the outside or through the oil-pan opening removes excess material, to save cost and weight, and reduces unsoundness in heavy die cast sections. Careful attention to design of the main-bearing bridge area results in the best compromise involving load distribution, gradual section changes, thickness of cast sections, and draft requirements of the casting process. In most designs, the main-bearing bridges are line bored to receive the precision shell bearings, against which the crankshaft rotates. The differential expansion between aluminum main-bearing bore and steel-backed bearing insert shells relieves the interference as operating temperatures are approached. Ferrous bearing caps, which reduce this differential expansion, are specified by automotive manufacturers in the United States, although European designers have employed aluminum bearing caps successfully.

The main-bearing cap is retained in the cylinder block in a lateral direction by an interference fit in the machined seat for the cap. The cap must be securely retained, so that it does not fret and wear at the parting line. The corners of the seat for the bearing cap should be generously filleted, to reduce a serious stress concentration at a highly loaded point. The main-bearing cap bolts should extend far enough into the bridge to distribute the very high loading adequately.

Because aluminum has a lower yield strength and modulus of elasticity than iron, hold-down bolt locations, diameter and thickness of washers, part rigidity, and assembly devices should be designed so that loads may transfer as directly as possible to supporting walls, with minimum distortion. Abrupt section changes and stress concentrations must be avoided, to keep the repetitive operating stresses within the fatigue limit of the alloy.

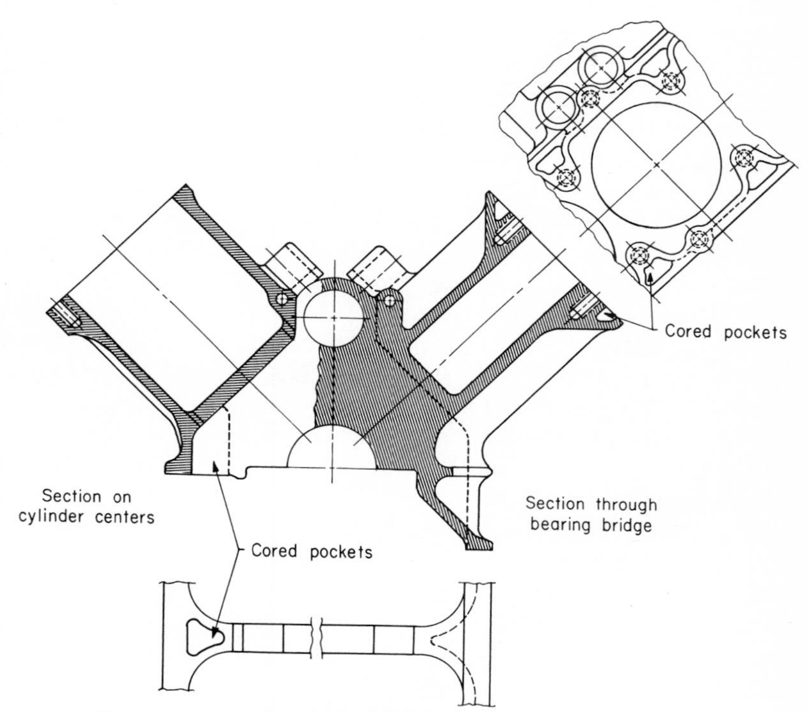

Fig. 2. Section through aluminum die cast V-type cylinder block, showing typical cored openings and proportional thickness of load-carrying members

Cylinder blocks for commercial-vehicle engines differ little from the configuration and function of lighter-duty passenger-car engines. The basic difference is the physically greater size and more substantial construction of commercial engines.

Bearings for Gasoline Engines

About a fourth of currently manufactured passenger cars are equipped with steel-backed aluminum bearings; aluminum is less often used with heavy-duty gasoline engines. The aluminum bearing conventionally employed for the main and connecting rods in passenger-car engines is made by bonding aluminum bearing-alloy sheet to a steel back with an overlay of electrodeposited tin or lead-tin alloy. Chapter 20 in this volume contains

Top view shows pressed-in iron valve guides, cored bolt holes, and gas passages; bottom view, combustion chamber with pressed-in ferrous valve-seat inserts.

Fig. 3. Four-cylinder liquid-cooled head for a 200-hp V-8 passenger-car engine, made as a semipermanent mold casting

an extensive discussion of bearing alloys, including forms and production methods, as well as their advantages, performance and design.

All passenger-car thin-shell bearings are steel shells with a lining of bearing material—babbitt, copper-lead with lead-tin overlay, aluminum alloy sheet with lead-tin overlay, or 20% Sn aluminum alloy X8081, which requires no overlay. The two precision half-shells forming one bearing assembly are located in the bearing bore and in the cap by lugs and also by predetermined interference fit.

Aluminum bearings in gasoline engines demonstrate excellent durability, compatibility with journal surfaces, conformability to misalignment, embeddability, and high thermal conductivity. They are highly resistant to organic acids formed by engine-oil oxidation, additives in heavy-duty inhibited oils, and contaminants acquired during engine operation.

Camshaft bearing loads and speeds are such that the journals could be operated directly against the aluminum cylinder block. However, practical service problems require that renewable thin-shell bushings be used instead. Both steel-backed and solid aluminum bearings are employed.

Cylinder Heads for Gasoline Engines

Liquid-Cooled Cylinder Heads. The almost universal adoption of the overhead-valve engine has resulted in great complication of the cylinder head (Fig. 3). The formerly popular L-head engine made frequent use of aluminum cylinder heads on iron blocks. The complexities introduced by the overhead-valve design increased the relative cost of producing semipermanent mold heads, so that today aluminum heads are less extensively used, except in all-aluminum engines.

Cylinder heads that are now produced include multiple combustion chambers with integral valve-port passages, bosses for spark plugs and valve guides, and provision for mounting the valve-actuating mechanism. Coolant passages are proportioned and located to cool the thermally loaded areas, while permitting symmetrical cylinder-head fastening. No acceptable design of this intricate part has yet been developed that can be cast by the full permanent mold or die casting process. Therefore, aluminum cylinder heads are cast in semipermanent molds, using sand cores for internal passages. For most economical design, the coring should neither be fragile nor complex, nor require pasting together of core sections. It should be possible to incorporate all cores in a one-piece unit for placement in the mold.

The physical size of the commercial heavy-duty engine requires multiple cylinder heads, each covering two or three cylinders. The shorter head lengths reduce thermal expansion problems but require slip joints in gas manifolds and the use of coolant-collection manifolds.

The cylinder head transfers heat to the coolant, maintaining thermally loaded areas at safe temperatures. Laboratory data show that the high conductivity of aluminum results in lower operating temperatures of valves, contributing to knock-free operation with fuels of lower octane.

Low temperatures at the combustion surface reduce heating of the unburned charge, and thus increase volumetric efficiency and specific output of the engine. Spark plug temperatures are lower in an aluminum head than in a similar head made of cast iron.

Alloys 333-F, 333-T5, or 355-T5 are commonly used for these semipermanent mold castings. The alloys have good foundry and machining characteristics and provide leaktightness and favorable resistance to corrosion.

Ferrous valve-seat and guide inserts conventionally are used in aluminum cylinder heads to withstand the high temperatures, pounding, and wear. These inserts usually are installed with interference fits; the seat inserts occasionally are secured by additional staking or rolling of the aluminum around the circumference.

Cylinder-head fasteners preferably are cap screws; they should be provided with hardened, flat-ground steel washers to prevent galling. Boss area and washer diameter and thickness must be sufficient to sustain and distribute the bolt load. To avoid valve-seat distortion, bosses and port passages should not be connected. Proportioning of metal sections can reduce thermal gradients in heavy-duty commercial engine heads, resulting in lower thermal fatigue stresses.

Air-Cooled Cylinder Heads. Cooling requirements of air-cooled engines, popular in small rear-engine passenger cars, demand the high thermal conductivity of aluminum alloys. Fins integral with the cylinder head dissipate heat to forced cooling air. Although the outside contours of the head are formed readily in a permanent mold, the gas passages of the most efficient designs require sand cores. Therefore, some production heads are cast by the semipermanent mold process (Volume III, Chapter 2) in alloy 356-T5. Alloys 333-F, 333-T5 or 355-T5 may be preferred for certain designs. For die cast heads, alloys 13 and 380 are suitable.

Pistons for Gasoline Engines

Trunk-type aluminum pistons, introduced in passenger-car engines before the first World War, were the predecessors of modern heavy-duty commercial gasoline engine pistons. The 1920 split-skirt and 1925 steel-strut designs set the pattern for today's passenger-car engine.

The universal acceptance of aluminum pistons by all gasoline engine manufacturers in the United States can be attributed to light weight and high thermal conductivity.

The effect of the lower inertia of aluminum pistons on bearing loading permits higher engine speeds and reduced crankshaft counterweighting. Although the piston crown (top surface of the piston head) is exposed to the high temperature of burning fuel, rapid heat conduction reduces crown temperatures to a level that does not promote combustion abnormalities.

Aluminum automotive pistons generally are permanent mold castings, although recently some interest has been evidenced in forged or impact-extruded pistons to achieve longer fatigue life for very-high-output automobile engines, especially if supercharged. However, the permanent mold design is superior in economy and design flexibility.

The alloy generally used for passenger-car pistons, F132-T5, has an excellent combination of foundry, mechanical, and physical characteristics, including low thermal expansion. Heat treatment increases hardness for improved machinability and eliminates permanent change in dimensions from residual growth (Volume I, Chapters 5 and 6) at operating temperatures. Forged 2618-T61 or 4032-T6 pistons have similar characteristics.

Piston alloys for heavy-duty engines include low-expansion alloys A132-T551 and F132-T5. Alloy 142-T571 also is employed in some heavy-duty pistons, because of its higher thermal conductivity and superior properties at elevated-temperature. However, it is more difficult to cast than competitive alloys, and thus more costly.

Forged pistons have not been applied widely in automotive vehicles. At temperatures above 400 F, the hardness of forged piston alloy 4032-T6 is lower than that of cast alloy A132-T551 or F132-T5. Until a satisfactory method is devised to bond a ring-groove insert in a forging or an elevated-temperature alloy is developed, forged pistons will be inferior in the important factor of groove wear.

Piston design has involved considerable exercise of individual ingenuity and thus represents a combination of science, art, and trial. Pistons must operate without scuffing over a temperature range of about −30 to +500 F, transfer heat effectively to the cylinder walls and lubricating oil, withstand and transmit explosion loads that may exceed 1000 psi, and retain oil and compression rings in correct alignment. All these functions must be accomplished with minimum noise.

Because the aluminum piston and the iron cylinder in which it operates are at different temperatures and differ in thermal expansion, clearance between them varies considerably. Design features that create a thermal barrier, such as suitable slots, permit the skirt (bearing surface) of the piston to expand independently of the high-temperature crown. The skirt is cam ground with a larger clearance in the wrist-pin direction than in the thrust direction. This allows free skirt expansion parallel to the wrist pin, which reduces expansion in the thrust direction. Thus, the cam grinding assists in maintaining a satisfactory clearance at the thrust faces of the skirt over a wide temperature range. The clearance is made low enough to prevent noise, yet high enough to provide for an oil film.

In controlling piston clearance, cast-in steel inserts are used to supplement the slots. Because of its lower coefficient of thermal expansion, the steel insert restrains the piston from normal expansion. It also reduces contraction at low temperatures.

Heavy-duty gasoline engine pistons require heavier sections than those for passenger-vehicle engines, to support the greater combustion loads at higher operating temperatures. These engines may be supercharged, which increases the pressure and temperature at or near full throttle, where they operate a large fraction of the time.

In heavy-duty engines, the thermal control slots employed in passenger-car pistons are not provided. This strengthens and stiffens the piston crown and ring-belt area by additional support from the skirt. However, the omission of slots requires larger initial piston clearance to satisfy full-load conditions. The cold starting clearance may be so large as to cause cold-piston slap noise. This usually is not discernible or objectionable because of higher engine noise level. However, passenger-car engines modified for heavy-duty use may employ slotted pistons.

Prolonged exposure to operating temperatures that occur at the top compression-ring groove (up to 550 F) causes a signifi-

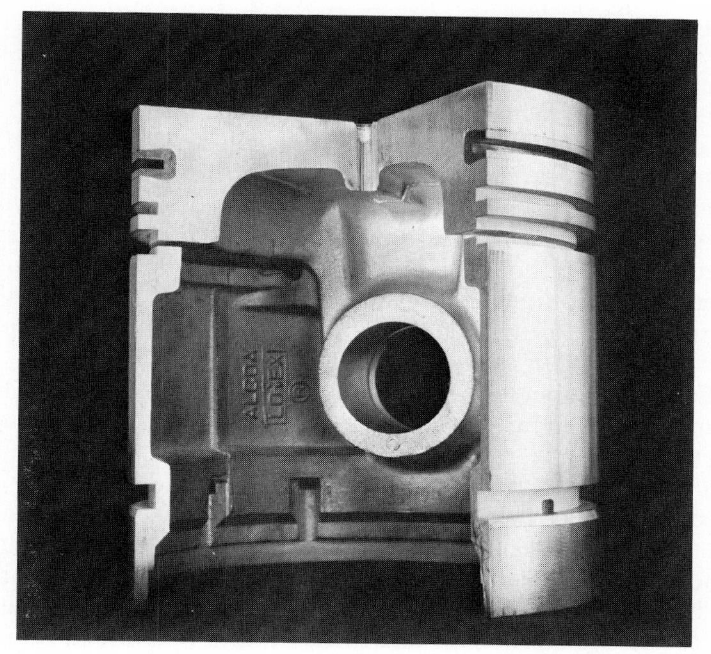

White Motor Co.

Fig. 4. Alloy F132-T5 permanent mold cast piston (shown in cutaway view). Ferrous insert reduces wear in top piston-ring groove in heavy-duty gasoline engine.

cant decrease in the hardness of aluminum piston alloys. This leads to enlargement of the ring groove, initiating a harmful sequence beginning with wear of the piston ring and groove. The wear results from ring rotation and sidewise oscillation in the presence of abrasive material; some of the abrasive material is breathed in with the combustion air and some results from corrosive and mechanical wear of the cylinder walls and piston rings.

Excessive ring-groove wear can be prevented by the use of ferrous inserts. A heavy-duty piston with a cast-in ring-groove insert of cast ferrous alloy is shown in Fig. 4. The thermal expansion of a high-nickel cast iron insert is similar to that of the aluminum-silicon piston alloys. Thus, the metallurgical bond between the insert and piston is free of differential expansion stresses, and the ring groove remains hard and wear-resistant at prolonged high operating temperatures.

Connecting Rods, Rocker Arms, Covers and Manifolds

Forged aluminum connecting rods presently are applied only in cars built or converted for racing.

The approximately 15% reduction in weight provided by aluminum reduces inertia loading, permitting higher rotative speeds, although at a higher cost. However, the larger physical dimensions required for aluminum frequently prevent this application in existing engines. Also, differential thermal expansion between an aluminum connecting rod and the steel crankshaft requires added design considerations, as described for main bearings, to prevent excessive bearing clearance variation.

Where design permits aluminum rods, forged alloy 2014-T6 is selected; its high fatigue and yield strengths permit minimum section size.

Recommended large-end fastenings are studs inserted into tapped blind holes in the rod. This eliminates a significant stress concentration that may develop when through-bolts are used.

Rocker arms of permanent mold or die cast aluminum alloy have been applied successfully in several passenger-car models. The cost saving from eliminating machining operations required for iron is the advantage of greatest interest, although the lower inertia is beneficial to valve operation. Reduction of the acceleration loads on the valve train permits higher engine speeds with satisfactory valve motion. This effect also is becoming significant in commercial engines as design speeds are increased.

Valve-mechanism components must be designed with minimum weight compatible with satisfactory rigidity. A pressed-in ferrous insert in an aluminum rocker arm resists wear of valve-stem contact; a staked-in-place, sintered seat receives the hemispherical end of the push rod. An alternate design utilizes a ball-end or hemispherically recessed valve-lash adjusting screw.

Alloys such as 333-T5 or 380 have satisfactory strength and bearing characteristics for this application.

Front engine covers close the open cylinder block end, where the camshaft drive usually is located. Aluminum covers, employed on most current automobiles, are alloy 13 or 380, die cast with integral subassemblies, such as the oil-pump body, distributor drive, fuel-pump mounting, and crankshaft front seal. The front surface of the cover forms the rear of the water pump impeller chamber, which is closed by the pump cover carrying the pump-shaft bearings. The front engine cover is representative of aluminum die cast parts that perform many functions, but require few machining operations.

Inlet manifolds are produced as semipermanent mold castings; their configuration is not adaptable to the die casting process. On high-performance engines, their light weight compared to cast iron, and improved fuel-mixture distribution resulting from high thermal conductivity, have justified a cost premium for aluminum. The alloys used are 333-F or 356-T5.

Both coolant and exhaust-warmed inlet manifolds are made of aluminum. Combining the two warming methods, with an integrally cast cylinder head and inlet manifold, is possibly best.

Heat Exchangers, Liquid Cooling Systems, and Air Conditioners

Many thousands of dip-brazed heat exchangers are in service in aircraft and military vehicles, dating from 1942. During recent years, over 150,000 dip-brazed automobile radiators have been placed in general service on one passenger-car model, mostly in conjunction with iron cylinder blocks and other iron parts containing the coolant. The good corrosion resistance on external surfaces and high thermal conductivity of aluminum are advantages in this application. Commercial coolant inhibitors, as well as those incorporated in ethylene glycol-based antifreeze solutions, are effective in reducing corrosion of all metallic areas in the cooling system. Radiator and engine-block cleaning solutions labeled suitable for aluminum have been found satisfactory.

Tubes, tanks, and headers are generally No. 12 brazing sheet; fins are alloy 3003. Aluminum heat exchangers are manufactured by three processes: dip brazing, furnace soldering, and tubes mechanically expanded against fins combined with soldered return bends. Dip brazing (Volume III, Chapter 13) is best for most heat exchangers; it is employed for the radiators now in production.

In the drawn-cup, tube-and-fin heat exchanger (Fig. 5), the line contact established between surfaces to be brazed assures adequate fillets. The contact is accomplished by a jig that applies pressure in holding the drawn cups together (7).

Aluminum is employed also for dip-brazed automatic-transmission oil coolers on passenger cars and commercial vehicles.

Liquid Cooling Systems. Aluminum die castings are applied successfully for various engine parts that contact the coolant,

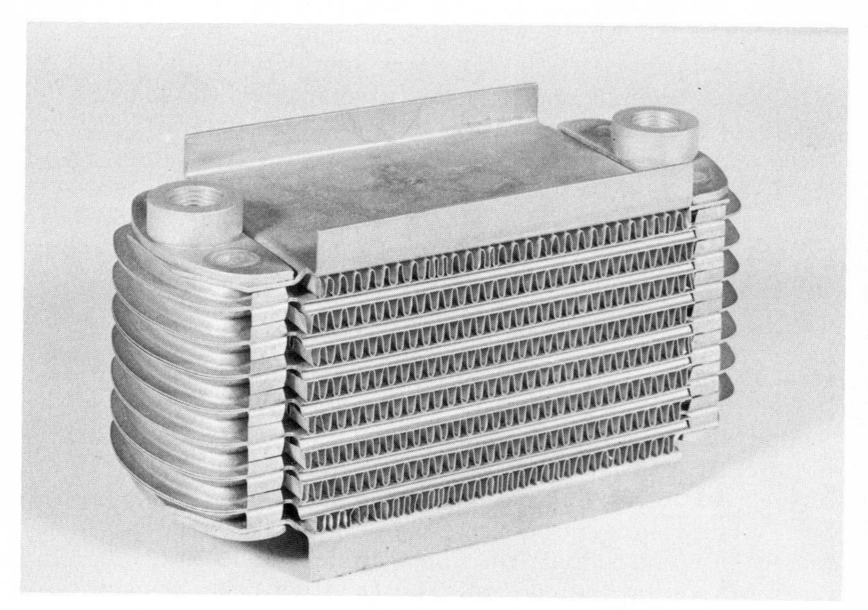

Fig. 5. Drawn aluminum sheet tube-and-fin heat exchanger that was joined by dip brazing

such as the cylinder block, thermostat housing, and water pump (4). The cost usually is lower than for alternate cast iron parts. Alloys 13 and 360 are satisfactory.

Coolant circulation rate in engines is high, reflecting a trend to the smallest components possible, to minimize engine size. Velocities over 30 ft per sec have led to erosion and cavitation problems. Although coolant systems are commonly under pressure, typically 12 to 25 psi, rapid circulation of hot coolant through restricted passages, with severe changes of direction and cross section, may create low local static pressures. These areas may be subject to formation of vapor bubbles that collapse on the metal surface, resulting in cavitation (Volume I, Chapter 7). To minimize the risk of perforation, coolant passages should be of ample size, with gradual changes of flow area and direction.

A relatively large, slow-speed pump reduces the possibility of erosion and cavitation problems in pump areas. Thorough production cleaning of all coolant-carrying sand cored parts minimizes entrained sand, which would be abrasive if circulated.

Alcohol-base antifreezes are not recommended in cooling

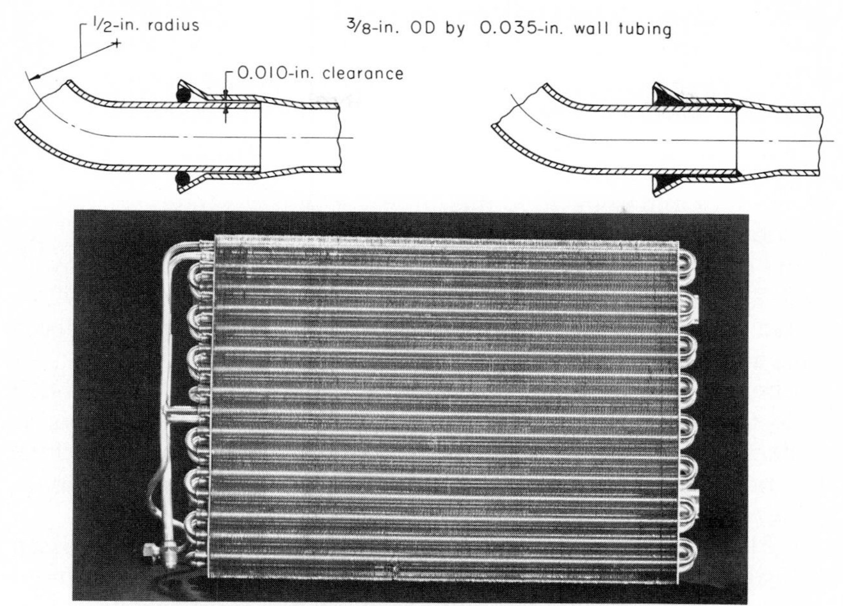

Fig. 6. Aluminum automobile air-conditioning condenser. Drawn alloy 3003 tube was expanded into alloy 7072 fins. Design details for soldered return bends are shown above.

systems combining aluminum with other metal parts, as they are likely to cause corrosion problems. Permanent-type, inhibited antifreeze solutions specifically recommended for aluminum should be employed.

Poultice corrosion can be avoided by using nonabsorbent gasket materials in the cooling system. To prevent water seepage under hose connections, wide, flat beads should be provided, with hose clamps located as close as possible to the bead to prevent accumulation of water that might cause a differential aeration corrosion cell.

Misregistry of ports carrying cooling water from one part to another can result in erosion. Where an aluminum part is connected to a dissimilar metal part, such erosion accelerates any galvanic corrosion that may occur. Considerable reduction in erosion and galvanic corrosion can be achieved by a gasket with a metering hole smaller than the openings on the mating parts. The gasket introduces a longer path for the corrosion currents.

The use of coatings to reduce erosion or corrosion, although plausible, is not recommended. Coating integrity is nearly impossible to achieve in production, and each slight discontinuity is a potential area of concentrated attack, which could penetrate the casting surface more rapidly than if there were no coating.

Air Conditioners. More than three million dip-brazed aluminum automobile air-conditioner evaporators are in service. Like automotive radiators, they are constructed of No. 12 brazing sheet tubes and alloy 3003 fins.

The condensers, located in front of automobile radiators, are made of aluminum. Two manufacturing methods are employed. In the first, alloy 3003 drawn tube is expanded into alloy 7072 or alclad 3003 fin stock; the return bends are flame soldered automatically (Fig. 6).

The second method consists of furnace soldering extruded 6063 tubes to alloy 3003 fins. A flux is required that reacts at soldering temperature to plate zinc on the aluminum surface (Volume III, Chapter 14). Under some conditions, no additional solder is needed.

Both types of condenser have shown excellent corrosion performance, on the surfaces exposed to highway environment and on those in contact with refrigerant. Joint strength has proved to be adequate under the cyclic stress conditions.

Aluminum hookup tubing and fittings perform well; they are used with most aluminum refrigerant systems and must compete on a cost-per-piece basis with other materials. Alloy 3003 tubing and 6262-T9 fittings are recommended, thus eliminating galvanic corrosion caused by heavy-metal contacts.

Aluminum is widely used for compressor crankcases, pistons, and connecting rods, generally as die or permanent mold castings, to attain low cost and to reduce machining requirements. Alloys 380 and 333-F are commonly employed.

Accessory Parts for Gasoline Engines

Engine-accessory parts include several commonly produced as aluminum die castings, such as carburetor bodies, throttle bodies, distributor housings, fuel and oil pumps, oil-filter adapters, fan spacers, and rocker-shaft supports. These parts are die cast in aluminum because the process provides superior dimensional accuracy, adequate strength under loading conditions, and integral design features at minimum cost.

Occasionally, cover plates are die cast in aluminum. For some commercial truck engines, die cast valve covers and oil pans achieve economies compared to fabrication in steel. Decorative effects are designed into the valve cover. These die cast parts generally are complex, incorporating bosses or mounting pads that would require costly assembly in other materials. Simple cover plates are usually uneconomical in aluminum unless a specific physical property is vital to the function of the unit.

End bells for starters and generators, and stator housings for alternators, are excellent die casting applications. The alloy for die cast engine-accessory parts is generally 13 or 380.

Distributor-cap inserts, formerly of brass or copper, are almost universally aluminum for economy, in alloy 2011-T3 or 3003-H18 (Volume III, Chapter 8).

Impact extrusions (Volume III, Chapter 4), typically in 6061-T6, are used for various parts, including speedometer drums, power-steering components, spark-plug tubes, oil-filter cans, and transmission torque-reaction shafts.

Various types of superchargers occasionally are employed for heavy-duty gasoline engines and have had sporadic use in the passenger-car field. They are discussed subsequently in this chapter. Parts commonly in aluminum are rotors, impellers, and housings, which are sand, plaster, or permanent mold cast.

DIESEL, DUAL-FUEL AND MULTIFUEL ENGINES

The diesel is a compression-ignition engine operating on fuel oil injected under high pressure into the combustion chamber, where it is atomized and ignited by the high temperature of compression. The fuel oil varies from a high-grade kerosene type to the low-grade residual type (Bunker C).

Diesel engines differ from gasoline engines not only in fuel, but in many design features and in kind of service (5). Their outstanding advantage is their use of cheap fuel of low flammability, a benefit gained by sacrificing ease and flexibility of operation and acceptability of exhaust products. Diesel engines also are noisier and more costly than gasoline engines. These limitations discourage their use in passenger cars.

However, diesels are used for many heavy-duty applications. They power a majority of the buses and virtually all heavy trucks. Their use in light trucks is substantial and growing. Since these engines are operated at or near full power capacity much of the time, and because of higher combustion pressures, they are somewhat more ruggedly constructed than gasoline engines.

Compression ratios are as high as 20 to 1 (compared to a maximum of about 11 to 1 in gasoline engines), and many models are turbocharged. Most medium-power to high-power units, ranging from 200 to 5000 bhp, are turbocharged, permitting up to twice the power from the same size engine.

Dual-fuel engines, also of the compression-ignition type, operate either on diesel fuel oil or on a mixture of gas with a small quantity of fuel oil that ignites the gas. These engines can utilize natural gas, manufactured gas, propane, and sewage gas or other suitable byproducts of industrial processes. However, some engines operating on natural gas have lower compression and require spark ignition.

The multifuel engine is a compression-ignition power plant variety of special interest for military applications. With its swirl-type combustion system, it can utilize diesel fuel, jet (JP4) fuel, or gasoline, whichever is available.

Fig. 7. Sand cast 585-lb crankcases used in 750-hp diesel engines to power vehicles

Continental Motors Corp.

Aluminum is employed extensively in these various types of heavy-duty engines, especially in those used for transportation, where increased payload is an important economic advantage.

Cylinder Blocks and Crankcases for Diesel Engines

Cylinder blocks and crankcases, the largest engine components, provide the maximum weight reduction opportunity through conversion to aluminum. The cylinder block and crankcase are integral in liquid-cooled engines; these castings are aluminum for some commercial and many military models. Wet cast iron cylinder liners are conventional, regardless of block material, to facilitate maintenance.

Air-cooled diesel engines, produced mostly for military applications, have separately cast cylinder heads and crankcases, both generally in aluminum (Fig. 7).

Aluminum cylinder-block or crankcase castings are designed so that the most economical casting process feasible (die, semipermanent mold, permanent mold, or sand) can be used. Die casting almost always is eliminated because of the large size of the casting, heavy sections, or production quantity.

The full permanent mold process is employed for economy where practicable. Castings are designed with direct core draws, or collapsible or multiple cores where back drafts and undercuts are unavoidable. More intricate sections require the semipermanent mold or sand casting process. Figures 8 and 9 show a typical diesel cylinder-block design.

Alloys 355-T77 and 356-T77, generally selected for these castings, provide good machining characteristics and a low level of residual stresses, leading to excellent dimensional stability.

Bearings for Diesel Engines

An extensive discussion of aluminum bearing alloys in Chapter 20 of this volume covers compositions, tempers, forms, and casting methods; information is included on advantages, performance, and design. Comments regarding their application in gasoline engines appear previously in this chapter, beginning on page 315.

Monometallic (solid) aluminum bearings are used extensively in large internal-combustion engines on the main and connecting rod journals (6). Other bearings made of aluminum alloys

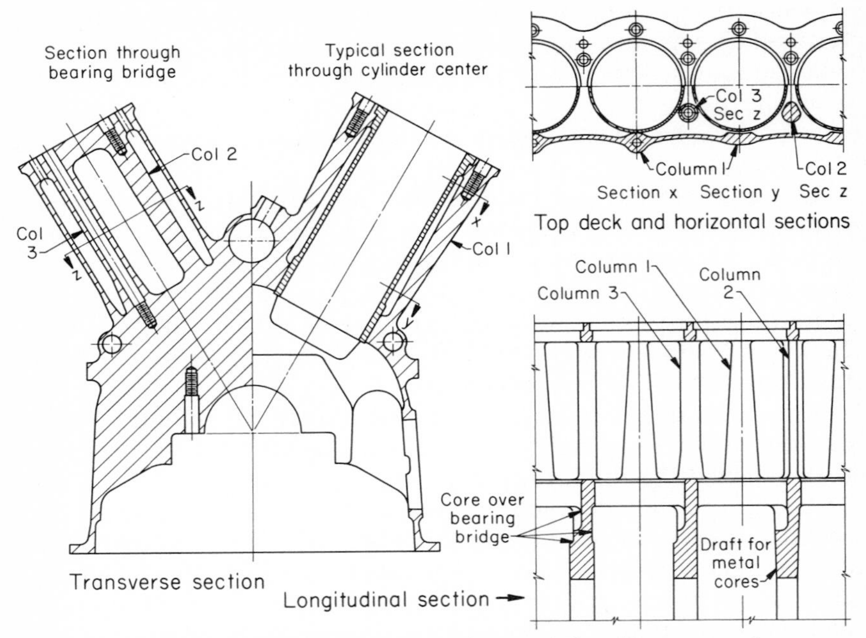

All outside and end walls were designed for direct core draws. Cylinder compartment is designed for shell or plain sand cores, with the lower end extending down into the bearing bridge for reduction of metal. Draft is shown for straight-draw metal cores at the bearing bridge. Columns 1, 2, and 3 illustrate methods of carrying firing load: Column 1 by sidewall ribs, Column 2 by solid column, and Column 3 by a long-necked stud through a cored or drilled hole in a column.

Fig. 8. Typical aluminum cylinder block for diesel engine

include the camshaft and piston-pin bushings, and thrust washers. Figure 10 shows a complete set of aluminum bearings for each cylinder of a multicylinder diesel engine.

Almost half the diesel engines with 2 to 6-in.-diam main journals have steel-backed aluminum main and connecting rod bearings; this application is increasing rapidly. Most engines with main-journal diameter exceeding 6 in. employ solid aluminum main and connecting rod bearings as standard equipment on new engines and replacement on old engines.

During recent years, the power output of a given-size diesel engine has been doubled, mainly by turbocharging. Since it generally has not been feasible to increase journal size, bearing loads have become greater. Aluminum bearings, with good pressure lubrication, can carry loads up to 10,000 psi on projected bearing area, and therefore they have been instrumental in obtaining this increased output economically from new engines, as well as applying turbocharging to engines in service.

The high resistance of aluminum to corrosive agents in lubricating oils is of extra value for diesel engines, because combustion of the heavy fuels can introduce corrosive elements into the lubricating oil.

At least half the solid aluminum bearings in diesel engines operate directly on crankshaft journals, without an electroplated overlay. Some manufacturers use a soft lead-tin overlay of 0.3 to

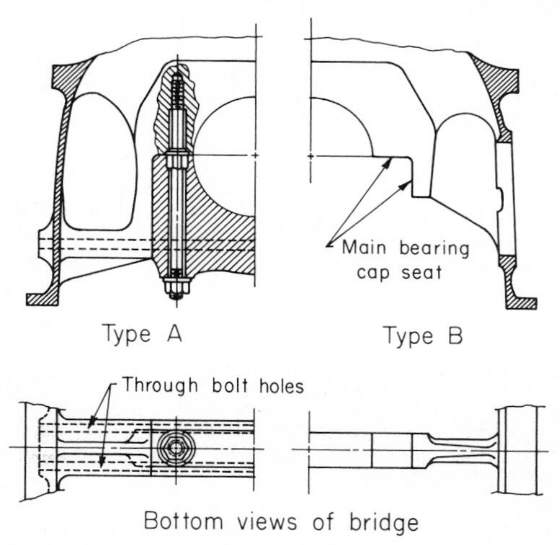

Saddles must be able to withstand severe stresses and keep crankshaft in alignment. Type A illustrates use of two through-bolts to secure bearing cap to sidewalls. Main-bearing studs should extend well up into bridge by counterboring the threaded hole. Type B illustrates conventional main-bearing retention with full surface fit of the bearing cap in the bearing saddle. Lower view shows removal of metal near main-bearing bridge.

Fig. 9. Design of main-bearing bridge in diesel cylinder block

0.7 mil to assist bearings during the run-in period, and to accommodate any slight misalignments or tight areas. An alternate method is to paint the bearing surface with a dry-film graphite-base material that is not removed by high oil pressure.

Bimetal and trimetal bearings generally have high-strength steel or bronze backing with a very thin, soft bearing-metal lining. With faulty lubrication, any failure of the lining or bond that allows the hard back to operate on the journal can cause

Fig. 10. (Top) Complete set of solid aluminum bearings required for each cylinder of a diesel engine rated at 1000 bhp per cylinder. (Bottom) Solid aluminum main bearings installed in diesel crankcase.

Fairbanks, Morse and Co.

damaging wear and scuffing of the journal. In contrast, a solid aluminum bearing seldom damages the journal if lubrication fails. One of the most valued assets of the solid aluminum bearing is that, when a crankshaft journal is damaged and must be machined to an undersize, the bearing replacement can be machined readily in the field to the necessary undersize. Bimetal bearings require either a heavier soft-metal layer, which produces a weaker bearing, or a complete new undersize back.

However, where the wall thickness of bearings is limited by available space, thin-wall solid or bimetal bearings must be used; wrought aluminum-tin bearing alloys such as 8280 or X8081 are employed for these applications. These bearings accept loads up to 10,000 psi with oil temperatures as high as 300 F, if oil pressure is adequate.

Cast solid bearings of alloy 750-T5, a relatively soft alloy, are used to replace heavy-wall bronze-backed babbitt bearings in large, slow-speed, naturally aspirated engines, for both original equipment and repair. These low-output engines have soft crankshafts (about 160 Bhn), fair lubrication pressures, and oil temperatures below 170 F.

Cast alloy 750 in the T101 temper (T5 treatment plus 4% cold work to increase compressive yield strength) is used for precision half-shell bearings as standard equipment in currently produced engines, for both naturally aspirated and turbocharged models. These engines have high bearing loads and good lubricating-oil pressure; bearing temperatures may exceed 200 F.

Alloy B750-T5 bearings, which have still higher compressive yield strength, can be used on turbocharged production engines where the loads are very high and adequate pressure lubrication is provided. This alloy also is satisfactory for loadings of 5500 psi on piston-pin bushings in standard two-cycle engines.

A unique application of B750-T5 alloy is for the master bearing in a 3000 bhp, 12-cylinder radial engine (Fig. 11). The bearing moves along a circular path on a crankshaft rotating at over 400 rpm. The center crankshaft hole has a 14-in. bore; the 12 knuckle-pin holes have a 5.5-in. bore. More than 125 of these master bearings have operated for over 10 years in standard two-cycle and turbocharged natural gas and diesel engines.

Alloy XC750-T6 is satisfactory for high loads of 7300 psi as piston-pin bushings in two-cycle turbocharged engines where the temperatures are high and the lubrication borderline.

Nordberg Manufacturing Co.

Fig. 11. Alloy B750-T5 master bearing for a 12-cylinder radial diesel engine (bottom). Bearing is 36 in. in OD and 12 in. thick, with a 14-in. bore, and weighs 715 lb.

Alloy A750-T5 bearings have good scuff resistance; they are used in large diameters for heavy machinery where the journal is relatively hard. The alloy is adaptable for casting complicated parts that perform both structural and bearing functions.

Concentric boring of precision half-shell solid aluminum bearings provides uniform wall thickness; eccentric boring is preferred to obtain more clearance at the parting line. This clearance allows foreign material to be flushed from the bearing by the lubricating oil.

Large eccentric-bored bearings in diesel engines should have oil clearance at 90° from the parting line of 0.001 in. per in. of shaft diameter. In many engines, 0.0008-in.-per-in. clearance is satisfactory, if oil pressure is adequate. The parting-line clearance should be the 90° clearance plus 0.003 in.

Cylinder Heads for Diesel Engines

Cylinder heads of aluminum are optional equipment on several models of liquid-cooled diesel engines. On air-cooled diesels, they are standard.

In both liquid-cooled and air-cooled engines, high-output turbocharged designs place exacting demands on the materials that constitute the combustion envelope. The high thermal conductivity of aluminum is especially advantageous; both in naturally aspirated and turbocharged models, high compression ratios are possible without detonation.

The low thermal-expansion stresses in an aluminum cylinder head reduce valve-seat distortion and prolong valve life; valve temperature is reduced. Valve-seat inserts have been made for many years from aluminum bronze, alloy steel, or cobalt-base alloy, for both intake and exhaust valves. Seat inserts up to 5.75 in. OD have operated successfully (Fig. 12).

Liquid-cooled diesel cylinder heads, with their multiple openings in the combustion chamber, have complicated coring, whether the head covers one or more cylinders. A head serving only a single cylinder may have an intake valve and up to four exhaust valves, a fuel-injection valve, and a starting air valve or heating unit.

Liquid-cooled cylinder heads sand cast in alloy 356-T7, specified for most designs, operate very satisfactorily. Where higher tensile and fatigue properties are required in the combustion area, C355-T77 is selected.

Air-cooled diesel cylinder heads are sand cast in 142-T77. This alloy is selected to provide high-temperature tensile and fatigue properties in the combustion area. Fins can be spaced up to six per inch over the combustion dome; fin depth is up to 3 in. Separate aluminum muffs contain ferrous cylinder liners, either cast-in or installed by shrink fitting. An integral cylinder head and cylinder has a one-piece ferrous combustion dome and liner with a finned aluminum member cast around it. An all-aluminum integral cylinder head and cylinder, cast with fins, has operated successfully. The cylinder wall is chromium plated, resulting in 0.5-mil-deep channels in the coating.

Pistons for Diesel Engines

Most four-cycle diesel engines have aluminum permanent mold cast or forged pistons, but most two-cycle diesels use pearlitic malleable or high-strength cast iron to resist high-temperature burning. Because they are subjected to higher temperatures and pressures than are encountered in gasoline engines, pistons are a critical component. Aluminum piston crown (combustion surface) temperatures range from over 700 F at the center to 450 F at the periphery. The temperature decreases to about 350 F at the top of the pin boss.

The piston head surface may be flat, crowned, or, in designs of over 12-to-1 compression ratio, recessed for the combustion pocket and possible valve pockets. The pistons are trunk type; high firing loads make design of the head rib-supports and pin boss critical.

Permanent mold cast pistons permit the greatest expression of design, both of the crown and inside contour. However, forged pistons have higher tensile and fatigue properties, especially in the pin-boss area, and they are specified where maximum firing pressures may reach 1500 psi.

Diesel pistons are permanent mold cast in A132-T551, D132-T5, F132-T5, or 142-T571 alloy. Hypereutectic aluminum-silicon alloys are used in diesel engine pistons to minimize wear of the top ring groove; their lower coefficient of expansion reduces running clearances.

Cast pistons less than 6 in. in diameter are mostly of the uncooled type, although some are oil-spray cooled under the piston head. Ferrous top compression-ring-groove inserts often are cast in. Pistons over 6 in. in diameter usually are oil cooled,

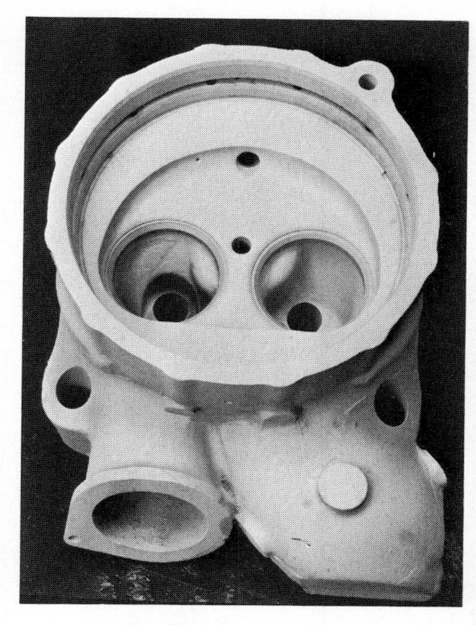

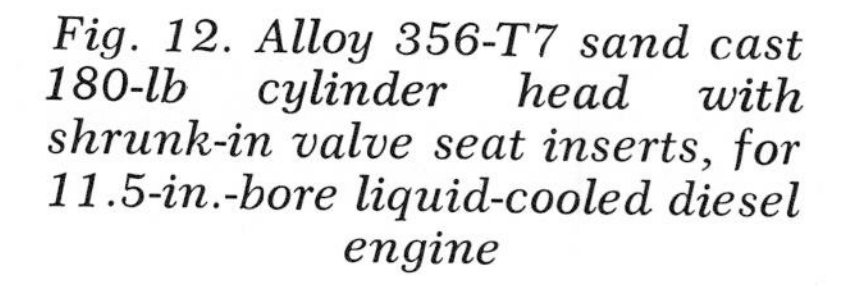

Nordberg Manufacturing Co.

Fig. 12. Alloy 356-T7 sand cast 180-lb cylinder head with shrunk-in valve seat inserts, for 11.5-in.-bore liquid-cooled diesel engine

Baldwin-Lima-Hamilton Corp.

Fig. 13. Alloy D132-T5 permanent mold cast, oil-cooled piston with cast-in top ring-groove insert, for a 12.75-in.-bore diesel engine (cutaway view)

with spray or "cocktail-shaker" cooling, or cast-in cooling passages located directly behind the compression-ring grooves to remove heat from that area. The prevalence of turbocharging and the associated higher piston-crown operating temperatures for these larger pistons increase the need for oil cooling.

The most efficient piston cooling is obtained by forcing lubricating oil through coil passages. Although a cored passage can be produced in an aluminum permanent mold cast piston, the most economical method is to cast-in a steel cooling coil, which also can be designed to cool the area under the piston crown.

Cast-in ferrous ring-groove inserts, containing one or two ring grooves, are employed to improve the life of the top compression-ring groove, with all sizes of diesel pistons (Fig. 13). The insert, generally an iron-base alloy having a coefficient of thermal expansion near that of aluminum, is metallurgically bonded to the piston. The same technique is used for a separately cast

Harnischfeger Corp.

Fig. 14. Combination 60-lb flywheel and timing gear housing for diesel engine was permanent mold cast in alloy 333-F with collapsible core on one side and straight drawn core on the other.

aluminum ring carrier that contains the ferrous ring-groove insert and all other ring grooves above the pin boss.

While forged aluminum pistons are one-piece with integral pin bosses, some have a separate, shrunk-on, cast or forged ring carrier, or a bolted-on piston-pin carrier. A recent improvement is a forged aluminum ring carrier containing a ferrous top ring-groove insert. The higher tensile properties of the forging allow the shrink fit onto the piston body to be a minimum of 0.002 in. per inch of piston diameter (more than double that of the permanent mold cast ring carrier).

Oil passages in a forged piston are machined into either the piston body or the ring carrier. The carrier is shrunk on the piston body and welded at the top joint to seal against leakage.

Alloys 4032-T6 and 2618-T61 are employed extensively for forged pistons. However, 2219 with a T7-type heat treatment is growing in use for both the piston and ring carrier, to utilize its excellent tensile, fatigue, and hardness properties at elevated temperatures.

A recent achievement is a forged piston produced from atomized aluminum alloy powder. These pistons have considerably higher yield, tensile, elongation, fatigue, and hardness properties after 1000 hr at 600 F than do pistons of any alternate aluminum cast or forged alloy. The powder metallurgy alloy shows virtually no decrease in hardness during extended time at this high temperature; thus, the top ring groove does not deform during service. Residual growth also is negligible. Forging and machining characteristics are suitable for pistons. Thermal fatigue cracking in the area of the piston head is minimized.

Miscellaneous Parts for Diesel Engines

Miscellaneous parts made of aluminum for diesel engines include head and side covers, and side doors for large engines; these are permanent mold cast in alloy 333-F or die cast in 380. Housings for flywheel and timing gear, and end covers are produced as permanent mold castings (Fig. 14) in 333-F, 355-F,

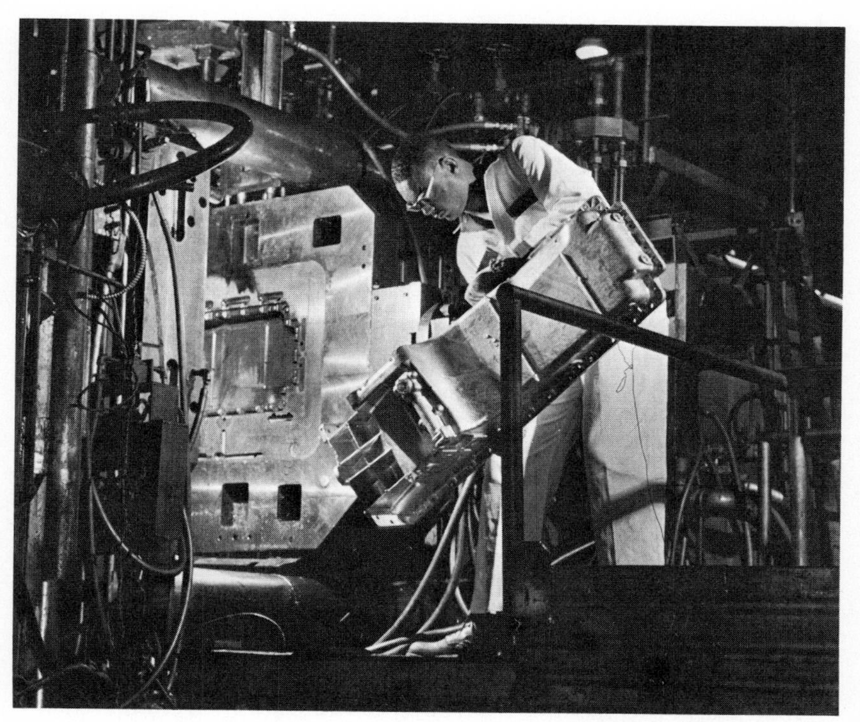

Cummins Engine Co., Inc.

Fig. 15. Die cast oil pan for a diesel engine is 15 in. wide and 47 in. long. It is one of the largest plan areas ever cast, weighing 33 lb.

or 355-T7, or in A356-T61 for especially severe service conditions. Fuel-injection pump housings are cast in 356-T7.

Oil pans are cast in aluminum for light weight, economy, and rapid heat transfer for cooling the lubricating oil (Fig. 15). They are permanent mold cast in 333-F or die cast in 380.

A 22-lb fan (26-in. OD) for an air-cooled diesel engine is produced as a premium-strength casting in C355-T61, to obtain smooth finished, contoured blade cross sections, high tensile and fatigue properties, and good resistance to stress corrosion.

Intercoolers (heat exchangers) remove compression heat from the air leaving the turbocharger, increasing the air density and volumetric efficiency, and thus boosting power output. The housing and cores of the heat exchangers employ aluminum because of its light weight and rapid heat transfer.

Superchargers and Other Rotary Compressors

The principal application of rotary compressors is to supercharge internal-combustion engines. They are used on four-cycle or two-cycle natural gas or diesel engines. Two main varieties are the blade type, called turbochargers, and the positive-displacement rotor type.

Engine superchargers and turbochargers supply compressed air for combustion, to obtain up to 100% more power from a given-size engine. The moving parts of turbochargers generally rotate at high speed; aluminum construction thus is important to provide low centrifugal forces for reduced bearing loads, and low inertia for rapid response when speed changes in the unit are required.

Turbochargers, the most common type of supercharger, are essentially high-speed, centrifugal air compressors with an impeller wheel driven by an exhaust-gas turbine. The impeller, diffuser, and compressor housing are aluminum.

Impellers are either shrouded or open face (Fig. 16). The shrouded impeller is used to obtain high efficiency at low and medium pressure/density ratios. It is sand or semipermanent mold cast in alloy 355-T61.

The open-face impeller is employed to produce higher pressure/density ratios. It is designed for minimum residual stress and maximum stiffness as a premium-strength C355-T61 plaster mold casting. The contoured-section blades are precision cast to high dimensional accuracy. The blade finish is smooth, less than

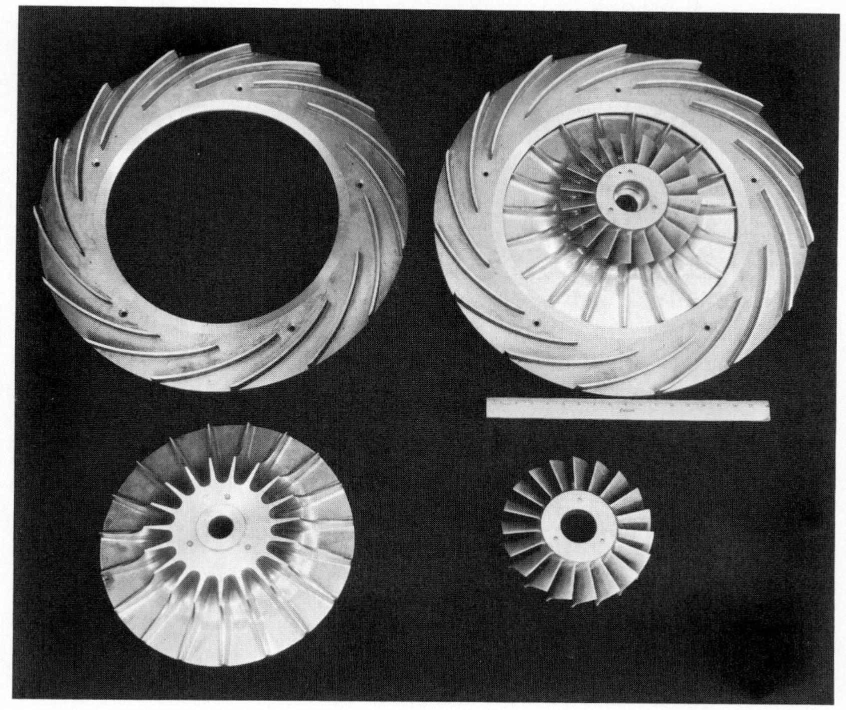

Alco Products, Inc.

Fig. 16. Aluminum turbocharger impeller assembly and diffuser used in high-output diesels (upper right), and component elements. Sand cast alloy 355-T61 inducer with cast-to-size blades (lower right), forged alloy 2014-T6 impeller with machined blades (lower left), and sand cast alloy 355-T7 diffuser (upper left).

100 micro-in. With proper design, units have been spun at a peripheral speed of 2000 ft per sec without failure.

Open-face impellers in which a straight blade is machined are forged in alloy 2014-T6 or 2025-T6. They are stronger than the cast impellers and have been spun successfully at 2500 ft per sec. Premium-strength cast C355-T61 inducers with contoured blades are mechanically fastened to the forged impellers.

Diffusers and compressor housings are semipermanent mold cast in 355-T61 or sand cast in 355-T7.

Positive-displacement superchargers have two or three lobes and a straight or spiral rotor. They are employed primarily for scavenging two-cycle engines, with limited use for supercharging four-cycle engines. They are mechanically driven, and are mounted on the side or overhang at one end of the engine. The overhung position adds importance to aluminum's light weight.

Alloys 355-T7 and 356-T7 permanent mold or sand castings are used for the rotors. The housings and end plates are permanent mold or sand cast in 355-T77 or 356-T77.

Slow-speed centrifugal blowers are separately driven units employed for scavenging heavy-duty two-cycle engines. The shrouded impeller with contoured blades is an alloy 355-T61 sand casting.

Gas turbines, similar in construction to superchargers, are in growing use in the industrial, marine, and vehicle fields. Units range from 75 to 50,000 bhp and operate on diesel fuel or natural gas. Applications of aluminum are limited to parts remote from the combustion zone, because of high operating temperatures. Some stators and compressor wheels are premium-strength castings in C355-T61. Since the weight of present designs is higher than desirable for automotive engines, the use of additional aluminum components is of interest.

References

1 J. M. Smith and R. M. Smith, Aluminum Engines — Design for Modern Fabrication, SAE Trans, **67**, 295–307 (1959)

2 "Aluminum Engine Symposium, Soc Automotive Engs Spec Publ 159, 1958

3 A. F. Bauer, Engine Blocks and Their Components in Aluminum Die Casting, SAE Trans, **68**, 385–395 (1960)

4 A. M. Montgomery, Corrosion Resistance of Aluminum Automobile Engine Components, SAE Trans, **69**, 24–30 (1961)

5 R. F. Schaefer, "Aluminum High-Output, High-Speed Diesel Engines", Paper 120U, SAE National Diesel Engine Meeting, Chicago, Oct 27–29, 1959

6 R. S. Frank and W. J. Lux, A Billion Engine Hours on Aluminum Bearings, SAE Trans, **64**, 655–664 (1956)

7 L. B. Larson, Trends in Castings for Automotive Applications, Metal Progress, **88**, No. 6, 52–57 (Dec 1965)

Chapter 15

Automotive Applications Outside the Engine

W. C. Keith, J. M. Smith and W. C. Weltman

IN 1896, the New York Sun accurately predicted large uses for aluminum in horseless carriages, because of its light weight and capacity to be shaped by many processes. The first such application was in the crankcase of the 1897 Clark three-wheel automobile. In the early 1900's, aluminum sheet was used for passenger-car panels, and aluminum castings for wheels and for engine, transmission, and body parts, by several automobile manufacturers.

By the 1920's more than a dozen car builders had converted to aluminum sheet for various body parts (Fig. 1). One company consumed 5000 tons for radiator shells in the 1925–1927 period. A short time later, development of improved methods for the deep drawing of steel sheet provided a cost advantage that recovered the applications for steel.

The most prominent advantage of aluminum in automotive applications is its combination of light weight and adequate strength. Operating costs are reduced and payloads increased for vehicles of all types. Low density is of extra value in the reciprocating parts of engines, and a larger tonnage of aluminum is utilized in engines than in body and chassis parts of automotive

W. C. Keith is manager, Application Engineering Div., Aluminum Company of America, New Kensington. Before his retirement in January 1965, J. M. Smith was manager for transportation, Sales Development Div., Aluminum Company of America, Cleveland. W. C. Weltman is an application engineer for transportation, Application Engineering Div., Aluminum Company of America, New Kensington.

Fig. 1. Body of 1923 Pierce-Arrow sedan, fabricated of cast and wrought aluminum

vehicles.* Other attributes of aluminum important to vehicle construction are resistance to corrosion, finishing characteristics, and easy maintenance of appearance, as-fabricated or finished.

Although engineering advantages and ultimate economy determine the use of aluminum in commercial vehicles, its applications in American passenger cars are based largely on first costs in manufacturing. For example, the effect of light weight in increasing payload or reducing operating costs justifies a somewhat higher price for aluminum parts than for iron parts in a commercial vehicle, but not in a passenger car. However, although the cost of iron in its basic form is about one sixth that of aluminum by weight or one half by volume, the die casting process (Volume III, Chapter 2) has made it possible for aluminum to compete for many parts.

Occasionally, a first-cost advantage for aluminum is found in economies introduced in machining or assembly, or by greater casting accuracy, lighter weight, or superior finishing characteristics. A realistic cost analysis should include any influence, adverse or beneficial, that the material under consideration for the part has on the cost of associated parts.

*Because of their diversity and relevance to both automotive and other industries, engine applications are discussed in a separate chapter, beginning on page 311.

Transmissions for Passenger Vehicles

Transmission cases of aluminum, conventionally die cast in 380 alloy, are almost universally specified for automatic-transmission assemblies (Fig. 2). Because of the mass of this component, the application constitutes the largest consumption of aluminum in passenger cars. Aluminum reduces weight and cost, compared to cast iron. The economic advantage results from the dimensional accuracy of die castings and appreciable saving in machining costs. Not only are some machining operations eliminated, but those necessary are performed at faster speeds and feeds than for iron.

The transmission case is a good example of the favorable influence of an aluminum part on the design and cost of an associated component. The lower-weight transmission housing reduces the cantilever load on the converter housing, permitting lighter construction for that part.

Some automatic transmission cases are integral with the converter housing. A choice is made between eliminating a part

Fig. 2. Automatic transmission cases and flywheel housings made as die castings being assembled to passenger-car engine

Dodge Div., Chrysler Corp.

with its interface machining and assembly operations, and retaining interchangeability of torque converters, housings, and transmissions. Another cost saving is available by casting the case with integral valve and servo bodies. Some transmissions have internal parts of aluminum, such as planetary-gear carriers and seal rings.

The comparatively large effect of a temperature change in an aluminum case on the center-to-center distance between the transmission main shaft and countershaft has been reported to contribute to gear noise. This effect can be counteracted by employing a gear tooth profile that allows a slight change in gear fit. Or, if extreme temperature ranges are anticipated, the shaft can be mounted in cast-in or bolted-in ferrous inserts. Ball-bearing or roller-bearing fits permit some bearing alignment with the shaft at normal operating temperatures.

Die cast synchronizer rings, employing aluminum-silicon alloy (16 to 22% Si) for wear resistance, are a potentially economical application, now limited by casting problems and low ductility of the alloys. Low inertia of rings improves transmission operation.

Aluminum cases for manual-shift transmissions, produced as alloy 356-T6 sand castings, presently are used only in military vehicles and European cars. Traditional manual-transmission cases are not suitable for die casting, although they could be designed and tooled to utilize this process.

Flywheel Housings. The member that connects the transmission case and the engine cylinder block is known as the flywheel housing, clutch housing, or converter housing, depending on the components enclosed. When not integral with the transmission case, they are almost invariably alloy 380 die castings. Safe fatigue-stress levels are insured by proper design. On both flanges, mounting-bolt boss diameter should be at least 2.25 times bolt diameter; fillet radius should not be less than $\frac{1}{16}$ in. Low-stress areas of the housing wall are cast to a minimum practical thickness of about 0.1 in., blending into thicker, more critically stressed sections. Stress concentrations around openings in the housing wall, such as for clutch lever or cooling air, are designed within fatigue limits of the alloy, including a 3-to-1 factor for rough-pavement shock loading.

Alignment of the transmission shaft and engine crankshaft must be maintained by rigidity of the housing, to prevent driveline noise and vibration. Rigidity can be increased in these aluminum assemblies by greater wall thickness or by wavy or corrugated walls, and adequate design of mating parts.

Torque converter stators are alloy 380 die castings or welded assemblies of two die castings. The smooth, close-tolerance contoured vanes required for efficient design are formed by removable steel cores.

Pump and turbine elements have been produced as alloy 355 plaster castings (Volume III, Chapter 2), with similar vanes. These castings require an expendable mold for each production piece; for many designs they cannot compete in cost with sheet steel units having slightly lower operating efficiency.

Transmission extensions, most often alloy 380 die castings, function as adapters that permit the vehicle propeller shaft to be driven by a choice of transmission and extension combinations. They usually contain the driveline bearings and seals and may serve as a rear-motor mount and speedometer-drive housing.

Wheels and Brakes for Passenger Vehicles

Wheels. Sand cast aluminum disk and spoke wheels were produced for automobiles as early as the 1920's. After a few years, they largely were discontinued because of higher cost compared to improved steel designs.

A forged aluminum wheel, chromium plated or color anodized, was successfully introduced in 1955 as a style innovation on several expensive passenger-car models. Development of one-piece forged or extruded ornamental wheels offers considerable promise, because of the attractive finishes applicable to the wrought alloys used, such as 6061-T6.

Most recently, passenger-car wheels have been produced as permanent mold castings. The rim disk is cast integrally with the hub, or the hub and drum are a single casting with a bolted or riveted steel rim. These ornamental wheels (Fig. 3), supplied primarily for sports cars, require no wheel covers. Since wheels are a style item, the reduction of weight is less important than the attractive finishes available. Because wheel weight is unsprung, any weight saving increases passenger comfort.

Wheels typically are permanent mold cast in A356-T6 alloy. Any alloy selected must have sufficient ductility to prevent service failures from abuse.

Aluminum wheels can be finished in a variety of ways. Buffing of highlights with contrasting paint in recessed areas, followed by a complete clear coating, is the most popular finish for cast wheels. Chromium plating is feasible on a casting of good

Kelsey Hayes Co.

Fig. 3. (Left) Permanent mold cast A356-T6 alloy ornamental sports car wheel; rim, disk and spokes are integral with spinner nut locking wheel to hub. (Right) Assembled wheel and tire.

surface quality. Wrought wheels are finished by color or bright anodizing, or by chromium plating.

In wheel design, the bead-seat and mounting-flange areas should receive careful attention, to prevent fatigue problems. Comprehensive testing to assure optimum wheel life is imperative; wheels must withstand abuses of tire changing, curb striking, and other road hazards, as these can cause stress concentrations that reduce fatigue life.

Wheel covers for conventional steel wheels also utilize the decorative qualities of aluminum. Die castings are used for the design freedom and sharp detail obtainable. A current model is die cast in alloy 360 and chromium plated. Wheel covers that are pressed or spun from aluminum sheet, polished and anodized, are popular in Europe.

Brake drums of aluminum, presently produced as permanent mold castings, are of two types. The finned functional drum is employed as standard equipment for the front wheels of certain automobiles, and is offered as optional equipment on some taxis and police cars. The second, or ornamental, integral wheel and drum is marketed as a four-wheel option. Aluminum is well suited for both types, primarily because of its high thermal conductivity and high heat capacity (twice that of steel on a weight basis). Both characteristics serve to prevent excessive drum and lining temperatures, and thus reduce lining wear.

Aluminum drums perform well with respect to the two types of brake fading (diminishing brake action at a given pedal position). "Mechanical fade", caused by thermal expansion of the drum, reduces effective reservoir capacity as limited by brake-pedal travel. The low operating temperatures of aluminum drums tend to counteract its high coefficient of thermal expansion. "Material fade" results from a decrease in coefficient of friction of the lining, caused by thermal decomposition of the lining material. This does not occur at the low operating temperatures of aluminum drums.

Reductions of up to 30% of ferrous drum weight have been accomplished by aluminum drums. When an aluminum drum is cast integral with a wheel disk to form an "ornamental wheel and drum", styling features can be incorporated, and heat transfer to the air is more rapid because of larger exposed area. Better heat dissipation can reduce tire bead temperatures.

In all permanent mold cast drums now in production, metallurgically bonded cast iron inserts form the brake-track surfaces. The drums are cast in 356-type alloys in the T5 temper. Solution heat treatments are avoided, because of the detrimental effect of the high temperature on the metallurgical bond.

Drums can be die cast with cast-in iron inserts for the brake track, by providing a roughened or mechanical, self-locking surface on the insert to resist braking torque. Thin fins, close tolerances, and reduced machining result in the economies typical of die castings.

In designing aluminum brake drums, sufficient mass must be provided to absorb as heat all the energy of a high-speed panic stop, without failure or fade. This type of heat absorption is so rapid that little is dissipated to the atmosphere. However, an aluminum drum must be provided with sufficient fin area to dissipate normally absorbed heat to the atmosphere rapidly enough to benefit substantially from the high thermal conductivity of aluminum.

Functional drums should be provided with ventilation through the wheel disk and cover. Thorough testing of drum design must be performed under rigorous conditions to insure adequate brake performance and life.

Brake Cylinders and Pistons. Pistons for wheel and master cylinders are aluminum impact extrusions or screw machine products in 6151-T6, or die castings in 380-T5. Advantages for aluminum are low cost and resistance to corrosion by brake fluids. The pistons generally are anodized for wear resistance and often are colored for identification. Some master cylinders have been produced as permanent mold castings in an aluminum-copper-silicon alloy. Power-brake units employ aluminum castings and stampings to reduce weight and cost.

Steering Gear Housings for Passenger Vehicles

Steering gear housings and covers of aluminum are produced extensively as die or permanent mold castings. Both processes offer lower cost than malleable iron when production quantities are high enough, especially where the part is designed to take full advantage of the superior machining characteristics of aluminum.

Die casting alloy 380 often is used — or A380 where additional ductility is desired. For permanent mold castings, alloys are 356-T6 or A356-T6 (the choice for higher ductility).

Safe performance is assured by housing designs that limit operating stresses to selected levels, achieved by blending ribs and wall sections to carry loads directly to the mounting bolts.

Axle Housings for Passenger Vehicles

Lower unsprung weight and improved ride are achieved with aluminum suspension parts, which are presently limited to axle housings used in Europe, because higher cost thus far has prevented their adoption in the United States. Extensive prototype testing has proven that aluminum performs satisfactorily. Most current designs require sand cores, but slight modifications could suit them for die casting, thus reducing the cost. Alloy choice is not critical. For permanent mold castings, 333 is suggested; for die castings, 380. No heat treatment is required.

Design must recognize bearing-load vectors so that metal distribution is efficient and produces maximum housing rigidity. Pinion-bearing cups should be installed so that some interference fit is retained at maximum operating temperature. Differential bearings require up to 0.002-in. interference at room temperature. To reduce thermal expansion problems, ferrous bearing caps are recommended.

The steel tubes commonly pressed into malleable housings can be installed similarly in aluminum; interference should be sufficient to hold the tubes at elevated temperatures. Design stresses in the radial wall section around the steel tube areas must be limited to an acceptable level. Mechanical locking of the tubes should be provided as a safety factor.

Passenger Vehicle Bodies

Aluminum bodies are employed commonly in automobile production in Europe, where the high price of gasoline emphasizes the value of weight saving. Another advantage of aluminum, resistance to corrosion, is especially significant in geographical areas where salt is used for de-icing streets. However, in the United States, the net balance of economic factors has not yet led to the adoption of aluminum bodies.

Body components of aluminum sheet are used in this country only in special applications, such as racing cars. In this field, aluminum hoods, rear decks, fenders, splash guards, bumpers, and bumper brackets are included in a weight-saving "kit". These kits also may contain high-performance items for the engine and running gear. With body parts, little attention is given to characteristics such as durability or corrosion performance, since a racing car's life is short.

Alloy 3003-O or 5052-O, typically 0.032 in. thick, is employed for racing bodies, depending on deep drawing and strength requirements. Alloy 6061 is formed in the O or T4 temper and then aged to T6. For production of passenger-car bodies, 0.040-in. alloy 3004 sheet would be the best selection for strength and formability. Paint systems for steel bodies are satisfactory for use with aluminum.

Complete one-piece die cast doors have been considered. Although tooling costs would be high, reduced assembly costs, excellent rigidity, and desirable contours can be attained.

Trim. Automotive stylists employ moldings, grills, bezels, fender strips, wheel covers, and so on, for ornamentation. These parts also may be functional. Bright aluminum trim alloys have been developed to provide high luster, corrosion resistance, formability, and adequate dent resistance at costs competitive with stainless steel (1).

Bright trim parts are fabricated from 5*xxx* series alloys. Mechanical properties of commonly used tempers are listed in Table 1.

Table 1. Typical Mechanical Properties of Automotive Trim Alloys in Order of Increasing Strength

Alloy and temper	Tensile strength, psi	Yield strength(a), psi	Elongation, %
5257-O	13,000	5,000	27
5257-H25	20,000	16,000	14
5257-H28	24,000	22,000	5
5657-H25	23,000	20,000	12
5657-H28	28,000	24,000	7
5557-O	16,000	6,000	25
5557-H25	25,000	21,000	10
5557-H28	30,000	28,000	8
5457-O	19,000	7,000	24
5457-H25	27,000	23,000	10
5457-H28	31,000	30,000	6
5252-H25	35,000	26,000	12
5252-H28	41,000	35,000	7
X5053-H25	38,000	29,000	10
X5053-H28	45,000	39,000	8

(a) Dent resistance of trim generally increases with yield strength.

An anodic coating 0.2 to 0.3 mil thick normally is specified for these aluminum parts, although thinner coatings are sometimes supplied. The sulfuric acid anodic process is employed for both exterior and interior trim. For extra brightness on interior parts, the process is modified (Volume III, Chapter 19).

Deeply drawn lamp bezels and housings are made of alloys 5257 and 5657 in various tempers. Alloy 5457, as well as 5557, is used for grills and stampings. Alloy 5252 is employed for rolled belt-line moldings and window reveals, for increased dent resistance. Its lower formability is acceptable in this application. The additional strength also is beneficial for assembly-line installation, as these parts must snap over preplaced fasteners. Where extremely bright finish is desired, alloys X5015 and X5053 are employed. Alloy X5015 is similar to 1100 in mechanical properties and thus provides the excellent formability required for interior trim. Alloy X5053 has the good mechanical properties needed for dent-resistant exterior trim.

Coined or pressed medallions and nameplates normally utilize high-purity alloys, such as 1065, 1199, or 5405, in the O temper. Brightness is excellent without mechanical buffing, which is difficult on these small, intricate parts. Several special clad alloys are offered that provide a satin effect after anodizing. The cladding generally is 1100 alloy on a core of 1100-H25 or 5050-H25; selection depends on the strength required.

Combination structural–bright work applications have utilized aluminum extrusions for several years. The upper doorframe (Fig. 4) employed in several automobile models is an extrusion that serves as the upper structural door member, the window support, the retainer for the weather stripping around both the glass and the door opening, and the interior and exterior reveal. For a specular anodic finish, either alloy 6464-T5 or 6563-T5 is chosen. These alloys also are used for extrusions for large grill openings with punched-out air passages.

Patterned aluminum sheet is utilized bare, lacquered, or anodized for trim applications. Door sill plates generally are patterned alloy 1100 or 3003 sheet in the O temper, or in the H25 temper (when increased dent resistance is required).

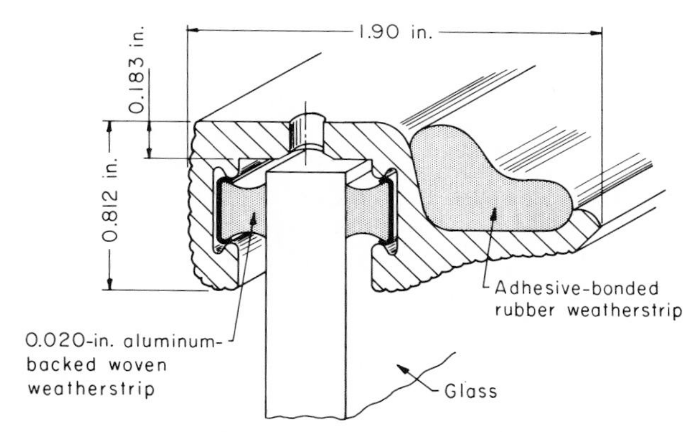

Fig. 4. Cross section of extruded aluminum upper doorframe serving as structural member, window support, weather-stripping retainer, and decorative reveal

Interior and exterior appliques are made from patterned sheet, using alloy 5457-H25 for brightness after anodizing. Patterned extrusions also can be applied as automotive trim.

Aluminum's light weight is an advantage in bumpers and bumper ends because of their overhung location. Lower modulus permits aluminum bumpers to absorb more impact energy than steel, although their lower hardness may result in gravel denting and scratching. Aluminum may be finished with an attractive bright anodic finish, as well as chromium plate. Industry has not yet accepted the anodized bumper; the chromium-plated aluminum bumper is not used because of a cost disadvantage. Anodized or plated bumpers are usually of 6*xxx* series alloys.

Bumper ends were produced as permanent mold castings of alloy 356-T6. Some automobile models have used die cast bumper guards in alloy 380. In addition to weight savings, cost is lower than for stamped and welded steel, especially in low-production models. High surface quality is required, since bumper castings are chromium plated to match other similarly plated trim parts.

Hardware items include ignition keys stamped from 7075-T6 sheet. Some rear-seat grab handles are chromium plated die castings. A large number of rear-door hinges are being made at low cost as alloy 13 die castings. Some hood ornaments and emblems are aluminum die castings or pressings. They are supplied bright or color anodized, or chromium plated.

Transmissions for Commercial Vehicles

Flywheel housings commonly are aluminum permanent mold or sand castings, typically in 333-F or 356-T6 alloy. Tooling cost of die castings may be warranted by production quantities if the same part can be adapted to several engine-transmission combinations. The transmission of a heavy truck may weigh 700 to 800 lb. Depending on the mounting points for the engine-transmission assembly, this weight may be overhung from the flywheel housing. This can result in loading from acceleration as high as three times gravity when negotiating rough terrain. In addition, the load may be alternately upward and downward, resulting in high fatigue cycles. Comprehensive testing, preferably in a vehicle in typical operation, is required before acceptance of a design for production. If engine supports are mounted on the flywheel housing, they must withstand engine torque multiplied by the maximum transmission gear ratio. High strength and good rigidity are attained in either sand or permanent mold castings by using blended ribs and deep sections.

Limited use is made of sand or semipermanent mold cast 356-T6 alloy transmission cases. Ferrous inserts, cast-in or bolted in the end walls, serve to withstand the gear loads and provide recessed bores for the antifriction bearings. In smaller, lighter transmissions, the bearings may be pressed directly into the aluminum case, as in passenger vehicles.

Wheels and Brakes for Commercial Vehicles

Since the weight saved by aluminum wheels and brakes is preponderantly unsprung, numerous advantages accrue in addition to increased payload. Included are reduced driver fatigue, increased tire mileage, easier tire changing, and decreased maintenance of tires.

Wheels for buses, trucks, and trailers are of two general types: forged disk and cast spoke. This discussion is limited to rim sizes of 20, 22, and 22.5-in. diameter, those most common for heavy-duty trucks.

An aluminum wheel provides a 25 to 50-lb weight saving compared to a similar steel product. Forged aluminum disk wheels of high-strength heat treated alloys (Fig. 5) have been employed on all types of commercial vehicles since 1948. They are standard equipment on some lightweight tractors and trailers, and customer option on many others. The wheel is forged in one piece, heat treated, and machined to close tolerances, providing a strong, true-running product. The wheels have standard 10-hole, 11.25-in.-diam bolt circles, common to axles on most highway vehicles. The rims are integral; the flat-rim type employs steel side and lock rings.

Although some early designs of cast aluminum spoke wheels for trucks and trailers were not notably successful, those pro-

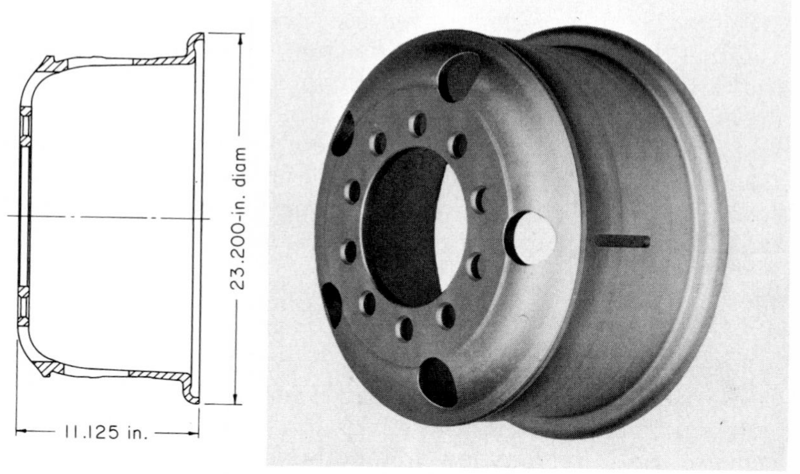

Fig. 5. Disk truck wheel, 22-in.-diam, forged of high-strength heat treatable aluminum alloy

duced in the last 10 years have been generally satisfactory.

Current spoke wheels are five-spoke design semipermanent mold castings in alloy 356-T7, selected for its mechanical properties, stability at elevated temperatures, and ease of casting and machining.

Design is undoubtedly the most important factor in the success of a cast aluminum spoke wheel. The wheel spiders are individually designed for the front axles, drive axles, and trailer axles of a vehicle, with demountable steel rims the only common component. A box-type spoke with a completely closed spoke end has become standard. Since each commercial vehicle has a wheel of different design, this basic spoke must be modified to make the wheel of dimensions compatible with other components of the axle-end assembly.

Brake drums for commercial vehicles can be made successfully of aluminum drum castings with segmented iron inserts bolted in place, forming the brake track. The drums weigh approximately 35% less than iron drums and 15% less than steel-iron composites. Fade and noise are reduced substantially; lining life is extended at least 50%. The bolted-in liners, although costly, provide a replacement feature that extends drum life. Experimental sand cast drums have performed for a million miles with several liner replacements.

Drums should be permanent mold cast in alloy 142-T571, selected for elevated-temperature properties and dimensional stability over long periods of service.

Other brake components for which aluminum is used are brake shoes, spiders, and diaphragm supports. These are produced for many heavy-duty trucks. Sand cast alloy 220-T4 parts and 356-T7 permanent mold products have served successfully for many years. Half the weight of the corresponding iron part is saved. In the air-brake system, aluminum is used for cooling tanks and valve parts, for its high thermal conductivity.

Steering-Gear Housings for Commercial Vehicles

Steering-gear housings, permanent mold cast in alloy 356-T6 or die cast in alloy 380, are produced for two manufacturers.

It is possible to utilize these high-production casting processes because the numerous low-volume builders of heavy-duty highway equipment frequently purchase complete standardized high-production steering-gear units. To permit the flexibility required of such units, provision is made to mount a single steering-gear design in several positions. Complications introduced by this feature, in addition to the high stresses common in commercial units, necessitate analytical consideration and experimental testing to establish the stresses induced in different positions. However, this flexibility permits production quantities that justify the permanent mold or die casting process.

Truck, Trailer, and Bus Chassis

The chassis members discussed consist of the frame, axles, and connecting members. Aluminum was introduced for these parts in both passenger and commercial vehicles in the late 1920's. Present consumption of aluminum for these components in commercial vehicles is 10,000 tons a year.

Suspension systems consist of components connecting the frame to the axles. Aluminum permanent mold castings and die forgings are employed for these parts to achieve weight savings of 40 to 60% over the corresponding ferrous parts.

Various manufacturers have slightly different names for the several components in a typical truck suspension. A representative list of these includes: 7 to 12-lb spring hangers, 50 to 60-lb main trunnions, 8 to 11-lb frame hangers, and 8 to 11-lb torque rods, all A356-T6 permanent mold castings, and 55 to 65-lb equalizer beams forged of 2014-T6.

Larger, more economical permanent mold castings sometimes introduce cost savings, and they are offered as standard equipment. Permanent mold casting occasionally permits extra weight saving through design. For example, the trunnion parts of one air-ride suspension also serve as air reservoirs, eliminating separate air tanks.

The severe service conditions imposed on truck, trailer, and bus suspensions involve both cyclic and shock loading, and demand both analytical and laboratory stress analysis to achieve successful aluminum application.

Axle Housings and Differential Carriers. Cast aluminum rear-axle housings were used in heavy-duty vehicles for some years beginning about 1940. Sand cast 356-T6 housings for axles with a load rating of 20,000 lb provided over 50% weight saving compared with malleable iron castings. The payload increase was about 140 lb, all unsprung weight. Later, attractively priced fabricated steel weldments, although heavier, replaced aluminum for this application.

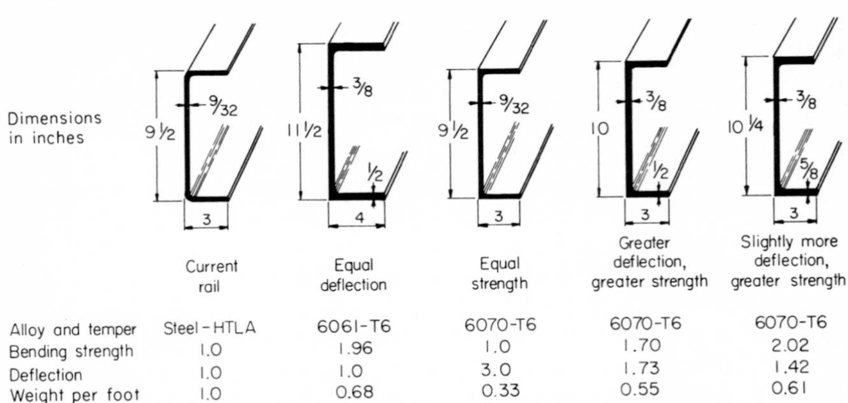

	Current rail	Equal deflection	Equal strength	Greater deflection, greater strength	Slightly more deflection, greater strength
Alloy and temper	Steel-HTLA	6061-T6	6070-T6	6070-T6	6070-T6
Bending strength	1.0	1.96	1.0	1.70	2.02
Deflection	1.0	1.0	3.0	1.73	1.42
Weight per foot	1.0	0.68	0.33	0.55	0.61

Fig. 6. Beam designs in 6061-T6 and 6070-T6 compared with high-tensile low-alloy steel beam, for various functions of strength and deflection

The differential carrier is the element in the rear-axle assembly that positions the gears and supports the gear loads. Weight reduction of 55% can be achieved using cast aluminum in place of malleable iron. The cost of the complicated sand castings required limits this substantial weight saving to military and very lightweight commercial vehicles. Alloy 356-T6 is recommended. It is important and possible in aluminum design to provide stiffness at least equal to the ferrous part, so that gears and bearings remain correctly aligned under load, for satisfactory life and quietness.

Frames. Frame rails for heavy-duty trucks and tractors often are produced as aluminum extrusions, with a saving of 300 to 600 lb per vehicle. Alloys 2014-T6 and 6061-T6 have been successful. Alloy 6070-T6, intermediate between these in both mechanical properties and price, is a recent recommendation.

Rail design involves compromises among beam depth, stiffness, and fatigue strength (Fig. 6). Typical size ranges are: beam depth, 9 to 11.5 in.; web thickness, 0.375 to 0.5 in.; flanges, 0.75 to 1.125 in. thick and 2.5 to 3 in. wide.

Cross-members of aluminum are used extensively in both steel and all-aluminum frame assemblies. In addition to maintaining alignment of the frame rails, the members may serve as cab, engine, and transmission supports, and torque-rod anchoring locations. Because members are subject to bending and twisting as the vehicle negotiates road obstacles, closed sections are preferred. Each cross-member must be strong enough to sustain imposed loads, yet sufficiently flexible to permit elastic deformation, thus avoiding damage to other vehicle members. Weight reduction of 45 to 55% of ferrous parts can be achieved.

Welded-plate box-section cross-members are constructed of alloys 5454-H311 and 5456-H321.

Cast aluminum cross-members, used where complex configuration is required for engine or transmission mounting, are 220-T4 sand castings and A356-T6 permanent mold castings.

Extruded, formed 6061-O alloy tube up to 6 in. in diameter and ⅜-in. wall, welded to sand cast A356-T4 end brackets, is a successful cross-member design. It provides maximum torsional rigidity, minimum weight, and easy assembly, but over-all cost is more than for welded-plate box-section members. After welding, the assembly is heat treated to the T6 temper, providing strong end-mounting brackets coupled with a center tube of the high ductility desired.

Aluminum cross-members are bolted to either aluminum or steel frame rails. Faying surfaces should be suitably caulked and painted, or otherwise treated to prevent corrosion.

Fuel and air-reservoir tanks of aluminum are offered as optional equipment. Gasoline tanks on commercial vehicles require Underwriters' approval, although diesel fuel tanks do not. The tanks may be cylindrical or rectangular, and they are of all-welded construction, typically 5052 sheet 0.090 to 0.125 in. thick. Tempers depend on forming and service requirements.

Compressed-air reservoir tanks for air brakes must conform to ICC and ASME specifications. In aluminum, they are drawn cylindrical shells in 6061 alloy sheet 0.090 to 0.125 in. thick. The shells and fittings, also 6061, are welded with 4043 filler metal. After welding, the assembly is heat treated to T6 temper.

Commercial Vehicle Bodies*

Truck cabs of aluminum, normally of welded or welded and riveted construction, are desirable for weight savings (2). Alloy 5052-O or 5052-H32 sheet is selected both for panels and formed structural members. Sheet thickness ranges from 0.050 in. for door, hood, and roof panels to 0.125 in. for interior structural components. Extrusions of 6061-T6 alloy also are employed in cab construction.

*Some of the structures to be discussed have counterparts in railroad equipment (Chapter 16 in this volume).

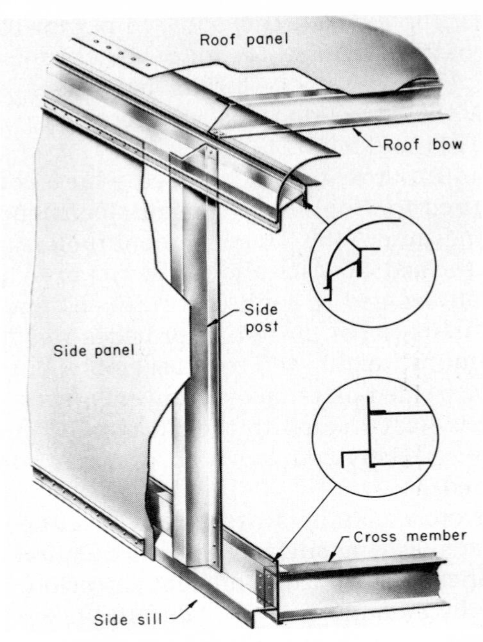

Fig. 7. Typical design of exterior-post van truck or semitrailer body using aluminum sheet and extrusions

Van truck and semitrailer bodies are constructed with aluminum vertical posts and side sheets in two general styles — exterior post (Fig. 7) and exterior side sheeting.

In truck bodies, low maintenance cost is the primary reason for using aluminum, as an attractive appearance is important (Volume III, Chapter 23). Because appearance is less critical with semitrailers, aluminum construction is of interest principally for increased payload (3).

Side-sheet alloys may be 5052-H38, 6061-T6, or alclad 2024-T3, 3003-H291, or 5155-H38. Selection is based on current sheet prices, surface finish, color uniformity, and mechanical properties. The posts are extruded 6061-T6 alloy, with a hat-shaped cross section for exterior-post construction and a Z-section for exterior side-sheet construction. In designing van trucks and semitrailers of either style, sheet thickness and post spacing are selected to sustain anticipated loads.

In exterior-post construction, the hat-shaped posts used for semitrailers are 1 to 2 in. deep and 4 to 5 in. wide, and weigh approximately 1.5 lb per ft. In van truck bodies, the posts weigh only 0.6 to 0.8 lb per ft. Side-sheet thickness in semitrailers is 0.050 to 0.080 in.; the sheet serves as a shear web. In trucks, the sheet is 0.040 to 0.050 in. thick. Rivet spacing generally is 4 in.; $\frac{3}{16}$-in.-diam brazier-head rivets of alloy 2117-T4 or 6053-T61 are used for appearance.

With exterior-sheet construction, the Z-posts weigh about 1.0 lb per ft for trailers and 0.5 lb per ft for trucks. The exterior sheet contains oval vertical corrugations approximately 0.375 in. deep and 1.0 in. wide at intervals of 6 to 8 in. Sheet thickness is typically 0.051 in. for both semitrailers and trucks; alloys are the same as those used for exterior posts.

One-piece metal roof sheet is available only in aluminum, an advantage from the standpoint of leaktightness. Roofing sheet usually is alloy 3003-H16, 0.032 to 0.040 in. thick and up to 102 in. wide. No fasteners are employed in the roof bows; peripheral rivet spacing is 1.5 in. Mastic caulking compounds are applied between the sheet and the roof rails and bows, serving as sound deadening for the "floating" roof sheet.

Refrigerated van truck and semitrailer bodies are almost universally of aluminum construction, using either exterior-post or exterior-sheet designs. Insulation of specified thickness applied to interior wall and roof surfaces is covered with a lining of anodized aluminum, galvanized steel, reinforced plastic, or plywood. Prefabricated insulated sandwich panels that provide structural strength and require no posts are being used experimentally. They are 2 to 6 in. thick, with aluminum surfaces

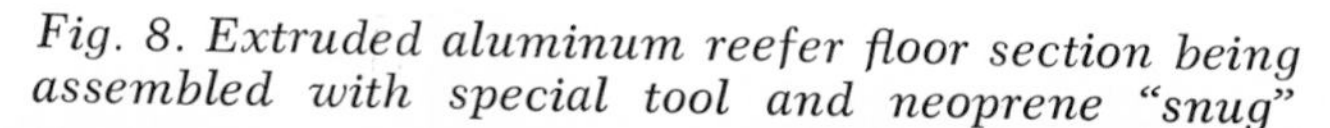

Fig. 8. Extruded aluminum reefer floor section being assembled with special tool and neoprene "snug"

The Heil Co.

Fig. 9. Off-highway end-dump body of welded alloy 5454-H32 plate with exhaust-heated floor and sides

forming the interior and exterior walls. Special joint designs are required to avoid thermal expansion problems, maintain insulation efficiency, and contribute to structural strength.

Both van truck and semitrailer bodies are employed without suspension systems, and with some modifications, they may be used as "containers" for through-handling of cargo by truck, railroad, or ship (see Chapter 16 in this volume).

Trailer Floors. Extruded 6063-T6 flooring is common in trailers. Lightweight "boards", 7 to 10 in. wide by 1.25 in. deep, are tongue-and-groove assembled to form a combination of widths for either dry-freight or refrigerated trailers. The dry-freight floors have a smooth upper surface, whereas the refrigerated-trailer floors are corrugated to permit moisture drainage and air circulation under the cargo. Designs are based on industrial-truck wheel loads of 5000 to 6000 lb on 12-in. cross-member spacing. Figure 8 shows assembly of a trailer floor section.

Bulk-haulage units are of several types; the most common is the end dump (Fig. 9). These structures are made both as trucks and semitrailers, and may be either frame mounted or self-supporting, depending on function. Alloy 5086-H34 or 5454-H32 sheets, 0.125 to 0.25 in. thick, are assembled using semiautomatic inert-gas metal-arc welding processes. The consumable electrode is alloy 5356.

Flat-bed trailers are used to haul commodities such as pipe, baled hay, or bulky machinery. Aluminum became competitive with steel for these trailers, on the basis of cost per pound of weight saved, with the development of high-speed welding techniques. A typical flat-bed trailer (Fig. 10) is constructed with alloy 2014-T6 extruded longitudinal T-shaped frame members that are butt welded stem to stem. At the deep portion of the beam, a 6061-T6 spacer plate is added by welding on with 4043 filler rod. Cross-members are 6-in.-deep 6061-T6 extruded channels, bolted into place.

A 7-ft by 39-ft trailer floor of extruded 6063-T6 welded to the cross-members weighs only about 1000 lb. Complete trailer weight in aluminum is approximately two thirds that in steel.

Truck and Trailer Tanks. Most trailer tanks and some truck tanks are aluminum. They normally are built to a specification; this is required if they are to be used to transport flammable commodities across state lines. There also are many local regulations based on National Fire Protection Association codes.

Williamsen Body and Equipment Co.

Fig. 10. In this high-strength 7400-lb aluminum flat-bed trailer, use of an alloy 2014-T6 extruded longitudinal frame welded to 6061-T6 cross-members and covered with 6063-T6 flooring results in a saving of 3600 lb dead weight over steel.

The alloys permitted are 5052, 5086, 5154, and 5454; tempers also are specified. Welding is with 5154 or 5356 electrode. Alloys specified for transporting hydrogen peroxide are 5254 and 5256, welded with an electrode of the same alloys.

The advantages of aluminum most pertinent to truck and trailer tanks are increased payload, economical maintenance, and resistance to corrosion. Aluminum tanks are employed for handling numerous chemical cargos, many of them discussed in Chapters 12 and 16 of this volume.

Full monocoque construction is used in tanks. Either ring stiffeners or bulkheads are allowable, with spacing determined by design or regulation. Sheet thickness is 0.141 to 0.250 in. It is used in the annealed temper for heads, bulkheads, and baffles, and in the H32 temper for the shell.

Tank shell joints are butt welded, to achieve maximum fatigue life. Heads and bulkheads must have a smoothly turned flange with a minimum bend radius three times the thickness.

Truck-mounted tanks are best supported with a three-point suspension; this relieves highly localized stresses caused by chassis flexure. Semitrailer and full-trailer tanks should be supported with stiff saddles that cradle and hold the shell in its round or oval shape. Some tanks are convertible for liquid or solid material handling, to meet seasonal demands (Fig. 11).

Intercity Bus Bodies. Most bus bodies for intercity service are of semimonocoque aluminum construction. Assembly is entirely by riveting, using 0.050 to 0.080-in. 5052-H34 sheet and 6061-T6 or 6062-T6 extruded shapes, typically 0.125 in. thick. Exterior structural sheet panels are ribbed in a bold pattern for appearance and strength. Both sheet and extrusions are given a relatively thick anodic coating (0.5 to 0.6 mil) to achieve a durable, attractive satin finish.

In bus interiors, alloy 3003 patterned sheet and expanded metal in various tempers are employed for decorative panels covering heating and air-conditioning vents and for "kick pads" on the sides at floor level. Extrusions are used above the window level to retain roof liners and side panels. Aluminum-framed window units are installed in the bus sides.

Off-highway equipment comprises two general categories: rock-body or end-dump trailers and bottom-dump trailers. Both are commonly constructed of aluminum for reduced weight and low-cost maintenance.

Fabrication is exclusively by welding, frequently with work-

The Heil Co.

Fig. 11. Welded aluminum 850-cu-ft bulk-commodity tank trailer weighing 9600 lb

hardened alloy 5454 or 5456 plate. The respective welding electrodes are 5356 and 5556. Extrusions of alloy 5454 in various tempers are used, because of their strength, weldability, and fatigue life.

The typical end-dump truck body in Fig. 10 was constructed entirely of alloy 5454-H32 plate and 5454-H112 extrusions. The floor is of sandwich design; the corners are hollow to permit exhaust gases to heat the body. (Exhaust heating is satisfactory with aluminum bodies.)

For lading that is only mildly abrasive and of small particle size, aluminum bodies are built with the same sheet gage used for steel, permitting a 60% weight saving. Side plates 0.375 to 0.5 in. thick and 0.5 to 0.75-in. floors usually are satisfactory.

Where the load is hard rocks of irregular shape, aluminum gage must be increased approximately 30% to absorb the highly localized impacts and to compensate for wear. For severe loading conditions, aluminum floors are up to 1.25 in. thick to assure satisfactory service life. This thickness results in the aluminum body weighing 40 to 50% less than its steel counterpart.

A steel wear plate bolted or adhesively bonded over an aluminum floor provides highly satisfactory service. The wear plate is maintained or replaced readily. The aluminum-steel combination need not weigh much more than all-aluminum, and costs less.

Scraper blade and apron attachments are constructed as aluminum weldments. A steel blade is bolted to the leading edge to provide a replaceable abrasion-resistant surface.

Mobile Homes and Travel Trailers

Mobile homes and travel trailers usually are constructed with aluminum sheet coverings nailed to wood frames, although there is a growing trend to riveted extruded aluminum frames. Appearance, weight, and maintenance features are important to the ultimate consumer.

The exterior walls of mobile homes are almost exclusively aluminum sheet in a wide variety of panel designs. The siding sheet is 0.019 or 0.024-in.-thick 3005-H25, or a similar alloy, used bare or with a mill-applied baked-enamel finish. Before attaching to the framing, the sheet generally is crimped, in widths up to 60 in., for stiffness and attractive appearance; sheet is applied with the crimping either vertical or horizontal.

Travel trailers, which are smaller than mobile homes, generally utilize formed or plain aluminum sheet panels for outside walls. The sheet usually is of the same alloy and thickness as for mobile homes. When an unpainted, uniformly bright surface is desired, alclad 6061-T6 or alclad 2024-T3 is used. Construction methods are the same as for mobile homes.

Most windows and interior trim in mobile homes and travel trailers are fabricated from alloy 6063-T5 extruded shapes.

Included in the travel trailer industry is a relatively new product, camper units. These units, covered entirely with aluminum skins, fit into the beds of pickup trucks to provide sleeping and living accommodations. Side and roof sandwich panels utilize alloy 3005-H25 as the outside face and plastic foam as the core, with either wood or aluminum sheet interior surfaces.

References

1 W. C. Cochran, E. T. Englehart, and D. J. George, Improved Methods, New Tests Upgrade Anodized Aluminum Auto Trim, Mod Metals, **16**, No. 9, 82–86 (Oct 1960); W. H. Tingle and D. J. George, Measuring Appearance Characteristics of Anodized Aluminum Automotive Trim, SAE Midyear Meeting, Chicago, May 1965, Preprint 650513

2 G. U. Brumbaugh, "Design Weight Reduction and Attendant Economies", SAE National Transportation Meeting, Baltimore, Md. (Oct 1964)

3 C. L. Burton and E. P. White, Lighter Trucks for Heavy Hauling, Mod Metals, **8**, No. 12, 26–30 (Jan 1953)

Chapter 16

Railroad Equipment

G. B. HAUSER

EARLIEST use of aluminum in railroad equipment in this country was in 1894, when the New York, New Haven and Hartford Railroad built a special lightweight car in which aluminum seat frames were used. In the following few decades, aluminum was adopted as a body material in many electric trolley cars and, more recently, has been used in several experimental rapid-transit trains.

Applications of aluminum continue to increase in railroad rolling stock construction (1, 2). In extensive use, these aluminum structures have demonstrated durability and capacity to withstand service shocks. The light weight of aluminum, compared to steel, permits larger cross sections in structural parts where advantageous. For example, railroad cars with larger-cross-section underframes and superstructures of aluminum are more capable of withstanding impact than cars made with thinner sections of heavier metals, because the thicker sections have higher resistance to buckling.

The principal effort toward weight reduction in passenger and freight cars has been in body, underframe, and related parts rather than in truck frames and running gear, although in some recent designs the weight of the trucks is almost half the total tare weight of the car. This emphasis is logical, however, because design problems with the upper structures are usually simpler and the returns in weight saving are greater. Application of aluminum to reduce truck weight is hampered by lack of space for parts large enough to meet deflection limitations. However,

The author is an application engineer for transportation, Application Engineering Div., Aluminum Company of America, New Kensington.

aluminum truck parts and running gear were operated experimentally in this country during the 1930's and are again receiving attention. The objectives are both to reduce weight and to achieve better dynamic qualities.

Because railroad cars and locomotives are used in motion, and in addition have moving parts, the weight advantage of aluminum in some applications is attributable primarily to its lower inertia. For example, low inertia is responsible for more rapid acceleration and deceleration of aluminum cars compared to steel units, and for the use of aluminum pistons in the diesel engines that are now the dominant railroad motive power. Aluminum is used in the superstructures of some designs of locomotives to save weight, but in others operating characteristics require the weight of steel construction.

Other characteristics of aluminum that are of value to railroads are high thermal conductivity (important in the diesel engine pistons), resistance to corrosion, finishing qualities, and economical maintenance of appearance. Many railroad applications, not only in rolling stock but in towers, buildings, signs, and signal systems, involve outdoor exposure. Surface maintenance of equipment, for protection or appearance, is a major cost item with railroads. Consequently, selection of material favors alloys with superior weatherability and finishing properties (Volume I, Chapter 7, and Volume III, Chapters 16 to 22).

Assembly methods have progressed over the years. Most aluminum passenger and freight cars, except for tank cars, at one time were of riveted and bolted construction. With the development of inert-gas arc welding, all-welded construction was introduced in 1956 for freight cars and has progressed rapidly. Passenger cars now employ a combination of welded, riveted, and bolted assembly for the main structure.

Passenger Cars

Active experimental use of aluminum for passenger car parts started in the 1920's. Next, complete superstructures were constructed of aluminum, especially in street and rapid-transit cars. The first two main-line railroad cars having all-aluminum underframe and superstructure were exhibited in the 1933–1935 Chicago World's Fair. Displayed with these was a three-car "streamlined" train entirely of aluminum except for trucks and running gear. In the next decade, many passenger cars with all-aluminum bodies were built.

Pullman-Standard

Fig. 1. Low-profile aluminum passenger cars designed for high-speed service

Corrosion troubles with the copper-containing aluminum alloys that had been used in early applications led to decreased use of aluminum for underframes. The open structure of the underframes was subject to dirt collection and to water drainage from within the cars, which created a damaging poultice corrosion effect. A notable exception was in the lightweight, high-speed trains built in 1955 with completely enclosed framing, and using Al – Mg_2Si alloy 6061 for the entire body, underframe, and underframe enclosure (Fig. 1). On one train, to meet the industrial designer's desire for an alternate light and dark natural aluminum pattern, anodized alclad 2024-T3 patterned sheet was used for the exterior.

Alloy 6061 and other 6*xxx* series alloys, the aluminum-magnesium alloys (5*xxx* series), and the aluminum-zinc-magnesium alloy 7005 are suitable for passenger car construction, to attain optimum combinations of strength, corrosion resistance, and weldability. Proper alloy selection permits effective use of aluminum for every part where it can be economically justified. As steel parts are used with aluminum in many of the railroad applications, there is the possibility of galvanic corrosion under certain exposure conditions. Dissimilar metal joints should be recognized as such and proper protection practices employed. Recommended methods are discussed in Volume I, Chapter 7.

The Association of American Railroads has established certain basic principles for passenger car design, which are published in its Manual of Standards and Recommended Practices. The aluminum industry, after studying these principles, issued a technical report on the use of aluminum that is utilized by the car builders (3). In passenger car construction, it is logical to use the highest-strength alloys meeting AAR specifications to assure both economy and passenger safety. These specifications do not permit selection of the high-strength aluminum aircraft alloys, except 2024. This alloy, 5083, and 6061 are currently recommended for basic railroad car structures.

Until the 1960's, aluminum passenger car body framing, sheathing, and underframing were of all-riveted construction. In the past few years, inert-gas metal-arc welding has been introduced for attaching structural members to the side sheathing and assembling certain portions of the underframing. Typical of passenger cars constructed with most recommended applications of aluminum is a subway car that weighed 10,930 lb less than the previous nonaluminum model.

The specifications impose no restrictions on aluminum alloys for interior trim and paneling; any alloy with suitable fabricating and finishing characteristics may be used (Volume III, Chapters 18 to 22). Alloys 3003 and 6063 are common. Virtually all passenger cars built today utilize aluminum for many parts of the interior finish, regardless of the material chosen for the car body. Many trains have cars with aluminum superstructures.

Freight Cars

The first important application of aluminum in freight train equipment was in hopper cars, because it was simple to transform the weight saving into extra capacity, gaining additional revenue at the same total weight on the rails.

The first ten aluminum hopper cars were built in 1931 and utilized ¼-in. 3004-H34 plate and 2017-T4 extruded sections. Thereafter, aluminum found extensive use in all types of freight cars, including gondola, box, tank, and mine cars, and associated equipment. A specific value of aluminum in freight cars is its excellent corrosion resistance in coal service, where most open hopper and high-side gondola cars are employed.

Early freight cars employed riveted construction almost exclusively, using alloy 6061 plate and shapes. Cars now generally are

Table 1. Comparison of 70-Ton Hopper Cars

Item	Aluminum	Steel
Loaded weight, lb	220,000	220,000
Tare weight, lb	36,900	51,000
Cargo limit, lb	183,100	169,000
Capacity, cu ft	2,949	2,700
Metal in body, lb	8,520	22,559
Ratio of tare weight in lb to capacity in cu ft	12.86	18.88
Ratio of cargo weight to tare weight	4.95	3.32

welded, utilizing 5083, 5454, 6061, and other alloys. As with passenger cars, stress analysis is an important part of the design of all freight cars. The AAR specifications for design, fabrication, and construction of freight cars should be followed.

Hopper Cars. A hopper car has a floor that slopes downward to one or more hinged doors to discharge bulk contents such as coal, ore or sand. Since 1931, 75 experimental aluminum hopper cars have been built, many of which are still in active service. Most were constructed of 6061-T6 extrusions and ¼ and 5/16-in. plate. Twenty-six of the cars, built in 1944, are of an extra-capacity design that provides 6.5 tons more payload on a given set of trucks. Tare weight and cargo capacity of a 70-ton aluminum hopper car are compared to a steel car in Table 1. Recent production orders will bring the total number of aluminum hopper cars in service during 1966 to 592.

Service tests show that, from the standpoint of resistance to corrosion by coal, aluminum hopper cars have a life expectancy of more than 30 years. At the end of 20 years of exposure (4), the average depth of pitting observed was about 10 mils, and the maximum 25.

Covered hopper cars, which evolved during the early 1930's, are the fastest growing type of freight car. Initial designs had only about 1300-cu-ft capacity. When aluminum was first used for these cars in 1960, they had reached the 100-ton (car plus full load) class. Aluminum design had stimulated interest in larger size. The prevalent size for regular service now is 4000 to 5000 cu ft. These cars are currently constructed of ¼ and 5/16-in. 5083-H113 plate, and of 5083-H111 and 6061-T6 extruded structural members (Fig. 2).

Designers from the aluminum industry devised the tank-type covered hopper car as an alternate to the rectangular shape. Each design is advantageous for certain types of service.

Covered hopper cars permit bulk shipping of dry granular or powdered materials, saving packaging and unloading costs. Their use is expanding. Table 2 compares aluminum and steel for various car sizes and cargo densities. Lading increases permitted by aluminum construction are 7 to 12.5 tons. Table 3 gives an analysis of weights and capacities of 100-ton cars.

Another factor in the economics of covered hopper cars is product compatibility. Resistance of aluminum to corrosion by specific chemicals and the nonstaining characteristic of aluminum compounds gives added justification for aluminum construction for many types of service.

Gondola cars are flat-bottom freight cars with sides and ends. An experimental high-side gondola with ¼-in.-thick 3004-H34 alloy side and floor sheets was constructed in 1937 for transporting sulfur. The car was in service for 23 years; as a result of this test, 200 large aluminum-bodied hopper cars with longitudinal doors were built for an expanded sulfur service.

Fig. 2. Covered hopper car, 4750-cu-ft capacity, loading 105 tons of corn through trough hatch. Note aluminum running boards.

Table 2. Data Relating Cargo Density to Economic Feasibility of Using Aluminum for Covered Hopper Cars

Cargo density, lb per cu ft	Total weight of cargo(a), 1000 lb, for cu ft capacities of: 2000	2500	3000	3500	4000	4500	5000
35	70	87.5	105	122.5	140	157.5	175
40	80	100	120	140	160	180	200
45	90	112.5	135	157.5	180	202.5	225
50	100	125	150	175	200	225	
55	110	137.5	165	192.5	220		
60	120	150	180	210			
65	130	162.5	195	227.5			
70	140	175	210				
75	150	187.5	225				
80	160	200					
85	170	212.5					
90	180	225					
95	190						
100	200						
105	210						
110	220						
Tare weight of cars at above capacities, 1000 lb							
Aluminum	42	44	46	49	51	54	58
Steel	56	60	64	69	75	79	83
Cargo limits of cars having 100-ton trucks, 1000 lb							
Aluminum	221	219	217	214	212	209	205
Steel	207	203	199	194	188	184	180

(a) The last two total cargo weights in each column are those possible in aluminum cars when standard designs are compared.

Table 3. Comparison of 100-Ton Covered Hopper Cars, Made of Aluminum and of Steel

Item	Aluminum	Steel
Loaded weight, lb	263,000	263,000
Tare weight, lb	51,000	74,700
Cargo limit, lb	212,000	188,300
Capacity, cu ft	3,930	3,930
Metal in body, lb	15,820	39,550
Ratio of tare weight in lb to capacity in cu ft	12.9	19.0
Ratio of cargo weight to tare weight	4.15	2.52
Minimum lading density for maximum load	54.0	48.0

Irwin-Sensenich Corp

Fig. 3. Aluminum mine car of 446-cu-ft capacity. Car being assembled by metal-arc inert-gas welding process, using alloy 5356 filler wire.

High-side gondola cars built in 1956 were the first freight cars, other than tank cars, of all-welded construction. They were welded of 5086 alloy ⅜-in.-thick plate, and eventually were shipped to Jamaica for bauxite service.

In 1960, 750 high-side gondolas of 100-ton capacity were built to haul coal in the Southeast. They were of all-welded construction; the bodies were aluminum except for the center sill and portions of the bolsters and cross bearers. Alloy 5083 was used throughout for shapes and plates, except the one-piece floor plate, which was of 5154 for easier formability. After five years of service, these cars are performing satisfactorily.

Aluminum covers supplied with a few low-side gondolas are constructed of 5050-H31 or 5052-H32, using 0.25-in. plate for framing and 0.092-in. sheet for roof panels. Riveted assembly is employed, with some welding. For a 50-ft car, the covers weigh 1600 lb, compared to 4300 lb in steel. They are easier to guide into place; if necessary, they can be placed or removed by man power. The tare weight saving in the car is also an important economic factor.

Mine cars are small gondolas. Aluminum designs have been tried at several mines. The car usually cannot be increased in size because of passage clearances, but aluminum construction permits more cars per train to be handled by the same size electric locomotive. When empty, the aluminum cars are controlled more easily by the locomotive on downgrades than are steel cars. These all-welded cars have extruded 6061-T6 framing, and 5083-H113 plate 0.25 to 0.375 in. thick. The high reflectivity of aluminum gives the cars good visibility in the mine, which helps to reduce accidents. With aluminum, the weight of a 446-cu-ft car can be reduced by 1.5 tons (Fig. 3).

Tank cars of aluminum are well past the experimental stage. The first unit, constructed in 1928, is still operating. About 6000 aluminum tank cars have been built in the United States.

Aluminum in tank cars not only saves weight but also resists reaction with many liquid chemical cargoes. With numerous cargoes, the primary advantage of aluminum is the long life of the tank in contact with the commodity. For example, fuming nitric acid attacks aluminum very slowly, making aluminum superior to competitive tank materials in long-term economy. With certain other cargoes, the principal benefit of aluminum is that it does not color or otherwise deteriorate the product. An example is acetic acid, which remains water white in aluminum tanks. Chemicals shipped in aluminum tank cars include:

Acetaldehyde
Acetic acid
Acetic anhydride
Acrylonitrile
Ammoniated ammonium nitrate solutions
Ammonium thiocyanate
Anhydrous ammonia
Aqua ammonia
Butane
Butyl stearate
Butynediol
Butyraldehyde
Cocoanut oil
Diamine (hydrazine)
Di-isocyanate
Dimethyl formamide
Epon resin
Ethanolamine
Ethylene diamine
Ethylene glycol
Fatty acids
Flammable solvents
Glycerol
Glycol
Hexamethylene diammonium adepate
Hexane
Hydrazine
Hydrogen peroxide
Methanol
Methyl acrylate
Napthenic acid
Nitric acid (over 85%)
Nitrogen fertilizer solutions
Nylon salts solution
Oleic acid
Polyvinyl acetate
Propionic acid
Rosin (hot or water white)
Sodium chlorate
Stearic acid
Styrene resins
Tall oil (refined)
Toluene
Toxophene
Trichlorobenzene
Urea solutions

Others could be shipped if needed in tank-car quantities. Chapter 12 in this volume and Volume I, Chapter 7 give additional information on compatibility of aluminum with chemical products.

The first aluminum tank car, built for experimental purposes, was of welded construction. Because no welded tank car specification existed at that time (1928), tanks were riveted for some years thereafter. Since about 1937, aluminum tank cars have been welded — starting in 1950, by the inert-gas metal-arc method (Volume III, Chapter 12). This method of fabrication permits selection of the high-strength work-hardened aluminum alloys, because good weld strengths are obtained across joints.

Aluminum-magnesium alloys 5052, 5086, and 5454 are the principal materials currently used for car tanks. These alloys are commonly employed in the H34 or H112 tempers, which have adequate formability and favorable mechanical properties for withstanding road shock. The minimum allowable plate thickness is ½ in. and, depending on design requirements, plate ranges up to 1⅛ in. Semi-ellipsoidal heads are used. Some cars have domes, others simply manway openings. All tanks are anchored to the center sill.

Tanks designed for 300-psi test pressure and 750-psi bursting pressure have been built. There are now nine Interstate Commerce Commission specifications and two issued by the Association of American Railroads for welded aluminum tank-car tanks. These specifications define the design criteria, which are much the same as required by the ASME unfired pressure vessel code. An exception is that certain greater minimum thicknesses have been found necessary to stand the rigors of railroad service. The largest aluminum tank built, having a capacity of 20,000 gal, uses only 50% more aluminum than the 10,000-gal size.

House cars are enclosed types such as boxcars, stock, automobile, automobile parts, and refrigerator cars. A few such cars having aluminum superstructures were built in the 1940's. In one car, most of the underframe was also aluminum. The first house car to be sheathed in aluminum was a boxcar constructed in 1944. During the following few years, another 50 were built with entire superstructures and floor stringers of aluminum.

The most common type of house car, the boxcar, is the workhorse of the railroads. It has been standardized in size, construction, and specialties to minimize its cost, although there is a trend toward special cars for specific types of service.

Aluminum has a prominent place in boxcar construction, even

though it may be difficult in many instances to justify the extra cost of an all-aluminum house car body for general freight. An aluminum boxcar has definite merit, however, for specialized service, such as head-end cars that carry mail, baggage, and express shipments in passenger trains, and for fast freight service on captive runs. In these applications, light weight is especially advantageous in permitting heavier payloads at the same total weight on the rails. For high-speed service, the allowable weight on rail is considerably under that permitted in freight train car loading. About 5 tons can be saved with an aluminum superstructure on a standard 50.5-ft boxcar.

The use of aluminum parts in boxcars is increasing, to counteract the loss in weight capacity caused by the trend to heavier floor systems, cushioned underframes, and load-protection devices, all of which increase tare weight.

Table 4. Weight of Doors for Boxcars

Door width, ft	Type of door	Weight of door, lb Aluminum	Steel
8	Sliding	222	460
9	Sliding	275	525
10	Sliding	325	700
15 (8 + 7)	Sliding	500	950
8	Plug(a), single-faced	500	1000
12	Plug(a), single-faced	830	1450
10	Plug(a), double-faced	750	1300
12	Plug(a), double-faced	850	1500

(a) Fits flush with inside wall of boxcar

Aluminum roofs and doors have been widely utilized on boxcars since 1960. About 13,500 doors and 10,000 roofs have been put into use. Aluminum roof sheets with galvanized steel seam caps save about 1200 lb per 50.5-ft car. Aluminum seam caps would reduce the weight another 400 lb at a higher cost. Aluminum boxcar doors, particularly those wider than 8 ft, operate more easily and wear the hardware less than other types do. A pair of 10-ft-wide doors saves 700 lb compared to conventional steel doors (Table 4).

The "all-door" car, of which 200 were built, is essentially a boxcar with garage-type rolling doors for sides. Three aluminum door sections form an entire side. When used with movable posts, they permit loading and unloading long material in large units, such as bundled lumber. The doors on a side operate easily from a single geared system (Fig. 4), and material-handling labor is reduced significantly.

Special, high-cubic-capacity steel "container" cars are now being built for fast handling of automobile parts from supplier to assembly plant. Parts are loaded into containers or baskets that are moved into the car through large door openings. In one fleet, these openings are closed by four aluminum doors, each 10 ft wide by 13 ft high, on each side of the car; in another fleet, two doors per side are used. The containers are held in place by bulkheads of 6061-T6 type alloy extrusions and steel framing in a fleet having one door per car side. The cars are equipped with cushioned underframes for further protection against shock damage. Other aluminum parts for these cars, such as roofs and running boards, are under consideration. An early experimental model had the entire body built of aluminum.

Aluminum sliding doors for boxcars are constructed of corrugated sheet panels and formed sheet shapes, commonly 0.109 in. thick. Alloy selection depends on the formability and strength required; alloy 5154 is the common choice for the corrugated panels and 5052 for the formed shapes. Plug (flush fitting) doors are fabricated of 5154 flat sheet of similar thickness, with 6061-T6 type alloy extrusions for the frame and for the stiffening members.

For boxcar roofs, aluminum sheet is formed to provide stiffness and watertight seams. Various aluminum-magnesium al-

Pullman-Standard

Fig. 4. All-door car using aluminum garage-type roll-up doors

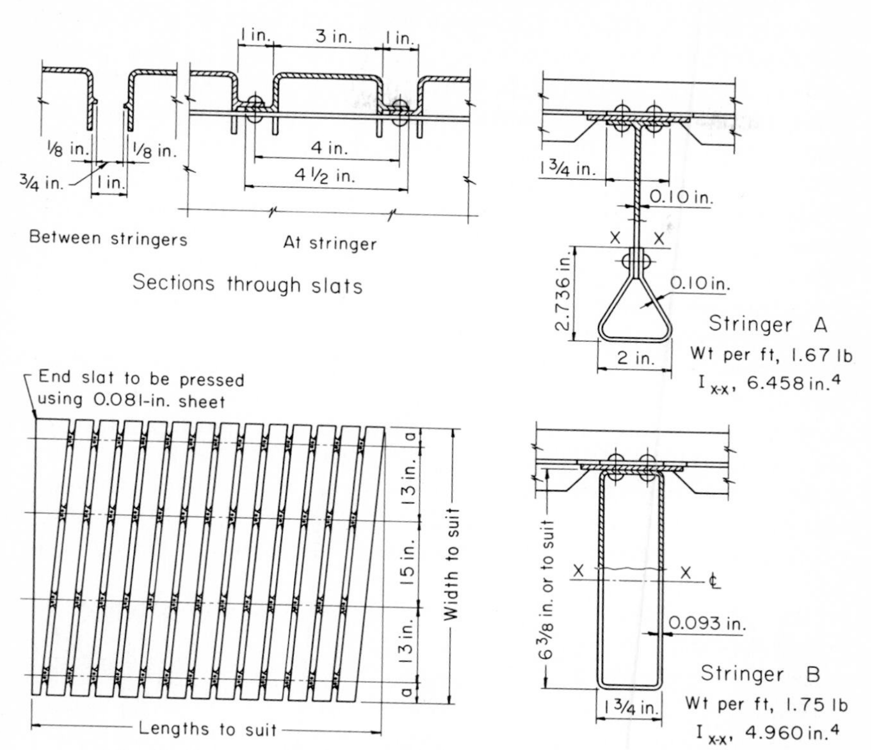

Fig. 5. Design of all-aluminum refrigerator-car floor rack

loys, in thicknesses from 0.081 to 0.102 in., are used. Both doors and roofs are made by riveting, usually with 6053 alloy rivets.

In all-aluminum cars, the sides are made of 1/8 to 3/16-in. flat sheet. The alloy usually is 5083 or 6061 for riveted construction, or 5083 for welded construction.

Three aluminum-bodied refrigerator cars built about 1947 are still operating. During the past few years, many all-aluminum refrigerator cars and boxcars, including single-sheathed cars, were designed, but few have been built.

All-aluminum floor racks (Fig. 5) for refrigerator cars were first tried in 1946. Trial results prompted the use of aluminum stringer and wood-slat floor racks in many cars built recently. The stringers, extruded in alloy 6061-T6, are screwed to the wood slats. Promising newer designs of all-aluminum welded racks usually comprise several different 6061-T6 extruded sections welded together.

Mechanically refrigerated cars generally require a roof duct for circulation of cold air; aluminum is standard for the ceiling sheets. The alloy usually is selected on a price basis, 3003 or 3004 being most commonly employed. Refrigerator cars are heavy, because of the insulation required. To compensate for this, aluminum applications that have proved technically and economically sound in this service, such as sheathing and all-aluminum floor racks, should be given full consideration by designers.

Lading protection devices are of aluminum for ease of handling. Aluminum provides sections that may bend but do not break, and that can be repaired by simple straightening. Lading bars that fasten the load by gripping an attachment in the sidewalls of the car are made of extruded rectangular shapes in alloy 6061-T6 or 6070-T6 (Fig. 6). In 1963, twice as many aluminum lading bars were sold as were the older steel and wood design, at a unit weight saving of 40%.

Upright partitions, called bulkheads, are another lading pro-

Evans Products Co.

Fig. 6. Aluminum lading bars (hollow extrusions) average 40 lb each, compared to 70 lb for conventional wood and steel units.

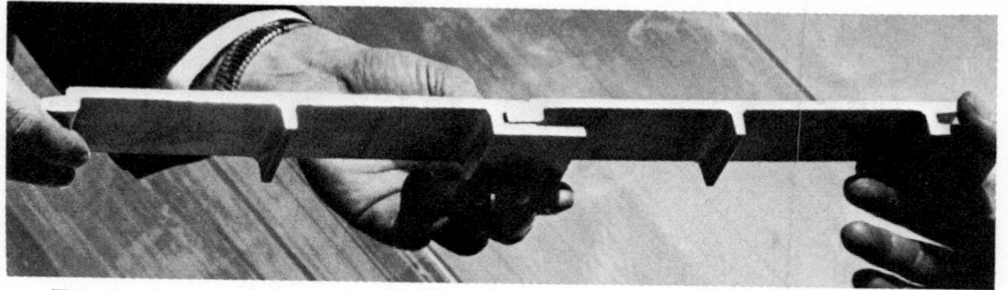

Fig. 7. Tongue-and-groove extruded boxcar side and end lining

tection device available in aluminum. Composite aluminum-steel versions also are used. Aluminum construction employs 6061-T6 extrusions, welded or bolted together.

Most boxcars have a wood lining to protect and contain the lading. The lower areas of the wood lining are subject to impact damage, because power trucks are generally used in servicing boxcars. Many railroads have adopted metal linings to minimize maintenance; aluminum linings have proved satisfactory. They are constructed of 6063-T6 extruded tongue-and-groove sections in thicknesses of ⅛ to ¼ in. (Fig. 7). In a 50.5-ft car with a 15-ft door opening on each side, the aluminum lining weighs 300 lb less than the wood it replaces, and 1400 lb less than neoprene-painted steel.

Other Freight Car Uses. An extruded aluminum floor design that could be nailed was introduced in 1960. Two depths were produced, 1.75 and 2 in.; ten car-sets of 6062-T6 were installed for trial service. In addition to a 30 to 40% saving in weight, the high cost of maintaining wood or steel floors is eliminated. A chart showing loads, spacing, and resultant deflection is given in Table 5.

Roof running boards are provided on most boxcars. Aluminum has not been used in this application, except for the early all-aluminum boxcars and for about 100 60.5-ft steel automobile cars that used aluminum boards to stay within the maximum load limit.

The largest use of aluminum running boards is on covered aluminum hopper cars; about 2500 are so equipped (Fig. 2). These aluminum running boards are of punched and stiffened alloy 5052 sheet, fastened to aluminum roof saddles with galvanized steel bolts. The saddles typically are formed of 5052 sheet ⅛ in. thick. Aluminum boards weigh about 5 lb per ft less than steel boards.

Table 5. Load-Deflection Data for Nailable Aluminum Floors

Span, in.	Load, psf(a)	Deflection, in. Steel(b) (1.75-in.)	6061-T6(c) (2-in.)	6061-T6(d) (1.75-in.)
12	11,600	0.009	0.009	0.013
14	8,525	0.012	0.012	0.018
16	6,525	0.015	0.016	0.024
18	5,155	0.019	0.021	0.030
20	4,175	0.024	0.025	0.037
24	2,900	0.034	0.037	0.053
30	1,860	0.053	0.057	0.083

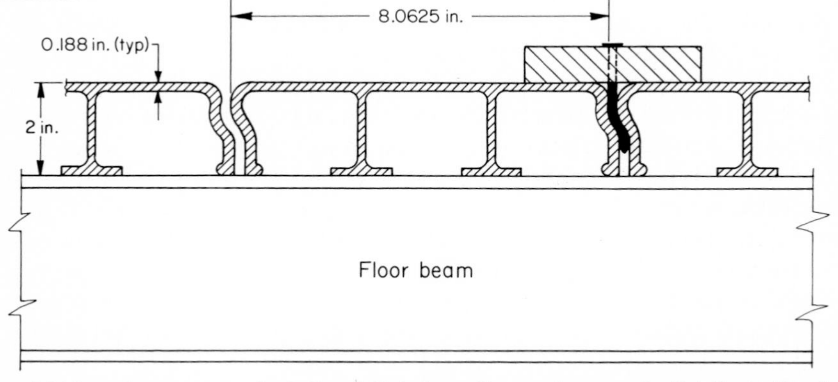

(a) Pounds per square foot. Loads listed are the maximum safe distributed loads for simple spans, based on a design stress of 20,000 psi for nailable steel flooring. At the listed loads, the maximum stress that occurs in aluminum flooring is only 10,000 and 7,650 psi for the 1.75 and 2-in. planks, respectively. (b) 8 by 1.75 by 0.10 in.; yield strength, 48,000 psi. (c) 8 by 2 by 0.188 in.; yield strength, 35,000 psi. (d) 8 by 1.75 by 0.188 in.; yield strength, 35,000 psi.

Containerization became commercially accepted in the late 1920's. Containers are essentially truck bodies without wheels or suspension systems, and the current concept is to design and use them for all modes of transportation. In railroad transportation, containers are generally shipped on flat cars. In 1931, several designs of demountable truck bodies were tested; in 1932, 50 all-aluminum bodies were placed in service. The all-aluminum model had a tare weight of 2600 lb, compared to 4000 lb for a design with steel framing and aluminum sheathing.

Aluminum construction has become almost standard for this application, because highway and air service require the lightest weight for the largest payload. Assembly is usually by riveting 0.040 to 0.080-in. sheet of alloy 5052-H38 or 6061-T6 to extruded 6061-T6 vertical posts. Alloy selection reflects mechanical property requirements and current sheet prices. Truck and trailer body builders are the major suppliers of containers. (For use of aluminum in trucks and trailers, see Chapter 15.)

Motive Power

Steam Locomotives. Although the steam locomotive probably has disappeared from the American railroad scene forever, except in isolated instances, it is appropriate to recount some of the applications of aluminum in the high-speed passenger locomotives before diesels displaced them, starting in the late 1940's.

The earliest application in steam locomotives was driving rods, used experimentally in the 1920's. Although the aluminum rods performed well and demonstrated the anticipated benefits, they were too expensive for the results obtained.

The only part of the crosshead found feasible in aluminum was the slipper or shoe (the sliding portion), which was aluminum on all of the most recent high-speed locomotives. Weight of each slipper was reduced from about 250 lb to approximately 100 lb, equivalent to about 6000 lb of dynamic augment at diameter speed (speed in miles per hour numerically equal to the driving wheel diameter in inches).

The aluminum alloy rods and slippers were of both forgings and extruded sections. The alloy was 7070 (10 Zn – 1 Cu – 0.75 Mn – 0.4 Mg), which was selected for optimum combination of mechanical properties and low cost. After they were heat treated to the T6 temper, the parts were hot tinned and lined to provide the required bearing surfaces.

The first application of aluminum in nonmoving parts was in 1932, for the locomotive cab and brake cylinders. By 1944, about 10,000 lb of aluminum per locomotive was utilized in nonmoving parts, effecting a weight saving of 19,000 lb. Included were the cab, streamlined jacketing, running boards and brackets, prow front, pilot casing, cylinder covers, dome casings, gage stands and supports, handrails, emblem plates, and miscellaneous other parts.

Crumpled aluminum foil 0.0003 in. thick was used as boiler insulation on some of the locomotives, in place of the usual lagging, to further reduce weight. In one instance, 65 lb of foil replaced 4000 lb of conventional magnesia block, without sacrificing insulation value.

Diesel locomotives were introduced in the 1930's; by the late 1940's, diesel engines had become the dominant railroad power source. Railroad diesel engines have used aluminum pistons from the beginning; these are permanent mold cast in alloy 142-T571 or forged in 4032-T62. Higher speeds of rotation were allowable because of aluminum's low inertia, and larger combustion loads were permitted by the high thermal conductivity of the metal. With some models, other aluminum components were also adopted; this is covered in a more extensive discussion of diesel engines in Chapter 14 of this volume.

Although in certain types of diesel locomotives, such as yard shifters, use of aluminum is impractical because weight is required for traction, in other types aluminum is employed to reduce weight. Some of the first diesel locomotives had aluminum superstructures. Aluminum conduit was an early application and has been used consistently; 3003 tube is employed.

In 1946, aluminum sheet was applied to the side panels of a diesel locomotive, to replace galvanized-steel-covered plywood

Fig. 8. Aluminum conduit on a main-line electric commuter car since 1926 and still in use. Photograph was made after 35 years of service.

that had presented corrosion difficulties. Similar replacements on eight yard and two road locomotives in 1949 and 1950 also were successful.

In 1952, one builder began using aluminum for the superstructure of export diesel locomotives. This program eventually covered 51 locomotives for Argentina and 22 for Brazil. The first lot employed 6000 lb of aluminum per unit, and the latter about 4000 lb. Aluminum was used for the cab structure, equipment covers, and shrouds — mostly 3004 and 5052 sheet, and 6061 and 6063 extrusions. The weight reduction was important, because railroad bridges and other structures in the South American countries were not designed for the heavier locomotives used in the United States.

Another application for diesel locomotives of reduced weight has been by military invasion forces. Prototype locomotives for this purpose, weighing 76 tons, were designed and built, using aluminum for the same applications mentioned above.

Electric Locomotives. Some early 4–4–4 and 4–6–4 electric passenger locomotives for main-line service used aluminum for the entire cab and the electrical apparatus decks, representing a 60% weight saving. Later, larger designs, such as the 4–6–6–4, had more efficient components and were able to conform to specified weight limitations with conventional steel construction, which is being used today.

Many electric traction units, such as street and subway cars, use aluminum parts in the electrical system; applications include motor housings, accelerator parts and cover, control and switch boxes, motor disconnector boxes, line switches, line relay boxes, receptacles and jumpers, controller parts, conduit, cable, and wire.

More than 3000 subway and commuter cars, some dating to 1926, employ aluminum in such applications as headlining, trim, seats, doors, floor plates, and electrical conduit (Fig. 8).

Other Railroad Applications

Electric-powered railroad systems such as rapid transit and commuter lines may use a third rail as the final distribution conductor, especially where the track is free from trespassing because of elevation or location in a subway. Experiments and test installations have shown that an aluminum third rail combined with a steel running surface provides better current

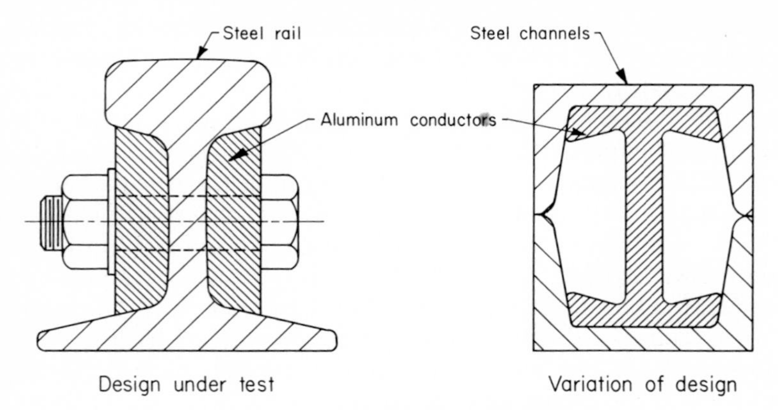

Fig. 9. Bimetallic third-rail designs

conditions at lower cost per foot of rail than an all-steel rail, and the number of substations along the line can be reduced. The aluminum portion of this bimetallic rail (Fig. 9) is extruded 6101-T6.

Railroad buildings that can be economically constructed entirely or in part of aluminum include passenger and freight stations, train sheds, warehouses, office buildings, shanties and shops of all kinds, and station canopies and shelters. All canopies of the stations on Chicago's recently built Expressway rapid transit system are made of alloy 3004 sheeting and 6061-T6 structural members. Details of a wide variety of building products are described in Chapter 10 of this volume.

Pneumatic tube systems of aluminum speed waybills and other papers from one department to another in the modern classification yard. These conveyor systems are discussed in Chapter 20 of this volume.

Bridge Plates. Piggyback trailers are normally loaded by the "circus" method (loading a series of flat cars from one end of the series), which requires car-connecting bridge plates that are easy to handle. Aluminum plates, which weigh about half as much as steel, are now a standard alternate. Both welded and bolted designs use 6061-T6 extruded stiffeners and 5083 or 6061-T6 plate, commonly ⅜ in. thick (Fig. 10).

Signs for railroad use include crossbucks (warning signs at railroad crossings), bridge markers, yard entrance signs, mile posts, whistle signs, switch stands, and station names.

The message is painted on some signs; on others a more reflective surface than paint is sometimes used or required, such as glass-bead products. Aluminum is used widely for the sign blanks and structures, because of its resistance to weathering, bare or coated. Alloy 3003 or 6061 sheet generally is employed. Long, narrow signs, such as crossbuck blades, that must withstand heavy winds utilize reinforced extruded sections in 6063-T6, at a lower cost than plate sections. There is detailed discussion of aluminum signs in Chapter 11 of this volume.

Fig. 10. An 82-lb aluminum bridge plate of bolted design

Signal Systems. Seven experimental aluminum signal cases, fabricated of 0.072-in. 5052-H32 alloy sheet, were installed in several different industrial locations in 1948. These cases contain electric and electronic switchgear; interiors must be free of dirt and dust. With conventional steel construction, frequent paint maintenance of the interior surfaces, as well as the exterior, is required. The aluminum test cases have performed well. In 1964, one company offered, as a standard alternate, a small case 8 ft long, 7 ft high, and 2 ft deep designed with interlocked 6063-T6 extrusions. Many other signal appliances benefit from aluminum construction to minimize maintenance, for applications such as lamps, lamp hoods, backgrounds, bases, frames, and brackets. Bare and insulated aluminum wire and cable (Chapter 21, this volume) are also used in signal systems.

Track maintenance equipment has improved steadily, become more mechanized, and adopted aluminum advantageously for many parts. An early application was for section and inspection cars. Often it is necessary for one man to move these cars on and off the rails. Extensive use of aluminum eases this task (cars weighing 265 lb have been built) and also reduces fuel and other operating costs.

Aluminum uses on these cars include housing side panels, timer and throttle levers, lever guide, lever grips, lift handles, axle bearing casings, idler pulley and arm, axle pulley, frame members, cab, and windshield frame. The gasoline engines use aluminum components for the water hopper, carburetor, timer body, timer cam, throttle valve, cylinder head, air cleaner bracket, and exhaust elbow.

Miscellaneous Railroad Applications. Among many other railroad equipment items made in aluminum are track and car jacks, track benders, tie tongs, track gages and spot boards, hoists, jigs and fixtures, ladders, scaffolds, dock boards, floor plates, nonskid plates, grating, and snow fences.

References

1 Aluminium in Railway Rolling Stock, Metallurgia, 62, 7–10 (1960)
2 O. Taschinger, The Technical and Economic Development of Aluminum Rail Vehicles, Aluminium, 41, 347–365 (1965)
3 "Association of American Railroads Passenger Car Construction of Alcoa Aluminum Alloys", 1944
4 E. T. Englehart and G. B. Hauser, Aluminum Alloys in Hopper Cars, Railway Locomotives and Cars, 128, 62–66 (May 1954)

Chapter 17

Marine Applications

W. A. PREY, N. W. SMITH and C. L. WOOD, JR.

ALUMINUM is used in hulls, deckhouses, and hatch covers of commercial ships, as well as in equipment items, such as ladders, railings, gratings, windows, and doors. The major incentive for employing aluminum is its weight saving compared to steel. Because it is common practice to use weldable aluminum alloys having strengths approaching or comparable to mild steel, equal-strength structures can be designed to a weight saving of 55 to 67%. However, to compensate for the lower modulus of elasticity of aluminum and to conform to normal deflection limitations, a somewhat lower, but substantial, reduction in weight is usually obtained. The weight saving normally ranges from 50% in hulls (although 59% is possible in this application) to 62% in commercial deckhouse structures.

The principal advantages of weight saving in many types of marine vessels are to increase payload, to expand capacity for equipment, and to decrease the power required. With other types of vessels, the chief benefit is to permit better distribution of the weight, improving stability and facilitating efficient hull design. The use of aluminum normally results in initial cost premiums that are justified over the life of the application by the benefits of light weight and low maintenance cost (1).

The weight saving achieved depends on the approach to design, which varies with different applications. Where known

W. A. Prey was formerly an application engineer for transportation, Application Engineering Div., Aluminum Company of America, New Kensington. N. W. Smith is an application engineer for consumer durable goods, and C. L. Wood, Jr., is an application engineer for aerospace and military, Application Engineering Div., Aluminum Company of America, New Kensington.

or rule loadings exist for specific structures, normal design principles are applied along with consideration of the mechanical properties of specific alloys. However, because of the difficulty of determining actual loadings on most ship structures, marine design commonly employs rule-of-thumb techniques coupled with extensive use of classification society specifications, such as those of the American Bureau of Shipping, which list scantlings for strength members for ships. Because of the minimal availability of basic rules and formulas for designing ship structures, aluminum members are usually proportioned from those in steel by applying conversion factors. These factors are calculated from differences between specific aluminum alloys and steels in strength and stiffness. Because the steel design normally includes a corrosion allowance, this calculation frequently results in an overdesigned aluminum structure.

Alloys. The 5*xxx* series alloys used for the majority of commercial marine applications have weld yield strengths of 15,000 to 26,000 psi. These aluminum-magnesium alloys retain good weld ductility without postweld heat treatment, and they can be fabricated with normal shipyard techniques and equipment. The weldable aluminum-magnesium-zinc alloys are also receiving attention in this field.

The corrosion resistance of the 5*xxx* series alloys is another major factor in the selection of aluminum for marine applications. Tensile strength reductions in 10-year sea-water corrosion tests of 0.064-in.-thick bare sheet specimens are only 2 to 5%. The 6*xxx* series alloys, widely used for pleasure boats, show a 5 to 7% decrease in similar tests. In addition to laboratory and field testing of small specimens, actual ship structures, such as the "Alumette", have been used to examine the corrosion resistance of these alloys (Fig. 1).

Alclad aluminum alloys are seldom required in construction of marine vessels. They are used, however, in a few applications, such as piping, for maximum assurance against excessive depth of pitting. Also, alclad 2*xxx* and 7*xxx* series alloys are selected where tensile strengths of 70,000 to 80,000 psi are required, considerably higher than now available in the 5*xxx* series alloys.

The high-strength alloys are employed where welding is not required, and where their higher strengths can be used to advantage. Because of their lower resistance to corrosion by sea water, protective measures such as cladding, painting, or cathodic protection must be used for satisfactory life in marine

Hull was exposed in tidal water continuously since construction, and was in excellent condition after 29 years of exposure. (Top) Inspection in 1949, showing little corrosion after 14 years of salt-water exposure. (Bottom) Bilge keel test racks, of series 5*xxx* marine alloys, added in 1948.

Fig. 1. The "Alumette", a hull test section fabricated in 1935 as a demonstration of the suitability of conventional shipyard fabricating techniques to aluminum

service. Some notable applications are in riveted truss unloader booms or in undersea structures, such as the submarine "Aluminaut", which is designed to have a service depth ranging to 15,000 ft (see Chapter 19 in this volume).

Protection of Aluminum Surfaces. In both salt-water and fresh-water service, the corrosion resistance of 5*xxx* and 6*xxx* aluminum plays a major role in maintenance. Salt-water service is much more severe, and although bare aluminum performs well in either fresh or salt water, its appearance deteriorates in salt water. This is not important in some commercial applications. However, in the majority of salt-water applications, aluminum is painted to insure an acceptable appearance (Volume III, Chapter 21).

The high-strength 2*xxx* and 7*xxx* series alloys must be coated with an appropriate anodic coating, paint system, or metal cladding, or be otherwise cathodically protected, for satisfactory service in sea-water environments. Although their corrosion resistance is superior to that of mild steel, it is not considered sufficient for unprotected service.

With either 5*xxx* series alloys or high-strength alloys, however, care is necessary in the design and fabrication of marine structures to avoid contact with other metals, such as steel, brass, copper, and certain of the stainless steels, because aluminum generally corrodes preferentially (galvanic corrosion) when connected in sea water with dissimilar metals. Where it is impractical to electrically isolate the aluminum alloy, cathodic protection is normally used to obtain satisfactory service (see Volume I, Chapter 7). In some instances, alclad products (Volume I, Chapter 9) or appropriate coatings (Volume III, Chapter 21) can alleviate galvanic corrosion problems.

Boats operated in salt water require antifouling paints to prevent marine growth. Aluminum is impervious to worms and borers, but the accumulation of marine organisms on the bottom of the boat can impair performance. To make coatings of antifouling paints adhere, care in surface preparation is required. A thorough precleaning and either a conversion coating or a washcoat primer, followed by a corrosion-inhibiting primer, under the finish coats, are necessary. Primers containing lead pigments should not be used. In salt water, zinc chromate primers are excellent, but they are not recommended for fresh-water service because of a tendency to blister.

Recently introduced antifouling paints employing organic tin compounds appear promising for eliminating the corrosion problems associated with copper-bearing or mercury-bearing antifouling compounds. The mercury paints should not be used on aluminum boats, due to possible severe corrosion. The copper-bearing paints can be used, but galvanic corrosion may result from inadequate anticorrosive or barrier paint coats between the aluminum hull plating and the antifouling paint.

Pleasure Boats

The use of small boats has expanded rapidly since 1945. Early applications of aluminum were mainly in canoes and small fishing boats, in which aluminum is now the dominant material.

Small Craft. Runabouts and small outboard cruisers up to 20 ft long generally are constructed either of aluminum or plastic. Styling often is more important than engineering superiority in these consumer products. However, only recently have builders emphasized styling in aluminum boats.

Light weight is advantageous, in that it reduces construction costs, allows a boat to be driven with less power, and provides portability. Furthermore, many accidents that would have caused fractures and extensive damage in wood or plastic boats result only in repairable dents with aluminum. Also, aluminum boats are damaged less than steel boats in service experience to date (even though aluminum plating and steel plating are usually of the same thickness), because the lower modulus of elasticity of aluminum results in a larger capacity to absorb energy. For both aluminum sheet and steel sheet, thickness is selected mostly on the basis of weldability, for which the requirements are the same for the two metals.

An example of aluminum's durability is the ramming of an aluminum catamaran, the "Lee Scott", by a 150-ton tugboat in a dense fog in 1959. The 45-ft "Scott" was struck amidships while moored at her berth. The force of the collision snapped off the 16-in. berth piling and the "Scott" absorbed an estimated 500,000 ft-lb of energy in stopping the tug. No weld failures occurred, and only one plate, where the tug's bow had made a small indentation, had to be replaced.

The practical minimum thickness of aluminum parts for repair welding is considered to be 0.090 in. Although lighter gages (common in small-boat construction) can be welded, usually they are repaired at perforated locations by riveting sheet patches in place. Dents are hammered smooth, as in automobile body repair.

Low maintenance reduces the cost of operating a rental boat service, and it is also an advantage with private pleasure craft, which are carefully maintained for appearance. Most aluminum boats are sold painted for fresh-water or salt-water service. For operation in fresh water, aluminum boats are commonly left unpainted for 10 years or more, whereas wood boats require annual caulking and painting. For salt-water service, the typical practice with aluminum is an annual touch-up plus repainting every three or four years.

Aluminum is used for boat trim and accessories, regardless of hull material. Anodized bright trim, either as extrusions or roll-formed sheet products, is widely used in boats of all types for rub rails, dash panels, and other parts.

Riveting is the major joining method used in fabricating small boats (Volume III, Chapter 11). It is economical and errors can be corrected easily. Its chief disadvantages are the appearance of the riveted joint and susceptibility of riveted seams to working and subsequent leakage. Recent advances in styling and design have alleviated appearance problems, and application of caulking tapes has minimized leakage.

Hull shapes for most small craft employ developable surfaces (single curvature contours) to which aluminum sheets can conform without permanent deformation. To allow more design freedom in hull form, stretch forming is used to obtain double curvature of hull sheets.

Jigging for welding assembly must provide for firm alignment of the aluminum sheet, to reduce distortion. Production welding of the light gages used for pleasure boats (0.050 to 0.090 in.) is a problem. Although tape sealing and caulking of seams are not required, exposed welds must be dressed for a good appearance. Welding is better suited to larger craft.

Small boats are fabricated from a wide range of aluminum sheet alloys, mainly in the 5*xxx* and 6*xxx* series. These have an optimum combination of strength, cost, ease of fabrication, and corrosion resistance. Generally, 5052-H32, 5052-H34, or 6061-T6 is used for small hulls that need no stretch forming. Where stretch forming is employed, 6061-T4 sheet, which may be subsequently artificially aged to the T6 temper, is utilized. Extrusions of 6061 or 6063 are used for structural and decorative sections, such as keels, chines, gunwales, and spray rails.

Rivets of 2117, 6053, or 6061 are recommended. Generally, a rivet should be neither much harder nor appreciably softer than the sheet to be joined, and it should have similar mechanical properties (Volume III, Chapter 11).

Larger inboard boats, 20 to 125 ft long, are fabricated of aluminum alloys for reasons similar to those for small craft. Normally, these boats employ welded construction for hull, interior structure, and cabins. The most popular alloy for hulls is 5086-H32, in thicknesses of $\frac{3}{16}$ to $\frac{1}{2}$ in. Bulkheads, fuel tanks, and cabins are usually of the same alloy as the hull, although 5052 or 6061 can be utilized. Structural members, either in special extrusions or standard structural shapes, can be of 6061-T6 or 5086-H112 in all-welded construction.

Sailing craft follow a pattern similar to that for power craft — the smaller boats using riveted construction of 5052 or 6061 alloy, and larger custom yachts using all-welded construction in 5086. The light weight of aluminum hulls in sailing craft allows the designer wide latitude in providing balance between sail area and ballast-displacement ratio. A recent study (2) of hull weights for wood, glass-reinforced plastic, and aluminum in a 30-ft Naval Academy yawl showed that plastic was 10% and wood 37% heavier than aluminum. The currently standard plastic yawls have a ballast-displacement ratio of 0.433, compared to 0.390 for the older wood design. Aluminum construction would permit a ratio of approximately 0.47.

Since ability to carry a given sail area depends on the inherent stability of the hull form plus that provided by fixed or movable ballast, it is common practice to increase the ballast ratios in aluminum hulls. This is especially prevalent in ocean racing yachts, such as the 58-ft "Dyna" and the 57-ft "Ondine", where ballast-displacement ratios are as high as 0.60 (compared to 0.27 to 0.425 for cruising yachts).

Attaching lead ballast to an aluminum hull in the form of a keel casting, as is done with hulls of other materials, could result in galvanic corrosion. For this reason, it is current practice to install solid or molten ballast inside the formed keel and the bottom plating. Fuel and water tanks are integral with the hull to save space and reduce costs.

Aluminum masts for sailboats are becoming standard in many boat sizes. The masts normally are drawn 6061 alloy oval tubes, but small-boat masts are frequently extruded of 6063 and include an integral track for carrying the sail. Small masts are not tapered, but large sizes are frequently tapered at the upper 10 to 20% of the length. Masts range in section size from 2.25 by 1.75 in. with 0.062-in. wall to 14.5 by 8.5 in. with 0.344-in. wall on ocean racing boats. Where larger sizes are required, masts are fabricated from plate.

Because of wide variation in rigging systems, and hence in loads imposed on the mast, there is no simple correlation between mast length and section dimensions. For example, a 12-meter boat competing in the America's Cup races has an aluminum mast 90 ft long with an oval section 9.652 by 11.925 in. with 0.23-in. wall, whereas the 65-ft mast on the ocean racer "Dyna" has a section 8.3 by 13.6 in. with 0.22-in. wall. The weight reductions compared to Sitka spruce spars are 10 to 50%, again following no definite pattern. Because the center of gravity of a spar is usually 30 to 50 ft above that of the hull, even small weight reductions significantly improve hull stability.

The required moment of inertia (I) for a mast section varies inversely as the modulus of elasticity for the material considered. Thus, an aluminum mast must have an I-value only 0.14 times that required for wood, permitting smaller aluminum mast sections. Where class sailing rules require aluminum and wood masts to have the same exterior dimensions, an aluminum mast is 10 to 30% stronger. Many classes that formerly restricted masts to wood now allow aluminum, to reduce mast breakage in hard-fought races.

Fittings for aluminum masts employ common marine alloys, in aluminum, brass, or stainless steel. Brass fittings must be insulated from the mast to prevent galvanic attack from seawater spray. This is accomplished by a nonmetallic gasket in the faying surface or caulking the edge of the joint. Sheaves are alloy 356 castings or plastic, and standing rigging is steel wire rope or stainless steel bars. Hand winches are normally chromium-plated brass; a recent design uses a 356 alloy casting, with the winch drum spray metallized with tungsten for wear resistance.

Commercial Small Craft

Personnel and work boat construction has accelerated with the expansion of the offshore oil industry since World War II. Initially, steel was established as the standard construction material for these craft, and it was not until the middle 1950's that the first aluminum personnel boat went into service. This

Fig. 2. Inert-gas metal-arc welding of small (54 ft long) offshore oil well personnel boat, built of 5456-H321 sheet, plate and extrusions, and some 6061-T6 tube. Framing system employs stiffeners welded to hull plating. In background is an 85-ft commercial boat, built with the same alloys and basic construction.

all-welded 6061-T6 boat quickly demonstrated the advantages of lighter hull weight, resulting in higher speed for the same horsepower. As time saved in transportation of personnel to the rigs offers significant wage savings, the industry rapidly adopted these craft. Over 400 were in service at the end of 1965.

Crew boats are normally of hard-chine, planing-hull type, using developable surfaces in the hull form. This results in an efficient hull that is economical to fabricate (Fig. 2). The builder also benefits from the lighter weight of the material being lifted into place, since fewer workers and pieces of hoisting equipment are required. One builder of personnel boats has shown that a 50-

ft aluminum hull requires a fabrication time 33% less that for steel. Typical time savings are 5 to 25%. With this saving to partially offset the higher cost of the metal, the total boat cost is generally only 10 to 20% higher than for a comparably equipped and powered steel boat. For this extra investment, a 4 to 8-mph speed increase is usually obtained. In one tank-tested hull design, a 12-mph increase was achieved for a 65-ft craft. The operators were able to recover the $24,000 premium for this boat in one year, permitting reduced charter rates, which expanded demand. They presently operate twelve 65-ft boats and nine 85-footers off the Gulf Coast.

The majority of aluminum personnel boats are fabricated of 5456-H321 sheet and plate 0.188 to 0.375 in. thick, and 5456-H111 or 6061-T6 extruded shapes. Alloy 5086 is also widely used for hull plating. Cabins are normally of 5052 sheet 0.125 to 0.25 in. thick, and 6061 extrusions.

Although speed increase may be the initial economic factor in selling aluminum personnel boats, the recurring maintenance savings can return as much or more to the owner during the life of the boat. Welded aluminum boats with five to seven years' service have shown annual painting costs only 5 to 20% of those experienced with similar steel craft. These savings are attributable to better corrosion resistance, which results in extended paint coating life. In addition, the entire interior structure can be left bare, whereas steel must be painted. Where fouling is not a problem, aluminum hull bottoms normally are left bare.

Cathodic protection is used on the majority of these personnel boats, to reduce galvanic corrosion adjacent to other metals employed for shafting and propellers.

Fishing Vessels. In these craft, the weight-saving and corrosion-resistance economies of aluminum have proven to exceed the initial investment premium. Following a short service test in 1957 of two 36-ft welded aluminum purse seine boats built of 0.25-in.-thick 5052-H32 plate and 6061-T6 shapes, an entire fleet was changed to aluminum. The original advantage attributed to aluminum was the weight saving, which was used to compensate for additional net-handling gear while retaining adequate stability. After four years of abuse of the boats in this rugged service, the owners were convinced that aluminum boats also had lower maintenance costs. No hull maintenance was required, whereas steel boats needed annual scraping, chipping, and painting (Fig. 3). Total annual maintenance costs averaged

Craft after 8 years of rigorous service (steel craft normally are replaced within 4 to 8 years). All-welded construction employed routed ¼-in.-thick plate, supplied by the aluminum producer, permitting material and fabrication economies. Painted when placed in service, craft has required no repainting.

Fig. 3. Aluminum purse seine fishing craft

$1200 for steel seine boats, compared to $100 for aluminum boats. The aluminum boats also outlast their steel counterparts, having almost twice the service life. About 250 aluminum purse seine boats are in operation off the Atlantic and Gulf Coasts.

A 57-ft Alaskan fishing boat constructed of 0.25-in.-thick 5086-H32 plate attained a loaded speed of 18 knots, more than double that of conventional boats. This resulted in an extra $5000 to $10,000 earnings per year, since more time could be spent at the fishing grounds. The craft is unpainted; maintenance savings are estimated at $2000 per year. The increased earnings and the maintenance savings quickly justified the 15% initial cost premium.

Similar savings were reported for 70 gill-netters with welded 5086-H32 0.25-in. hull plating, operating in the Pacific Northwest. These 36-ft craft earn 30% more in a normal season than the standard wood-hull gill-netters they replaced. The hull weight is approximately 6500 lb, resulting in a fish capacity of 35,000 lb, nearly double that for the wood boats. The aluminum boats are not painted, and maintenance costs are further reduced because of the simple cleaning procedures required for fish holds — hosing down with fresh water.

Equipment aboard fishing vessels is often aluminum. The aluminum fishroom, common in Europe, is used in some vessels in the United States. Extruded or roll-formed aluminum hold sections in 6061-T6 or 6063-T6 result in fishroom systems that are nonabsorptive, sanitary, and easily rearranged by the crew. Fish spoilage is reduced and more fish can be carried, as the aluminum sections are less than one third the weight of wet-wood fish or pen boards (portable boards for dividing the hold into small compartments).

Refrigerated fish tanks of unprotected 5052 or 6061 sheet and plate $3/16$ to $5/16$ in. thick have proven more sanitary and less expensive to maintain than coated or treated steel tanks. With brine as the normal coolant, steel tanks require the protection of organic or metallic coatings to achieve useful service life; in addition, coating maintenance is a continuous problem.

Government survey boats with aluminum hulls normally carry more surveying equipment than the conventional steel boats, although some use the weight saving to expand shallow-draft operations. Both state and federal government agencies operate these aluminum boats. The survey boats are fabricated by the builders of personnel boats, and they are made with similar alloys and construction practices.

Commercial Ships

Passenger vessels utilize large quantities of aluminum in superstructures and equipment. The 4.5 million pounds in the "SS United States", built in 1952, resulted in an 8000-ton decrease in displacement. The lighter topside weight permitted a beam reduction, saving hull weight and allowing reduced power capacity, while still providing the high service speeds necessary on modern ocean liners (3). The superstructure uses approximately half the 4.5 million pounds. Riveted 6061-T6 plate was employed for the deckhouse structure, superstructure decks, and bulkheads. The remainder of the aluminum was utilized in furniture, equipment, ventilation ducts, ladders, stair treads, and railings.

Major European-built liners have used aluminum extensively in superstructures and equipment, ranging from 1000 to 2000 tons per ship. The "Oriana", "Canberra", and "France" employed welded construction, using sheet, plate and extrusions of aluminum-magnesium and aluminum-magnesium-manganese alloys. Since appearance is important in this class of ship, the structures are painted; aluminum allows at least 50% longer time until repainting is required.

Dry cargo ships have been affected by new design trends that emphasize a need for lower topside weight. Heavier cargo handling gear and related machinery, and more narrow, hydrodynamically contoured, high-speed hulls have increased stability problems. Thus, weight saving is required to permit more efficient hull designs. Approximately 100 tons of welded 5086 plate and shapes 0.25 to 0.75 in. thick was used in the midship structures in each of ten ships built recently. Aluminum structures normally weigh only 40% as much as steel structures, using construction details similar to steel practice (welded plate and stiffeners bracketed at the decks). In some instances, additional weight is saved by application of special extrusions.

Cargo ships, as well as passenger liners, have been affected by changes in international regulations, administered by the U. S. Coast Guard, covering fire safety of deckhouse structures. This has resulted in a greater emphasis on insulation requirements for fire protection, which generally are greater for aluminum structures than for steel, because of the difference in melting temperatures (1200 F versus 2600 F). The full effect of this added insulation on weight ratios and cost will depend on the results of fire tests being sponsored by the Society of Naval

Architects and Marine Engineers; present regulations do not adequately define requirements for aluminum.

Bulk carriers normally can take direct advantage of any weight saving by carrying additional cargo. Six Canadian ore carriers (5) utilized 150 to 250 tons of aluminum in deckhouse structures, hatch covers, and equipment such as railings and lifeboats. All-welded construction using an alloy similar to 5086

Deckhouse of 450-ft bulk carrier was not painted, as an experiment, and successful experience led to adopting this as standard. Carrier has been in service for 10 years. Added revenue and maintenance savings have totaled $180,000.

Fig. 4. All-welded aluminum deckhouse of "Sunrip"

was employed for most applications. The weight saved — 60% in deckhouses, 50% in hatch covers — was reflected directly in increased cargo capacity. As a further experiment, the aluminum structures were left unpainted on the first ship of the series. The success of this experiment proved that painting was unnecessary (6), and the subsequent ships followed the lead, saving $2000 per year for each ship (Fig. 4).

The Great Lakes iron ore carrier "Edward L. Ryerson" holds the record for ore carried in one season — partially attributable to the use of 19 aluminum hatch covers weighing approximately 4.5 tons each. These one-piece covers are 21 by 54-ft all-welded construction, fabricated of 5083 plates and shapes. By careful design and close cooperation with the American Bureau of Shipping, a weight saving of 64% was achieved compared to conventional steel construction. Similar hatch cover applications have been made on Canadian lake vessels. Prior to this, aluminum hatch cover designs were normally limited to a 50% weight saving due to restrictive regulations.

Aluminum booms of riveted 2014-T6, 6061-T6, or 6070-T6 extruded or rolled shapes on self-unloading ore carriers enable operators to achieve economies in converting older ships to update their usefulness. In a typical installation, a 190-ft steel boom on the "J. R. Sensibar" was replaced with a 256-ft aluminum boom, increasing the dockside unloading area available to the ship without having to alter the existing boom support structure.

Passenger ferries use aluminum superstructures to maintain safe stability while carrying more passengers (4). In 1939, New York City's Staten Island ferries initiated this application of aluminum with three riveted superstructures, involving a total of 100 tons of 6061-T6 plates and shapes. This resulted in a reduction in fuel consumption of 220 gal per round trip for each ferry and an annual operating cost that was $107,000 less than for a similar ferry with an all-steel superstructure. Similar ships followed in 1950. The latest group of three ships, built in 1964, used 100 tons of welded 5086 plates and extrusions for the topside structure. Smaller ferries in operation off the Pacific Coast and in the St. Lawrence River have hulls of welded 5086-H32 plate, 3/16 or 1/4 in. thick.

Barges. Aluminum barges, carrying various chemical products, have been operated on the American inland waterway system since 1960 (7). A 5200-bbl barge is 97 ft long, 35 ft wide and operates at an 8.5-ft draft. A 9000-bbl barge is 100 ft long, 50 ft wide, and carries 1200 short tons at an 8.5-ft draft. The aluminum barges have 7⁄16-in.-thick welded 5086-H34 hull plating; the cargo tanks are 5⁄16-in. 5052-H34 plate. Approximately 120 short tons of aluminum was used in constructing the 100-ft barge, resulting in a weight saving of 150 tons compared to a similar steel barge. This permitted 15% more cargo to be carried, but the corrosion resistance of the aluminum alloys employed in tankage, piping, and hull was the major factor in selection of aluminum for these chemical barges.

These barges have also been used to move such commodities as lubricating oils, fuels, nitrogen fertilizers, petroleum solvents, and glycols. Recent inspections by the United States Coast Guard, the American Bureau of Shipping, and the owners have shown virtually no corrosion of the aluminum structure or structural damage from handling in river tows.

A larger aluminum barge, 195 by 50 ft, was built in 1963. All-welded 5083 plate 5⁄16 to 9⁄16 in. thick and structural shapes were used to fabricate this barge. It carries acetic anhydride, although classed for a range of other chemical products also. The rated capacity is 2264 short tons at an 8.5-ft draft. This capacity is approximately 14% more than a stainless-clad tank barge of the same size; hull weight of the aluminum barge is only 200 short tons, compared to 486 tons for steel construction.

Hydrofoils. These high-speed craft are used for commuter and excursion service. Although their use in Europe has been an economic reality for over a decade, the availability of competing forms of transportation has restricted application in this country. Early European applications dictated minimum hull weight to utilize practical power sources. This led to the exclusive use of a 6061-type alloy and riveted construction for the hull, cabin, and bulkheads. Craft built recently in the United States have employed welded construction with the 5*xxx* series alloys.

The 90-ton, 105-ft-long hydrofoil "H.S. Denison" was built in 1961 for the Maritime Administration. A combination of riveting and welding was used in fabricating the hull, cabin, and bulkheads of 5456 sheet, plate, and extrusions. Alloy 7079-T6 forgings formed part of the steel foil structure. Piping systems were of aluminum or plastics, following aircraft practice.

Smaller hydrofoil craft have also been constructed of aluminum. Two 45-ft-long craft of welded 5456 were built, with 10 more planned for similar construction. Welded 5086 sheet, plate, and extrusions were used to build the 34-ft "Albatross", which can carry 24 passengers at speeds up to 40 mph.

Aluminum is not only the accepted material for hydrofoil hull structure, but is used also in small foil systems in the form of alloy 356-T6 castings and 6061-T6 extrusions. However, in large craft, such as the "Denison" and the Navy's PCH and AGEH (discussed in the next section), high-strength steels are employed for the foil structures. Although many questions remain concerning the relative importance of the various factors in material selection, it has been established that the strength and stiffness provided by the high-yield-strength steels (150,000 to 200,000 psi) are necessary in the large craft.

Naval Vessels

Destroyers. About 6000 tons of aluminum per year — more than any other type of marine application — is used on destroyers. During the 1930's, extensive application of aluminum in destroyers was developed, and design practices were refined. During World War II, construction reverted to steel because of the shortage of aluminum. Following the war, with growing emphasis on electronic equipment, deckhouse structure weight became a critical factor, and aluminum was reinstated to combat this problem.

Alloy development in the past decade has resulted in an almost standard application of 5456 plate and extrusions in the welded deckhouse structures of destroyers. Quantities now used range from 100 to 350 tons per ship, depending on the type of destroyer. The weight savings in the aluminum deckhouse structure, normally about 40 to 45%, are utilized to maintain sufficient ship stability while employing the narrow hull necessary for high service speeds. Additional equipment installations also are permitted topside.

Over half the aluminum used is in the deckhouse structure, the remainder being employed in a variety of equipment applications. These include lockers, desks, chairs, bunks, doors, windows, ladders, gratings, and galley equipment. A wide range of the more corrosion-resistant wrought and cast alloys is found in these items, including 5052, 5086, 6061 and 356.

Aircraft Carriers. Aluminum applications totaled over 1750 tons on the carrier "Enterprise" (CVA-65) completed in 1961. The largest single item (8) was the four deck-edge elevators (Fig. 5). The first such elevator platforms, employing welded 6061-T6 members in a tubular-truss structure, had been in-

Elevator being assembled by consumable-electrode (MIG) welding. Alloy 5456 plates up to 2 in. thick were welded with alloy 5556 filler wire. Four elevators, each weighing 105 tons and 52 ft wide by 85 ft long, were installed.

Fig. 5. Large aluminum elevator for aircraft carrier "Enterprise"

stalled on the carrier "Shangri-La" (CVA-38) in 1955. Later, alloy 5154-H36 was used for the welded elevators on CVA-61. Alloy and welding developments led to application of alloy 5456 plate and extrusions in the elevators on the "Enterprise". These were designed with an open grillwork structure; the deep girders were fabricated from plate ¾ to 2 in. thick. The 52 by 85-ft structures weighed 105 tons each, 35 tons less than similar steel units. Reduced inertia, during operation between the flight and hangar decks, permitted reductions in operating machinery.

The "America" (CVA-66), completed in 1965, employs elevators of stiffened-plate configuration, using high-strength steels; they weighed 115 tons each. A similar design but employing alloy 5456 resulted in aluminum being specified for the elevators on carrier CVA-67, now under construction, at a weight reduction of 15 tons each.

Other uses included the items of equipment mentioned for destroyers, along with radar masts, superstructure, cooling panels in the flight deck, and comparable structures.

Hydrofoils. The Navy's antisubmarine warfare program has resulted in the construction of two of the largest aluminum hulls of any type in this country. Now under test is the 115-ft-long PCH (Patrol Craft, Hydrofoil), with fully submerged foil system and an all-welded 5456 hull. Extrusions 26.5 in. wide, with integral T-section stiffeners, form a large part of the hull structure.

The 219-ft-long research hydrofoil ship, AGEH, utilizes similar wide, integrally stiffened extrusions of 5456 in welded construction. This structure represents the most economical way to obtain the strength-weight ratio necessary for successful performance of these hydrofoils.

Motor gunboats had been limited to under 90 ft long, but the latest class are 165-ft-long, all-welded aluminum ships (9) that are expected to achieve useful speed increases economically (Fig. 6). The main hull structure employs 5086-H32 plate in thicknesses of 5⁄16 to ½ in. Deckhouse, decks, and bulkheads use 5086 and 5456 plate and extrusions in all-welded construction.

In 1965, 104 50-ft patrol boats were ordered for service in Vietnam. Each weighs only 16 tons and is capable of over 30 mph. Hulls were constructed of 5456 plate.

Shipping Containers

Marine containers are similar to highway trailers, using the stressed skin or semimonocoque principle, in which the side sheet carries the load (see Chapters 15 and 16 in this volume). The marine container, however, requires stronger construction at the end posts or corners, as several containers may be stacked one on top of the other (10). In addition, side sheet gages may be thicker than for van trailers, to prevent perforation from dockside handling. Side posts may be thicker and deeper to absorb the load punishment as the containers are nested aboard ship.

Alclad 3003 roof sheet, normally 0.032 to 0.040 in. thick in

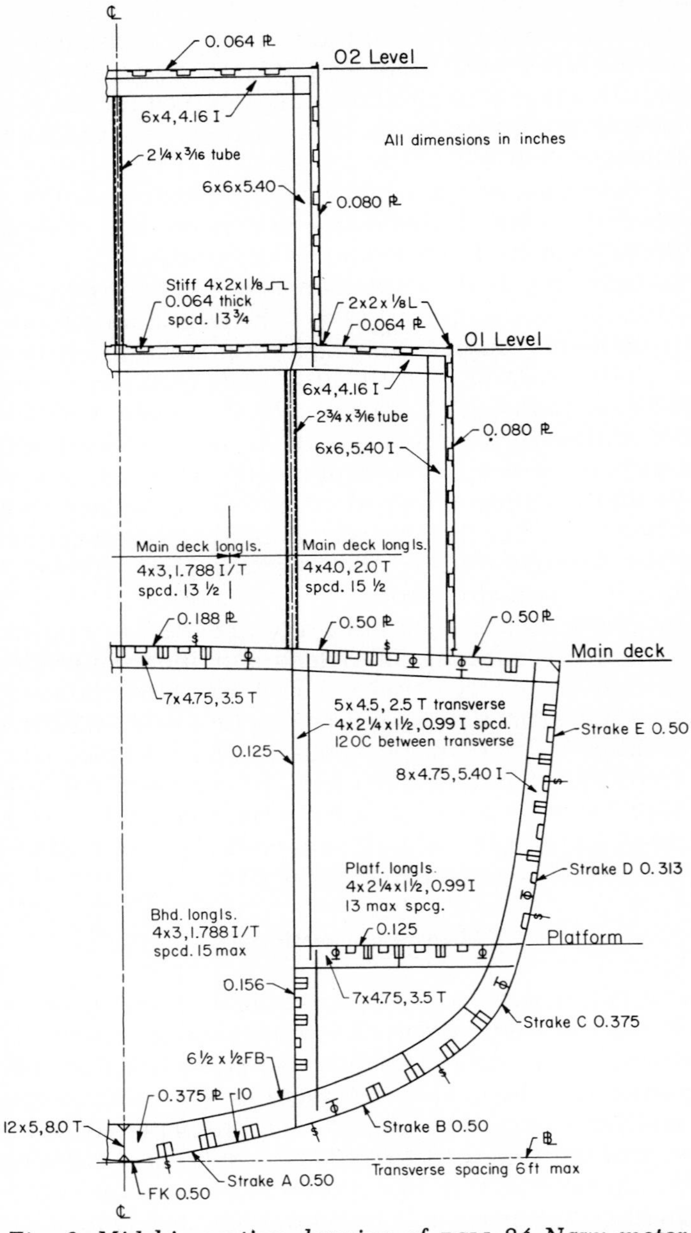

Fig. 6. Midship section drawing of PGM *84 Navy motor gunboat. The 165-ft craft is of all-welded construction, employing alloy 5086 for principal structural members.*

van trailers, can be as thick as 0.060 in. in marine containers. Side sheet of alclad 2024-T3, alclad 5155, or alclad 6061-T6 is used in thicknesses up to 0.081 in. Extrusions are normally 6062-T6; joining is with 6053-T61 rivets.

Corrosion performance of aluminum containers in marine environments indicates that painting is not required. Only superficial etching attack occurred in constant exposure for 45 months. Galvanized or stainless steel bolts and fittings are employed; faying surfaces are treated with asphaltic compounds to reduce galvanic attack from dissimilar metal contact.

Motive Power

Present 50-hp outboard motors weigh no more and occupy less space than the 25-hp unit of 30 years ago, a direct result of increased use of aluminum. Inboard engines have more than doubled their propulsion capabilities, while reducing both weight and silhouette.

Outboard motors for small pleasure boats have an average output of 30 hp and weigh about 125 lb. These 2-cycle engines produce nearly 1 hp per cubic inch displacement. A 1.5-hp air-cooled outboard motor weighs as little as 25 lb, whereas the 90 to 100-hp V-4 or inline six-cylinder engine weighs 240 lb. Aluminum die and permanent mold castings, and high-strength aluminum forgings represent 70% of the total engine weight.

A typical cylinder block and crankcase is of die cast 13 or 380 alloy, and has iron cylinder liners, cast in place (Fig. 7). The entire inlet and exhaust manifold systems, the upper and lower crankcase covers, cylinder heads, and carburetor body utilize die castings of 13, 380, or similar alloys. Upper and lower motor leg castings, lower gear cases, and water pump housings are similarly fabricated. In a few designs where minimum underwater profile is required, a semipermanent mold lower gear case of 356-T6 is used. This process allows more design freedom, since the casting interior need not be based on core withdrawal.

Cast or forged pistons are employed at the discretion of the engineer. Permanent mold pistons in F132-T5 and 142-T5 are in general use. Alloy F132 has a satisfactory history in 2-cycle and 4-cycle engines, whereas 142, with superior thermal conductivity, appears to reduce piston temperatures and preclude crown burning in certain engines. Forged pistons of 4032-T6 are used throughout one entire outboard line.

Mercury Outboard Motors

Fig. 7. Aluminum die cast six-cylinder block for 60 to 70-hp outboard motor. Iron cylinder linings are cast in place.

Outboard motor transom clamps vary from 218 alloy die castings for small-output to medium-output engines, to aircraft-type 2014-T6 forgings for some 60 to 100-hp units. Some outboards merely rest in a centering device and are through-bolted to the transom with 2024-T4 fasteners.

The alloy used for propellers depends on method of production, size, and selling price. Most original-equipment propellers of low horsepower rating are die cast of 13 or 380 alloy; if cracked or bent, they can be replaced more economically than repaired. Die cast propellers for the 60 to 100-hp engine are usually 218 alloy, and can be straightened, welded, and reworked to a limited degree. Replacement-part manufacturers produce sand castings, because of a multitude of diameter and pitch variations, and favor an Al – 7 Mg alloy, such as Almag 35 or A218, that allows extensive repairing. The application of aluminum has two important advantages over heavier propeller materials: The low inertial forces involved in shifting from forward to reverse prevent wear and damage to the shift mechanism, and the aluminum does not form a galvanic couple with the immersed motor leg.

It is industry practice to give all aluminum engine components a chemical conversion coating. A sealing compound usually is applied to all interior passageways, to prevent water or gas leaks and to improve salt-water corrosion resistance. Exterior surfaces receive a spray coat of zinc chromate primer, and a decorative and protective finish of lacquer, enamel, or epoxy paint (Volume III, Chapter 21).

Inboard engines in 20 to 60-ft commercial and pleasure craft are, with few exceptions, adaptations of automotive, truck, or industrial power plants (see Chapter 14 in this volume). The few refinements that might be designed into an engine built strictly for marine service cannot be economically justified. The marine engine manufacturer employs a highly developed mass-produced engine with cast aluminum or iron cylinder block, steel crankshaft and connecting rods, aluminum alloy pistons, and cast aluminum or cast iron cylinder heads. His contribution is designing, fabricating, and testing those specialized additional components necessary for heavy-duty marine service.

The stamped steel oil pan, normally air cooled, is replaced by a larger-capacity sand or permanent mold aluminum casting of 319, 333, or 356 alloy with a T5 heat treatment. Integrally cast water passages are sometimes included for oil cooling. To reduce over-all heights, low-profile intake manifolds, generally sand cast in 319 or 356, in the T5 condition, are used. Flame arrestor bodies for carburetors are sand cast or permanent mold cast components of 319 or 333 in the as-cast condition.

The starter and generator mounting brackets and the flywheel housing and engine mounting points are usually grouped into one large engine cover casting. Both sand and semipermanent mold aluminum castings are employed, generally 356 alloy in a solution heat treated and aged temper. At the propeller-shaft end, an aluminum alloy casting is used as an adaptor from the engine block to a marine transmission or reduction unit. The rear engine-mounting brackets are usually a part of this adaptor. Sand cast alloy 319-T5 and permanent mold cast 333-T5 and 356-T6 are employed successfully in this application.

Sand cast water-cooled exhaust manifolds of 319 and 356 with a T5 aging treatment showed little water jacket corrosion in 2 to 3 years of service in sea water. High rates of corrosion have occurred in the mixing area, where raw sea water enters the exhaust stream and provides exhaust pipe cooling aft to the transom. Cathodic protection and proper gasketing procedure may solve these difficulties.

Aluminum die castings are successfully used as distributor housings, generator and alternator end bells, alternator rotors, and oil-filter adaptors. Alloys 13, 360, and 380 are usually chosen, and require no heat treatment. Aluminum sand and permanent mold castings are used in transmissions and reduction housings, with 319-T5, 333-T5, and 356-T5 the most common selections.

With many of the advantages of both inboard and outboard installations, the inboard-outboard, or outdrive, is steadily gaining in popularity. A typical installation mounts an inboard-type engine against the transom. Power passes through the transom and into a right-angle gearbox, then down to propeller shaft level and through a second right-angle gearset. Aluminum sand, permanent mold, and die castings are universally used for structural components in the drive unit. A typical 150-hp installation employs 60 lb of 356-T6 permanent mold and semipermanent mold castings. These castings offer resistance to corrosion, adequate mechanical properties, consistent leakproofness, and acceptable machining characteristics. Die castings in 13 or 380 alloy are equally successful for these components and are used on installations up to 325 hp.

Pump or water-jet propulsion is being refined and has outstanding advantages in shallow water, rivers, lakes, and bays. Because no part extends below the keel, the boat can operate in a few inches of water. Aluminum sand and permanent mold castings have found favor for intake housings, impeller housings, and the transom casting that combines the functions of steering and reversing. Alloy 356-T6 is usually selected, and it performs well when given an anodic or chemical conversion treatment and then is painted.

V-drives allow the engine to be placed against the transom, conserving floor space. The engine output shaft extends forward and is coupled to the V-drive gearbox. Through a gearset or V-belts, the drive line is reversed and angled to pass through the keel to the propeller. Aluminum alloy gear cases perform satisfactorily, reducing the off-center hull loading and assisting in the

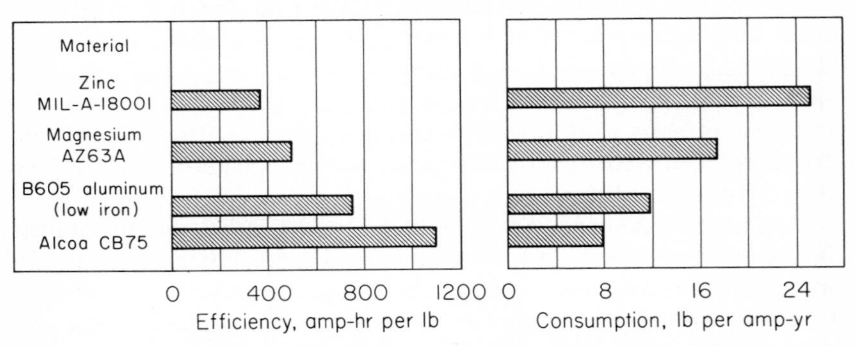

Fig. 8. Comparative efficiency and consumption of four anode materials for use in cathodic protection systems

dissipation of gear-generated heat. Sand cast 319, 355, or 356 alloys in the T6 condition are commonly selected.

Inboard assemblies are degreased and given a protective coat of enamel or epoxy paint. The resultant high-gloss finish eliminates unsightly but harmless surface corrosion and simplifies cleaning of the engine (Volume III, Chapter 21).

Heavy-duty diesel engines tailored for marine service range upward from 25 hp. Only two domestic engines are offered with aluminum blocks (Chapter 14 in this volume).

Other Applications

Dock and marina construction has paralleled expansion of boating as a recreational activity. (The term "marina" was coined to describe a docking facility that provides more than boat storage space.) Aluminum docks normally require only minor seasonal repainting. Alloys used are the same as in boat construction. Some docks are designed with aluminum decking, but most employ wood decking to effect initial cost savings. Alloys 5052, 6061, 6063, and 356 are employed as structures, decking, and fittings.

There are many architectural aluminum applications in marina buildings, as well as in the large covered marinas. Aluminum roofing and siding, both natural and painted, is applicable (see Chapter 10 in this volume). Handrails, light standards, and guardrails are often made of aluminum tube or pipe. Standard structural pipe and fittings are widely used for these purposes.

Individual homeowners requiring docks also use aluminum, either in prefabricated structures or "do-it-yourself" assemblies. Framework made of tube or structural shapes, decking of formed sheet or extrusions, and cast fittings are employed, using the same alloys. These docks normally have fixed means of support, and are assembled on site or positioned in sections.

Weather buoys are part of an expanding program of continuous weather metering under the direction of the United States Navy. More than 20 unmanned automatic weather buoys, called NOMAD, are anchored off the Atlantic and Gulf Coasts. The 20 by 10-ft all-aluminum buoy hull and superstructure support weather recording and monitoring devices, as well as automatic radio broadcasting equipment. Aluminum is chosen for its nonmagnetic properties, and 5086-H32 plates 3⁄8 to 1½ in. thick are used for the deck, bulkheads, keel, and shell plating. Extruded and rolled 6061-T6 structural shapes are employed for stiffeners in the all-welded construction of the hull and support structures. The resistance to corrosion of these alloys is necessary to obtain the planned 10-year service intervals of these unmanned buoys.

Aluminum anodes are used for cathodic protection (see Volume I, Chapter 7) of steel or aluminum structures in marine service and in industries such as chemical processing or oil and gas production and distribution. Anodes made of alloy B605, a commercial-purity Al – 5 Zn alloy, were introduced in 1955. Higher efficiencies and hence lower consumption rates are offered by anodes made of the recently introduced alloy CB75, a commercial-purity aluminum-zinc-tin alloy. Comparative data are shown in Fig. 8. Marine applications include stern frame, ballast, and cargo tank anodes. Heat exchangers, lubricating oil coolers, pumps, and other marine equipment also can be protected with aluminum anode alloy CB75 more economically than with other anode materials.

References

1 "Aluminum Afloat", Aluminum Company of America, 1964

2 R. G. Henry and Captain R. T. Miller, USN, Sailing Yacht Design — An Appreciation of a Fine Art, Trans SNAME, **71**, 425–490 (1963)

3 W. Muckle, "The Design of Aluminum Alloy Ships' Structures", Aluminum Development Assoc., England, 1963

4 Th. Domes, The Part Played by Aluminum in the Progress Made in Rhine Passenger Ship Construction, Aluminium, **41**, 582–588 (1965)

5 A. Lana-Serrate, "Application Record — S. S. Sunrip", Aluminum Company of Canada, Limited, 1956

6 E. Balfour, "The Use of Aluminum in Ships", Society of Naval Architects and Marine Engineers, Eastern Canadian Section, Jan 13, 1959

7 C. H. Holtyn, "Aluminum — From Boats to Ships", Society of Naval Architects and Marine Engineers, Pacific Northwest Section, April 5, 1963

8 F. M. Daly, "Welded Fabrication on Aluminum Airplane Elevator", Society of Naval Architects and Marine Engineers, Hampton Roads Section, Dec 5, 1958

9 C. W. Leveau, "Marine Aluminum Applications", Society of Naval Architects and Marine Engineers, South California Section, Feb 13, 1964

10 "Aluminum Van Containers: Concept, Construction, Capabilities", Aluminum Company of America, 1963

Chapter 18

Aircraft and Aerospace Applications

C. L. BURTON, L. W. MAYER and E. H. SPUHLER

PRIOR to 1900, the activity that now is the aerospace industry was represented by such projects as the Schwarz rigid airship, built in 1887, the first application of aluminum in aircraft; a Danish inventor's 1894 proposal to reach the North Pole assisted by nine hollow, 6-ft-diam aluminum globes, equipped with paddles for air-sailing and spikes for travel over ice; McMouillan's construction in Cairo, Egypt, of a soaring machine, employing aluminum shipped by Pittsburgh Reduction Company; and the first Zeppelin, built in 1900 with a framework of aluminum longitudinal girders and transverse rings.

As the twentieth century progressed, aluminum became an essential metal in aircraft. The cylinder block of the engine that powered the Wright brothers' plane at Kitty Hawk in 1903 was a one-piece casting in an aluminum alloy containing 8% copper; aluminum parts were used in control mechanisms in 1908, the first aircraft application in the United States other than for engine components; aluminum propeller blades appeared as early as 1907; and aluminum covers, seats, cowlings, cast brackets, and similar parts were common by the beginning of the first World War (1). In 1916, L. Brequet designed a reconnaissance bomber that marked the initial use of aluminum in the working structure of an airplane. By war's end, the Allies and Germany employed aluminum alloys for the structural framework of fuselage and wing assemblies.

The authors are with the Application Engineering Div., Aluminum Company of America. C. L. Burton is manager for cast and forged products — aerospace and military, Cleveland. L. W. Mayer is an application engineer for aerospace and military, and E. H. Spuhler is manager for aerospace and military, New Kensington.

Aluminum alloy sheet first appeared as fuselage and wing skin in 1919 on the Junkers F-13. Sheet corrugations corresponded to the line of flight; the craft was the first of semimonocoque stressed-skin design (2).

Early development activities, many involving only prototype projects, led to the all-aluminum structure of the CO-1 observation airplane, designed in 1921 by the Engineering Division at McCook Field (now Wright-Patterson Air Force Base). A year later, the United States Navy issued a production order to the Glenn L. Martin Company for the MO-1, the Navy's first essentially all-aluminum land-based monoplane (3).

A method of cladding alloy 2017 with commercial-purity aluminum to improve corrosion resistance was developed during the middle 1920's. Alclad 2017-T4 sheet 0.0095 in. thick was used for the skin of the ZMC-2, the first all-metal airship. Concurrently, the famous Ford Trimotor airplane also employed the new clad alloy. By the early 1930's, aluminum alloys were firmly established as the major airframe material.

Aluminum now is used extensively for airframes, landing gear and wheels, reciprocating and turbine engine components, propellers, systems elements, and interior trim. The attributes of aluminum alloys primarily responsible for this usage are lightness, strength and weatherability. For engine applications, thermal conductivity also is an important property.

Alloys for Airframe Components

The aircraft airframe has been the most demanding application for aluminum alloys; to chronicle the development of the high-strength alloys is also to record the development of airframes. Duralumin, the first high-strength, heat treatable aluminum alloy, was employed initially for the framework of rigid airships, by Germany and the Allies during World War I. Duralumin was an aluminum-copper-magnesium alloy; it was originated in Germany and developed in the United States as alloy 17S-T (2017-T4). It was utilized primarily as sheet and plate. Its 40,000-psi yield strength was surpassed in 1931 by alloy 2024-T3, with a yield strength of 50,000 psi. Alloy 2024-T3 was introduced initially as alclad sheet; one of its first applications was in the DC-3 airliner. Alloy 2014-T6, with 60,000-psi yield strength, was the predominant alloy in aircraft forgings from 1928 to 1945.

Alloy 7075-T6 (70,000-psi yield strength), an Al-Zn-Mg-Cu alloy, was introduced in 1943. Since then, most aircraft structures have been specified in alloys of this type. The first aircraft designed in 7075-T6 was the Navy's P2V patrol bomber. A higher-strength alloy in the same series, 7178-T6 (78,000-psi yield strength), was developed in 1951; it has not generally displaced 7075-T6, which has superior fracture toughness. Alloy 7178-T6 is used primarily in structural members where performance is critical under compressive loading.

Alloy 7079-T6 was introduced in the United States from Germany in 1954. In forged sections over 3 in. thick, it provides higher strength and greater transverse ductility than 7075-T6. It now is available in sheet, plate, extrusions, and forgings.

Alloy 2020-T6 was introduced in 1957 as an aluminum structural alloy with good strength properties up to 350 F; it has a modulus of elasticity 8% higher, and a density 3% lower, than 7075-T6. Although these characteristics are highly desired by aircraft designers, 2020-T6 has been employed as the major structural material in few aircraft in the United States, because of its relatively low fracture toughness. However, it was specified for the British TSR 2 because of its elevated-temperature characteristics, and was evaluated for possible application in the C-5A transport, because of its ambient-temperature characteristics. Also, it is being used in the thrust structure of the Saturn S-II, which is the second stage of the Saturn V.

Alloy X7080-T7, with higher resistance to stress corrosion than 7079-T6, is being developed for thick parts. Because it is relatively insensitive to quenching rate, good strengths with low quenching stresses can be produced in thick sections.

Cladding of aluminum alloys (see Volume I, Chapter 9) was developed initially to increase the corrosion resistance of 2017-T4 sheet and thus to reduce aluminum aircraft maintenance requirements. The coating on 2017 sheet — and later on 2024-T3 — consisted of commercial-purity aluminum metallurgically bonded to one or both surfaces of the sheet. The cladding provides a more corrosion-resistant surface than the base alloys. It also protects these strong alloys electrolytically at small areas where the coating is removed by corrosion, accidental abrasion, fabrication, or similar actions (Volume I, Chapter 7). Protection is equally effective at edges where bare core alloy is exposed.

Electrolytic protection, present under wet or moist conditions, is based on the appreciably higher electrode potential of commercial-purity aluminum compared to alloy 2017 or 2024 in the T3 or T4 temper. When 7075-T6 and other Al-Zn-Mg-Cu alloys appeared, an aluminum-zinc cladding alloy 7072 was developed to provide a relative electrode potential sufficient to protect the new strong alloys.

However, the high-performance aircraft designed since 1945 have made extensive use of skin structures machined from thick plate and extrusions, precluding the use of alclad exterior skins. Maintenance requirements increased as a result, and these stimulated research and development programs seeking higher-strength alloys with improved resistance to corrosion without cladding.

Aluminum alloy castings traditionally have been used in nonstructural airplane hardware, such as pulley brackets, quadrants, doublers, clips, ducts, and wave guides. They also have been employed extensively in complex valve bodies of hydraulic control systems. The philosophy of some aircraft manufacturers still is to specify castings only in places where failure of the part cannot cause loss of the airplane. Redundancy in cable and hydraulic control systems "permits" the use of castings.

Casting technology has made great advances in the last decade. Time-honored alloys such as 355 and 356 have been modified to produce higher levels of strength and ductility. New alloys such as 354, A356, A357, 359 and Tens 50 were developed for premium-strength castings (Volume I, Chapter 8). Alloys A357 and Tens 50 contain small but useful amounts of beryllium. Attainment of premium strength with these alloys requires application of advanced casting technology (Volume III, Chapter 2). The high strength is accompanied by enhanced structural integrity and performance reliability.

The Federal Aviation Agency must approve aluminum alloys and their design mechanical properties for use in civil aircraft registered in the United States. In military aircraft, similar approval is the responsibility of the procuring agency. To guide aircraft designers and achieve standardization, a joint effort by the Federal Aviation Agency and the Department of Defense is maintained to approve materials and adopt design mechanical properties. These are published in MIL-HDBK-5, "Metallic Materials and Elements for Flight Vehicle Structures". Most alloys and tempers discussed in this chapter are approved by these agencies for general aircraft use. In choosing an alloy for a specific application, many of its characteristics generally need consideration; most important are static and fatigue strengths, corrosion, fracture toughness, and fabricability. Before an alloy is specified, its presence in the handbook or its acceptability to the licensing or procuring agency should be verified.

Joining Methods in Airframe Manufacture

Joining aluminum structure in airframes is primarily by riveting (Volume III, Chapter 11). This method is readily controlled and inspected, and it does not require application of heat that might partially anneal or significantly impair the corrosion resistance of the heat treated alloys used. The limited heating required in dimpling sheet of some alloys and tempers prior to riveting does not impair properties. Sheet less than 0.080 in. thick generally is dimpled for countersunk head fasteners, and thicker material is machine countersunk.

Countersunk head rivets are employed almost exclusively for attaching outer skins, whereas universal head (modified round) rivets are utilized extensively for interior structure, where protruding heads are generally not objectionable. Wing panels often are riveted by automatic machines, which form one or both heads of the rivet. The machines are fed with rivets or slugs (short chamfered lengths of rivet wire), and the heads usually are shaved flush with the exterior surface.

Rivet alloy 2117-T4 is the most popular for general structures, especially for automatic riveting, because it retains good driving characteristics indefinitely after solution heat treatment. Rivets of 2024-T4 often are utilized where high strength is required, even though they must be driven within 30 minutes after heat treatment, or refrigerated until needed, to prevent age hardening prior to driving. Alloy 2017-T4 rivets are driven easily within approximately one hour after heat treatment, without refrigerating, and provide strength intermediate between that of 2117-T4 and 2024-T4 rivets. Alloy 5056-H32 rivets often are selected to join magnesium alloy parts, to minimize galvanic corrosion.

Rivets of the newer alloy 2219 can be driven in the T6, T62, or T81 tempers, and are suitable for elevated-temperature service. They are utilized in a few recently produced aircraft.

Alloys 7075-T6 and 7178-T6 are employed for high-shear-strength fasteners that are retained in joints by means of swaged collars rather than driven heads. Alloy 7075-T73 rivets have good driving characteristics, provide high shear strength (47,000

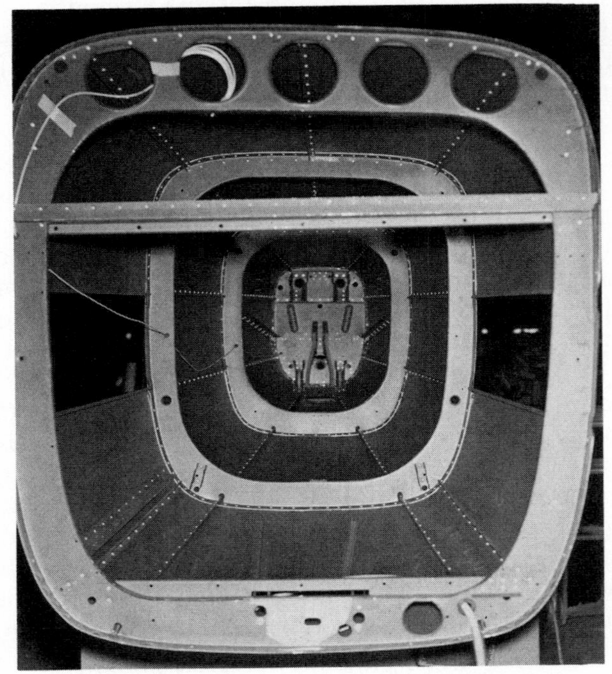

Cessna Aircraft Co.

Fig. 1. Rear fuselage of light aircraft showing typical semimonocoque structure of alclad 2024-T3

psi), and good corrosion performance for airframes. Virtually all aluminum rivets are anodically coated prior to driving, for increased protection against corrosion; it is beneficial to have a coat of zinc chromate primer on countersunk holes.

Electric resistance spot and seam welding are used to join secondary structures, such as fairings, engine cowls, and doublers, to bulkheads and skins. Difficulties in quality control have resulted in low utilization of electric resistance welding for primary structure.

Ultrasonic welding offers some economic and quality-control advantages for production joining, particularly for thin sheet. However, the method has not yet been developed extensively in the aerospace industry.

Adhesive bonding (Volume III, Chapter 15) is a common method of joining in both primary and secondary structures. Its selection is dependent on the design philosophy of the aircraft manufacturer. It has proven satisfactory in attaching stiffeners, such as hat sections to sheet, and face sheets to honeycomb cores. Also, adhesive bonding has withstood adverse exposures such as sea-water immersion and atmospheres.

Fusion welded aluminum primary structures in airplanes are virtually nonexistent, because the high-strength alloys utilized have low weldability and low weld-joint efficiencies. Some of the alloys, such as 2024-T4, also have their corrosion resistance lowered in the heat-affected zone if left in the as-welded condition. It is not practical to apply stress-relief methods to the structures to reduce residual welding stresses and achieve good fatigue performance. The complexity of aircraft structures restricts weld inspection by radiography. Distortion resulting from welding impairs aerodynamic and load distribution characteristics of the design. A contributing deterrent to welding is that riveted and bolted designs employed in airplanes were highly developed by the time the efficient, high-energy-input welding methods currently used on aluminum missile tanks became available.

The improved welding processes and higher-strength weldable alloys developed during the past decade offer new possibilities for welded primary structures. For example, the weldability and strength of alloys 2219 and 7039, and the brazeability and strength of X7005, open new avenues for design and manufacture of aircraft structures (Volume III, Chapters 12 and 13).

Light Aircraft

Light aircraft have airframes primarily of all-aluminum semimonocoque construction, as shown in Fig. 1; however, a few light planes have tubular truss load-carrying construction with fabric or aluminum skin, or both.

Aluminum skin is normally of the minimum practical thickness: 0.015 to 0.025 in. Although design strength requirements are relatively low, the skin needs moderately high yield strength and hardness to minimize ground damage from stones, debris, mechanics' tools, and general handling. Other primary factors involved in selecting an alloy for this application are corrosion resistance, cost, and appearance. Alloys 6061-T6 and alclad 2024-T3 are the primary choices.

Skin sheet on light airplanes of recent design and construction generally is alclad 2024-T3. The internal structure comprises stringers, spars, bulkheads, chord members, and various attaching fittings made of aluminum extrusions, formed sheet, forgings, and castings. The alloys most used for extruded members are 2024-T4 for sections less than 0.125 in. thick and for general application, and 2014-T6 for thicker, more highly stressed sections. Alloy 6061-T6 has considerable application for extrusions requiring thin sections and excellent corrosion resistance. Alloy 2014-T6 is the primary forging alloy, especially for landing gear and hydraulic cylinders. Alloy 6061-T6 and its forging counterpart 6151-T6 often are utilized in miscellaneous fittings for reasons of economy and increased corrosion performance, when the parts are not highly stressed.

Alloys 356-T6 and A356-T6 are the primary casting alloys employed for brackets, bellcranks, pulleys, and various fittings. Wheels are produced in these alloys as permanent mold or sand castings. Die castings in alloy A380 also are satisfactory for wheels for light aircraft.

Severely formed sheet members normally are produced from bare or alclad 2024 in the O temper. When not severely formed, parts can be formed immediately after quenching, in the W or mill-supplied T3 tempers.

For low-stressed structure in light aircraft, alloys 3003-H12, H14, and H16; 5052-O, H32, H34, and H36; and 6061-T4 and T6 are sometimes employed. These alloys are also primary selections for fuel, lubricating oil, and hydraulic oil tanks, piping, and instrument tubing and brackets, especially where welding is required. Alloys 3003, 6061, and 6951 are utilized extensively in brazed heat exchangers and hydraulic accessories. Recently developed alloys, such as 5086, 5454, 5456, 6070, and the new weldable aluminum-magnesium-zinc alloys, offer strength advantages over those previously mentioned.

The external skin sheets in larger light aircraft have thicknesses up to approximately 0.070 in. This thickness, however, occurs only in a few areas, such as the center section of the wing. The major requirements are strength, fatigue durability, and corrosion resistance; therefore, alclad 2024-T3 and alclad 7075-T6 are the alloys usually selected.

Sheet assembly of light aircraft is accomplished predominantly with rivets of alloys 2017-T4, 2117-T4, or 2024-T4. Self-tapping sheet metal screws are available in aluminum alloys, but cadmium-plated steel screws are employed more commonly to obtain higher shear strength and driveability. Alloy 2024-T4 with an anodic coating is standard for aluminum screws, bolts, and nuts made to military specifications. Alloy 6262-T9, however, is superior for nuts, because of its virtual immunity to stress-corrosion cracking.

The exteriors of many light planes are painted to reduce the effort required to maintain a bright, polished appearance and to avoid superficial corrosion of the aluminum. Painting also is the most economical way to obtain decorative colors (Volume III, Chapter 21). Interior structures generally need not be painted. However, bare 2*xxx* and certain 7*xxx* series alloys should be protected by at least a good-quality wash-coat primer, to avoid superficial corrosion, and aircraft operated in seacoast atmospheres should have more extensive paint protection.

Transport Aircraft

Transport aircraft of the types operated by commercial airlines, by corporations for executive travel, and by the military, including the new C-5A (4) and Concorde craft now under development, are generally of semimonocoque and sheet-stringer aluminum construction.

The alloys primarily utilized today are 2024-T4 and the alloys having still higher strength (2014-T6, 7075-T6, 7079-T6 and 7178-T6). Where sheet is used, the alclad form is preferred. The upper skins and spar caps of wings often are of 7075-T6 and 7178-T6, because the critical requirement is high compressive strength, and the structure generally is not critical in tension loading or fatigue.

For wing tension members, shear webs, and ribs, alloys 2014-T6, 2024-T4, and 7075-T6 are used extensively. For these applications, fatigue performance and fracture toughness, combined with high strength, are the alloy characteristics of chief concern. Although 7075-T6 is stronger than 2024-T3 or 2024-T4, it is more sensitive to notches and has a higher fatigue-crack propagation rate. However, structures designed and fabricated in 7075-T6 have somewhat less weight than is possible in a 2024-T3 or 2024-T4 structure for equivalent performance.

Although extruded members in 2014-T6 and 2024-T4 have given satisfactory service in aircraft of all types, 7075 in the relatively new T73 temper is superior in resistance to exfoliation and stress-corrosion cracking. In this temper, the alloy is virtually free of intergranular attack; any corrosion is predominantly a pitting type. This alloy should be considered for relatively thick members (over $\frac{3}{16}$ in.) when severe salt or industrial atmosphere environments are expected. For fatigue-critical sections, the allowable stresses for 7075-T73 should be no higher than those normally specified for 2014-T6 and 2024-T4.

Wing skin machined from wide ribbed extrusions, preferred by some designers, is an economical approach when high (generally more than 1 in.) integral stiffeners are required. This type of skin is more likely to be required for wings of high aspect ratio (ratio of the square of the wing span to the wing area). Some of the major advantages are elimination of stiffener fasteners and availability of thick bosses, pads, and lands for

Lockheed Aircraft Corp.

Fig. 2. Integrally stiffened wing skin panel for large transport airplane, machined from 7075-T651 plate

attaching other hardware and to reinforce cutout boundaries. Fail-safe design is achieved by using relatively narrow panels.

Rolled sheet and plate 0.040 to approximately 0.375 in. thick are employed for wing skins by other manufacturers who prefer as wide and as few pieces as possible. Fail-safe design in this type of construction is achieved by many separate stiffeners, formed from sheet or milled from standard extrusions, or machined from stepped extrusions to accommodate integral end fittings.

Alclad sheet and plate are preferred for wing skins to obtain good corrosion resistance. Roll-tapered alclad sheet and plate provide skins that are structurally efficient without extensive machining. Also, optimum spacing and design of stiffeners are practicable with this approach. Adhesive bonding, instead of riveting, is employed by some designers for attaching doublers and stiffeners to the skin sheet.

Wing skins also can be produced from sculptured plate, which involves extensive machining of plate up to 3 in. thick, leaving integral stiffeners, lands, pads, and bosses where needed for optimum structural efficiency (Fig. 2). The procedure minimizes the number of skin penetrations required for fasteners, and provides minimum weight when wide, long plates are used to avoid splices. Fail-safe or safe-life requirements can be met by selecting an alloy and temper having a low crack propagation rate and high fracture toughness. Plate and extrusions in tempers stress relieved by stretching are machined easily to close dimensions. Because they often are machined on their flat surfaces to obtain the desired smoothness and tolerances, clad surfaces are not feasible.

Chemical milling, which is discussed in Volume III, Chapter 17, is utilized in the manufacture of transport-type aircraft.

Leading edge skins, subjected to hot air for anti-icing, frequently utilize alclad 2024-T81 sheet. Depending on the time at temperature requirement, alclad 7075-T6 or alclad 2219-T81 or T87 may be a better choice.

Fuselages on virtually all modern airline transports and executive aircraft are pressurized. The pressurization cycles and safety requirements dictate the design parameters of high-load, fatigue-resistant and fracture-resistant structures for this application. Although the design (spacing of stringers, formers, bulkheads, windows and other factors) is the most important consideration in achieving a desired performance, the fracture toughness (closely related to tear resistance) of the alloy probably has the most influence on the weight of the structure. Alloys and tempers with good combinations of static strength, fracture toughness, and corrosion resistance are the best for this application. Alclad sheet 0.040 to 0.187 in. thick in 2014-T6, 2024-T3, 7075-T6, and 7079-T6 is utilized. Alclad 2219-T81 and 2219-T87 have good fracture toughness, but their tensile strengths at room temperature are lower than those of the other alloys.

Fuselages have extruded and roll-formed sheet longerons primarily of 2024-T4 and 7075-T6. The latter alloy is favored for the larger aircraft, which have higher stresses (Fig. 3). The forming rings are fabricated from bare and alclad 2024-O and 7075-O, subsequently heat treated to the T42 and T6 tempers, respectively. Keel members on larger aircraft utilize high-strength extrusion alloys 7075-T6 and 7178-T6, because their major design requirement is for a high static stress rather than a fatigue loading.

Tail surfaces are constructed of the same alloys utilized for wings. Full-depth single-piece spars and ribs are employed in smaller aircraft; some are machined from thick plate, others from die forgings.

For skin sheet in the engine areas, where temperatures may range to above 400 F, bare and alclad alloys 2014, 2024, and 2219, all in an artificially aged temper, often are utilized. Of the commercial sheet alloys, 2219 in artificially aged tempers has the most stable properties at elevated temperatures.

Thin skins (0.010 to 0.025 in.) are required for such components as trim tabs, servo tabs, control surfaces, flaps, and non-load-carrying access doors; they are applied in both skin-rib and sandwich-type construction. Alclad 2024-T3, alclad 7075-T6, and alloy 6061-T6 are the primary selections. Aluminum honeycomb core generally is made from 3003-H19, 5052-H19, or 5356-H19 foil (Fig. 4). Foil of 2024-T81 is produced and used advantageously for core for long service at high temperatures.

Landing gear structural parts for heavy airplanes are often produced as aluminum alloy forgings. The main cylinders are made on hydraulic presses as conventional closed-die forgings, with the parting plane at the center of the cylinder. In the past, alloy 2014-T6 was employed extensively, but in recent years alloy 7079-T6 or T611 has been used. Alloy 7075 in the new T73 temper and alloy X7080-T7 also should be considered, because of their good resistance to stress-corrosion cracking, and in the case of X7080-T7, its good properties and low quenching

(Top) Aft section showing internal structure and pressure bulkhead. Skin is alclad 7075-T6 and internal structure predominantly 7075-T6. (Convair Div., General Dynamics Corp.)

(Bottom) Semimonocoque section. Stretch-formed skin is alclad 2014-T6, longerons are roll-formed alclad 7075-T6, Z-sections are formed 7075-T6 sheet, and doublers at each frame are titanium rip stoppers. (Douglas Aircraft Co.)

Fig. 3. Jet transport fuselage sections

stresses in thick (over 3 in.) sections. Other landing gear members, attached to the main cylinders, also are produced as aluminum forgings, including structural forgings in the fuselage and wings, which distribute the landing gear loads into other structures, and forged parts for the retracting mechanism.

Aircraft wheels have been produced in aluminum alloys for many years. From the 1920's until World War II, they were made as sand and permanent mold castings. Beginning in the late 1940's, wheels for heavy airplanes have been required to carry greater loads with each new generation of aircraft. This factor and the adoption of the tubeless tire have led to almost universal application of forged wheels for heavy airplanes to obtain maximum strength and to minimize air loss. Heavy-duty forged wheels most often are produced in 2014-T6 or T61. Alloy 2014 has proven to be excellent for this application, because of forgeability, strength, mechanical properties at elevated temper-

Fig. 4. Expanded and machined aluminum foil honeycomb core for trailing edge structure

The Boeing Co.

atures, adequate resistance to corrosion, and favorable response to pre-stressing treatments applied to increase fatigue strength.

Wheels for heavy civilian or military airplanes generally are designed on a safe-life basis. They are replaced at regular intervals during the life of an airplane, allowing use of lighter-weight designs than are required for long-time fatigue resistance. The wheels are subjected to extensive experimental stress analysis, fatigue testing, and application of pre-stressing techniques, to optimize design. The loads carried are high in relation to wheel size and weight, necessitating tire air pressures ranging as high as 200 psi.

Integral fuel tanks are incorporated in the wings of nearly all modern transport aircraft. Kerosene-type jet-engine fuels contaminated with water constitute a breeding medium for certain forms of bacteria. Products of their life cycle, in conjunction with other contaminants, are corrosive to most metals, including aluminum. It is essential that a good-quality, impervious coating be applied on these surfaces, especially those in the lower portion of the wing, to protect the structure. Coatings for this purpose are under intensive development. Integral fuel tanks for aviation gasoline also have a suitable protective coating, such as a polysulfide synthetic rubber type, in the sump areas, where contaminating water accumulates. The use of alclad sheet where feasible minimizes any corrosion of the aluminum structure.

High-Performance Aircraft

High-performance aircraft required by the military services are designed to withstand 9 to 12-g loads (9 to 12 times greater than those imposed by unaccelerated flight). The maximum loads are infrequent, and on some aircraft may never be encountered. Since the 1-g stresses prevalent during most of a flight period are low, and the life of the aircraft in terms of flying hours is also generally low, high-cycle fatigue is not a major problem. However, the high stresses that occasionally may be imposed in maneuvers demand consideration of the high-stress fatigue characteristics of the structure material. Another characteristic of this type of aircraft is high wing loadings, which dictate thick wing skins, typically 0.5 to 1.5 in. at the root. Design requirements resulting from aerodynamic heating at high speeds are discussed subsequently, under supersonic aircraft.

Since about 1945, all high-performance aircraft have been manufactured of the highest-strength aluminum alloys approved by the military services. Alloy 7075-T6 has been the workhorse, complemented in specialized applications by 2014-T6, 2024 in both naturally and artificially aged tempers, 7079-T6, and 7178-T6. In one large Navy carrier aircraft, 2020-T651 plate is used for wing and tail surfaces to obtain the advantages of its low density (0.098 lb per cu in.) and high modulus of elasticity (11.4 million psi). The notch sensitivity of 2020-T6 requires care in design and fabrication to minimize stress concentrations and to realize the full structural capabilities of the alloy.

Extrusions 1 to 5 in. thick in alloys 7075-T6 or 7079-T6 are utilized as machining stock for spar caps, which in some designs are continuous from one side of a wing to the other. Appreciable sweepback and dihedral angles present forming problems for continuous spars; therefore, in some swept-wing aircraft, stepped extrusions are employed as machining blanks for spar caps with integral attachment fittings. These are attached to carry-through members (structures connecting the left and right wing spars to each other and to the fuselage), machined from thick plate, hand forgings, or die forgings.

Some highly swept wing designs have numerous ribs and bulkheads generally fabricated of sheet and extrusions or ma-

Fig. 5. Wing skins for high-performance aircraft machined from alloy 2020-T651 plates, 0.781 by 128 by 335 in.

North American Aviation Co.

chined as monolithic members from forgings or plate. Alloys 7075-T6, 7075-T73 and 7079-T6 predominate.

Wing skins are attached to the inner structure with high-shear-strength fasteners, usually titanium or cadmium-plated steel, that impose high bearing loads on the skins. These loads are accommodated by leaving thick lands for fastener rows. Chordwise lands are also effective in reducing stresses at splices and attachment points, so that stress concentrations do not become a fatigue problem. To obtain the lightest structure, a tapered thickness skin is essential. All requirements mentioned are obtainable by machining stress-relieved plate to the finished configurations, as shown in Fig. 5. Alloy 7075-T651 plate is the principal material used, except where 2020-T651 or 2024-T851 is required for added stiffness or elevated-temperature strength.

Roll-tapered alclad plate is desirable for corrosion resistance, but it does not permit machining of integrally stiffened panels without removing the cladding on one side. In addition, distortion problems would occur from machining, because a satisfactory method for stress relieving roll-tapered plate has not yet been developed. Where roll-tapered alclad sheet or plate is utilized, the stiffeners are separate pieces attached to the skins with fasteners.

The primary disadvantage of the machined-plate skin is its elimination of the use of an alclad exterior surface for greater corrosion resistance, thus requiring effective coating systems for adequate corrosion protection. In general, the military services approve systems involving a conversion coating, one or two coats of zinc chromate primer, and one or two coats of high-quality organic coating. If the coating fails or is damaged, aircraft operating in very severe and tropical salt atmospheres may encounter exfoliation corrosion on top surfaces of 7075-T6 and 7178-T6. Alloy 7075-T73 and the artificially aged tempers of the 2*xxx* series alloys do not exfoliate, but they have lower yield strengths than the 7*xxx* series alloys in the T6 temper. A recent development is 7178-T76, which approaches the structural capability of 7075-T6 and the exfoliation resistance of 7075-T73.

Premium-strength aluminum alloy castings are used in some high-performance airplanes. They are employed in structural components such as canopy supports and frames (Fig. 6), fuselage members, and heavily loaded pylons (Fig. 7) that support external loads. With closely controlled foundry practices, guaranteed strength levels of 50,000-psi tensile strength

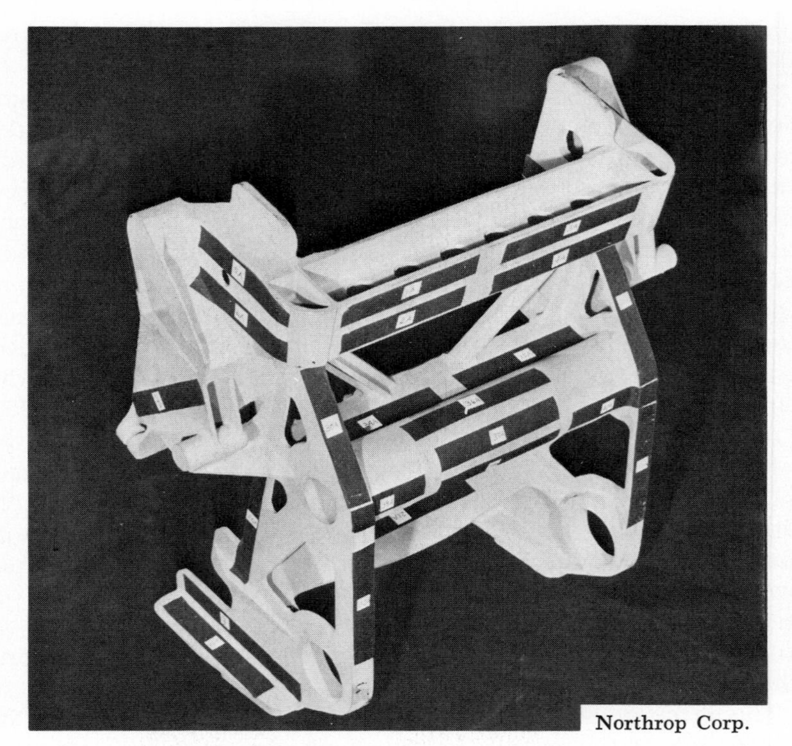

Northrop Corp.

Fig. 6. Aft canopy support casting in alloy A357-T6 for supersonic fighter. Strips show location of test specimens for checking specification properties of 38,000 psi tensile strength, 28,000 psi yield strength, and 5% elongation.

and 40,000-psi yield strength (and 5% elongation) are obtained in substantial portions of large and complicated castings with sections as thin as ⅛ in. Close dimensional tolerances and smooth surfaces also are produced. Alloys 354-T6 and A357-T6 are usually specified for these premium-strength castings. New alloys of the 2*xxx* series, not yet in production, show a capability of 20% increase in mechanical properties for simple shapes.

Supersonic Aircraft

Supersonic aircraft, designed to withstand aerodynamic heating to 250 F for over 100 hr (the time in service is accumulated in small increments), generally utilize the 2*xxx* series alloys in artificially aged tempers for skin sheet (5, 6).

Alloys 2024-T81 and T86 are the most extensively employed; 2014-T6 and 2024-T62 or T81 are used for extruded members. Alloys 2014-T6 and 2618-T61 are employed for forged products located in heat-affected areas; alloy 2024, which can be forged, also can be considered for parts of this type. Alloy 2219 has had limited application in engine pods as sheet, rivets, and forgings.

The designers of one supersonic bomber have made extensive use of honeycomb core sandwich construction for wing panels, to achieve a stiff structure that does not buckle when stressed in compression near the yield strength of the material. The honeycomb in these sandwich panels is 5052 aluminum foil, except where fiber glass is applied to further insulate the fuel from

Fig. 7. Premium-strength alloy A357-T62 cast pylons for supersonic fighter. Minimum properties in most areas are 50,000 psi tensile strength, 40,000 psi yield strength, and 5% elongation.

aerodynamic heating. Honeycomb panel frames are predominantly 7075-T6, machined from plate to eliminate corner joints. Aluminum honeycomb is also used in the beaded areas of skin doublers, to help stiffen the fuselage skin. At elevated temperatures, 2024-T81 foil provides higher strength than is obtained in work hardened alloys, such as 5052-H39 and 5056-H39.

Concurrent with the development and production of supersonic aircraft, the removal of metal by chemical etching (Volume III, Chapter 17) emerged as a manufacturing process; it is extensively applied to remove surplus metal from skins and complex parts. This process is largely credited with the reduced amount of skin-doubler construction now utilized in supersonic and high-performance aircraft. Etchants have been developed for all high-strength aluminum alloys. When chemically milling the 2*xxx* series alloys, a smoother surface generally is obtained with the annealed and artificially aged tempers than with the naturally aged tempers.

The supersonic transport being developed by British and French interests makes general use of alclad and bare 2618-T6 for the structure. This alloy, which has served many years in forged engine parts, is available also in other wrought forms. Alloy 2219-T81 or T87 has approximately the same tensile strength for design purposes as 2618-T6; however, limited data show 2618-T6 has higher creep strength. These alloys or modified versions of them are promising candidates for any aluminum transport expected to cruise up to Mach 2.4. Alloy 2219-T87 also should be of interest as fuselage skin material in supersonic transports, because of its high fracture toughness.

Helicopters

Helicopters have critical structural requirements for rotor blades. Alloys 2014-T6, 2024-T3, and 6061-T6, in extruded or drawn hollow shapes, are utilized extensively for the main spar member.

The blade skins, typically 0.020 to 0.040 in. thick, are primarily alclad 2024-T3 and 6061-T6. The trailing-edge portion of rotor blades does not carry the major rotor loading and often is made of alclad sheet only 0.016 to 0.025 in. thick. The leading edges sometimes are hard anodized for greater resistance to erosion and to dents from debris when operating close to the ground. In other designs, a high-hardness, high-density metal shields the leading edge.

Some blades have alloy 3003-H19 or 5052-H39 honeycomb core; others depend on ribs and stringers spaced 5 to 12 in. apart to prevent excessive buckling or canning of the thin trailing edge skins. Adhesive bonding is the most common joining method.

The cabin and fuselage structures of helicopters generally are of conventional aircraft design, utilizing formed sheet bulkheads, extruded or rolled sheet stringers, and doubled or chemically milled skins. The formed sheet members usually are made in alloy 2024-O, 0.025 to 0.063 in. thick, and heat treated to the T42 temper if parts cannot be formed in the mill-finished T3 or T4 tempers. Some alclad 7075-T6 is also utilized. Landing skids primarily are extruded or drawn 2024-T3 or 7075-T6 tube, 2 to 4-in. OD by 0.070 to 0.375-in. wall. Close-tolerance 2024-T3 drawn tube also is employed extensively for synchronizing and drive shafts; the size depends on torque load.

Aircraft Engines

In-Line Reciprocating Engines. The airplane flown by the Wright brothers in 1903 was powered by a four-cylinder in-line, liquid-cooled gasoline engine, with a sand cast integral crankcase and cylinder block of aluminum alloy. Since that time, reciprocating aircraft engines usually have been constructed largely of aluminum alloys. The famous Liberty 400-hp liquid-cooled in-line engine, developed by a joint American industry effort during the first World War, made extensive use of cast alloy 112-F in block, crankcase, heads, pistons, intake manifold, and miscellaneous covers and fittings.

The Allison and Rolls Royce Merlin in-line, liquid-cooled engines made famous during the second World War likewise had integral crankcase and cylinder blocks, of casting alloy 355-T71. Cylinder heads, manifolds, covers, and various fittings were cast in the same alloy and heat treated to T6, T51 or T71, depending on service requirements for each part. The pistons for these engines were 4032-T6 forgings. Radiators and oil coolers were furnace brazed from tubing in 3003 and sheet in 6061 or 6951 brazing sheet.

Through the years, many in-line engines have been developed for light personal and military aircraft. A popular construction uses horizontally opposed cylinders. Many thousands of light planes are equipped with four-cylinder and six-cylinder air-cooled engines of this type, employing cast aluminum crankcases of 355-type alloys, and cylinder heads typically of 142-T7.

In recent years, the alloy used for cast crankcases, cylinder blocks, and cylinder heads for liquid-cooled engines has been of the 355 type, usually in the T5 or T7 temper. Crankcases in air-cooled engines with horizontally opposed cylinders also are cast in this material. Separately cast cylinder heads are produced in 142 or A355 alloys in T7-type tempers.

Radial reciprocating engines emerged into great prominence following Lindbergh's 1927 flight from New York to Paris. The radial engine of his airplane had a forged aluminum alloy crankcase, cast cylinder heads, and forged pistons, applications that have continued in radial engines. The high-horsepower radial engines, which reached maximum use during World War II and the early 1950's, use forged crankcases, cast or forged cylinder heads, forged pistons, and many other forged or cast parts. Some engines in the 500-hp range also have forged aluminum connecting rods.

Large radial air-cooled engines have forged crankcases of 6151-T6. This alloy was selected on the basis of service tests; other materials that seemed more suitable did not perform as well. Cast cylinder heads used on large radial engines are produced in alloy 142-T77, poured in special dry-sand precision molds having good chilling and feeding to develop soundness and high mechanical properties. Forged cylinder heads for these engines are produced in alloy 2218 or a modified version, and heat treated to a T6-type temper. Forged pistons for large radial air-cooled engines are made of 2018-T6, 2218-T6 and 4032-T6.

Turbine Engines. Turbojet engines were under development in the late 1930's in England and Germany. Germany succeeded in bringing one turbojet powered aircraft, the ME262, into combat operations during the second World War. Developments in America were stimulated by the test bench success of the Whittle engine in England during the war. The P-59A, flown in 1945, was the first American jet-powered fighter, but the P-80 was the first jet aircraft ordered into mass production (a few years later) by the U.S. Air Force. The early jet engines utilized alloy 2014-T6 for compressor, diffuser, and impeller parts; now 2618-T6 is more commonly employed.

Turboprop engines were placed into operational test in military aircraft in the early 1950's, leading to development of the engines for the transport airplane Lockheed Electra, which entered production late in the decade. A few years prior to the Electra, turboprop engines developed in England became operational in airline transports; they are used in the Vickers Viscount. Small turbine engines, both jet and propeller types, have reached a high state of development, and the current trend indicates their use in small aircraft. They already are the major type of engine for large executive aircraft and for helicopters.

The bypass turbojet engine (some of the compressor air bypasses the combustion chamber) was developed shortly after introduction of turbojet airline transports in this country in 1959, and it is now the principal kind of large transport engine.

Applications of aluminum in turboprop and turbojet engines are limited, compared to reciprocating engines, because of the higher operating temperatures in many zones of the turbine engines. Some models use aluminum castings and forgings for housings. The front frame is produced in certain models as an aluminum casting in a 355-type alloy in the T6 temper and, in other models, as an assembly of extruded vanes, furnace brazed or welded to a forged or fabricated ring of 6061-T6.

In the compressor stage, the stator and rotor blades and the structure to which they are attached often are alloy 2618-T61. In a few designs, afterburner eyelid actuator parts utilize extrusions, forgings, and impacts in powder metallurgy alloy XAP001.

Propellers

Propeller blade forgings of aluminum were developed during the 1920's to replace laminated wood. The first two-blade propellers were not adjustable in pitch and were forged as single units. Adjustable-pitch propellers soon appeared and were necessarily forged as single blades.

In forging heavy-duty blades, ground steel bearing rings must be installed at the blade shank. The shank is then heated locally and flanged on a horizontal mechanical upsetter, providing a configuration for attaching the blade to the hub with its adjusting mechanism.

The solid aluminum blade was predominant on heavy planes built before the beginning of the jet age in about 1950. These blades have attained a high degree of reliability. During the 1950's many commercial airliners converted from newer nonsolid blades back to solid aluminum forgings.

In recent years, forged aluminum propellers for light planes have become popular. High-speed models have variable pitch and are attached to the hub mechanism by special threads.

Slower types have two-blade integral propellers, efficient over the limited range of operating conditions encountered. The largest blades are produced in alloy 7076-T6, whereas alloy 2025-T6 generally is used for aircraft propellers in smaller sizes.

Aircraft Systems

Systems other than airframe structures utilizing aluminum include electrical, fuel and oil, hydraulic, oxygen, and air-conditioning systems.

Electrical. Aluminum electrical and radio-frequency (rf) conductors are now employed by some manufacturers to achieve significant weight savings compared to copper. The principal problem was obtaining low-resistance terminals and splices. With the appearance of good low-resistance terminal connections in aluminum during recent years, the problem has become less serious.

Housings for multiple-point electrical connectors are made of aluminum, primarily in accordance with military specifications. Alloy 380 is used in die cast parts, and 2014-T6 and 6061-T6 in parts machined from impact extrusions, forgings, or screw-machine stock. The parts are anodized or painted, or both, or are plated, as required for the intended service. Conduit normally is made from drawn tube in alloys 2024-T42, 3003-H14, and 6061-T4, and is employed extensively in the wing areas.

Stranded conductor meeting military specifications has a minimum of 19 strands of No. 24 AWG wire, and is made of EC (electrical conductor) aluminum. Significant weight is saved by specifying aluminum for stranded conductors larger than No. 8 AWG and more than 6 ft in length. Because of its low density and elevated-temperature characteristics, aluminum conductor is suitable for hot areas of supersonic aircraft. As magnet wire, it is used extensively in motors and solenoids, primarily to save weight. Coaxial radio-frequency cables generally use aluminum tube for the outer conductor, which also is the armor.

Electrical cables and cable bundles are shielded by aluminum foil, with and without a resin backing. Braid of alclad 5056-O wire is sometimes used if an armor-type shielding is required.

Fuel and oil lines are alloy 5052 or 6061 tube in various tempers, except in fire zones. Corrosion and fatigue resistance and weldability are important characteristics for this application. Tube outside diameter ranges from 0.25 to 5 in. and the wall thickness from 0.020 to 0.065 in. for most aircraft. Diameters over 0.75 in. are usually of harder alloy 6061 in the T4 or T6 temper. Fittings machined from 356-T6 castings or 6061 forgings or bar stock are generally welded or brazed to the tubes.

Valves and sumps that are not integral parts of primary structure are made from appropriate products in the same alloys employed for fuel lines. Internal fuel and oil tanks are fabricated from 5052 sheet 0.040 to 0.080 in. thick, and tip and external tanks are usually made in a higher-strength alloy, primarily 6061-T4 and T6. High-strength aluminum-magnesium alloys 5083, 5086, and 5456 also may be used for tanks, and are specified on some recently designed aircraft; newer alloys of the weldable aluminum-magnesium-zinc type may be utilized in the future, because they possess advantages in strength and manufacturing cost.

Heat exchangers typically are brazed assemblies of sheet, fittings, and small tubes of alloys 3003, 6061, and 6951. Alloy X7005 offers possibilities for higher strength and lighter weight. Certain small tubes, typically 0.125-in. diam and 0.010-in. wall thickness, are produced as Hooker tubing on impact extrusion presses or rivet headers.

Water tanks for both engine injection and drinking supply have been made of aluminum; there is a current preference for stainless steel or titanium. Where aluminum is employed, alclad 3003 is recommended. Stainless-steel-clad aluminum should have advantages for this application.

Hydraulic and pneumatic systems in aircraft can be defined to include systems for dispersion of anti-icing fluids, and for actuation of brakes, flaps, control servos, and landing gear. Drawn tube $\frac{3}{16}$ to $1\frac{1}{2}$ in. thick in alloys 2024-T3, 5052-O, and 6061-T6, produced under hydraulic tube specifications, meets flaring and pressure-testing requirements. In low-pressure (primarily return) lines, 5052-O, H32, or H34, and 6061-T4 or T6 tubing are used, because of their formability and resistance to corrosion.

Hydraulic fittings meeting military standards and approved by the Federal Aviation Agency generally are machined from 2024-T851 alloy screw-machine stock or forged in 2014-T6. Alloy 7075-T73 is used for some hydraulic components to obtain immunity from stress-corrosion cracking, which has been a problem with parts having high surface tensile stresses resulting from manufacturing or assembly.

Valve bodies are often made from 356-T6 castings or 2014-T6, 6061-T6, or 6151-T6 forgings. Cylinders are generally forged from 2014-T6, 7075-T6, or 7079-T6. Hard anodic coatings are applied on many surfaces subject to wear. Alloy 7075-T73 is utilized in some instances, to overcome stress-corrosion problems. In hydraulic systems with pressures of 1500 to 3000 psi, the lines are often stainless steel instead of aluminum.

Reservoirs are usually fabricated from 6061 sheet, tube, or impacts, to obtain corrosion resistance and weldability. Fittings are made of 356-T6 castings or 6061-T6 forgings, rod, or bar. In many systems, the accumulators also are of these alloys, although some are made of 2014-T6.

Oxygen systems comprise both liquid oxygen storage, used primarily in military aircraft, and high-pressure gaseous oxygen storage. Storage bottles for liquid oxygen typically are made of alloy 5052, which has good fracture toughness at the low temperature involved. High-pressure gaseous oxygen bottles are made of stainless steel. In both types of systems, the oxygen is delivered to flight personnel and passengers at low pressure. Alloy 5052 tubing is employed extensively for low-pressure lines, although copper tubing is used in at least one commercial transport model.

Air-conditioning ducts utilize drawn tube of alloys 3003 and 6061 for sizes up to 4-in. diam. Larger ducts are fabricated of formed and welded sheet. For ducts that may serve at temperatures over 200 F, other alloys are sometimes specified; 2219-T81 is used in one design. Flexible aluminum ducts in many aircraft deliver air to the cabin, carburetor, and heat muffs.

Aircraft Interior Trim

Interior trim in aircraft involves aluminum alloys that are easy to fabricate, especially into extrusions, and that can be finished with attractive anodic or paint coatings. Rolled patterned sheet is utilized as the decorative exterior material in applications such as hat racks and partitions. Miscellaneous trim is fabricated from extrusions and sheet of aluminum alloys developed specifically for good finishing characteristics.

Aluminum sandwich panels, with face sheets less than 0.010 in. thick, are used as backup for padded and fabric-covered installations. The thin sheets are of alloys 5052-H38 or 6061-T6, providing good yield strength to resist denting.

Missiles and Boosters

Design and material selection for guided missiles and space vehicles are basically outgrowths of conventional aircraft practice. Many missiles, such as Matador (1950), Regulus (1950), Snark (1954), Bomarc (1954), and Hound Dog (1958), are in essence pilotless aircraft built along more or less conventional lines. Possibly the largest single difference between conventional aluminum aircraft construction and missile construction is in the extensive use of structural aluminum weldments in many of the missiles.

The fuel tank of the Bomarc antiaircraft missile forms a cylindrical element of the fuselage to which two ramjet engines are attached. It initially was a welded tank fabricated from 6061-T6 sheet, plate, and rolled ring forgings. In the B version of the missile, higher design loads and more severe thermal exposure were expected. Because of its weldability, alloy 2219 was chosen over stronger alloys for an upgraded fuel tank.

The Hound Dog air-to-ground missile utilizes weldments extensively in the fuselage; these consist primarily of 2014-T6 alloy forged rings and 2024-T3 sheet about 1/8 in. thick.

Ballistic missiles and space boosters are generally classified into two broad categories by propellant: solid or liquid. Examples of liquid-fueled missiles are the Redstone, Thor, Titan, and Saturn; the Pershing, Polaris, and Minuteman use solid-fuel propellants.

Liquid-fueled rockets employ a large portion of the total structure for fuel and oxidizer tankage, which usually is cylindrical with the tank walls forming the exterior skin of the vehicle. As internal pressure in the tanks generally is less than 50 psi, tank design and materials selection are influenced primarily by static loads resulting from vehicle weight (including propellants) and dynamic loads caused by acceleration and maneuvering. For these conditions, monocoque or semimonocoque construction with minimum skin thicknesses of 0.050 to 0.250 in. is normally employed, which usually favors the selection of low-density materials. These fuel and oxidizer tanks, although under relatively low internal pressure, are nevertheless pressure vessels; hence, fusion welding generally is the preferred method of joining, to assure pressure integrity.

None of the wide range of liquid fuels and oxidizers used react chemically with aluminum alloys. Among the oxidizers are hydrogen peroxide, inhibited red fuming nitric acid, liquid oxygen, liquid fluorine, and nitrogen tetroxide. Fuels include those based on kerosene (such as RP-1), ammonia, liquid hydrogen, hydrazine, and UDMH (unsymmetrical dimethyl hydrazine).

Some fuels and oxidizers are in the category of cryogenic fluids (liquid oxygen, liquid hydrogen, liquid fluorine), which require tank materials not adversely affected by prolonged exposure to temperatures as low as −423 F. Aluminum experiences no sudden transition from ductile to brittle behavior at low temperatures, and in general aluminum alloys display higher tensile and yield strengths and greater ductility at cryogenic than at room temperatures (see Chapter 13 in this volume).

Redstone, an early liquid-fueled ballistic missile, utilized non-heat-treatable alloy 5052-H38 for fuel and oxidizer tankage, due to its adequate strength level and excellent weldability. The development of stronger 5*xxx* series alloys contributed to the design of the longer-range, more efficient Jupiter ballistic missile, which used alloy 5086-H34. Engine fairing for the 105-in.-diam Jupiter missiles was of corrugated alclad 2024-T3 sheet.

The S-I and S-IB stages of Saturn I are essentially a cluster of eight Redstones surrounding a Jupiter. They make use of an even stronger alloy of the 5*xxx* series, 5456-H343, for tank walls and retain 5086 for tank ends. The degree of work hardening in the ends varies as a result of the forming process.

---

1 Forward skirt structure, alloy 7075-T6
2 Gox distributor, alloys 2219-T87, T81 and T6
3 Oxidizer tank, alloys 2219-T87, T81 and T6
4 Antislosh baffles, alloys 2024-T3 and 7178-T6
5 Antivortex device
6 Cruciform baffle
7 Intertank structure, alloy 7075-T6
8 Fuel tank, alloys 2219-T87, T81 and T6
9 Suction line tunnels, alloy 2219-T81
10 Oxidizer suction lines
11 Fuel suction lines
12 Center engine support, alloys 7075-T6 and 7079-T6
13 Thrust column, alloy 7075-T6
14 Holddown post, alloy 7079-T6
15 Upper thrust ring, alloy 7075-T6
16 Lower thrust ring, alloy 7075-T6
17 Engine fairing, alloy 7075-T6
18 Fin, alloys 2024-T3 and 7075-T6
19 F-1 engine
20 Retro rockets
21 Gox line
22 Helium line
23 Helium bottles, alloy 2014-T6
24 Helium distributor
25 Oxidizer vent line
26 Instrumentation panels
27 Cable tunnel
28 Umbilical panel

Key to S-IC stage of Saturn V launch vehicle on facing page

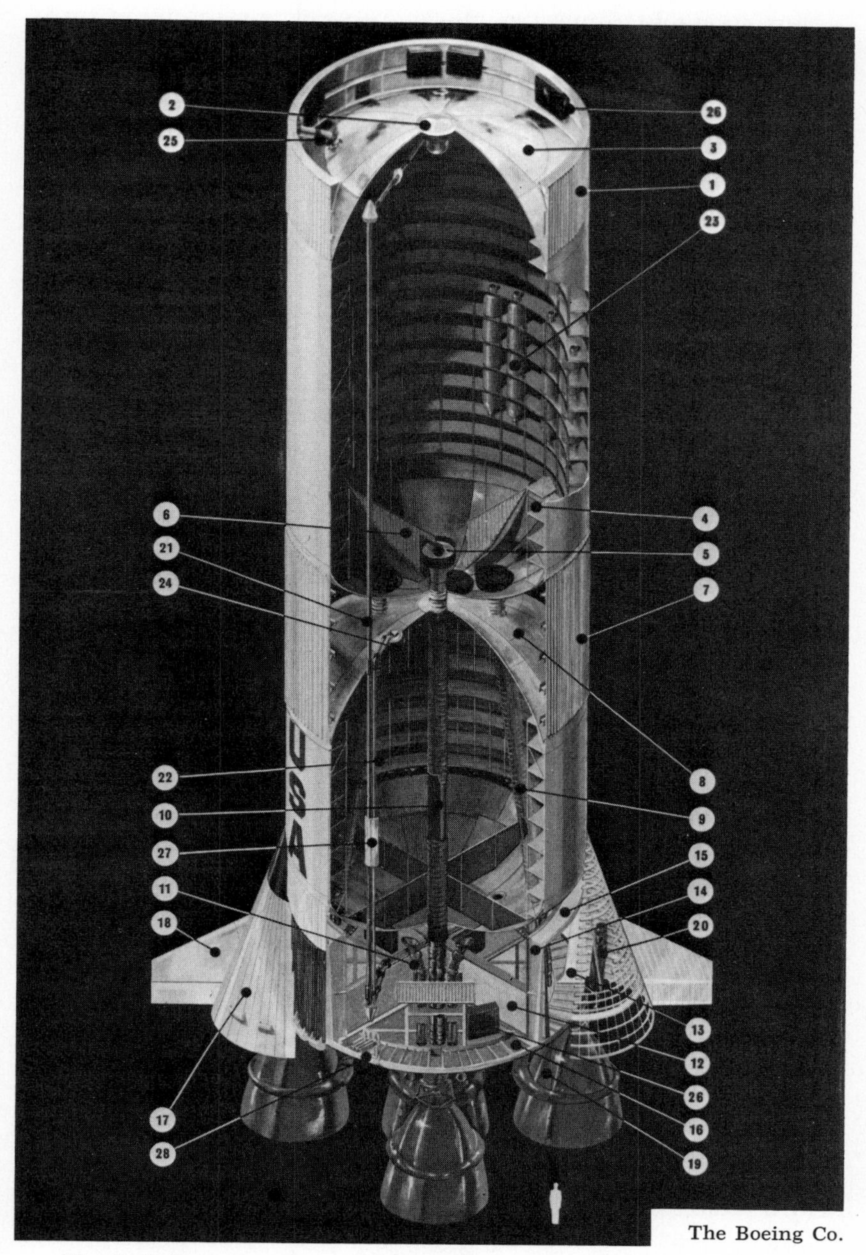

The Boeing Co.

Fig. 8. Schematic view of S-IC (first stage) of Saturn V vehicle. (See facing page for identification of numbered parts.)

Heat treatable aluminum alloys are well represented in tankage applications and, although less readily weldable, are likely to supersede the non-heat-treatable alloys, of lower strength. Alloy 2014-T6 is widely employed for tankage applications, including the upper Saturn stages, Thor, and Titan.

The first stage (S-IC) of the Saturn V (Fig. 8), which has a 7.5-million-lb thrust capability, utilizes heat treatable alloy 2219, primarily in the T87 temper, for fuel and oxidizer tankage. This alloy has lower strength but better weldability than 2014-T6.

The highest-strength aluminum alloys, 7001-T6, 7075-T6, and 7178-T6, are difficult to weld (Volume III, Chapter 12) and therefore are not favored for fuel and oxidizer tankage.

Most large liquid-fueled missiles and space vehicles have tank walls fabricated from large aluminum plates in which integral reinforcing ribs are machined. For example, the sidewalls of the S-IC stage of the Saturn V utilize 2219-T87 plate 2.25 in. thick, 11 ft wide, and 27 ft long. This thickness is required to provide stock for machining integral T-stiffeners. The machined sidewall segments are creep formed to the tank contour in the T37 temper, during artificial aging to T87 (Fig. 9).

Ends, or domes, for these large tanks are produced from 2219-T37 plates 0.25 to 0.50 in. thick, cut into wedge-shaped segments, or they are machined to final thickness leaving thick weld lands, then formed to the proper curvature by either explosive forming or hydraulic bulging. Subsequently, the gores are welded to form the completed dome, which is then aged to the T87 temper. Sidewalls, domes, and thrust structures are joined together through a Y-shaped member machined from a 33-ft-diam alloy 2219-T851 ring, fabricated from three pieces of plate, each 5½ in. thick by 27 in. wide by 27 ft long.

The pressure vessels for gaseous helium, shown in Fig. 8, item 23, are fabricated from extruded tube (Fig. 10). The tubes are fabricated into final form by a combination drop-hammer and forging operation, heat treatment to the T6 temper, and machining. Operating pressure of these large vessels is 3000 psi while submerged in liquid oxygen at −297 F.

Nonpressurized parts of most liquid-fueled ballistic missiles and space boosters employ large quantities of high-strength, heat treatable aluminum alloys 7075-T6, 7079-T6, and 7178-T6, in all of their common forms. Built-up aluminum beams and trusses of these alloys are employed in thrust structures, which transmit the propulsion forces from the engines to the tank walls.

There generally is a cylindrical intertank structure to transmit thrust loads between fuel and oxidizer tanks, except where a common pressure bulkhead is incorporated. The intertank structure often is produced from corrugated 7075-T6 thick sheet or light-gage plate. The interstage structure, which transmits the load from one stage to the next, also uses high-strength 7*xxx* series alloys, either in corrugated form or semimonocoque sheet-

The Boeing Co.

Fig. 9. Age forming of machined 2219-T37 plate for sidewalls of Saturn S-IC

stiffener design. Some 2020-T6 extruded compression members are used in the Saturn V.

Liquid rocket engines utilize high-quality precision aluminum castings and forgings for housings and impellers in both fuel and oxidizer pumps. Figure 11 shows a precision-cast C355-T61

Fig. 10. Alloy 2014-T6511 extruded tubes, 21.6-in. OD by more than 1-in.-thick wall by 18½ ft long, weighing 2320 lb each, for production of Saturn S-IC gaseous helium pressure vessels (see Fig. 8, item 23)

pump body for the RL-10 engine using liquid oxygen and liquid hydrogen. Forgings in 7075-T73 are rapidly being adopted for rocket engine components, because of their attractive combination of high strength and resistance to stress corrosion.

Smaller liquid-fuel missiles incorporate precision castings in

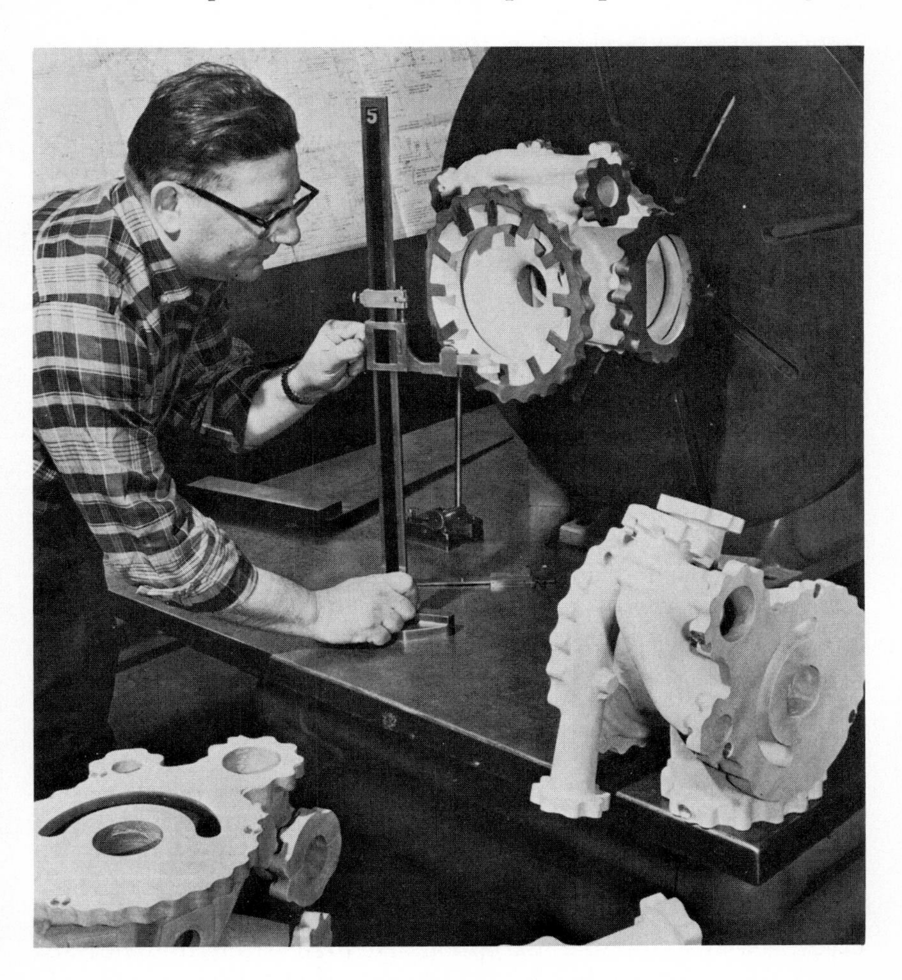

Mechanical properties are 42,000 psi tensile strength, 33,000 psi yield strength, and 3% elongation; surface finish, 100 micro-in.; dimensional tolerance, ±0.010 in. at critical locations.

Fig. 11. Precision cast alloy C355-T61 pump bodies for RL-10 liquid hydrogen–liquid oxygen rocket engine

alloys C355-T61, A356-T61, and A357-T61, and forgings in alloys 2014-T6 and 2618-T61, in place of complex built-up assemblies for parts such as wings and fins. For instance, Bullpup A uses permanent mold fins in alloy A356-T61, quality being maintained by x-ray inspection and destructive testing. The high-production air-to-ground Bullpup employs forged and welded 2014-T6 tanks (Fig. 12) for its liquid fuel and oxidizer. During firing, the tanks are highly pressurized by burning a slug of solid propellant, expelling fuel and oxidizer to the combustion chamber. The Army's Lance, for ground-to-ground use, is of this same type. Its tanks are produced from shear-spun tube and forged bulkheads.

Solid-fueled rockets have internal pressures greater by an order of magnitude than those existing in the tankage of liquid-fueled missiles. As a result, the hoop load is usually the critical design load. This application was initially dominated by steel, principally because fusion welding is more common for high-strength steels than for the highest-strength heat treatable aluminum alloys. Alloys such as 7001-T6, 7075-T6, and 7178-T6 develop strength-to-density ratios comparable to all except the highest strength, highly alloyed or cold worked steels, but they are less readily welded.

Aluminum alloys 2014-T6, 2024-T3, 6061-T6, and 7075-T6, however, are widely employed for small, air-to-air, air-to-ground, and sounding rockets, because the small-diameter motor cases employed can be fabricated from seamless tubular products. To date, these small cases have been 6 to 8 in. in diameter and 0.040 to 0.080 in. thick; however, the feasibility of seamless motor cases 12 in. and larger in diameter has been proven (7).

It has been shown also that the performance of an all-aluminum motor case can be further increased by circumferential reinforcement with a high strength-to-density ratio filament material, such as fiber glass or high-strength steel wire (8).

Composite construction incorporating high-strength fiber glass filaments and organic resins is being utilized for some motor cases, because of the exceptionally high strength-to-density ratios obtainable in the cylindrical portion of the vessel. Aluminum components often are employed, especially where machining is required. Aluminum forgings of alloys 7075-T6, 7075-T73, and 7079-T6 are used in the skirt area and in the heads to accommodate holes through the fiber glass wall for nozzle and igniter ports and other parts.

Reaction Motors Div., Thiokol Chemical Corp.

Fig. 12. Alloy 2014-T6 forgings and impact extrusions used in welded tanks of Bullpup prepackaged liquid-fuel rocket engine

The airframe structure of the solid-fuel missile or space vehicle is fabricated by methods similar to those used in making the liquid-fuel type.

Aluminum particulate usually is one of the fuel elements in solid propellants, and aluminum thus is generally the most prevalent metallic material in a loaded motor. Aluminum powder inhibits pressure variations during firing, thus promoting even burning of the solid fuel. Aluminum increases specific thrust when used as one of the fuel elements. Most current and planned solid fuel rockets employ aluminized propellants.

The electronic and guidance portions of missiles and space boosters use cast aluminum components extensively, generally in the form of electronic housings, gyro gimbals, and intricate wave guide assemblies. Most of these are cast in C355-T6 or A356-T6. In many of these applications, aluminum is chosen because the sections can be cast as thin as 0.080 in. with precision as close as ±0.005 in.

Aluminum is used in other missile and booster subsystems and components, as in aircraft. The T73 temper of alloy 7075 was

Fig. 13. Alloy 2014-T6 monolithic precision forging weighing 100 lb. Forging is nose-wheel well truss of turboprop transport airplane.

initially developed for hydraulic system components in space boosters, a critical application where high strength and high resistance to stress-corrosion cracking are required.

Satellites and Space Vehicles

Satellites and spacecraft designed for re-entry into the Earth's atmosphere and eventual recovery, do not use aluminum alloys for principal structure, because of the high-temperature environment encountered during re-entry. However, satellites and space vehicles designed to operate above the atmosphere during their useful lives do utilize aluminum alloys in principal structure, for essentially the same reasons that have made aluminum successful for aircraft and missile construction.

In addition, the range of surface finishes producible on aluminum has led to its wide application as external satellite skin. Thermal balance is maintained in most satellites by designing the structure to conduct to the skin excess heat generated by electronic gear. The skin must dissipate this heat by radiation, and also reflect enough solar energy to maintain the internal satellite temperature within design limits. The optical qualities of an aluminum skin can be varied as desired: by polishing, by anodizing (clear or in color), or by applying one of many paint systems. The high thermal conductivity of aluminum is helpful in minimizing thermal gradients.

The Apollo manned lunar expedition program makes structural use of aluminum alloys in the Saturn V booster tankage, the Command module, and the LEM (lunar excursion module), which is to make the actual moon landing. However, the command and re-entry capsules have nonaluminum materials of higher heat resistance for the skin and principal structure.

A good example of both structural and optical uses of aluminum in a satellite is the NASA orbiting astronomical observatory (OAO). The basic satellite structure consists primarily of alloy 2014-T6 sheet and extrusions. Aluminum reflector sheet 0.032 to 0.125 in. thick is employed extensively as the external skin. This product has 1178 alloy cladding; after electropolishing and anodizing, the sheet develops high reflectivity.

Massive Monolithic Members

Massive monolithic members are utilized in large or high-performance aircraft to transfer or distribute high loads to adjacent structure. Some of these components, machined from large pieces of stock, are landing-gear-attachment bulkheads and trusses (Fig. 13), wing carry-through structures, fuselage and wing bulkheads (Fig. 14), landing gear cylinders and trunnions, wing spars (Fig. 15), and ribs and thrust structures for large rockets.

Factors affecting the choice of alloy, temper, and product for large monolithic structures are the directional properties (particularly elongation), service temperatures, thickness at final heat

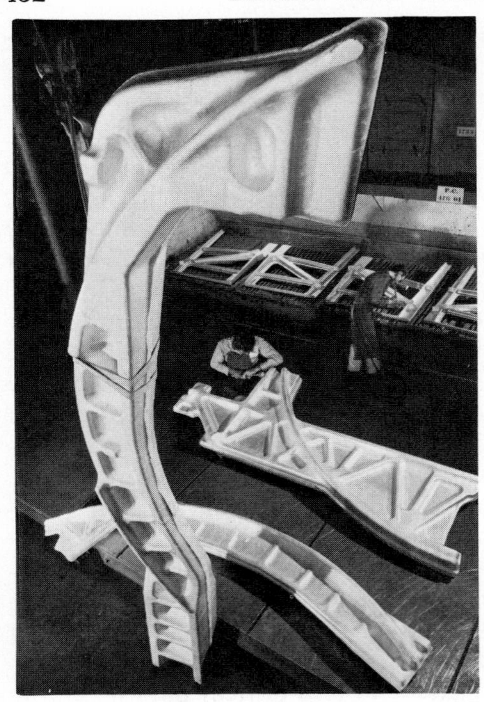

(Top) Forging in foreground is 15½ ft long and weighs 1680 lb. (Bottom) Fuselage section utilizing members machined from forgings of the type shown on the skid in top photograph.

Fig. 14. Large die forged 7075-T6 structural members for military jet transport

Lockheed-Georgia Co.

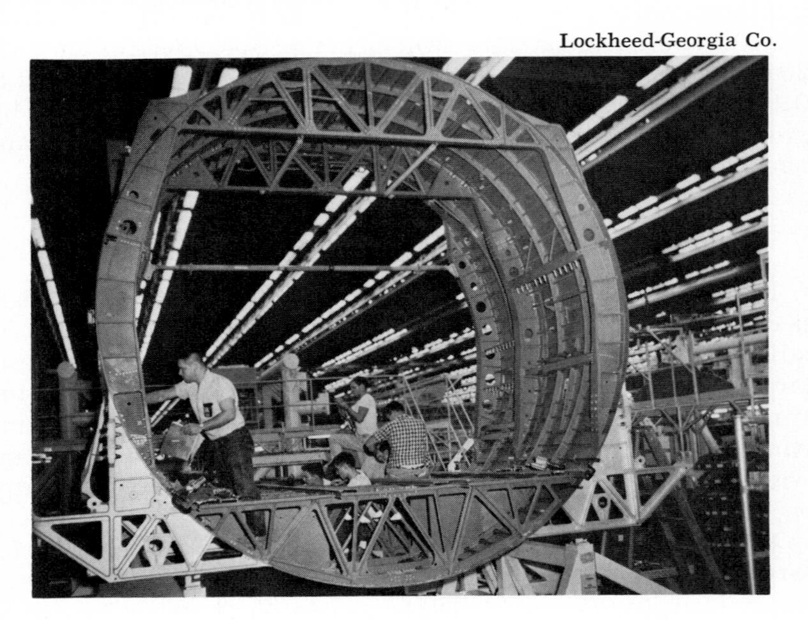

treatment, methods of joining, and relationship of any sustained stresses to grain orientation.

Selection of product is strongly dependent on the economics of manufacturing (9). Die forgings and extrusions usually minimize the quantity of raw stock required, but their dimensional tolerances are seldom close enough to obviate the need for extensive machining. Plate, extrusions, or rectangular or contour hand forgings are preferred for parts that must be stress relieved, because of the difficulty and tooling expense of compression stress relieving large closed-die forgings. High-speed automated milling machines have made machined solid stock competitive with die forgings in many designs. Stress-relieved material is economically machined to the thin webs (0.040 to 0.060 in. thick) often required. The use of stress-relieved material not only avoids costly distortion problems during machining, but also reduces the possibility of stress-corrosion cracking due

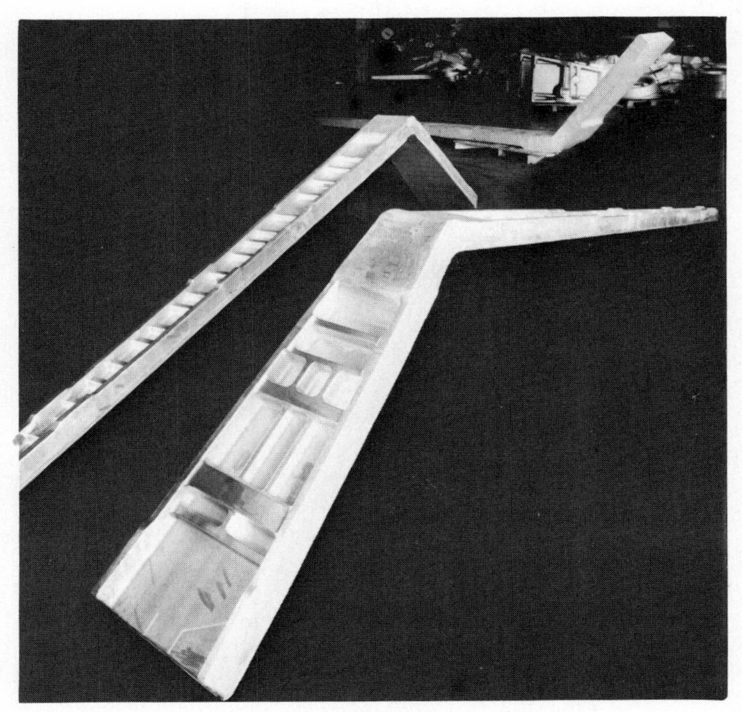

Fig. 15. Wing spar forging for supersonic fighter in stress-relieved 7079-T652. Part is 17½ ft long and weighs 1600 lb.

High Vacuum Equipment Corp.

Finned tubes are alloy 6063, return-bend tubes 6061-T6, structural shapes 6061-T6, and welding filler 4043. Operational limits: vacuum to 10^{-10} torr, internal brine or liquid nitrogen pressure to 150 psi, and temperatures from −320 to 500 F.

Fig. 16. Cryopanel for space chamber

to residual quenching stresses in susceptible alloys and tempers (Volume I, Chapter 7, and Volume III, Chapter 10).

The high-strength heat treatable alloys are employed almost exclusively for these monolithic structures. Alloy 7079-T6 has been the most popular, except for use in heat-affected areas where 2014-T6, 2024-T81 or 2618-T61 is preferred. The development of X7080-T7 offers promise of forged parts with higher resistance to stress corrosion than obtained with 7079-T6; the low residual quenching stresses minimize distortion during machining. Alloy 2219 is selected because of its weldability, and 7075-T6 and 7178-T6 for thrust structure parts to be rough machined to 3 in. or less before final heat treating.

Ground Support and Test Facilities

Space chambers, enclosures evacuated to sufficiently low pressures to simulate outer space, must be designed to withstand ambient external pressure. Weldable alloys, such as 5083, 5454, and 5456, are satisfactory for this construction. Advantages of aluminum include buckling strength, low outgassing, and fracture toughness at cryogenic and room temperatures.

Cryopanels (panels maintained at a cryogenic temperature to simulate the heat absorption characteristics of space) are generally fabricated from aluminum sheet and tube, tube-in-strip, or finned tubular extrusions of alloys 3003 or 6063 (Fig. 16). Cryopanels usually have a dull black organic coating applied for maximum thermal absorption.

Aluminum reflector sheet is used for reflectors associated with simulation of solar radiation.

Nuclear engine test facilities require structural elements made of materials that form primary isotopes having very low radiation and short half-lives. Because activated pure aluminum has a short half-life, interest centers on its alloys containing the lowest practical content of elements having long half-lives, such as beryllium, cobalt, iron, nickel, and zinc. Aluminum alloys containing only elements of short half-life, such as magnesium, manganese, and silicon, with other elements restricted to very low percentage as impurities, are available. The impurity elements are in such low concentration that it is necessary to test for them analytically with nuclear radiation instrumentation. Other important requirements are weldability, resistance to corrosion, and sometimes elevated-temperature strength.

Alloys 1100, 6061, 6063, and the weldable 5*xxx* series generally with specially controlled impurity limits are those predominantly used. Extruded tubular shapes, pipe, structural shapes, sheet, plate, and fasteners are employed extensively for general structure, cooling water, shielding, and transfer tracks. Boral plate, a sandwich material made of aluminum plate and enclosed boron carbide filler, was developed by the United States Atomic Energy Commission for fast-neutron shielding and absorption. It is produced commercially and is utilized in nuclear reactor test facilities.

Aircraft landing mats have been used since before the second World War to provide a satisfactory surface on raw terrain with minimum preparation for landing and take-off of military aircraft. The increasing weight and speed of modern jet aircraft have forced improvements in landing mats over the pierced aluminum (0.156-in.-thick 6061-T6 sheet) or steel plank products of World War II. Continuing development has resulted in a formed and welded assembly of 6061-T6 sheet, 0.156 in. thick. Advanced designs undergoing tests include a lightweight multicell extrusion 24¾ in. wide by 1½ in. deep in a 6*xxx* alloy, and adhesive-bonded sandwich panels with cellular cores using alloys 5052, 6061, alclad 2014 and alclad 7178. They must withstand loads of 50,000 lb with 100 psi tire pressure.

The United States Marines' SATS (short airfield for tactical support) concept, involving power-assisted launches and arrested landings, must handle jet planes weighing 60,000 lb and with tire inflation pressures of 400 psi. The tail hooks used to engage arresting gear impose high local stresses in landing-mat panels. The current panel design utilizes a hollow multicelled 6061-T6 extrusion, 24¾ in. wide and 1½ in. deep.

Helicopter airfields have lower load requirements for landing mats, making it easier to achieve the light weight desired for mobile operations. One floatable mat being evaluated utilizes alclad 2014-T6 sheet for the skin and corrugated core, adhesive bonded to each other and to a frame of welded 6061-T6 extrusions.

Missile loaders, launchers, carriers, and erectors use many aluminum parts to provide high mobility (see Chapter 19 in this volume). The popular structural alloys 2014, 5456, and 6061 are the wrought alloys usually employed. Large castings for complex structures are normally of 356-T6. Large van-type trailers use materials and design practices given in Chapter 15, this volume.

The possibilities of welded designs for missile loaders were enhanced with the availability of alloy 2219 and the recently developed weldable aluminum-magnesium-zinc alloys. Some hollow shapes are produced in 7075-T6 for shipboard missile handling equipment. The launching rails on several aircraft designs also are made of 7075-T6 extruded shapes. Hard anodic and other types of electrochemical finishes are utilized on wear surfaces to obtain low friction and long life.

Missile and engine containers generally are of welded construction to obtain moistureproof packages. Small and medium-size containers, normally handled with power equipment, usually are made of materials other than aluminum for economy. Larger containers, and those that must be handled by troops or be highly mobile, are fabricated from aluminum alloys. Sheet in alloy 6061 and extrusions in 6061 and 6063 are employed. A few designs are specified in 5*xxx* series alloys and some utilize honeycomb sandwich construction.

Electronic cabinets used in GSE (ground support equipment) range from small "black box" sizes, generally made from 3003-H14 sheet, to large console units, designed in high-strength aluminum alloys such as 2024-T3 or 7075-T6. In certain large consoles, alloy 7075-T6 is specified for extruded sections that must be thin because of space limitations, and consequently require higher strength. For a combination of strength and anodizing characteristics, alloy 5052 is used extensively.

Multiple-void hollow extrusions in alloys 6061 and 6063 are utilized in electronic cabinets for structures with integral coolant passageways. Extruded shapes in 6061-T6 and 6063-T6 and castings in alloy 356-T6 are used extensively for corner members, racks, and chassis.

Antennas for radar and radio ground support equipment employ aluminum in the supporting structure, reflector surfaces, and feed mechanisms, because of its light weight and resistance to weathering. Aluminum contributes an important reduction in loads on bearings and base structure, and also permits the desired stiffness in the reflector surfaces without excessive weight. (Figure 13 in Chapter 11 illustrates the use of aluminum tube in supporting project Haystack's reflector surface.) Sandwich construction often is employed for reflector panels; the core is either fiber glass, a lightweight foam, or aluminum.

Alloys 5083, 5456, and 6061 are used extensively in antenna structural components. Weld filler wire is usually 4043, 5356, or 5556, and cast fittings are 356-T6. Alloys 5052 and 3003 are employed for expanded-mesh and solid reflector surfaces. Stretch forming has proven effective in achieving desired contours; sheets are welded or bolted to the supporting frames.

Tubular supports for feed mechanisms are of 6061-T6. Lower-strength alloy 6063-T5 or T6, with superior finishing characteristics, may be an acceptable alternate, depending on loading conditions. Alloy 2024-T4 bolts, with an anodic finish, and alloy 6262-T9 nuts are standard for mechanical assemblies in the field. Bolts can be produced in alloy 7075-T73 if higher strength is desired. Alloy 6070-T6 may be specified for extruded shapes and sheet, to obtain strength higher than 6061-T6 and good corrosion resistance. The new weldable 7*xxx* series alloys offer advantages for welded designs.

Aircraft maintenance docks, hangars, alert shelters, and missile assembly and check-out buildings are engineered in accordance with local codes and those of the American Society of Civil Engineers. Aluminum applications are similar to those described in Chapter 10 of this volume for industrial buildings. Additional reasons occasionally prompting the use of aluminum in these aircraft maintenance applications include low transportation costs to remote installations supplied primarily by air, a requirement that the structures be movable, or the high cost of foundations for a heavier structure.

References

1 Orville Wright, private communication, December 9, 1939
2 C. F. Jenkin, "Report on Materials of Construction Used in Aircraft and Aircraft Engines", H. M. Stationery Office, London, England, 1920, p 68
3 "A Chronicle of the Aviation Industry in America", Eaton Manufacturing Co., Cleveland, Ohio, 1948, p 27
4 J. Mecklin, The C-5: The Biggest, Cheapest Lift Ever, Fortune, 72, No. 5, 179 (Nov 1965)
5 The Selection and Application of Aluminum and Aluminum Alloys, "Metals Handbook", Vol. 1, 8th edition, American Society for Metals, 1961, p 880
6 J. Fielding, Materials and Processes, in "Supersonic Engineering", John Wiley & Sons, New York, 1962, p 226–257
7 L. W. Mayer, High Performance, Low Cost Motor Cases of Aluminum, ARS Journal, 32, 1044–1050 (July 1962)
8 L. N. Odell and W. E. Albert, The Filament Reinforced Motor Case, Aerospace Eng, 21, No. 4 (April 1962)
9 Examples of Light Metal Parts for Aeronautical Construction, "Metals Handbook", Vol. 1, 8th edition, American Society for Metals, 1961, p 901–915

Chapter 19

Military Vehicles and Equipment

J. F. FAULKNER and E. W. JOHNSON

THE EARLIEST military use of aluminum was for torpedo boats, ordered in 1892 by the French Government (1). The United States Army acquired aluminum picket and tent pins and aluminum canteens in 1896; in fact, Teddy Roosevelt carried an aluminum canteen in the famous charge up San Juan Hill during the Spanish-American War (2). Also, during the 1890's, the United States Navy procured 94-in.-wide aluminum sheets for a large assembly, possibly a ship superstructure (3).

As described in Chapter 1 of this volume, the first World War generated an urgent need for aluminum in several forms and for a variety of military applications. Germany, faced with shortages in iron and steel, employed aluminum in army tanks and industrial machinery (4).

The second World War added many naval uses in structural, functional, and personnel equipment aboard fighting ships. Other notable military adaptations were in bridges and pontons, walkie-talkie sets, fuel drums for air transport, aircraft landing mats, and searchlights.

This chapter discusses current military defense uses of aluminum other than those dealt with under marine and aerospace applications (Chapters 17 and 18 in this volume). Although many military designs and materials are relatively stable, there

J. F. Faulkner is a development engineer, Product Development Div., Aluminum Company of America, Cleveland. E. W. Johnson is an application engineer for aerospace and military, Application Engineering Div., Aluminum Company of America, New Kensington.

W. A. Woodburn, a research engineer, Fabricating Metallurgy Div., Alcoa Research Laboratories, New Kensington, assisted in the preparation of this chapter.

is a strong trend toward innovation, especially in combat equipment. Thus, many products described here are likely to be changed within a short time. Design details and most applications in the development stage are omitted because of military security restrictions or uncertainty concerning final selections.

Armor

Military requirements of combat vehicles establish their specifications for armor. The 5*xxx* series strain-hardenable alloys have been used in all aluminum military vehicles produced to date. The ballistic merit of these alloys relative to rolled homogeneous steel armor varies with the angle of impact. The 7*xxx* series heat treatable alloys provide improved protection at all angles. Because minimum weight for a given level of protection is essential to mobility, aluminum armor is used extensively in combat vehicles.

The ultimate selection of armor material depends also on requirements other than ballistic criteria. For vehicular applications, weldability is a primary need, because welding most economically produces structural integrity and the watertightness necessary for amphibious operation. Satisfactory machinability and formability are needed for shop fabrication. Strength must be adequate to resist service stresses, including shocks encountered in airdrops and cross-country operation.

Completed vehicles may be used or stored for long periods under extreme conditions of temperature (−80 to 165 F) and humidity. Operations also include movements through corrosive waters. Armor material must retain its mechanical and ballistic properties, and resist corrosion under such conditions. Aluminum alloy armor provides the characteristics required.

Additional advantages offered by aluminum over steel are freedom from low-temperature embrittlement and greater rigidity, resulting from thicker sections, for equal protection. Increased rigidity, up to nine times that of steel, usually eliminates the need for secondary structural support.

As an example of fabrication economies, edge preparation for welding aluminum requires simple sawing and high-speed edge machining only, whereas the slower, more expensive procedure of flame cutting and edge grinding is necessary for steel armor. An important effect of these and other advantages is lower cost per vehicle with aluminum armor than with steel.

Production forms of aluminum alloy armor are rolled plate, extrusions, and forgings. For alloys with ballistic properties developed by strain hardening, use primarily is in the form of rolled plate.

Heat treatable aluminum alloys that can be welded effectively are being developed as weldable armor, making it possible to employ more forged and extruded armor components. These forms offer reduced fabricating costs and greater versatility than plate.

Cast aluminum armor components are being introduced for applications where requirements other than ballistic performance dictate section thicknesses greater than those necessary for wrought armor.

Military specifications for weldable aluminum armor cover strain-hardened 5*xxx* series alloy plate and heat treatable 7*xxx* series plate, extrusions, and forgings in various tempers (5).

Vehicles

Aluminum's greatly increased use in military vehicles in the past few years has resulted from requirements for reduced weight for improved vehicle mobility, "swimmability", air transportability, increased payload (6), and ease of maintenance. Many successful, economical, commercial highway vehicles of aluminum construction have been employed by the services. However, most combat and tactical vehicles have no civilian counterparts, and their aluminum components have been developed specifically for military service (7).

Wheeled vehicles for general-purpose duty are used predominantly for logistics (support and supply) operations. Aluminum 5*xxx* series alloy sheet and 6061-T6 and 6063-T5 extrusions are employed extensively in the bodies of large buses, cargo trailers, liquid-transport tanks, and comparable vehicles.

Bus and cargo-trailer bodies usually are riveted assemblies of aluminum sheet and extrusions, whereas tankers are welded 5*xxx* series alloy sheet assemblies. Tanker pumps, filters, and plumbing are made of aluminum castings and tube. Chapter 15 in this volume describes these and other aluminum applications in commercial vehicles.

Special-purpose wheeled vehicles have standard military functions or characteristics that are outside normal commercial requirements. These vehicles can be categorized as single or

Highway Products, Inc.

Transporter, which is essentially an all-aluminum structure, has very low rolling resistance over all types of terrain, and can be towed, either singly or in tandem, by any prime mover with a simple pintle hook. Permanent mold casting (inset) is both wheel and hub. It is 38½ in. long and 21 in. in diameter; each end weighs 148 lb.

Fig. 1. The M-6 1000-gal rolling liquid transporter

multipurpose, for highway, "off-road",* or cross-country missions, or combined use.

The Minuteman missile transporter is illustrative of single-purpose highway vehicles. Its aluminum components include: 2024-T6 alloy forged disk wheels; 2014-T6 forged front hubs, fifth-wheel control arms and cross braces, and equalizer beams in the tandem axle assemblies; 6061-T6 plate and bar stock weldments in the trailer-frame cross-assembly rear hinge structure (for support of the trailer body when raised upright to transfer the missile), and in several suspension system brackets; 220-T4 alloy sand-cast support brackets for the auxiliary transmission and the gasoline tanks; welded 5052 sheet gasoline tanks; and 1100 alloy brazed tube-and-fin radiator.

*Partially prepared or otherwise reasonably negotiable surface

Welded assemblies in the vehicle are heat treated after being welded. Where strength requirements permit, the operation is limited to artificially aging material welded in the T4 temper. In many instances, however, stock in the O or F temper is welded and the assembly is completely heat treated.

The adjustable-height aircraft-loading trailer, another single-purpose vehicle for use on prepared surfaces, employs forged 2014-T6 actuating beams, and several extruded 6061-T6 parts.

Others in this class of vehicle are simple, four-wheel trailers for nuclear ordnance. These are built primarily of 6061-T6 forgings, 5083 extrusions, and A356-T6 castings.

Equipment vans (electrical, shop trailers, and detection and control centers) normally have some off-road capability. They are more rugged, and often better thermally insulated, than conventional trailers. Typical construction includes body sandwich panels of 5052-H34 alloy sheet facings on an insulating core, and 6061-T6 tread-plate floors on 6061-T6 extruded beams.

An unusual off-road vehicle is the ART-30 airborne fork-lift truck for the Marine Corps. This 1.7-ton vehicle lifts 1.5 tons and operates effectively on mud, snow, and rough terrain. All structural components, including forks and fork carriage, are aluminum. The 2014-T6 alloy forged fork weighs 36 lb, in contrast to 165 lb for the conventional steel design of the same capacity. Welding and mechanical fasteners provide the 6061-T6 body structure with watertightness to a depth of 5 ft.

Another off-road vehicle, the rough terrain trailer, weighs 1 ton and has a 4-ton capacity for loads with low centers of gravity. Its deck, frame, and chassis are constructed mainly of 6061-T6 sheet and extrusions.

The rolling liquid transporter (Fig. 1) is an unorthodox cross-country vehicle concept, with a minimum of structure for the payload it carries. The liquid cargo is contained in tires mounted on permanent mold cast 356-T6 alloy "axle wheels" attached to a tongue of 6061-T6 drawn tube.

The M-102 trail-gun-type 105-mm howitzer, a lightweight weapon carriage for rough terrain, is fabricated almost entirely of aluminum. Fusion welded box sections of 5086-H32 sheet and 5086-H112 extrusions provide structural efficiency and low weight in the trail, body, and base assemblies. Several functional extruded tubes, such as those in the cradle structure, are 5086-H32 alloy. Forged 7075-T6 and 7079-T6 structural brackets support the trunnion and cradle; ground stakes are 7075-T6 forgings, hard anodized for abrasion resistance; wheel hubs are A356-T61 castings. With a gross weight of approximately 1.6 tons, the M-102 is by far the lightest 105-mm conventional gun yet designed. Transport by helicopter for maximum tactical effectiveness takes unusual advantage of its light weight.

The Hawk missile launcher is a two-wheel "trailer" with cross-country capabilities to match the tracked transporter-loader vehicle that pulls it. The launcher has an essentially all-riveted aluminum body of 2024-T3 and T4 sheet, plate, and extrusions. The superstructure consists primarily of large aluminum sand castings in 356-T6 alloy.

A new family of lightweight truck designs — the XM-561, XM-410, and XM-656 — is replacing the traditional group; capacities range from 1¼ to 5 tons. The combined objectives of cross-country capability and lightness for maximum mobility and air transportability demand efficient structural design.

The XM-561 (Fig. 2) is a 1¼-ton-capacity, articulated 6 × 6 (six wheels, all driving) vehicle, combining a two-axle tractor with a single-axle carrier. Tractor and carrier have resistance welded, hull-type bodies of 5086 alloy extrusions and sheet. Other aluminum components include welded 5086-H32 sheet fuel tanks and cast 356-T6 differential cases.

The XM-410, a 2½-ton, 8 × 8, four-axle truck, has an integrated chassis, frame, and cab ("drivable chassis"), plus fuel

U.S. Army

Fig. 2. XM-561 aluminum truck and trailer-carrier is articulated, with power available to all six wheels, providing agility in rough terrain, compared to other wheeled vehicles.

Fig. 3. M-60 main battle tank, showing forged aluminum wheels and hubs, and welded sheet fender boxes. As-forged wheel with unusual re-entrant interior shape is pictured in inset.

tank and demountable cargo body of aluminum. These structures are assembled from 5083-H32 and 6061-T6 sheet, plate, and extrusions employing weldments, and 2017 alloy rivets and other mechanical fasteners. Several A356-T61 and 356-T6 castings are used in the body fittings. The power-transfer cases are 356-T6 castings. Truck weight is about one ton less than the previous standard 2½-ton truck.

The XM-656 is a 5-ton, 8 × 8 truck with conventional chassis that employs 6061-T6 aluminum sheet and extrusions in cab, cargo body, and cab arctic hard-top assembly. Forged 2014-T6 alloy arms carry fore and aft thrust between axles and frame. Wheel hubs are either cast 356-T71 alloy or forged 2014-T6. The power train contains 356-T6 castings in the transfer cases and 356-T71 castings in the differential cases.

FMC Corp.

Aluminum components include complete hull, cupolas, and wheels. Welded joints apparent in this photograph are typical of aluminum-armored vehicles. Aluminum paint points out use of aluminum.

Fig. 4. The M-113 armored personnel carrier

Tracked Armored Vehicles. Armored combat vehicles (tanks) are produced in a wide range of sizes, and include several types designed for specific missions. This general class is illustrated by the M-60 (Fig. 3) and the M-113 (Fig. 4).

The M-60A1 main battle tank usually is considered a "medium" tank, because its 51-ton gross weight is significantly less than the heaviest tanks previously built. Alloy 2014-T6 die forgings are used for road wheels, track-support wheels, and hubs, comprising a large portion of the aluminum used. Other applications include: welded 5086-H32 sheet fuel cells; shroud of 3003-H14; fender boxes and fan shroud of 5052-H32 and 5052-H34 sheet; and numerous components in the power plant.

The armored vehicle launched (AVL) bridge is an aluminum and steel structure transported, launched, and retrieved by a launcher mounted on a modified M-48 or M-60 tank chassis. The bridge contains approximately 8½ tons of aluminum, and has a total weight of approximately 14 tons.

The M-113, an armored personnel carrier, must be air-droppable and transportable and capable of swimming with full combat weight; its mass thus is held to a minimum. Structural integrity also is critical, because the vehicle is exposed to extremely rough cross-country service and is air-dropped routinely. Its weight is less than half that of the steel vehicle it replaces (6). It was the first production vehicle to use aluminum armor, and is typical of several models in current production: the M-109 self-propelled 155-mm howitzer (Fig. 5); the M-114 command reconnaissance vehicle; and several vehicles developed directly from the M-113 basic design, including the XM-106 and M-125A1 mortar carriers, the M-132 flamethrower, and the M-577 command post vehicle. These vehicles employ 5*xxx* series aluminum armor, as-rolled plate and, in some parts, extrusions and forgings.

Nonballistic parts on all vehicles mentioned utilize sheet, plate, numerous extrusions, and a few forgings, mainly in the softer tempers of 5083, but also in other alloys of the 5*xxx* series and in 6061-T6. The various complex parts, ranging from small fittings to gear cases and structural members, primarily are cast in 356-T6, A356-T6, or ASTM GM70B alloy, with a notable exception: the 220-T4 "spade" used to stabilize the M-109 as a gun platform. Wheels for the vehicles are drawn from alclad 2014 or 2024 plate.

The XM-551 Sheridan-Shillelagh employs heat treated aluminum armor (8). The Sheridan, weighing 16 tons, is the heaviest vehicle to date designed and tested for airdrop; its weight thus is critical. It is unique in its use of forged aluminum armor in the hull and its cast aluminum cupola.

Tracked logistics vehicles differ from combat types in several ways, a major difference being absence of armor. This saves considerable weight, permitting substantial payloads. Two important vehicles in this class are those used to handle the Hawk and Pershing missiles.

The Hawk transporter-loader is a small, tractor-type vehicle equipped with a powered, manipulator-type superstructure. It was one of the earliest vehicles of its type, and is mostly of steel construction, but it was the first to employ aluminum wheels and tracks. Wheels are alclad 2014 drawn plate. The forged 2014-T6 single-pin track shoes have rubber grouser pads and steel-capped guides to minimize wear. It also has permanent mold cast 356 alloy housings for the transmission, differential, and cross-drive.

The XM-474E2 support vehicles for the Pershing missile are typical of the unarmored group that use the M-113 power plant and suspension. They have frame-and-panel-type bodies rather than monocoque hull structures. Superstructures vary with function. Alloy 5083 sheet, plate, and extrusions, joined by welding and mechanical fasteners, are employed in the body, frame, and superstructures.

The M-116 general-purpose tracked logistics vehicle is a lightweight (5.5-ton) design, constructed principally of 5086-H34 sheet on an extruded aluminum frame, joined by welding, rivets, and bolts. Its drawn 2024-T4 plate wheels, and 6062-T6 extruded clamping plates on the track bands are characteristic of current lightweight tracked vehicles.

The most recent light logistics vehicle, the XM-571, is articu-

General Motors Corp.

This is one of the largest aluminum-armored vehicles. Recoil from the 155-mm howitzer is dissipated by rear-mounted cast aluminum "spades". Flotation kit is stored in welded aluminum containers.

Fig. 5. The M-109 self-propelled howitzer

U.S. Army

Tractor is aluminum armored for protection of cargo, which can include personnel. Forged aluminum wheels help minimize weight, and provide high strength to withstand the extreme loadings experienced by this multipurpose vehicle.

Fig. 6. Universal engineer tractor spreading a load of gravel on a road-construction project

lated, with power transmitted through the coupling to a second unit. It is a tracked counterpart of the XM-561 wheeled vehicle. Aluminum is used for 42% of the vehicle, chiefly as: 5083 alloy sheet (honeycomb panels) and 6061-T6 extrusions in hull and body; 356 alloy castings in wheels, engine, and power-train cases; and 6151-T6 forged track shoes.

The universal engineer tractor (UET), which has the appearance of a bulldozer with a front-loading scraper, can perform dozing, scraping, hauling, and prime moving functions (Fig. 6). The UET weighs 15 tons empty, and can transport or carry as dozing ballast an additional 12 tons. Its light empty weight makes it air-droppable, amphibious and highly mobile; the ballast capability permits it to perform as a 27-ton bulldozer. Aluminum applications in frame and body include armor plate and nonballistic parts of 5456 alloy. Forgings include 2014-T6 wheels; castings include 356 alloy power-train housings.

U.S. Army

Fig. 7. The LARC*-15 (lighter, amphibious, resupply, cargo). This 15-ton-capacity all-aluminum vehicle is the largest of its type in current service.*

Earthmovers. Military tracked vehicles for other than combat or logistics are mostly earthmovers. Typical is the commercial bulldozer, where aluminum generally is limited to power-plant applications.

Amphibious vehicles of aluminum construction include the Army LARC (lighter, amphibious, resupply, cargo) group and the Navy experimental LVH (landing vehicle, hydrofoil), both general-utility craft for ship-to-shore operation. Also included is the Army MFAB tactical bridge and ferry.

The LARC group of vehicles, which replaces the World War II "Duck", includes 5-ton and 15-ton capacities (Fig. 7). The two models are similar except in size. The exacting requirements of these vehicles are met by all-aluminum welded construction, primarily of 5086 alloy sheet and thin plate on extruded ribs, longerons, and other framing. A large number of 356-T6 sand and permanent mold castings serve as fittings; several A356-T6 castings are important structural members, including the permanent mold cast propeller shroud. Alloy 2014-T6 forgings are used in wheel assembly, lifting links, and other high-stress areas.

The Navy LVH is a cargo or general-utility hydrofoil boat with wheels. It differs from the LARCs by having retractable wheels, foils, and propeller. High speed and efficient performance are achieved by sophisticated structural and hydrodynamic design, and extensive use of aluminum. Sheet, plate, and extrusions of 5083 alloy in the H112 and H113 tempers are welded to form a stressed-skin hull and superstructure. The foils are hollow welded assemblies of 5083 extrusion and tube. Forged 2024-T6 wheels, cast 356-T6 power-train cases, and the normal castings, forgings, and weldments in the turboshaft engine are other aluminum applications. Land and water speeds up to 40 mph are the highest available in an amphibian.

The Army mobile floating assault bridge (MFAB) is a unique wheeled boat with a rotatable "roadway" superstructure. The MFAB can launch itself and ferry other vehicles (Fig. 8), or form a floating bridge in conventional fashion. Hull and deck are 5456-H343 sheet, welded or riveted to 6061-T6, 2014-T6, or 5456 alloy extrusions in the framework, using 2117 or 6061 rivets. The roadway consists of 12-in.-wide ribbed 2014-T6 extrusions laid across beams welded from large 2014-T6 extruded shapes.

Motive power for production military vehicles includes gasoline, diesel, and multifuel engines (see Chapter 14, this vol-

Fig. 8. Ferry, consisting of four Army mobile floating assault bridge (MFAB) amphibious vehicles of aluminum, can carry a 60-ton tank. Time and crew needed to assemble ferries or bridges of this type are much less than with previous equipment.

ume). In most military vehicles, power-plant components are aluminum only where the application has been adopted by a commercial vehicle producer as a standard item.

The use of engines containing substantial amounts of aluminum is not extensive, but does include diesel engines in three tracked vehicles and one truck.

Outstanding is the AVDS-1790, a V-12 air-cooled engine for the M-60 tank. Crankcase, oil pan, turbocharger, and accessory housings are 355-T71 sand castings. Cylinder heads are sand cast in 142-T77; muffs are 142-F permanent mold castings, used as-cast to avoid heat treatment damage to the bond with the cast-in iron cylinder liner. Alloy C355-T61 castings with premium strength, tolerance, and smoothness provide the characteristics required in cooling fans and turbocharger impeller. Forged 4032-T6 pistons and brazed oil coolers complete the aluminum applications.

The XM-571, a tracked vehicle, is powered by an automobile air-cooled aluminum engine, with only minor modifications.

The XM-561 wheeled vehicle is a truck using a three-cylinder diesel engine (the 3-53) based on a "standard" 53-cu-in. cylinder. Aluminum components of the engine include sand cast 356-T7 cylinder blocks and heads, and 355-T7 flywheel housing.

One other engine, the LD-465, used in the XM-410 truck, is important because it will operate on several fuels and is indicative of intensive efforts by the services to reduce logistics problems in fuels. Aluminum pistons are 20% Si alloy forgings, and the flywheel housing is a 355-T71 or C355-T61 permanent mold casting. The LDS-465 that powers the XM-656 truck has 355-T71 or A356-T61 permanent mold castings in the flywheel housing, a 355-T7 turbocharger case, and a C355-T61 premium-strength cast turbocharger impeller.

Ordnance

Ammunition. Lower cost and equal or better performance have led to increasing use of aluminum in recent years for parts such as projectiles (both cartridge-launched and rocket-launched), cartridges, mines, bombs, and their components.

The smallest projectiles employing aluminum are several varieties of the conventional 20-mm round. These have a conical aluminum nosepiece, machined from rod or bar of 2024-T4. Two

40-mm projectile models have a drawn 1100 alloy sheet ogive and machined tubular skirt of 6061-T4.

Larger projectiles use aluminum in various components, including die cast nosepieces; forged or extruded spikes, bodies, chambers, and booms; and extruded, sheet, or die cast tail-fin sections. Other aluminum items are mainly screw-machine parts, plus some die castings and impacts in fuse, base, and firing assemblies. Another significant application involves impacts for "burster" tubes in special shells, such as the 155-mm chemical round.

The 6066-T6 cartridge case of the 40-mm grenade-launcher shell is made by impact extrusion or multiple drawing; a more recent, longer 40-mm case is an impact. Substantial use is made of 6061-T6 impacts for 90-mm blank ammunition cartridge cases, with limited application also in the less common 75, 76, and 105-mm sizes. Although not a cartridge, the 7001-T6 motor body impact for the 66-mm rocket houses the propellant. The motor closure for this rocket, which joins motor body to warhead, is machined from a double-end impact, also of 7001-T6 alloy.

Land mines utilize several aluminum components, although the cases, like projectile and grenade bodies, are of ferrous material, to produce the most damaging fragments. Aluminum items are principally small screw-machine parts, including fuses, firing pins, charge caps, and various holders.

The need to clear paths through mined areas has led to development of the M-157 shaped-charge snake, a 400-ft-long assembly of 5-ft sections that can be positioned remotely in a mine field by a combat tank. The sections are hollow 6061-T6 extrusions containing linear explosive charges that destroy or explode mines. The high stiffness-to-weight ratio possible with aluminum tube permits long lengths without buckling, and assemblies light enough for proper positioning by the tank vehicle.

Bombs employing aluminum are mostly practice types, ranging up to a foot or more in diameter. Use of aluminum facilitates control of center of gravity, provides repairability and resistance to corrosion, and minimizes cost.

Retardation attachments for conventional bombs reduce falling speed and eliminate risk to the aircraft that dropped the bomb from a low altitude. These devices are mechanically assembled from 7075-T6 impacts, 2024-T4 sheet, 2014-T6 and 7075-T6 hollow extrusions, and 7075-T6 bar.

Aluminum components forged to size with extreme precision ("net" forgings, with tolerances smaller than normal even for finish machining) are economical for certain mass-produced ammunition items.

Guns and launchers utilizing aluminum range from the M-16 rifle to the superstructure of the M-474 used to transport key equipment of the Pershing system.

One model of the M-16, with a 5.56-mm bore, has forged 7075-T6 upper and lower receivers, in addition to several smaller parts. The M-14 standard automatic rifle employs a 7075-T6 butt-plate assembly, both for light weight and capacity to accept a hard, durable anodic coating. The M-60 machine gun has several small aluminum parts, such as the bipod, that help prevent excessive over-all weight.

Another weapon with aluminum components is the Vulcan aircraft-mounted multibarrel gun. Its drum feed uses sheet and

Fig. 9. Section of Zuni rocket launcher, showing drawn and extruded aluminum shapes comprising the assembly. Top hollow extrusion is main strength member and attaches to airplane wing pylon.

other aluminum parts; barrels are held in alignment by a forged aluminum "spreader".

The M-72 recoilless rocket launcher LAW (light antitank weapon) has a 6061-T6 impact extruded chamber (9). A variation of the World War II "Bazooka", it is carried complete with its rocket, fired once, and discarded. Therefore, low cost is essential. An aluminum impact extrusion that is utilized as part of the shipping container and as a barrel to fire the rocket contributes greatly to the low cost, as well as to keeping maximum weight below a 4.5-lb limit. A die cast 380 alloy firing-pin housing is used for the same reasons. The 66-mm rocket fired by this weapon was described on page 473.

A somewhat similar, but larger, shoulder-fired weapon is the Redeye antiaircraft rocket launcher. It employs aluminum as a 2024-T3 drawn-tube barrel, some small extrusions, and incidental fittings.

Rockets up to about 5 in. in diameter, used in large quantities, require multiple launchers. These typically are 5052-O tube assemblies attached to the vehicle serving as the launching platform.

The Zuni rocket is fired from a typical aircraft-mounted launcher assembled from various tempers of 3003 and 6063 alloy drawn tubes and complex 6061 and 6063 extruded shapes. The launcher is placed in an outer tube of welded sheet to streamline the pod and provide for attachment to a pylon that extends from the airplane wing (Fig. 9). Aluminum die castings and screw-machine parts are used to complete this four-barrel assembly.

Other launcher-type infantry weapons that make important use of aluminum are the Mauler, the M-79 grenade launcher, and the M-7 portable flamethrower. The 7075-T6 impact (Fig. 10) employed as the barrel of the M-79 is mainly responsible for keeping the weight down to a limit of 6 lb. Integral boss detail obtainable by the impact extrusion process eliminates the cost of manufacturing and assembling extra parts. The M-7 flamethrower operating assembly uses eleven 380 alloy die castings and a forging for levers, grips, covers, and bodies.

Other ordnance items employing aluminum include free-fall (unguided) devices, illuminating shells, and equipment for handling, shipping, and storing ordnance.

Baseball-size smoke "bomblets" are dispensed from aircraft in great numbers to provide smoke screens. Use of 3003 alloy for

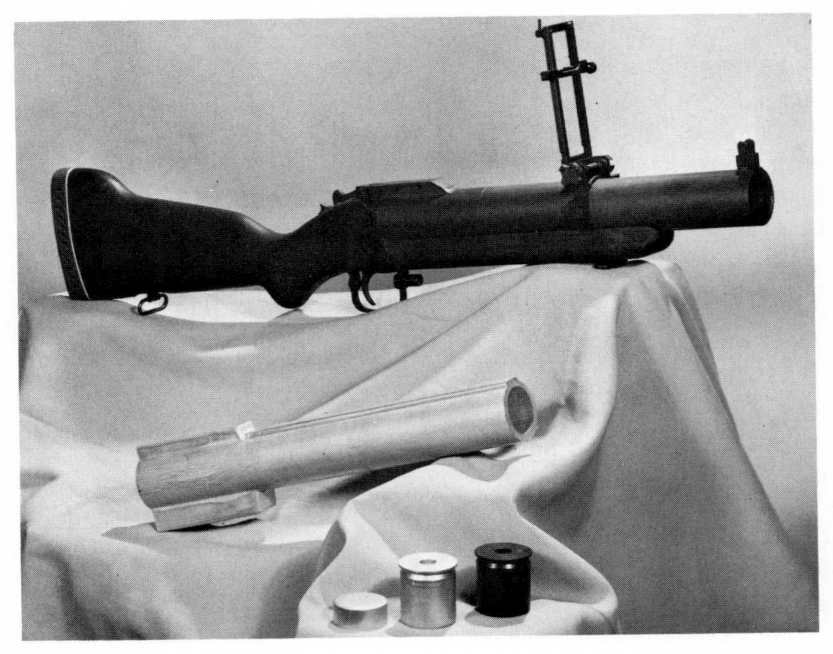

Fig. 10. M-79 grenade launcher and the impact extrusion used for the barrel, along with the cartridge case, shown in three stages (slug, impact, finished part). Black anodized finish reduces reflection and helps avoid detection.

the drawn-sheet bomblet cases provides minimum weight and cost. The grapefruit-size E-134 combat bomblet (Fig. 11), formerly a brazed assembly of steel stampings, employs 6061-T6 forgings and sheet. The aluminum design reduced by nearly one half the cost and the number of parts and manufacturing operations.

Antiradar chaff, introduced during World War II, is cut-up light-gage aluminum foil ejected from aircraft in flight. Aluminum is selected because of light weight, low cost, resistance to corrosion, and microwave opacity.

Typical of aluminum usage in equipment to handle, ship, and store ordnance items is the Weapons Ready Service for Marine Corps advanced airfield operations. Stiffness, strength, and ruggedness are provided at minimum weight and cost by 6061-T6 extrusions, tube, forgings, and sheet, in the double A-frame, strongback, tracks, cradles, and stacking frames.

Fig. 11. Army E-134 bomblet, showing very sharp detail and re-entrant shape of integral fins on forged 6061 alloy hemispheres

Supply and Maintenance Equipment

This broad class of military equipment consists of general utility items. Most have civilian counterparts and are described elsewhere in this volume. Typical items, with the main aluminum products involved, are listed below:

Item	Products
Clothes lockers	Sheet, extrusions
Conveyors	Extrusions, rod
Fire-fighting suits (Fig. 12)	Foil
Food packaging	Foil
Fuel, water, and LP gas tanks	Sheet, plate, weld wire
Kitchen utensils, refrigerators	Sheet, extrusions
Ladders, scaffolding	Extrusions, tube
Medical, tool, and ice chests	Sheet
Portable radio and battery cases	Impacts
Prefabricated building panels	Sheet, extrusions
Tent frames and poles	Tube

Other applications, associated with aircraft, are discussed in Chapter 18 of this volume; they include shipping pallets for general cargo use and platforms for airdrop.

Numerous aluminum utility equipment items are peculiar to the military services, such as the mess kit, canteen, and tent peg. Hand splints, litters, and ship berths are more recent uses.

Fig. 12. Army's new fire fighting suit, made of flame-retardant, aluminized paper laminated to aluminum foil. Suit fits over soldier's uniform, helmet, and breathing apparatus.

Underwater

The high resistance to seawater corrosion of most aluminum alloys, especially the 5*xxx* and 6*xxx* series, has contributed to their extensive use in surface craft and shallow subsurface equipment (see Chapter 17 in this volume). High strength-to-weight and stiffness-to-weight ratios of the 7*xxx* series alloys make them important also as depths and pressures increase. These properties are essential to minimize weight of a structure capable of resisting collapse under external pressure.

Torpedoes and Mines. Torpedoes commonly are subjected to several practice firings during their service lives. They are designed with a slight net positive buoyancy to permit floating and recovery after practice runs.

Weight saved in torpedo shells or machinery can be added as instrumentation or payload. Aluminum is employed extensively for weight reduction in the Mark 37, 44, 45, 46, and 48 torpedoes. Products vary with models, but aluminum-silicon alloy castings are used most frequently for such major parts as outer casings (aft, center, and nose sections), propellers, shroud rings, internal rings and bulkheads, and smaller components.

For some models, the propellers are plaster mold cast to finish size. At least one part on the MK-46 is a premium-strength C355-T61 alloy casting with minimum properties in the casting of 50,000-psi tensile strength, 40,000-psi yield strength, and 5% elongation. Some designs utilize 2014-T6 or 6061-T6 die forgings for propellers and several other parts. Welded sheet skins are used on certain models. Some torpedoes employ a large number of rolled or die-forged rings machined to serve as frame and reinforcing members.

In one underwater mine design, extruded 6061-T6 multiple-hollow "planks" are welded together to form the walls of a unique cylindrical case.

Detection devices and associated gear are being intensively developed. Most independent-type devices use aluminum extensively, because it offers the lowest cost per pound of net buoyancy and long service life. Flooded structures that rest on or near the ocean floor and support detection devices in a desired pattern are assembled from aluminum extrusions, tube, castings, and drawn-plate hemispheres. Flotation force to maintain vertical orientation of support structures is provided by spheres adhesive bonded from hemispheres; spheres with diameters of 22 in. to over 40 in. employ 6061-T6 and alclad 7178-T6.

Spheres made of cast A356-T61 hemispheres also have been tried successfully for flotation, despite a lower buoyancy-to-weight ratio than wrought spheres. Because of this lower efficiency, cast spheres usually are more expensive per pound of net buoyancy. It is advantageous, however, to use cast spheres in small quantities in those sizes for which drawing tools are not available to make wrought spheres.

A small sound-signal device deployed in predetermined patterns detonates under water to detect submarines by reflected sound waves. It is nearly all aluminum, using impacts, extrusions, die castings, screw-machine parts, and sheet.

Research vehicles for investigations at great depths pose a severe design problem of maintaining net positive buoyancy, because of the high strength required. The "Trieste", which has taken man to the bottom of the deepest known part of the oceans, uses the buoyancy of a large gasoline-filled tank, which severely limits speed and maneuverability of the vehicle.

The use of aluminum in the "Moray" and the "Aluminaut" provides a less cumbersome solution, at least for the intermediate depths permitted by the capabilities of present aluminum alloys and fabricating processes. Both vehicles have buoyant hulls that are capable of withstanding high service pressures.

The "Moray" employs sand cast A356-T61 aluminum hemispheres assembled by bolts to provide spherical pressure hulls, each large enough to house a man plus necessary controls and instrumentation, and mounted in a flooded structural housing.

The "Aluminaut" is a cylindrical vehicle not unlike conventional submarines in configuration. It is about 51 ft long by 8 ft in outside diameter, and carries a crew of three. The cylindrical portion of the hull is 7079-T6 alloy forged ring sections, mechanically assembled with O-ring seals; the ends are 7079-T6 forged hemispheres. This approach circumvents problems associated with welding the highest-strength aluminum alloys (Volume III, Chapter 12). Integral bolting flanges on the 4-ft-long rings provide sufficient section stiffness to prevent elastic buckling of the cylinder wall at design stress. The buoyancy required

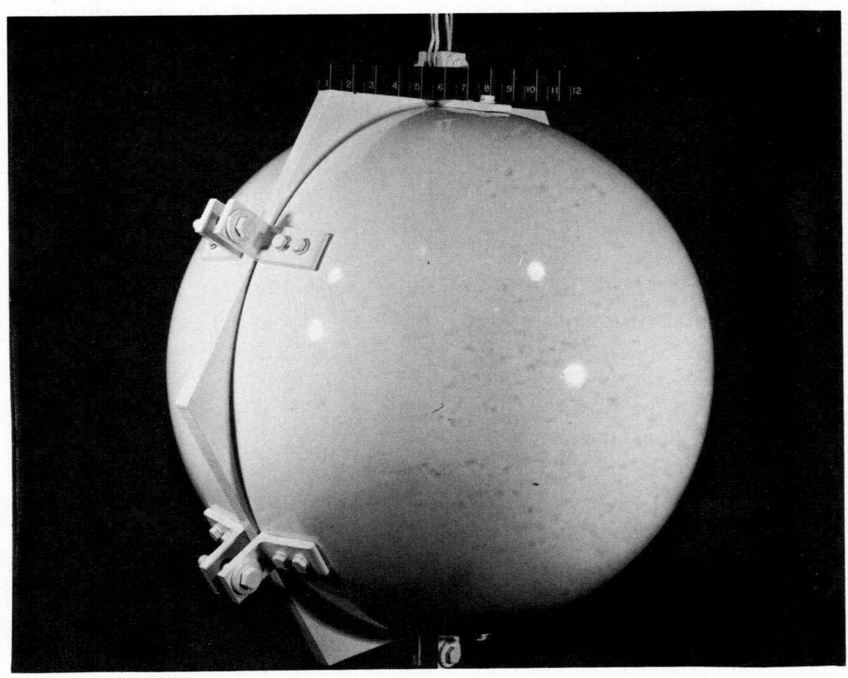

Fig. 13. Spherical aluminum instrument case is employed in undersea research. Flange positions sphere in assembly; bolted brackets provide pre-stress on joint to assure water tightness.

could not be obtained at reasonable cost using any other construction material within present technology.

Another class of vehicle that extensively employs aluminum is a remotely controlled, torpedo-size, research device. Launched from torpedo tubes and monitored from the parent vessel, it is powered for lengthy excursions. One model has a forged 7079-T6 hull with integral stiffening elements machined on the inner diameter. Forged ends and miscellaneous internal items also are aluminum.

Deep-sea housings of aluminum are employed for instruments and photographic equipment. They are extruded 6061-T6 or 7075-T6 alloy cylinders in sizes from a few inches to over 1 ft in diameter. Ends are closed mechanically, often with flat plate circles, O-ring sealed.

Aluminum flotation spheres also are used to house instrument packages. They are assembled mechanically to permit reopening and reclosing without damaging the seal at the joint (see Fig. 13 on the facing page).

Certain large sonar transducer housings, up to several feet in diameter, are made from aluminum forgings; they normally are a 5*xxx* series alloy for best combination of weldability and resistance to corrosion.

Atomic Energy

Atomic-energy devices have made substantial use of aluminum. Many hardware requirements are very sophisticated, introducing unique problems in forming, joining, and other fabrication details, demanding exceptional flexibility in the choice of alloys, products, and assembly methods. Atomic-energy applications are discussed also in Chapter 12 of this volume.

Weapon hardware frequently is constructed with alloy 6061-T6 medium-strength parts, and high-strength components of 7079-T6 or a similar alloy. Such factors as control of center of gravity can affect alloy and product selection, but high strength-to-weight ratio is usually the major requirement. The chief products involved are forgings, extrusions, and plate. Assemblies of these products employ most of the conventional joining procedures, including welding and mechanical methods.

Because of limitations on weapon-case size, and other critical performance requirements, above-normal strength and ductility are required in some hardware. In certain parts, for example, the normal longitudinal properties are maintained in all directions, requiring special alloy, stock, and metalworking modifications. The design and testing of most weapon hardware are probably unique in attention to structural performance. Exhaustive investigation of details is common practice. As a result, Atomic Energy Commission design agencies have established for aluminum and its use rigorous engineering and quality-control criteria that exceed those of any other consumer.

Other Military Equipment

Bridges and electronic hardware are typical of other military equipment making extensive use of aluminum. A ponton bridge, designed in World War II and still in production and use, is constructed mostly of 2014-T6 alloy extrusions. Assembly involves considerable welding, especially along the neutral axes of tubular beams made from extruded channels, of which the upper web forms the roadway. To improve traction of vehicles, the roadway face has longitudinal extruded and transverse press-formed depressions.

U.S. Army

Fig. 14. M-60 armored vehicle-launched (AVL) bridge unfolds into a 60-ft aluminum structure that supports the heaviest military vehicles, including tanks and self-propelled artillery.

U.S. Army

Fig. 15. A 50-ft portable antenna as packed for storage and shipment

Several other types of aluminum ponton bridges also are in service, including a footbridge that employs extrusions and plates of 2014-T6 and 6061-T6 alloys in the superstructure. The ponton is fabricated of 6061-T6 alloy.

The armored vehicle-launched (AVL) bridge illustrates the increasing mobility of military bridging. This aluminum and steel structure (Fig. 14) is attached to the front of a modified tank, folds to ride atop the vehicle, and operates hydraulically without exposing personnel. Aluminum's high strength-to-weight and stiffness-to-weight ratios contribute significantly toward maximum portability and mobility. Although 2014-T6 has been the alloy most widely employed since first used in World War II, the weldable, more corrosion-resistant type of 7*xxx* series alloys probably will be used extensively in new designs. Their high strengths as welded permit more welds at sites other than neutral axes, allowing better designs and fabricating economies.

The familiar hand-held mine detector utilizes an aluminum wand and electronics package for corrosion resistance and to reduce the weight an infantryman must carry so carefully.

A portable antenna mast for infantry use (Fig. 15) makes outstanding use of sectionalized design in aluminum. It is assembled from light-wall, drawn tube sections and sand castings; a two-man team is used to transport and erect the 50-ft mast. (See discussion of antenna systems on page 457.)

References

1 J. D. Edwards, F. C. Frary, and Zay Jeffries, "The Aluminum Industry", Vol II, McGraw-Hill Book Co., New York, 1930, p 9
2 C. C. Carr, "Alcoa: An American Enterprise", Rinehart Publishing Co., New York, 1952, p 111
3 *Ibid*, p 129
4 *Ibid*, p 151
5 H. P. George, Light Armor Materials, Journal of Metals, 13, 131–134 (1961)
6 C. B. Salter and R. J. Fabian, Lightweight Ordnance Equipment, Materials in Design Engineering, 54, No. 1, 100–104 (July 1961)
7 N. M. Lloyd, Aluminum and the Military Vehicle, Automotive Industries, 133, No. 11, 59–62 (Dec 1965)
8 H. B. Croskery, Sheridan Rides Again, Ordnance, L, No. 271, 68–70 (July–Aug 1965)
9 F. V. Youngblood, NATO Arms with LAW, Ordnance, L, No. 272, 184–186 (Sept–Oct 1965)

Chapter 20

Bearings, Tooling, Instruments and Other Mechanical Applications

P. I. NIELSEN, H. H. NUERNBERGER and C. G. SHIRING

CLEARLY DEFINED fields of application of aluminum are discussed in the other chapters on applications in this volume. This chapter considers various important mechanical uses that are outside the scope of the major application categories.

Aluminum Bearing Materials

Aluminum alloys with desirable bearing properties are used in a wide variety of applications (Fig. 1). Steel-backed and solid aluminum bearings are employed as connecting rod and main bearings in internal combustion engines (Chapter 14, this volume) and industrial compressors. Other aluminum bearing applications are in heavy tooling, such as boring mills, presses, lathes, milling machines, and grinding mills, and as hydraulic pump bushings. Aircraft landing gear assemblies, power shovels, and track rollers utilize solid aluminum bearings to withstand high-shock loads. Rolling mill bearings are cast of aluminum alloys to increase load and speed capability.

Aluminum bushings are normally employed for relatively light, low-speed duty, compared to bearings, and they are made

P. I. Nielsen is manager for cast and forged products — machinery and equipment, Application Engineering Div., Aluminum Company of America, Cleveland. H. H. Nuernberger and C. G. Shiring are development engineers, Product Development Div., Aluminum Company of America, New Kensington.

R. W. Irwin, a product engineer, Aluminum Company of America, New Kensington, assisted in the preparation of this chapter.

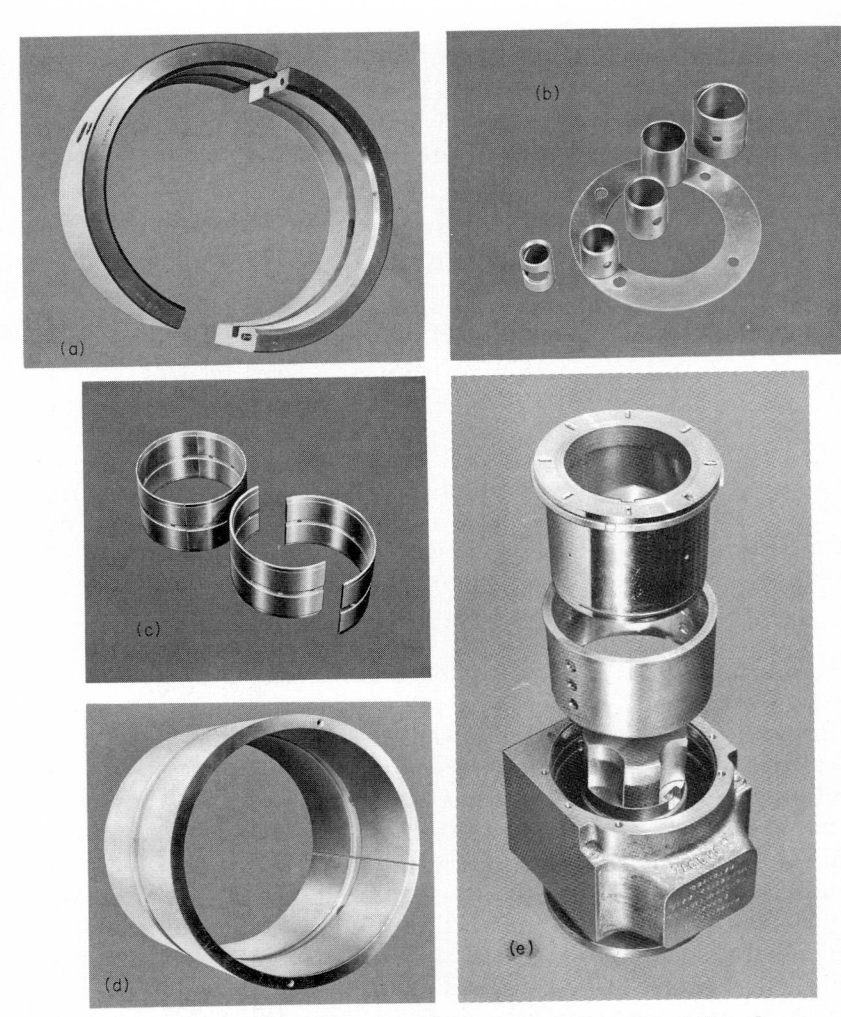

(a) Fixed bearing, consisting of two half-shells. (b) Solid aluminum bushings and thrust washer. (c) Full-floating aluminum bearing used in diesel engine. (d) Full-floating bushing used in compressor. The split in the bushing allows for heat expansion. No stress is imposed on bushing until surfaces of split meet. (Ingersoll-Rand Co.) (e) Semifloating aluminum bushing (center), used in roll-neck bearing of rolling mill, is fixed to housing by dowels. Precision-finished steel sleeve (top) rotates freely with the shaft in the aluminum bushing, on an unbroken film of lubricant.

Fig. 1. Major types of aluminum bearings

from aluminum bearing or other alloys, depending on the frictional and mechanical properties required for the application. Self-lubricating bushings are produced by compressing mixtures containing aluminum powder (see Volume I, Chapter 10).

Aluminum bearing alloys combine to a greater degree than any other single bearing material these desired characteristics: low cost, long life, high resistance to corrosive agents in lubricants, high mechanical compatibility with journal steels (no damage to shaft), high heat conductivity, good compressive and fatigue strength, light weight, conformability, embeddability, high speed capability, and monometallic (solid) design.

Cast or wrought monometallic (solid) aluminum bearings have high load-carrying ability, and can withstand very high speeds. They serve in engines and machinery as heavy-duty bearings under loads as high as 10,000 psi on projected areas of the bearing half shell, and at surface speeds up to 275 fps. In many laboratory tests, bearings have completed thousands of hours of successful operation at 12,000-psi loading. With proper shaft preparation, modern lubricants, and excellent oil filtration, even higher load and speed levels can be tolerated.

Monometallic aluminum bearings give excellent service on either hard or soft steel shafts, which is an advantage when shaft cost must be low. However, under identical conditions, hard shafts show less wear than soft shafts. The choice depends on an economic analysis that considers the expected useful life of the machine or the wear limit for part rejection. For steel shafts of low Brinell hardness (125 to 250), bearings cast in alloy 750 are employed. When shaft hardness exceeds 250 Bhn, casting alloy B750 is a better choice, particularly if the bearing lubrication system is not optimum.

If moving parts fail, an aluminum bearing does not damage the journal, largely because of its good embeddability. Any aluminum adhering to a shaft can be removed with chisel, polishing cloth, and caustic solution. This attribute of aluminum bearings saves equipment downtime and often avoids replacing an expensive shaft.

Choice of a method to cast bearings, which precedes alloy selection, depends on the number of pieces per order and the size and design of the part (1). Choice of alloy and temper depends on the casting process, part design, and service conditions.

The nominal compositions of three cast bearing alloys, 750, A750 and B750, are tabulated in Volume I, Chapter 8, and of the wrought bearing alloys, X8081 and 8280, in Volume I, Chapter 9. Alloys 750, A750 and B750 can be cast in sand or permanent molds, but not as die castings. Alloy X385 is preferred for die cast bearings; although not equal in bearing characteristics to the 750-type alloys, it is considered to have good machining and bearing properties.

Alloys 750 and A750 have similar mechanical properties, but A750 is easier to cast and better adapted to the production of complicated parts. Cast bearings of alloys 750 and A750 are supplied in the T5 or T101 temper, the latter attained by cold working after a T5 heat treatment. The T101 temper substantially increases compressive yield strength, improving the ability of a bearing housed in a material of lower thermal expansion to maintain an interference fit through cycles of heating and cooling. The cold working has little influence on hardness or tensile strength.

Such parts as gear housings and pump bodies may have both structural and bearing functions, and a bearing alloy in the T101 temper provides the additional strength needed above bearing requirements. For more highly loaded parts, such as wrist-pin

Table 1. Typical Mechanical Properties of Cast Aluminum Bearing Alloys

Property	Sand cast			Permanent mold cast			Die cast
	750-T5	A750-T5	B750-T5	750-T5	A750-T5	B750-T5	X385-F
Tensile strength, psi(a)	20,000	20,000	27,000	23,000	20,000	32,000	36,000
Tensile yield strength (0.2% offset), psi(a)	11,000	11,000	22,000	11,000	11,000	23,000	20,000
Elongation, % in 2 in.(a)	8.0	5.0	2.0	12.0	5.0	5.0	3.0
Compressive yield strength (0.2% offset), psi(b)	11,000	11,000	22,000	11,000	11,000	23,000	...
Brinell hardness (500-kg load, 10-mm ball)(a)	45	45	65	45	45	70	...
Shearing strength, psi(c)	14,000	14,000	18,000	15,000	14,000	21,000	...
Endurance limit, psi (R. R. Moore-type specimen, 500 million cycles)	...	...	10,000	9,000	9,000	11,000	...

(a) Tension and hardness values determined from standard 0.5-in.-diam tensile test specimens cast in green sand or permanent molds, and 0.25-in.-diam die cast specimens. Tension tests made without machining the cast surface. (b) Compression values obtained from 0.25-in.-diam specimens with l/r ratio of 6. (c) Estimated, except for permanent mold cast 750-T5 and B750-T5.

bushings, tractor-track roller bushings, and connecting rods, the still-higher-strength casting alloy B750-T5 is preferred. Die casting alloy X385 also has sufficient strength for use in parts designed for structural loads. Typical mechanical properties of cast aluminum bearing alloys are given in Table 1.

Typical mechanical properties for bearing alloys X8081 and 8280, supplied as sheet and plate in annealed and various cold rolled tempers, are listed in Table 2. Other wrought bearing

Table 2. Typical Mechanical Properties of Wrought Aluminum Bearing Alloy Sheet and Plate

Alloy and temper	Condition	Tensile strength, psi	Yield strength (0.2% offset), psi	Elongation, % in 2 in.
X8081-H25	Partially annealed	24,000	21,000	13.0
X8081-H112	As fabricated	28,000	25,000	10.0
8280-O	Annealed	17,000	7,000	28.0
8280-H12	Cold rolled	21,000	19,000	12.0
8280-H14	Cold rolled	24,000	22,000	6.0
8280-H16	Cold rolled	27,000	25,000	5.0
8280-H18	Cold rolled	32,000	30,000	4.0

alloys include Al − 4 Si − 1 Cd, and Al − 20 Sn. As with casting alloys, temper selection depends on bearing load and any additional structural strength requirements. Solid wrought aluminum bearings also have very high load-carrying ability and can meet requirements for heavy-duty bearings.

Design of Aluminum Bearings. Typical recommended bearing loads for cast and wrought monometallic aluminum bearings are:

Reciprocating load, pressure lubrication — 5000 psi
Unidirectional load, pressure lubrication — 3000 psi
Unidirectional load, doubtful lubrication — 1000 psi

These values are guides only. Associated components and other factors specific to an application influence allowable bearing loads.

Aluminum bearings, depending on the application, run with pressure-times-velocity (*pv*) values from 10,000 to 750,000. They withstand very high speeds, as evidenced by successful tests conducted at a surface speed of 275 fps. Commercial applications include water-air type turbines operating at 35,000 rpm.

Aluminum bearings are plated for applications involving heavy loads at low speeds or to assist all types of bearings during the run-in period. An overlay of 90% Pb, 10% Sn is electrodeposited on the bearing to a thickness of 0.3 to 0.7 mil.

Minimum bearing wall thickness for monometallic aluminum engine bearings is frequently determined by the formula:

$$0.035 \times \text{shaft OD} = \text{wall thickness}$$

However, under certain conditions, wall thicknesses appreciably less than those given by this formula are used satisfactorily. Ample wall thickness allows the bearing to be properly fixed in the housing.

For full-round monometallic aluminum bushings, the following average interference fits are recommended: alloys 750 and A750, 0.0004 to 0.0006 in. per in. of bearing outside diameter;

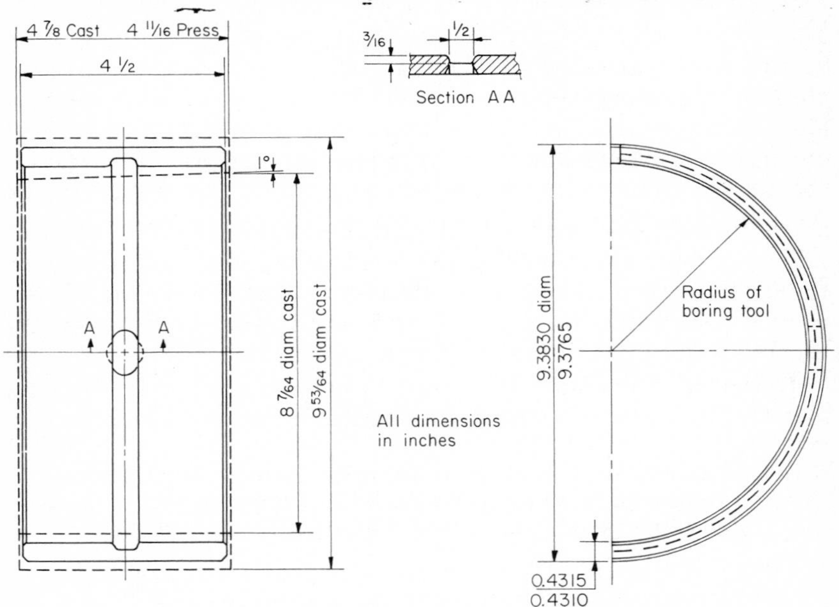

Fig. 2. Typical design of a main bearing in aluminum

B750, X8081 and 8280, 0.0006 to 0.0010 in. per in. of bearing outside diameter. Clearance of 0.0015 in. per in. of shaft diameter is recommended for oil lubricants. With grease as the lubricant, a clearance of 0.002 in. per in. of shaft diameter should be used.

Factors governing the practical clearance of aluminum bearings include the journal, bearing, and housing materials; journal hardness and finish; type and degree of lubrication; bearing loading and type (unidirectional, rotating, or reciprocating); speed; average size of dirt particles; and quantity of dirt in circulation (Fig. 2). Clearance must be increased or decreased based on evaluation of all these factors and actual experience. In many applications, aluminum monometallic bearings are operating with oil clearances appreciably below those of equivalent bronze or babbitt bearings.

Good lubrication is vital with aluminum bearings, as with bearings of other materials. Lubricants can be applied in several ways, including gravity, wick, and pressure methods. Best results are obtained with pressure lubrication, provided the design details are effective. Variables that should be considered in the design include speed and load; misalignment; length-to-diameter ratio; grooving; size and quantity of dirt particles; operating conditions; viscosity, stability, pressure, and cooling properties of the lubricant; and finish of adjacent parts.

The recommended surface finish for an aluminum bearing is 16 to 25-micro-in. roughness. Experience has shown, however, that an accurately machined surface, without drags or burnishing, is more important than a smooth finish. Steel shaft finish should be 5 to 35 micro-in., depending on the application.

Pumps

Among the main components of a gear-type pump for which aluminum may be used are the housing and end covers. In some instances, an aluminum design incorporates the housing and an end cover in a one-piece casting, maintaining a close fit between gears and housing for high efficiency. Using die castings in pumps frequently permits a design providing cast O-ring grooves and other close-tolerance cavities that otherwise would require machining.

Pump components made in large quantities usually are die castings employing alloy 13 or 380. Permanent mold castings in alloys 333-T6 and 356-T7 are recommended for such components as housings, covers, and adapters, when a specific design or production quantity does not justify the cost of die casting equipment. More stringent design or quantity limitations may call for sand cast components, generally in 319-T6 or 356-T7.

Precision parts such as centrifugal pump impellers and rotary pump lobes frequently are plaster mold or investment cast (Chapter 5, this volume, and Volume III, Chapter 2).

Fig. 3. Cutaway of automotive air conditioning compressor with die cast pistons, head, base plate, and cover plate. The connecting rods are forgings, and the main body is a permanent mold casting.

Compressors

Common types of compressors are single-acting piston, double-acting piston, and centrifugal. With single-acting enclosed compressors, such as used in automotive air-conditioning systems, the chief concern is obtaining pressure tight crankcases. This is accomplished by using permanent mold castings or die castings impregnated with a sealant (Fig. 3).

Die casting is employed for high-volume production of small-diameter trunk-type pistons of aluminum-silicon alloys. Permanent mold or sand casting is used for larger designs or lower production rates.

Aluminum connecting rods are made as 380 or X385 alloy die castings, 333 alloy permanent mold castings, or forgings, depending on size, loading, and economics. Connecting rods can be run directly on a steel crankshaft, if the projected bearing area is large enough and the oil supply adequate.

Alloy 380 generally is specified for die cast compressor parts, although alloy 13 is preferred when pressure tightness is a problem. Alloys 333-T5, 333-T6, and 356-T7 are used for permanent mold castings; alloys 319-T5, 319-T6, and 356-T7 are selected for sand castings; and forgings are fabricated in 2014-T6 and 4032-T6. Crossheads generally are made of an aluminum bearing alloy. Impellers and diffusers used in centrifugal compressors require precise dimensions and usually are made as plaster or investment castings in alloys 355-T61 or 356-T7. These casting processes are capable of dimensional accuracy within several thousandths of an inch, section thicknesses under 0.125 in., and surface finish of 120 micro-in. roughness or better, when suitable pattern equipment is available.

Fans and Blowers

Components of aluminum fans and blowers are either riveted or welded, using alloy 5154 or 6061 sheet for blades with hubs cast in 356-T6 or forged in 2014-T6. High-speed impellers for pumping corrosive gases in certain industrial processes are aluminum weldments.

Large propeller-type fans fabricated from sections extruded in alloy 6061-T6 are used for applications such as preventing frost in fruit orchards and moving air in industrial cooling towers. The extrusion process produces efficient airfoil sections.

Hydraulic Circuits

Hydraulic circuits normally consist of a pump, valves, filter, accumulator, and operating cylinder.

Hydraulic valves made of aluminum cost less than brass valves. Because of intricate passageways throughout the valve

Hydreco Div., New York Air Brake Co.

Fig. 4. Die cast hydraulic filter head designed for operational pressures of 3000 psi

body, sand casting and semipermanent mold casting are the best fabrication methods. Aluminum-silicon alloys such as 355 and 356 are used for pressure tightness and resistance to corrosion. Successful application of expendable cores could permit die casting of high-production valve bodies. Although forgings and bar stock sometimes are employed, considerable machining is required to obtain body cavities. If an aluminum valve spool is used, the outside diameter can be anodized for improved wear resistance. The spool can be a wrought screw-machine product or a casting. Alloys having approximately the same coefficient of thermal expansion can be chosen for the body and spool.

Filter components incorporate aluminum even on a high-pressure unit, where the head is made as an alloy 13 die casting (Fig. 4). The tank (or element container) is either an impact extrusion or a forging of 6061 or 2014.

Accumulator heads and bodies have aluminum components. High-pressure systems utilize forged accumulator heads, and

molds produce tires for passenger cars, trucks, buses, farm tractors, and earthmovers.

Both castings and forgings are used extensively for tire molds. The most common passenger and truck mold construction is a

Goodyear Tire & Rubber Co.

Fig. 5. A two-section integral mold for producing mammoth tires for earthmoving equipment. Each section weighs 7500 lb and is 9 ft in diameter.

precision cast 214-type alloy tread ring, including all tread detail, placed in a cast or forged aluminum back. The tread rings are cast of A214-type alloys in special mold materials to extremely close dimensional tolerances; the high degree of surface smoothness achieved is of utmost importance. Precision aluminum castings also are employed for one-piece tire molds, which combine the tread details and the mold back in an integral unit (Fig. 5). Forgings in alloy 2618 or 5086 are used in aluminum passenger tire molds as upper and lower bead rings and mold backs.

Vacuum equipment for molding plastics does not require the high-hardness materials necessary for injection and compression molding equipment. Therefore, these multiple-cavity molds utilize aluminum, because of its heat conductivity, and castability and machinability. The molds generally are made with plaster castings, tooling plate, and hand forgings.

Aluminum patterns other than match plates usually are produced as sand castings. A few are fabricated from wrought aluminum products. Virtually all aluminum match plates, and many designs of cope and drag equipment, with integrally cast patterns now are pressure cast in plaster molds. The best reproduction of mold cavity shapes is obtained with an alloy containing 7% Cu and 5% Si, although 108-type or 319-type alloys are also used. The light weight of aluminum is a labor-saving advantage in this application.

Die Sets. Experimental aluminum die sets (press equipment to hold die and punch) have been fabricated and tested in a number of stamping plants. These service tests indicated that aluminum die sets perform as well as conventional cast iron sets, and also offer advantages.

Outstanding benefit of an aluminum die set is a 50% weight reduction in comparison with a ferrous die set. The resulting lower inertia permits higher-speed press operation without exceeding load limitations.

Mechanical properties of aluminum alloy and cast iron die-set materials are comparable. The softer aluminum die set is protected by placing steel inserts at points of impact or wear. Aluminum also achieves considerable savings in freight charges.

Tests reveal no corrosion problems with aluminum die sets. Therefore, repeated greasing and cleaning as they enter and leave storage are unnecessary.

Aluminum die sets generally are fabricated from tool and jig plate. However, some are cast in 356 or similar alloys. All die sets receive a heat treatment that virtually eliminates residual stresses, after which they can be machined without distortion.

Caul plates are large, flat metal sheets (typically $3/16$ by 54 by 250 in.) on which a raw product is assembled and carried through a curing cycle in a heated platen press. Aluminum caul plates made of alloy 2024-T81 or 6061-T6 sheet or plate are used extensively by manufacturers of plywood, chip board, veneers, and high-pressure overlays. The high thermal conductivity of aluminum reduces the time required for a curing cycle. High-strength, heat treated alloys are selected to minimize the warpage and buckling resulting from stresses thermally induced by the hot press.

Nameplates are usually fabricated from alloy 1100, 3003, or 5005 sheet or foil, and receive a variety of finishes, including anodizing, lithographing, relief etching, and such mechanical treatments as brushing or buffing. Colorful effects are obtained through combinations of these processes. One nameplate system commercially available uses aluminum sheet or foil having an anodic film impregnated with light-sensitive compounds. Processing is similar to a photographic print.

Agricultural Machines and Equipment

Although aluminum is employed extensively on farms for roofing and siding (Chapter 10, this volume), applications in the construction of large farm implements are limited because of economic factors.

Irrigation systems provide the largest area of application for aluminum products in the agricultural industry. The principal items are cast aluminum pump parts, extruded and welded tubing, cast and formed couplers, and valves.

Flood irrigation employs formed tubes 1.5 to 6-in. OD by 6 to 8 ft long as siphons, to lift water from the head irrigation furrow to the crop row. More advanced systems of flood irrigation replace the head irrigation furrow and siphon tubes with "gated pipe". This is aluminum tube 8 to 12 in. OD with "gate" valves spaced along the bottom, designed to release varying amounts of water to the crop row. In both applications, the water pressure is below 50 psi; wall thickness in the range of 0.040 to 0.064 in. is used for all sizes.

Sprinkler irrigation systems operate at pressures up to 300 psi, and require stronger pipe. Pipe ranges from 1 to 10 in. OD and is either extruded in alloy 6063-T6 or welded from plain or alclad 3004-H34 or 5050-H38 sheet. Walls are 0.050 to 0.094 in. thick.

In either type of irrigation system, the pipe is handled manually, so light weight is important (Fig. 6). High strength and adequate wall thickness are necessary to resist denting and other deformation. Some pipe is produced with double wall thickness for about 6 in. at one end to provide added resistance to dimensional change. Other methods of end reinforcement are a rolled bead, or a protective fitting.

Many irrigation fittings, such as couplers, valves, and tees, are

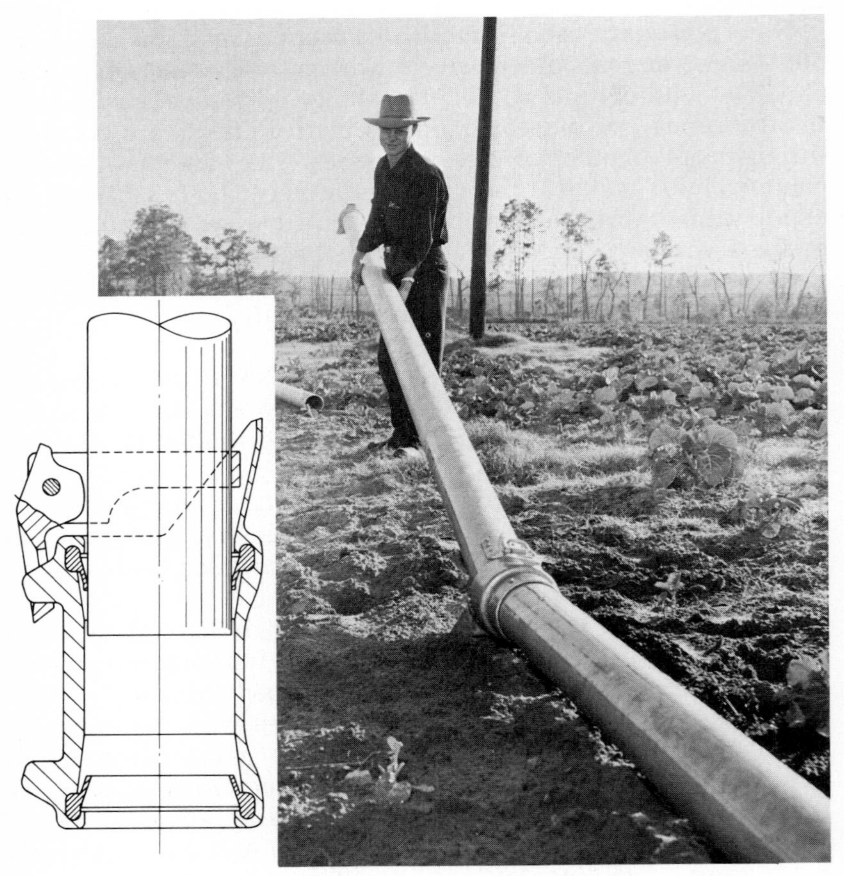

Fig. 6. A 40-ft length of 6-in. irrigation pipe being coupled. Inset shows quick coupling action and pressure seals of the cast coupling, typical of the several coupling designs.

either sand or permanent mold cast in alloy 356-T6 or roll formed from 6061-T4 tube.

Chemical Application Equipment. Production, transportation, and storage of fertilizers, insecticides, and herbicides utilize aluminum equipment to resist chemical attack (see Chapter 12 in this volume). The 300 to 1000-gal tanks employed in field equipment are constructed of alclad 3003 or 3004 sheet. Aluminum pumps, valves, and fittings also are common, and alloy 6061-T6 or 6063-T6 tubing is fabricated into spray booms and wands.

Miscellaneous Equipment. Aluminum grain scoops, drawn in alloy 6061, provide a 3-lb reduction in the load to be lifted, compared to steel scoops. Modern materials handling equipment, discussed subsequently in this chapter, is gaining acceptance on farms. Aluminum portable tools (see Chapter 22 in this volume) also are used extensively.

Chicken coops of aluminum are easy to handle and clean and they resist corrosion. Hovers for poultry brooders are made of aluminum because it reflects the infrared rays to the chicks. Aluminum farm gates are attractive and easy to open.

Business Machines

Aluminum die castings, extrusions, and sheet are employed extensively as frames and covers for a wide variety of office machines, such as typewriters, calculators, and accounting equipment. The die casting process economically produces in volume complex parts incorporating numerous bosses, ribs, slots, attach pads, and other details of casting design. Die cast enclosures can be made with complex curvature for aesthetic effects; through design, they can incorporate high rigidity and minimum weight. Alloys vary according to cost and foundry considerations, with 13, 360, and 380 predominating.

In electronic computers, aluminum die cast plug board frames of alloy 13 or 380 combine geometric detail with economical fabrication. Forgings in alloy 2014-T61 and some castings are employed as rotating memory storage drums. Nonmagnetic aluminum provides a base for magnetic memory coatings. Precision balance is easy to obtain with lightweight aluminum drums. Aluminum components are heat treated to insure minimum residual stress and maximum dimensional stability. Preferred tempers include T7, T61, and T65*x*.

Computers having random-access memory systems use aluminum-alloy disks as substrates for the memory units. The disks are fabricated from alloy 5086-H111 or 7075 sheet in the T6 temper, thermally treated by the customer to maintain dimensional stability, and machined accurately and polished to a high finish for deposition of the magnetic memory coating.

Magnetic and punched-tape reels utilize aluminum sheet extensively. Aluminum reels of alloy 3004 or 5005, anodized for appearance and easy cleaning, provide dimensional stability and rigidity with minimum inertia.

Addressing-machine plates of aluminum alloy 5052-H34 sheet are becoming common. They are formed of thin sheet and anodized for wear resistance. Their light weight is an advantage in handling stacks of plates in large-scale addressing operations. Because anodic films are able to absorb dyes, the plates can be color coded readily, for rapid identification of categories.

Instruments

Timing Devices. Most timing devices are controlled clocks having an index-type mechanism. Clock brass is the historic material for such devices, and it was the basis for the standards established for other metals. Most of these devices are now made in aluminum.

Aluminum performs as well as, and in some designs better than, clock brass, producing an equal or superior mechanism at lower cost. Choice of alloy depends on tool design, finish, tolerance, and service requirements. Clock-face sheet is 1100-H25 (bright rolled); frames and gears are 2024-T4 or 6061-T6.

Geophysical and Well Survey Instruments. Wrought and cast aluminum alloys are used with other materials in assembling certain measuring and recording instruments, including geophone cases, airborne magnetometers, gravity meters, drift indicators, single-shot and multiple-shot survey instruments, and well-logging instruments. Because of low-cost nonmagnetic characteristics, aluminum is used for cases, spools, working parts, and structural components.

Surveying. An engineer's transit must maintain accuracy over an indefinite period of years despite weather and climatic conditions. A transit manufactured by W. and L. E. Gurley in 1876 (5) was one of the earliest, if not the first, commercial use of aluminum in the United States. This transit was in service for

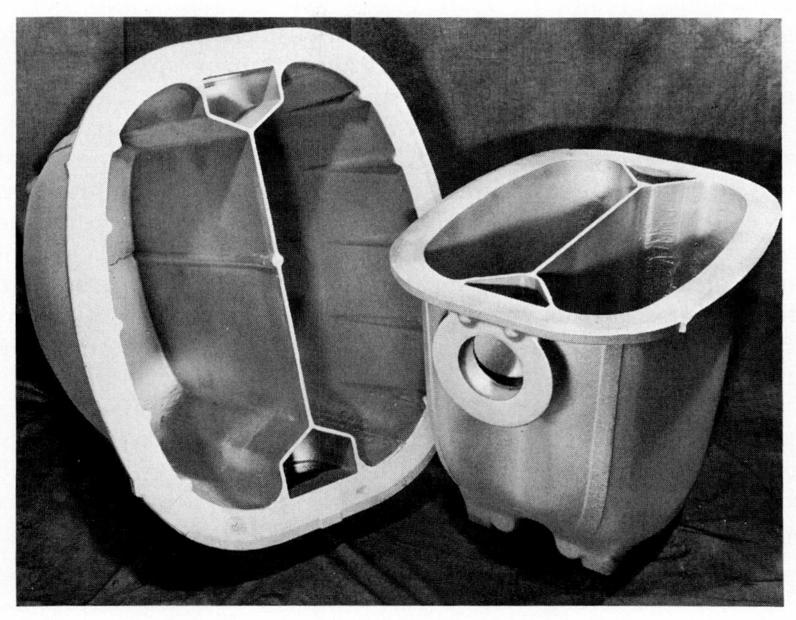

Fig. 7. Pressure-tight gas meter cases produced as permanent mold castings

50 years. Mechanical-property limitations of the first aluminum products hindered their use for instruments. These disadvantages were overcome by the modern alloys and products.

Comparatively small and intricate parts for surveying instru ments now are fabricated in aluminum alloys by casting, forging, swaging, spinning, or machining. The use of die castings with cast-in bearing-material inserts reduces the number of parts. Minor assemblies are combined into single parts, permitting more accurate manufacture and eliminating the inconvenience of parts slipping out of adjustment in service. This feature is effective because the aluminum alloys employed do not "grow" or distort with age, differing from some materials of instrument construction. Transits made from aluminum alloys have shown good stability under conditions that induce vibration.

Alloy 13 or 360 die castings are employed for transit parts such as levels, level spider, rod target, telescope housing, tripod clamps, and truss standard.

Pressure devices and recorders utilize aluminum forgings, castings, sheet, plate, structural shapes, tube, and fittings. These instruments include pressure gages, gas regulators and meters, petroleum product meters, rupture disks, recorders, and pneumatic control systems. A choice of aluminum product usually is based on individual design and specifications.

Aluminum products for gas meters, both small-capacity domestic and large-capacity, high-pressure industrial types, have been commercially available as standard production items since the early 1950's (Fig. 7). High-production, small-capacity meters employ die castings in alloy 13 or 380 as outer cases and valve plates. Larger, industrial-type, high-pressure meters usually are produced as permanent mold castings of alloy 333 or 356. For small-production runs, sand castings in the same alloys are common.

One type of die cast gas meter for small homes weighs approximately 9 lb, less than one fourth the weight of a comparable cast iron meter. In this 150-cu-ft design, the density ratio advantage of 1:3 is augmented by design details permitted by the die casting process. The aluminum meter costs less than

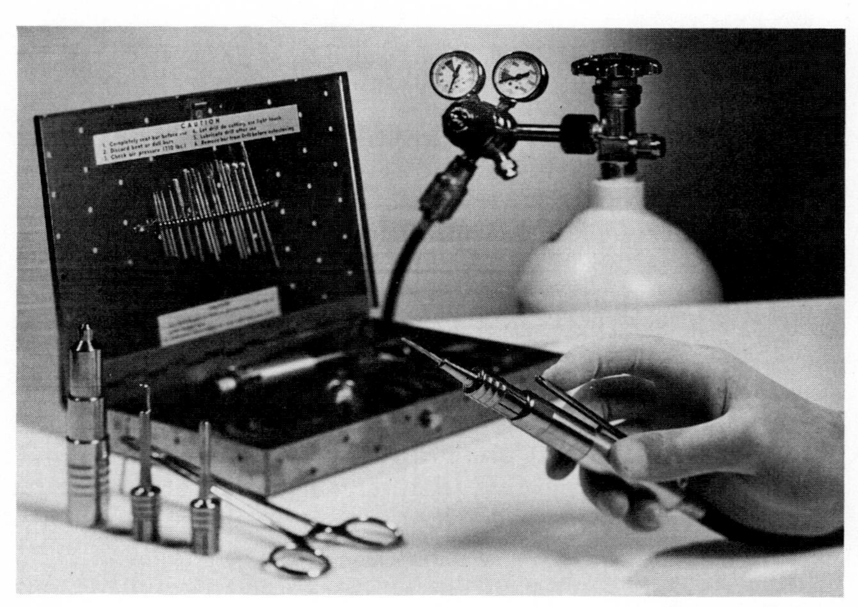

R. M. Hall Corp.

Fig. 8. The drill used by orthopedic surgeons has an aluminum body and air motor. The entire drill is autoclaved at 300 F and then chilled before use.

one fourth as much to ship as a cast iron meter. Larger industrial meters provide comparable weight reductions. One 5000-cu-ft meter with a 100-psi working pressure weighs 635 lb in cast iron and 176 lb in aluminum.

Pneumatic control systems (6, 7) utilize large quantities of aluminum tube in applications formerly dominated by copper. Lower costs and longer coil lengths than are available in copper are attractive features. However, the mechanical tube fittings used for joining aluminum control systems are more expensive than the sweat-soldered type of fitting used with copper tube.

Room-temperature and heat-curing types of high-strength adhesives are used increasingly for joining aluminum tube, replacing solder bonding or mechanical fittings. When suitable, adhesive joining procedures (Volume III, Chapter 15) provide additional economies with aluminum.

Surgical and Sanitary Equipment. Numerous medical and surgical items are manufactured in aluminum (Fig. 8). General-purpose clinical utensils and equipment are standard products, including special basins, urinals, irrigators, medicine cup racks, instrument trays, graduates, and jars for forceps, hydrometers, and thermometers. Both steam and dry sterilizers utilize aluminum alloys for many components. These sterilizers may be stationary or portable, for laboratory or small office use. A wide variety of aluminum alloys are approved by the ASME Boiler and Pressure Vessel Code (8) for sterilizer applications where design and fabrication features are governed by the code.

Aluminum is excellent for handling and storing distilled or deionized water, and operating steam condensate (9), any of which may be used in sterilizing operations. The purity of these waters and of the vapors is maintained at a high level.

The more corrosion-resistant aluminum alloys (10) are selected for surgical and sanitary applications. Alloys used for preserving water purity are 1100, 3003, 5050, 5052, 6061, or 6063, or castings of alloy 43, B214, or 356.

"Clean Rooms". In certain manufacturing operations, room temperature, relative humidity, and the size and quantity of airborne dust particles must be controlled to an exact degree to obtain products of high reliability. Clean rooms are large enclosures that provide such working environments (11). Selection of materials and equipment for these rooms is based on resistance to corrosion, flaking, peeling, and cracking. Wood is excluded; extensive use is made of anodized aluminum, stainless steel, chromium plate, porcelain, plate glass, and vinyl and acrylic plastics. Aluminum items used to construct and equip clean rooms include ductwork, exposed surfaces, door casings, handles, air-lock passages, mop handles, and ladders.

Commercial Heating, Ventilating and Refrigeration

Heating Equipment. Most heating systems and equipment utilize aluminum for one or more components. Aluminum is employed for blowers, chimney liners, ducts, electrical unit and baseboard heating, grills, heat exchangers, heat shields, instruments, mobile-home water-heating tanks, pumps, radiant ceiling systems, reflectors, regulators, and solar heaters.

Aluminum is used for direct-fired or electrically heated tanks (9, 10) where noncontamination of heating fluids, or high resistance to corrosion of metal contacting the fluids, is of primary concern. For example, in cleaning or washing certain electronic components, aluminum tanks and pipe are employed for heating and distributing distilled water. Another application is steam-jacketed cookers utilized for many years by the commercial food industry.

Aluminum and the other materials presently employed in hot-water heating equipment (8, 12, 13) are subject to corrosion by some domestic and well waters, particularly in systems where new water continually enters the equipment. The economics and expected performance of the equipment guides the selection of the most suitable materials. Alclad sheet, plate, and tube products usually are chosen for aluminum equipment in corrosive applications, because they offer superior resistance to perforation. The core alloy is typically 6061-T4, but special alclad coatings are frequently used. Dissimilar metal connections should be avoided or protection provided to eliminate galvanic corrosion. Where it is not feasible to insulate such connections electrically, disposable protector sections of 6061, 6063, or alclad (inside) 3003 are incorporated (Fig. 9).

Closed, recirculated water systems, where little or no new water is added after the system is filled, generally do not present corrosion problems as extensive as those encountered in once-through systems. In recirculated systems, nonclad aluminum products may perform well, even in the presence of common dissimilar metals, including brass, copper, and iron. This is possible when the recirculated water has become stabilized, when the metal surfaces in contact with the water have acquired a coating from the action of the water, or when the aluminum and dissimilar metal surfaces have become polarized to the same level. Stabilized water has lost an appreciable portion of its ions by precipitation and has become weak as an electrolyte for promoting galvanic action. Polarization functions as a surface barrier to the galvanic currents. A complete change of water or the addition of new water to a closed recirculating system can alter markedly these favorable conditions for a period of time.

If corrosion of aluminum is found to be a problem in a specific closed system, effective inhibitors are available (see Chapter 7, Volume I). Inhibition of the recirculated water may be econom-

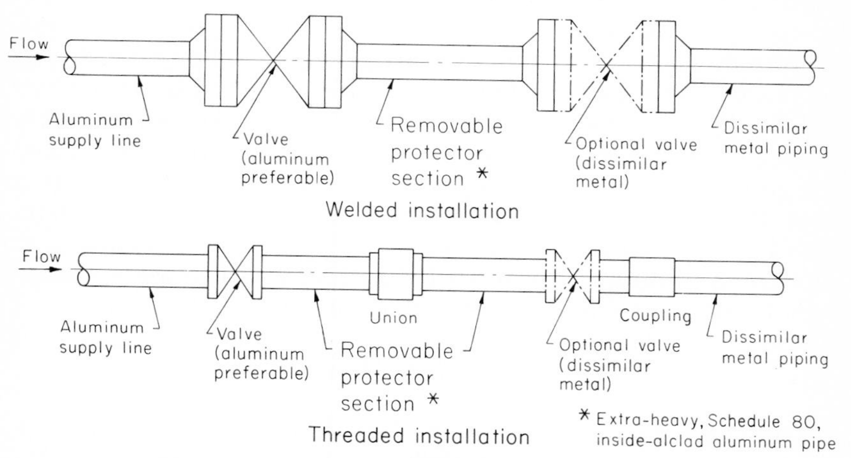

Fig. 9. Method of installing disposable protector sections between dissimilar metal piping

ically justified in installations where the light weight or high thermal conductivity of aluminum is important.

Government and industrial standards and procedures influence the use of aluminum in heating and ventilating systems.

Ventilating Equipment. Considerable tonnages of aluminum in various forms and alloys are consumed annually in fabrication and installation of blowers, ducts, fans, grills, louvers, and control systems for air-moving and conditioning equipment.

Aluminum duct, usually of an alloy selected for satisfactory formability and minimum cost, has a lower installed cost than galvanized steel sheet in certain applications, such as vertical ducts in high-rise buildings. Installation cost is reduced by handling longer lengths. In hot-air ducts, increased heat efficiency results from aluminum's low emissivity.

Some installations of air-moving equipment justify aluminum products even at a higher installed cost. For example, in textile mill systems conveying high-humidity air, no iron oxide can be tolerated, as it would stain the product.

Commercial refrigeration applications of aluminum are similar to domestic (Chapter 22, this volume).

Fire-Fighting Equipment

High reflectivity of aluminum in the infrared range is beneficial in heat-resisting emergency clothing. Suits made of asbestos cloth, shielded by a surface layer of vacuum-deposited aluminum, protect personnel entering zones of intense heat.

Pressure-containing components of highly portable, dry-chemical fire-fighting machines for airport use are formed of 5052 sheet and assembled by fusion welding. Cast hose fittings of 214-type and 612-type alloys and portable valves are available with a hard anodic coating for wear resistance and surface protection. Aerial ladders made of 2014-T6 or 6061-T6 extrusions are popular. Aluminum is also used extensively in fire truck bodies and engines (see Chapters 14 and 15 in this volume).

Materials-Handling Equipment

Bulk and Package Handling. Many of the devices in this category can handle either bulk or packaged materials. The principal types of equipment commonly constructed of aluminum include bags; barrels; baskets, pallets, skids; bins (storage and hopper); boxes and cartons; bulk cargo containers; cable reels; chutes; closed cans; conveyors (belt, bucket, roller); crates; elevators; open drums, cans, and pails; tanks and cylinders; tote trays and bins; and trucks (Fig. 10) and dollies. Some related items in aluminum are dockboards, hoists and jacks, movie reels and cans, scoops and shovels, shelving, towbars, and wheels.

The aluminum alloys used in materials-handling equipment vary with the specific application. Selection depends on requirements for strength, resistance to corrosion, forming characteristics, or other attributes pertinent to the use. Information to guide alloy selection is given in Volume I, Chapters 8 and 9, and

Chapter 4 of this volume. Sheet and plate are the forms of aluminum most widely used, although extrusions and some castings are incorporated.

Pneumatic conveyor systems (air conveyors) use air under positive or negative pressure to transport materials. Employed in their manufacture are aluminum pipe, cast or forged fittings, and structural shapes. Systems that must be dismantled periodically for inspection and cleaning utilize aluminum to reduce weight and handling costs.

The major tonnage of aluminum is in thin-wall extruded or drawn tube. Sheet, plate, and structural shapes are used for fabricating bins and hoppers. Welded tube is not acceptable unless the interior weld bead is removed to provide a uniform smooth surface contoured the same as the wall of the tube. Some materials routed through tube conveyors cause little or no wear on aluminum in the straight runs, but appreciable wear may result at abrupt changes of direction, such as at elbows and tees. The use of a more abrasion-resistant material such as steel, or bends of more generous radii, at these locations greatly alleviates this wear.

Pipe alloys include 3003-H112, 6061-T6, and 6063-T6; and structural shapes are 2014-T6 and 6061-T6. Sheet and plate

Fig. 10. An aluminum fork-lift truck that can lift its own weight (3000 lb). All structural components, including forks and fork carriage, are aluminum.

alloys and products for bins and hoppers are specified in accordance with service requirements. Where welded fabrication is desired, alloys 3003 and 6061, and various alloys of the 5*xxx* series, offer a wide selection of mechanical properties.

Mining Equipment

Aluminum's resistance to corrosion is beneficial for mining equipment because of the humid and acid conditions. Light weight is of more than usual advantage because the temporary nature of certain installations results in a large amount of moving and handling. Table 3 lists the items of mining equipment utilizing aluminum. Table 4 indicates the aluminum products and alloys, and other materials employed for mining equipment. The more corrosion-resistant alloys predominate, such as wrought alloys 3003 and 6061 and casting alloys 43, 220, and 356. The heat treatable aluminum-copper alloys are used where their high strength justifies acceptance of lower resistance to corrosion, or supplemental coating or painting.

Table 3. Items of Mining Equipment Using Aluminum

Beams for underground roof support and structures	Portable equipment
Blower, fan and ventilation pipes	Posts
Buckets	Powder for treatment of silicosis
Cable (bore-hole and feeder cable)	Pry bars
Cages	Rail benders
Cars, car loaders	Removable or portable attachments on heavy equipment
Chutes and chute liners	Roof jacks
Clamps	Safety hats
Compressors	Scaling bars
Conveyors and conveyor buckets	Screens
Drill-feed bars, housings, posts, post fittings, and rods	Shaft haulage equipment
Idler wheels and idler rolls for sheaves	Shaker conveyors
Jacks	Shovels
Ladders	Skips
Lamps	Surveying rods and stakes
Pipe—air-supply, drainage, steam, vent, water-supply	Tools
	Tramway carriers and buckets
	Wrenches

Materials Handling in Mining. In 1931, a large belt conveyor was installed in a coal mine. Six 60-ft aluminum booms carried the belts. The weight reduction compared to steel achieved sufficient savings in operating costs within a few years to recover the cost premium. Mining equipment installed at other coal mines during 1931 included cages, pit car loaders, skips (Fig. 11), vibrating screens, and tramway buckets and carriers (14). Coal mining usually is less abrasive to haulage equipment than is ore handling, but the combination of corrosion, abrasion, and rough usage in coal mining makes the applications comparable.

A mine in Renton, Pa., employed two aluminum aerial tram buckets to haul refuse and bony coal. In handling approximately 3 tons of refuse each trip, the buckets produced a significant power saving and increased the safety factor for both the cables and the supporting towers. After 10 years of service, the buckets were replaced with steel because aluminum could not be obtained for such items during the second World War. Later experience demonstrated that the aluminum buckets had dumped "cleaner" and had provided greater resistance to corrosion than the steel replacements.

Installation of aluminum conveyor buckets to replace steel in coal and coke operations has shown net economy in long service life. One foreign corporation reported that aluminum conveyor buckets remained in service six times longer than the steel buckets they replaced.

In shaft haulage equipment, light weight results in fuel savings and less wear on other components of the lifting

Table 4. Aluminum Alloys and Products Used in Mine Equipment(a)

Typical alloy	Product
6061-T6	Shapes, bars, and plate used in skips, cages, cars, roof beams, drill posts, pry bars, and other items requiring good strength
Alclad 2014-T6	Plate subjected to extremely rough usage, as in skip bodies
3003-H14	Nonstressed sheets, as in man-cage doors
6063-T5	Pipe for air, drainage, steam, vents and water supply(b)
6053-T61	Rivets(b)
2024-T4, Alumilite 205	Bolts(c)
220-T4	Castings requiring high strength, hardness, and very good corrosion resistance
356-T6	Castings requiring good strength, weldability, and very good corrosion resistance
43	Castings requiring only moderate strength, weldability, and very good corrosion resistance

(a) All bearing surfaces, wheels, shafts, wear plates, and liner plates are made in steel. Steel wear plates are used where abrasion, and not corrosion, is the principal cause of serious deterioration. (b) Steel rivets should be used only if aluminum rivets are not available. (c) A compound that meets Federal Specification TT-A-580a should be used on all pipe and bolt threads. Stainless steel or heavily galvanized steel bolts can be used.

mechanisms. Aluminum coal shovels made of alloy 6061-T6 provide adequate life while reducing personnel fatigue.

Piping Systems. Aluminum tubular products in standard and thin-wall sections were used in mining operations as early as the 1940's. Both temporary and permanent lines for water supply, drainage, air, steam, and vents employ bare and alclad alloys, including 3003, 5052, 6061, and 6063. The installations utilize such common joining procedures as threaded connections, clamping devices, and welded and flanged joints. In some of

Fig. 11. The aluminum double-bottom Kimberly skip permits a 25% weight saving over a fabricated steel skip of the same size

these piping systems, it may be necessary to insulate aluminum electrically from dissimilar metal connections, to avoid galvanic corrosion. However, where stray-current corrosion is experienced in the system, this insulation is not possible because the entire system must be electrically grounded, defeating electrical isolations. In such instances, disposable protector sections are included at dissimilar metal joints to accept the galvanic corrosion. Stray currents are more prevalent in subsurface mining operations where moisture and electrically operated equipment are present.

Structural Applications. Aluminum beams, posts, jacks, and rock bolts are familiar items in some mining areas. Sixty tons of aluminum rock bolts, washers, and nuts was used to support the roof of a 50-ft-diam discharge tunnel during construction of the Chute-des-Passes hydroelectric project in northern Quebec. The bolts were made from 6 to 12-ft lengths of 6061-T6-type alloy 1.25-in. round bar stock. Because of the high elastic limit of this alloy, these bolts are nearly as effective as mild steel and more resistant to corrosion. Grouting or other corrosion protection required for conventional rock bolts was not employed.

Roof beams in 6061-T6 are common in some mines. They are re-used and rehandled numerous times, and therefore offer long-term economies over oak or steel. Special extruded shapes can provide marked economies for mine structure assemblies.

Mining Tools. Cast and wrought aluminum products in various alloys are incorporated in clamps, drill rods, fasteners, hand-operated and pneumatic drills, pry bars, surveyors' rods and stakes, wrenches, and like tools. Aluminum's nonmagnetic characteristic is significant in the design of tool parts used in the assembly or adjustment of magnetically operated instruments.

Printing Equipment

Aluminum sheet in alloys 1100 and 3003 is employed extensively for lithographic printing plates, because of its response to a wide variety of mechanical and chemical surface treatments. The stability of the hydrophilic surface produced on aluminum litho plates is of benefit both in preparing and using the plates. Aluminum plates are prepared quickly and easily for the press, where a stable operating condition is achieved and maintained with less effort than with other litho plate materials. Light weight is a convenience in handling large plates.

Lithographic sheet is rolled to a three-quarter to full-hard temper (H26 to H19), depending on size and alloy. Such sheet has relatively high yield strength, which eliminates stretching and distortion during long press runs. Thus, register is consistent throughout the operation. High yield strength also reduces the risk of damage from buckling caused by improper handling. Aluminum litho sheet is available 0.007 to 0.029 in. thick and up to 60 in. wide.

In rotary letterpress operation, speeds were increased and plate life greatly extended by replacing much of the thickness of electrotype plates with alloy 3003-O or 5052-O sheet, resin bonded to the back of the plate. The lighter plate structure permits higher press speeds without increased rotational forces. The aluminum backup improves structural strength, offers resistance to fatigue at the plate clamps, and greatly increases plate life. This means fewer press shutdowns for plate changes on long runs.

Printing cylinders for rotogravure presses are fabricated from heavy-wall extruded tube in 6061-T6 or 6063-T6, aluminum castings in 356-T6, or, for very large cylinders, rolled and welded 6061-T6 plate. The light weight of aluminum minimizes the cost of repeated shipments between printer and engraver. The cylinders also are easily handled.

In some flat-bed letterpress equipment, cast alloy 356-T7 beds are employed, at a cost premium over conventional cast iron beds. The higher cost is justified by the high-speed operation permitted by lower inertial forces during bed reciprocation.

Cameras used in printing procedures employ aluminum castings and extrusions for structural rigidity.

Textile Machinery

In yarn preparation machinery, alloy 3003-H18 tube is used for cotton and wool card rolls. Whiteness of the oxide reduces the possibility of fiber contamination by colored corrosion products. Spinning frames utilize 6061-T6 extrusions for spindle rails, roller beams, and ring rails. With ring-rail extrusions, flanges are incorporated for stiffness to allow thin webs that facilitate subsequent blanking of openings for ring holders. The dimensional accuracy obtainable in extrusions virtually eliminates machining of these parts. Other spinning frame applications include alloy 360 die cast spindle holsters and ring holders, spindle adapters from screw-machine stock, separator blades of sheet or die castings, and numerous small parts produced as die castings or cut from extruded shapes.

In warp preparation equipment, an important development was the all-aluminum warp beam using alloy 6061-T6 extruded tube for the barrel and cast 356 or forged 6151 alloy aluminum heads (Fig. 12). These high-strength materials resist barrel pressures up to 2500 psi and beam head loads to 100,000 lb

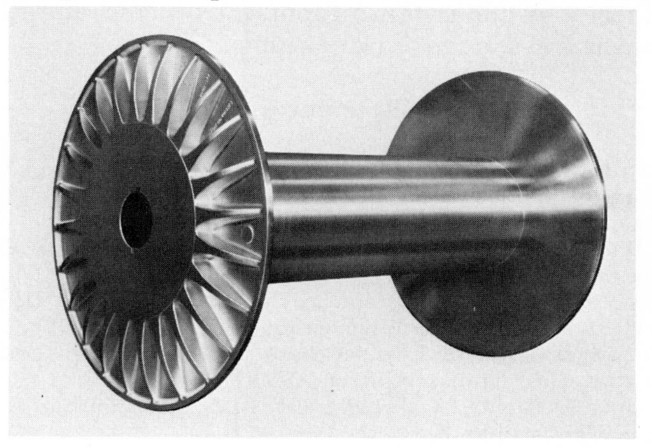

Hayes Industries, Inc.

Fig. 12. A 21-in. tricot warp beam with forged heads and extruded barrel

created by synthetic fibers. The light weight of the warp beam facilitates balancing and reduces tare weight in shipment. As with card rolls, staining of fibers is virtually eliminated.

Weaving and knitting machines have numerous components subject to oscillatory motion with consequent high accelerations. In weaving looms, aluminum lay beams of alloy 2014-T6 extrusions provide a light, fatigue-resistant structure. Their use permits higher weaving speeds with lower power consumption, and reduces deterioration of bearings and frames. Flanges are placed at several locations for attachments such as shuttle boxes and feelers. In warp knitting machines, extruded 2014-T6 or 2024-T4 needle bars reduce power consumption by lowering inertia.

Spools and bobbins of all types are made of aluminum, because they are easy to balance and have low inertia. As in warp beams, the spools must resist fiber pressure and must not stain the fibers. Alloy 6061-T832 and 6063-T6 drawn tubing are used extensively for barrels; flanges, if employed, may be fabricated from 5052 or 6061 sheet. Some spools are die cast in one piece, of 218 or 380 alloy, for special applications.

Hosiery boarding forms, used in a steam atmosphere, are generally made of alloy 2024 or 6061 sheet, to obtain good corrosion resistance in this application.

Miscellaneous applications in textile plants include sheet for ductwork and slasher hoods, sheet and extrusions for carts and trucks, sheet and tubing for lint-removal systems, and racks for the shipment and storage of warp beams.

References

1 H. Y. Hunsicker, Aluminum Alloy Bearings — Metallurgy, Design, and Service Characteristics, in "Sleeve Bearing Materials", American Society for Metals, Metals Park, Ohio, 1949

2 R. H. Wagner and W. C. Milz, "Aluminum — A Material of Construction for Lubricating Systems", Alcoa Research Laboratories

3 E. E. McDole, Use of Aluminum in Lubrication Systems Design and Specifications, Lubrication Engineering, **17**, 488–493 (1961)

4 D. W. Sawyer, Catalytic Effect of Several Metals on the Oxidation of Lubricating Oils, Transactions of ASME, **74**, 113–122 (1952)

5 Combining Durability and Lightness with Precision for Surveying Transits, Die Castings, **8**, 32–33 (Jan 1950)

6 D. W. Humphrey, Experience with Aluminum Tubing for Instrument Air Connections, Proceedings of the Instrument Society of America, **7**, 73–75 (1952)

7 E. T. Wanderer, Aluminum Piping's Applications, Heating, Piping and Air Conditioning, **25**, 116–119 (Nov 1953)

8 Section VIII, ASME Boiler and Pressure Vessel Code

9 R. H. Wagner and B. H. Wyma, "Aluminum Equipment for Handling High-Purity Water and Steam Condensate", presented at American Power Conference, Chicago, Illinois, April 27–29, 1965

10 W. W. Binger and C. M. Marstiller, Aluminum Alloys for Handling High-Purity Water, Corrosion, **13**, 591t–596t (1957)

11 R. O. Young, The Special Techniques of Clean Room Construction, Test Engineering and Management, **7**, 11–15 (May 1962)

12 C. J. Zetler, Aluminum Pipe Was the Answer, Plant Engineering, **10**, 85–86 (July 1956)

13 D. W. Sawyer and R. H. Brown, Resistance of Aluminum Alloys to Fresh Waters, Corrosion, **3**, 443–457 (1947)

14 E. P. White, Aluminum in the Mining Industry, Engineering and Mining Journal, **149**, 85–89 (July 1948)

Chapter 21

Electrical and Electronic Applications

H. H. CALDWELL

COPPER was the metal first used for conductors during the great development of electrical engineering in the early 1880's. However, the simultaneous rapid growth of the aluminum industry soon reduced the price of aluminum so that it could compete in electrical conductor applications.

For overhead transmission lines, aluminum is now used almost to the exclusion of copper. Although the increasing use of aluminum bus conductor is credited largely to economics, advances in joining techniques and general experience have prompted its use in many manufacturing, chemical, and utility installations. The most recent aluminum conductor development, magnet strip, owes its success to savings in coil manufacturing costs as well as to the lower initial cost of aluminum.

Many other electrical, mechanical, and structural applications of aluminum in electrical industries developed along with the growth of aluminum wire and cable. Non-current-carrying applications of aluminum are numerous in transformers, capacitors, motors, and other types of electrical equipment.

Wire and Cable

The use of aluminum for overhead transmission and distribution conductors in the United States is almost as old as the

H. H. Caldwell is a sales engineer, Aluminum Company of America, Pittsburgh.

D. H. Sandell, formerly senior transmission engineer, Rome Cable Div., Aluminum Company of America, Rome, N. Y., assisted in the preparation of this chapter.

aluminum industry itself. As early as 1895, when the price of aluminum per pound was about five times that of copper, the Pittsburgh Reduction Company sponsored electrical resistance tests at the laboratories of the Westinghouse Electric and Manufacturing Company and at Lehigh University. Data on copper and aluminum wires were obtained and translated to commercial comparisons. The favorable attributes of aluminum for electrical applications are: relatively high electrical and thermal conductivities, low density, nonmagnetic properties, ease of drawing down to the smaller wire sizes, and high resistance to weathering.

The first recorded sale of aluminum conductor occurred in April 1897: One half mile of solid No. 11 gage aluminum telephone wire was installed at the Chicago Stock Yards, where locomotive gases corroded copper wire.

Because of technological advances and favorable price as compared to copper, there has been continuous significant growth in the volume, sizes and varieties of aluminum conductors. Bare stranded conductor for power transmission and distribution consumed the major portion of the 180,000 tons of aluminum conductor sold in the United States in 1963.

Aluminum Conductor Materials. It was early learned that the electrical resistivity of aluminum is markedly increased by impurities; electrical conductor grade (EC) metal, containing approximately 99.5% Al, was established for most conductor uses. At present, aluminum producers offer EC with a minimum of 99.6% Al and conductivity of 62.0% IACS on a volume basis, although ASTM specifications permit 99.45% Al minimum and 61.0% conductivity. EC wire has a tensile strength range of 12,000 to 29,000 psi, depending on temper.

In the 1920's, experiments were made with an aluminum-magnesium-silicon heat treatable alloy for electrical conductors. With higher strength and lower conductivity than EC, these conductors found favor in Europe but only minor use in the United States, because of lack of economic incentive.

Transmission Conductor. The first major aluminum transmission line was completed in 1898: a 46-mile, three-phase line for the Standard Electric Company of California, from Blue Lakes to Stockton. In 1899, the Hartford Electric Light Company built a line (still in service) using a seven-strand all-aluminum EC-type conductor, each strand 0.221 in. in diameter. Aluminum overhead line was erected according to the standards used for

(Top) Typical smaller size of ACSR of 300,000 cir mils, 26/7 (aluminum strands/steel core strands), and two 500-kv EHV conductors. The large EHV conductor is 2⅜-in.-diam 108/37 ACSR and the special design is 2½-in.-diam air-expanded ACSR.

(Bottom) Expanded 2⅛-in. conductors used in 460-kv experimental test lines. From left, aluminum alloy conductor stranded around a flexible aluminum conduit; paper-expanded ACSR; rope lay-expanded EC aluminum conductor.

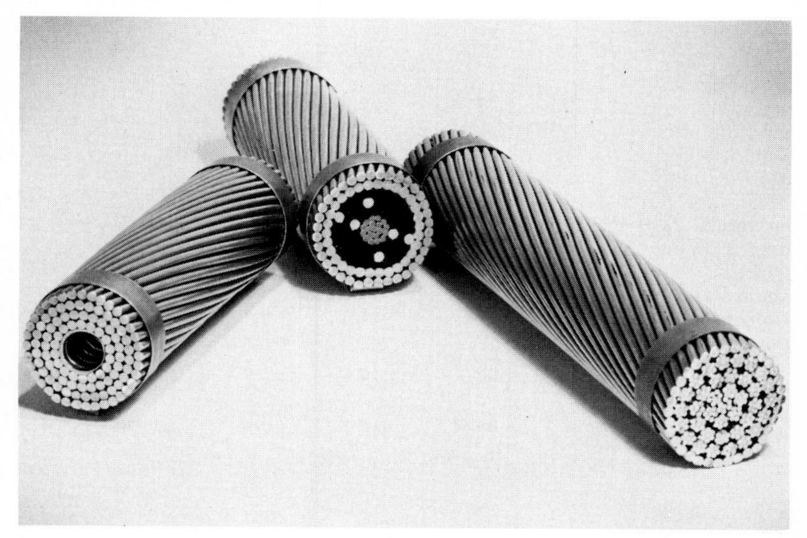

Fig. 1. ACSR (*aluminum conductor , steel reinforced*)

Table 1. Properties of Electrical Wires

Electrical Properties

Wire type	Conductivity, % IACS (min) 20 C	Resistivity, ohms: cir mil per ft 20 C	cir mil per ft 25 C	sq mm per m 20 C	sq mm per m 25 C	Temperature coefficient of resistance, per °C 20 C	25 C
Commercial EC aluminum wire..	62.0	16.727	17.069	0.027808	0.028377	0.00410	0.00401
Aluminum alloy 5005 wire(a)....	53.5	19.385	19.727	0.032226	0.032795	0.00353	0.00346
Aluminum alloy 6201 wire(b)....	53.5	19.754	20.097	0.032840	0.033373	0.00347	0.00340
Commercial hard-drawn copper wire...........	97.0	10.692	10.895	0.017774	0.018113	0.00381	0.00374
Standard annealed copper wire.....	100.0	10.371	10.575	0.017241	0.017579	0.00393	0.00385
Aluminum and zinc-coated steel core wire.......	9.0(c)	115.23	...	0.19157	...	...	...
Aluminum-clad core wire.......	20.33	51.01	51.52	0.0848	0.08563	0.0020	0.00198

Physical Properties Other Than Electrical

Wire type	Density at 20 C (68 F): g per cu cm	lb per cu in.	lb per million cir mils per 1000 ft	Coefficient of linear expansion, millionths per deg F	C	Modulus of elasticity: million psi	kg per sq mm
Commercial EC aluminum wire..	2.703	0.09765	920.3	12.8	23.0	10	7030
Aluminum alloy 5005 wire(a)....	2.703	0.09765	920.3	12.8	23.0	10	7030
Aluminum alloy 6201 wire(b)....	2.703	0.09765	920.3	12.8	23.0	10	7030
Commercial hard-drawn copper wire...........	8.89	0.321	3027	9.4	16.9	17	11950
Standard annealed copper wire.....	8.89	0.321	3027	9.4	16.9	17	11950
Aluminum and zinc-coated steel core wire.......	7.78	0.281	2649	6.4	11.5	29	20400
Aluminum-clad core wire.......	6.59	0.2380	2243	7.2	13.0	23.5	16500

(a) 0.8% Mg. (b) 0.7% Si, 0.75% Mg. (c) Typical.

copper; while many miles were strung in the early 1900's by these standards, all did not operate successfully. All-aluminum stranded conductors, although having the advantage of light weight, had to be strung with large sags, because of their low yield strength compared to stranded copper.

Experiments were conducted with several alloys of aluminum, and with combinations of aluminum with other metals, to obtain higher mechanical strength combined with suitable electrical characteristics. These experiments culminated in the development of aluminum conductor, steel reinforced (ACSR), introduced to the industry in 1909 with the sale of some No. 2 AWG (American Wire Gage) ACSR to the Western Ohio Railway Corporation for a 33-kv transmission line. The new conductor was accepted immediately by many engineers for use on the expanding transmission systems. A typical ACSR section is shown in Fig. 1.

A record-making early sale of ACSR was negotiated with the Southern California Edison Company for its Big Creek Line, completed in 1913. The conductor was 605,000 cir mils ACSR, consisting of 54 aluminum wires in three layers over a seven-strand steel core. For years it was the world's longest and highest-voltage line, operating at 150 kv and consisting of two 240-mile circuits. Voltage was increased to 220 kv in 1922; for many more years it continued to be the highest-voltage ACSR line in the world. It is still operating.

The core wire originally used for ACSR was Grade A double-galvanized steel. The early Alcoa specification for the galvanized steel formed the basis for the present ASTM specification for galvanized steel core wire.

Aluminized and aluminum-clad core wires recently have been employed to reinforce aluminum conductors. For many years, it was believed that a superior ACSR could be produced if the zinc coating of the steel wire were replaced with aluminum. In 1957, hot-dipped aluminum-coated (aluminized) steel wire was produced as an acceptable core wire for ACSR. The excellent resistance to atmospheric corrosion of aluminized wire resulted in its acceptance for service in coastal and severely corrosive industrial atmospheres. Aluminized steel core wire is covered by ASTM B 341.

Another method of covering steel wire incorporates an aluminum cladding that is about 10% of the composite diameter, representing approximately 25% of the total cross section,

Table 2. Tensile Property Specifications for EC Aluminum Wire

Nominal wire diameter, in.	Hard-drawn aluminum wire, EC-H19 (ASTM B 230) Tensile strength, psi (min) Average for a lot	Individual tests	Elongation in 10 in. for individual tests, % (min)	Three-quarter-hard aluminum wire, EC-H2 (ASTM B 262) Tensile strength, psi Min	Max	Half-hard aluminum wire, EC-H24 (ASTM B 323) Tensile strength, psi Min	Max
0.2600–0.2101	23,500	22,500	2.2	17,000	22,000	15,000	20,000
0.2100–0.1601	24,000	23,000	2.0	17,000	22,000	15,000	20,000
0.1600–0.1501	24,000	23,000	1.9	17,000	22,000	15,000	20,000
0.1500–0.1401	24,500	23,500	1.8	17,000	22,000	15,000	20,000
0.1400–0.1201	25,000	23,500	1.7	17,000	22,000	15,000	20,000
0.1200–0.1101	25,500	24,000	1.6	17,000	22,000	15,000	20,000
0.1100–0.1001	26,000	24,500	1.5	17,000	22,000	15,000	20,000
0.1000–0.0901	27,000	25,500	1.5	17,000	22,000	15,000	20,000
0.0900–0.0801	27,500	26,000	1.5	17,000	22,000	15,000	20,000
0.0800–0.0701	28,000	26,500	1.4	17,000	22,000	15,000	20,000
0.0700–0.0601	28,500	27,000	1.3	17,000	22,000	15,000	20,000
0.0600–0.0501	29,000	27,000	1.2	17,000	22,000	15,000	20,000
0.0500–0.0105	25,000	23,000	..	17,000	22,000	15,000	20,000

bonded to a high-strength steel core. It is utilized as a highly corrosion-resistant core for ACSR, and as an overhead ground wire for transmission and distribution lines.

In recent years, both heat treatable alloy 6201-T81 (0.7% Si, 0.75% Mg) and non-heat-treatable 5005-H19 (0.8% Mg) have been employed as stranded aluminum conductors for transmission and distribution lines. Material selection involves comparing the estimated installed cost of these and other conductors with expected service requirements, considering current-carrying capacity, thermal overload characteristics, line electric-energy losses, and atmospheric exposure characteristics.

The physical and electrical properties of EC metal, 5005 and 6201 alloys, and steel core wires are compared in Table 1 with those of copper. The tensile properties of EC, 5005 and 6201 wires are given in Tables 2, 3 and 4.

Rapid expansion of extra-high-voltage (EHV)* transmission lines in recent years has given impetus to prospects of a nationwide supertransmission grid. The EHV program helped to create a need for unusual conductor designs, and a larger demand for overhead aluminum conductors than might have accompanied the normal growth of electric energy consumption alone.

* Presently defined as lines operating at 345 kv and higher

A grid employing EHV transmission lines now connects most sources of electric power generation in the United States. Thus, if a power failure occurs in a major generating plant in one region of the country, adjacent plants, systems, and regions should assume the load without interruption.

Utilities can participate most effectively in this grid service if they operate at the highest voltages possible. The load capacity of a line varies approximately with the square of the operating

Table 3. Tensile Property Specifications for Aluminum Alloy Wire 5005-H19 (ASTM B 396)

Nominal wire diameter, in.	Tensile strength, psi (min) Average for a lot	Individual tests	Elongation in 10 in. for individual tests, % (min)
0.2600–0.2101	33,000	31,500	2.2
0.2100–0.1601	34,000	32,500	2.0
0.1600–0.1501	36,000	34,500	1.9
0.1500–0.1401	36,500	35,000	1.8
0.1400–0.1201	37,000	35,000	1.7
0.1200–0.1101	37,500	35,500	1.6
0.1100–0.1001	38,000	36,000	1.5
0.1000–0.0901	38,500	36,500	1.5
0.0900–0.0801	39,000	37,000	1.5
0.0800–0.0701	39,500	37,500	1.4
0.0700–0.0601	40,000	38,000	1.3

Table 4. Tensile Property Specifications for Aluminum Alloy Wire 6201-T81 (ASTM B 398)

Nominal wire diameter, in.	Tensile strength, psi (min) Average for a lot	Individual tests	Elongation in 10 in. for individual tests, % (min)
0.1883–0.1318	46,000	44,000	3.0
0.1317–0.0657	48,000	46,000	3.0

voltage: A 500-kv line carries more than four times the power of a 230-kv line (1). To operate successfully at higher voltages, the conductor must be sufficiently large, either singly or in bundles, to avoid creating too high a voltage stress on the air surrounding the conductor. When voltage stress is too high, the air gases ionize and produce a luminescent phenomenon, termed corona.

Corona discharges from the conductor represent a direct energy loss, and also may cause annoying radio interference.

Examples of conductors that have been used for EHV lines are illustrated in Fig. 1 (on page 519, top figure). Single

Fig. 2. Bundled four-conductor installation. The spacers used (inset), which maintain separation between grouped conductors, are typical of several designs, and consist of aluminum clamps at the ends of helical stainless steel springs.

aluminum conductors as large as 2.5 in. in diameter and 4 million cir mils in cross section are required for these lines. Bundled conductors employed in EHV lines provide the same equivalent cross section and diameter by combining up to four conductors. Bundled conductors are usually separated about 13 to 18 in. to achieve balance of mechanical and electrical properties (Fig. 2).

Distribution Conductor. Although transmission lines have dominated the technical literature, distribution conductors are the major product of many cable manufacturers. One estimate is that two pounds of conductor is needed for distribution for every pound employed in transmission.

The use of aluminum conductors for urban distribution has increased rapidly since World War II, stimulated by the change in the aluminum-copper price relationship. The per-pound price of copper, formerly much lower than that of aluminum, has been as high or higher than that of aluminum since the end of World War II. Aluminum has over twice the conductivity of copper on a weight basis, and aluminum conductor is used for virtually all overhead subtransmission and distribution lines.

For many years, predating even the introduction of ACSR, weatherproof distribution conductors were covered with cotton braid and impregnated with asphalt. After World War II, the cotton braided coverings were displaced by neoprene and, later, by polyethylene. In addition to excellent weathering characteristics, neoprene and (especially) polyethylene have high electrical insulating properties.

Utilizing these properties, multiplex cable, a new secondary and service-drop multiple conductor, was developed. These cables are either duplex, triplex, or quadruplex, consisting of one, two or three insulated conductors wrapped around a bare aluminum or ACSR neutral. The bare neutral acts as the messenger, supporting the entire cable when strung as an aerial line.

Although bare conductor is employed on many distribution lines, weatherproof conductors or insulated multiplex overhead cables are more popular.

Connection, support, and protection of overhead transmission and distribution conductors require both mechanical and electrical terminating and joining devices, as well as means for frequent electrical connections at intermediate points. At pole or tower supports, the conductors must be tied into the insulator grooves or held securely in clamps. At these same locations,

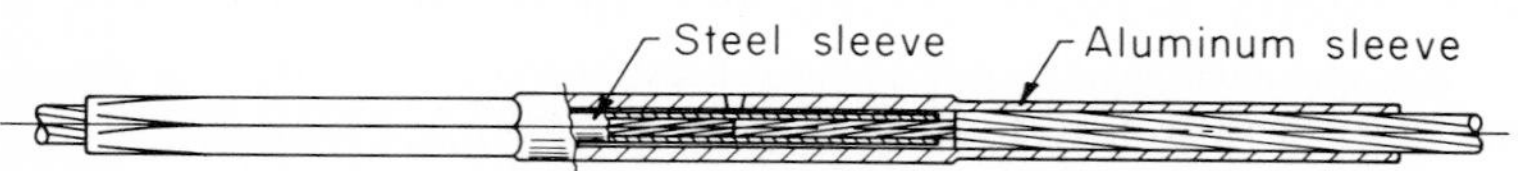

(Top) Applying dead end to large 2½-in. EHV conductor with powered compression equipment. (Bottom) Cross section of tubular compression joint for ACSR. The steel sleeve is compressed on the core, and the aluminum sleeve is compressed at both ends over the entire conductor.

Fig. 3. Aluminum conductor accessories

protection from vibration, wear, and flashover burning is usually required. If conductors are bundled for either high-voltage or high-current applications, suitable spacing devices are needed.

The aluminum alloys employed for conductor accessories, including drawn, extruded, and cast products, vary with the specific application and with the preferences of the individual manufacturer. However, the alloys are generally selected to provide suitable conductivity, high resistance to atmospheric corrosion, galvanic compatibility with conductor grade (EC) aluminum, and satisfactory mechanical properties. Typical suitable alloys are 6061-T6 for wrought forms and 356-T6 for castings.

A compression joint correctly applied to stranded conductor develops tensile strength approximating that of the conductor. The electrical resistance of a completed joint is less than that of an equal length of the conductor. A compression connector for an all-aluminum conductor consists of a cast, extruded, or drawn aluminum tube into which the conductor ends are placed; the tube is then compressed with suitable tools. A compression joint for ACSR includes a steel tube for the core and an aluminum sleeve over the entire conductor (Fig. 3).

Aluminum clamps, frequently 356-T6, are preferred to other metals for supporting stranded aluminum conductors. They eliminate heating and power waste from hysteresis losses that occur in ferrous materials. Because the use of dissimilar metals is avoided, the possibility of galvanic corrosion is minimized. The body and keeper components of suspension clamps and dead-end clamps are aluminum castings or forgings. The bolts and other hardware may be aluminum or one of the other common metals (Volume III, Chapter 11). Compression-type dead-end connectors employ cast or tubular aluminum parts in combination with the necessary steel members. Hardware items such as pins and bolts usually are steel.

Terminal and T connectors for stranded cable include a wide variety of bolted or compression devices. The main bodies and keepers are either aluminum castings or extrusions, depending on the required configurations. The hardware is aluminum or steel. On bolted aluminum connectors, aluminum fasteners have the same coefficient of thermal expansion as the rest of the assembly, thus maintaining uniform tightness at different temperatures. Tubular compression T connectors and terminals usually are assemblies of cast, drawn tubular, or extruded components. Field welding often is convenient and economical. Accessories are either aluminum castings or wrought shapes.

Aluminum armor rods are spiraled around the conductors at points of support. They provide some vibration damping and reinforce the conductors against the effect of vibration. Two general types of armor rods are available. One is straight rods that are applied by winding them on the conductor with special wrenches. The other is pre-formed during manufacture, and usually can be worked into place on the conductor by hand. The pre-formed type is generally easier to install; however, the straight rods applied with wrenches have considerably better damping characteristics. Rods have additional useful functions, including protection of the conductors from flashover damage and mechanical wear at points of support, and restoring the strength and conductivity of conductors where strands have been previously damaged.

Insulated aluminum conductors require a wide variety of terminals. Bolt-type connectors frequently are alloy 356-T6 castings with aluminum, steel or copper alloy bolts. Most types of set screw connectors are extruded 6*xxx* series alloy sections with aluminum, steel, or copper alloy screws. Aluminum components are preferred for terminals intended for use on either aluminum or copper conductors. These terminal components are often tin plated, or occasionally cadmium plated, in an effort to provide stable, low contact resistance. Compression-type aluminum fittings are excellent for aluminum-to-aluminum joints and have a good record for aluminum-to-copper joints. These fittings should be manufactured of high-conductivity aluminum, such as EC, in a relatively soft temper. Compression splices are usually tubular sections; compression terminals are castings, or drawn and partially flattened tube.

Insulated Power Cable. Aluminum conductors have been used in insulated cables for nearly 60 years in Europe and for at least 35 years in the United States. Today the choice between aluminum and copper for the metal in insulated conductors is based primarily on cost considerations for the particular application. The cost comparison should be based on the final installed cost of the circuits involved. For a specific application, the construction of insulated cable with aluminum conductor is essentially the same as that with copper conductor. However, there usually is a difference in conductor size, compensating for aluminum's lower electrical conductivity.

The minimum conductivity of EC grade aluminum is 62.0% that of copper. A convenient and reasonably accurate guide derived from this relationship is that, for equal voltage drop, an aluminum conductor should be two AWG sizes larger than a given copper conductor.

If, however, circuit design is based primarily on ampacity (current-carrying capacity), conductor size is determined by the temperature rating of the cable and its rate of heat dissipation. The ampacity of a cable of specific size depends on the details of construction and on the metal used for the conductor. For insulated cables of identical size and construction, those with aluminum conductors have 78 to 84% the ampacity of those with copper conductors. Thus, for equal ampacity an aluminum conductor need be only about one AWG size larger than a copper conductor. Complete ampacity tables for power cables with aluminum conductors have been published jointly by the Insulated Power Cable Engineers Association and the American Institute of Electrical Engineers (2).

Splicing and terminating procedures for insulated aluminum conductors differ from those used for copper. All manufacturers of aluminum cable furnish detailed instructions and recommendations for these operations.

The aluminum conductors normally used in insulated cable are EC grade, in either the H24 or H26 temper. Where unusually high strength is required, 5005 or 6201 alloy, or sometimes ACSR,

Table 5. ASTM Specifications for Aluminum Conductors Used in Insulated Cable

ASTM designation	Title
B 262	Three-quarter-hard aluminum wire for electrical purposes
B 323	Half-hard aluminum wire for electrical purposes
B 231	Concentric lay-stranded aluminum conductors
B 232	Concentric lay-stranded aluminum conductors, steel-reinforced (ACSR)
B 396	Aluminum alloy 5005-H19 wire for electrical purposes
B 397	Concentric lay-stranded aluminum alloy 5005-H19 conductors
B 398	Aluminum alloy 6201-T81 wire for electrical purposes
B 399	Concentric lay-stranded aluminum alloy 6201-T81 conductors

is used. A list of ASTM specifications for the various conductor types and strandings employed for insulated conductors is given in Table 5. The most common specifications for conductors in insulated cables are B 323 for solid conductors and B 231 for stranded conductors.

Specifications for the construction of insulated power cables are issued jointly by the Insulated Power Cable Engineers Association and the National Electrical Manufacturers Association (3, 4). These and other industry specifications provide for aluminum conductors in virtually all types of insulated power cable, including those insulated with plastics, rubber, paper, or varnished cambric.

Construction wire and cable includes types commonly known as building wire, service entrance cable, and nonmetallic-sheathed cable. Wire gages range from No. 14 AWG to 1 million cir mils for building wire, No. 6-1/0 for service entrance cable, and No. 4-14 for nonmetallic-sheathed cable. The use of aluminum conductors in these products is recognized in appropriate sections of the National Electrical Code. Specifications for each of these product types are published by Underwriters' Laboratories, Inc., to assure compliance with the National Electrical Code.

Communication Cable. Most telephone cables require a metallic shielding over the assembled conductors for electrical reasons. Alloy 1100 is used widely for this purpose, typically as a strip of sheet about 0.008 in. thick, folded longitudinally around the cable and held in place by an outer sheath of extruded thermoplastic material, such as polyethylene or polyvinyl chloride. The shield may be corrugated if desired, to provide improved flexibility.

Co-axial cables for high-frequency communication and data transmission typically consist of a central conductor surrounded by insulation and an outer conductor that forms a concentric sheath. For some applications, there is a protective covering over the outer conductor. Aluminum is widely used as the outer conductor of such cables, and is almost always much more economical than copper. It is applied either as a longitudinally folded strip, as in shielding of telephone cable, or in other forms described subsequently for aluminum-sheathed cables.

Specialty Wire and Cable. There are several specialty wire and cable constructions where aluminum may be advantageous for one or more components.

For example, portable power cables and welding cables having aluminum conductors usually cost appreciably less than equivalent copper-conductor cables. Conductor weight is reduced almost half by using aluminum instead of copper. The aluminum cable is larger in diameter when the lower conductivity of aluminum makes this necessary.

Applications of aluminum for wire and cable exist where the diameter difference is small or unimportant and the lighter weight of the aluminum cable is of major significance. If ultimate fatigue failure of the cable is expected, as a result of repeated flexing, somewhat shorter life is anticipated.

Cable Sheathing. An aluminum sheath often is more economical than other metal sheaths, and may provide several other advantages. Aluminum's high conductivity permits it to be used as a neutral or grounding conductor, while providing the necessary mechanical protection. In high-frequency co-axial cable, the aluminum sheath serves as a circuit conductor.

IPCEA specifications for insulated cable provide for aluminum sheaths. The National Electrical Code recognizes aluminum sheathed cable (type ALS) and permits the use of aluminum as a sheath on metal-clad cable (type MC). Alloy 1060 or 1080 is commonly selected for sheathing.

Aluminum sheathing can be applied by extrusion and by several other methods. In one process, the cable first is pulled into a length of seamless aluminum tube having an inside diameter slightly larger than the cable. In another, a strip of aluminum is formed continuously around the cable as a longitudinal fold; the butting edges are continuously joined as the assembly passes through welding electrodes. With both processes, the assembly is then drawn through a die to reduce the sheath until it grips the cable. The die can be replaced with a corrugating device to produce a corrugated sheath. In a third method, a narrow strip of aluminum is wrapped helically around the cable and formed with the overlapping edges of the strip interlocked. All these configurations may employ an outer protective nonmetallic covering, depending on use.

Bus Conductors

What is believed to be the first aluminum bus system in the world for industrial use was installed in 1895 for conducting direct current to the aluminum reduction cells at the Niagara Works of Pittsburgh Reduction Company (5). Aluminum busbars subsequently were employed widely for connections to direct-current conversion equipment and in aluminum smelter installations, heavy-duty feeder lines, and switchboards. Since the mid-1950's, aluminum bus has been employed increasingly in a wide variety of manufacturing, chemical, and utility installations. This recent growth is credited largely to economics: aluminum bus now costs only one third to one half as much as equivalent copper bus.

Bus Conductor Materials. Aluminum bus conductors are produced in different grades of aluminum and in several alloys. Physical properties are given in Table 6; mechanical properties, in Table 7.

The strength of EC aluminum is controlled by the amount of cold work introduced; conductivity decreases slightly with increasing strength. EC in the H12, H111 and H112 tempers is used primarily for low-voltage, high-current buses where conductivity is important. EC-H13 is preferred where somewhat greater strength and close dimensional tolerances are required.

Alloy 6101, also designated 2EC, is an aluminum-magnesium-silicon alloy with minor impurities controlled to give a guaranteed minimum conductivity of 55 to 60% IACS, depending on temper. The T6 temper of 6101 (55% conductivity) is used primarily for enclosed buses, where both high strength and high conductivity are important. The T63 temper (56% conductivity) is employed where more critical forming characteristics are required. The T61 temper (57% conductivity) is the general-purpose temper for applications where higher strength is not required. The T64 temper has the highest conductivity of the alloy conductors (59.5% IACS), along with excellent formability.

Since 1946, 6063-T6 has gradually displaced 1100-H18 for tubular bus conductors. Alloy 6063-T6 is about 45% stronger than 1100-H18; its current-carrying capacity is only 3% lower. Alloy 6061-T6 tubular conductor is recommended where still higher strength is desired and conductivity requirements are

Table 6. Physical Properties of Aluminum Bus Conductor Alloys

Property	EC grade	6101 T6	6101 T61	6101 T63, T8	6101 T64	6063-T6	6061-T6
Electrical conductivity at 20 C, % IACS (min)	62.0	55.0	57.0	56.0	59.5	53(a)	40(a)
Electrical resistivity at 20 C, microhms/sq in./ft (max)	13.137	14.81	14.29	14.55	13.69	15.37(a)	20.36(a)
Temperature coefficient of electrical resistivity at 20 C, per °C	0.00410	0.00363	0.00377	0.00370	0.00393	0.00350	0.00264
Thermal conductivity at 20 C, w/sq in./in./°C (min)	6.0	5.3	5.5	5.4	5.7	5.1	3.9
Weight at 20 C, lb/cu in. (typical)	0.098	0.098	0.098	0.098	0.098	0.098	0.098
Specific gravity at 20 C (typical)	2.70	2.70	2.70	2.70	2.70	2.70	2.70
Coefficient of linear expansion, millionths per °C (typical)	23	23	23	23	23	23	23
Modulus of elasticity, million psi (typical)	10	10	10	10	10	10	10

(a) Typical value

Table 7. Mechanical Properties of Aluminum Bus Conductor Alloys

Alloy and temper	Bar thickness, in.	Tube wall thickness, in.	Minimum strength, psi	
			Tensile	Yield (Offset = 0.2%)
EC-H111	All	All	8,500	3,500
EC-H112	0.125 to 0.500	...	11,000	6,000
	0.501 to 1.000	...	10,000	4,000
	1.001 to 1.500	...	9,000	3,500
EC-H12	0.125 to 1.000	...	12,000	8,000
EC-H13	0.125 to 0.750	...	13,000	11,000
EC-H17	0.125 to 0.500	...	17,000	15,000
6101-T6	0.125 to 0.500	...	29,000	25,000
6101-T61	0.125 to 0.749	...	20,000	15,000
	0.750 to 1.499	...	18,000	11,000
	1.500 to 2.000	...	15,000	8,000
6101-T63	0.125 to 0.500	...	27,000	22,000
6101-T64	0.125 to 1.000	...	15,000	8,000
6101-T8	0.125 to 0.500	...	29,000	25,000
6061-T6 (extruded)	...	All	38,000	35,000
6063-T6	...	Up through 0.500	30,000	25,000

lower. Where maximum conductivity is required and the low strength is acceptable, EC aluminum is recommended. Where both strength and high conductivity are important, alloy 6101 frequently offers the most suitable combination.

Forms of Bus Conductor. The most common form of aluminum bus is extruded rectangular bar. Rolled bar and plate, and cast bar are also produced. Rectangular bus conductors are easy to fabricate, store, handle and install. Through multiple-bar design, a large surface can be provided for dissipation of heat. Joints and taps are made readily by simple overlapping. Rectangular bus bar usually is fabricated from EC metal or 6101 alloy. Temper selection is based primarily on strength and bending characteristics desired for fabrication and installation.

Round tubular aluminum bus offers advantages that have led to its wide adoption for outdoor substation and switching station construction. It is typically ¾ to 6-in. extruded Schedule 40 pipe. Its shape provides equal rigidity in all directions, which is of advantage in withstanding ice, wind and short-circuit loads that can occur in almost any installation. The smooth, curved surface helps prevent corona discharge at high voltages. In the design of high-voltage switching stations, long bus spans are utilized to reduce the number of supporting structures. Because current-carrying requirements are relatively low, thin-wall aluminum tube can be used to advantage. Its rigidity prevents unsightly sags in spans. Tubular shapes also are employed for heavy-duty generator and switching bus in central stations. However, square tubes are popular because their flat surfaces simplify the making of bolted connections.

Rolled structural shapes were introduced for electrical conductors in 1928. One type, channel bus, combines a pair of EC or 6101 aluminum channels into a hollow, ventilated square (Fig. 4). Channel flanges are placed toe-to-toe, with a small gap between them. This box-shaped conductor has high strength and rigidity (high resistance to short-circuit forces) when the channel flanges are connected by either a continuous lacing system or sufficient spacers to make the assembly perform as a box girder. Long spans can be designed readily. Channel bus is efficient and practical for high-amperage direct or alternating current, especially above 2000 amp per circuit. It approaches the high electrical efficiency of a split tube, with the added convenience of flat surfaces for making taps and connections.

Fig. 4. First installation in the United States of aluminum channel conductors; installed in 1930 and still in operation. Three-phase, 440-volt circuits consist of pairs of ½ by 5-in. aluminum channels supported on insulated pipe by aluminum clamps.

Public Service Electric and Gas Co.

Fig. 5. Post-type insulators with special rectangular caps eliminate need for bus support clamps in suspending 11-in.-square IWCB (integral web channel bus).

In industrial plants of limited space, it often is desirable to install power distribution buses on roof trusses, building columns, or similar locations where no working space is consumed. Aluminum channel conductors are more conveniently proportioned and generally require less space than equivalent "modified hollow squares" assembled from rectangular bars. The lightness and rigidity of aluminum channel bus conductor usually permit installation on existing roof trusses without changes in the building structure. It also is convenient for bus risers and generator leads.

For direct-current circuits, where skin effect is not a factor, aluminum channels sometimes are placed back-to-back, with flanges pointing outward. The channels provide the section modulus necessary to resist short-circuit forces. Additional cur-

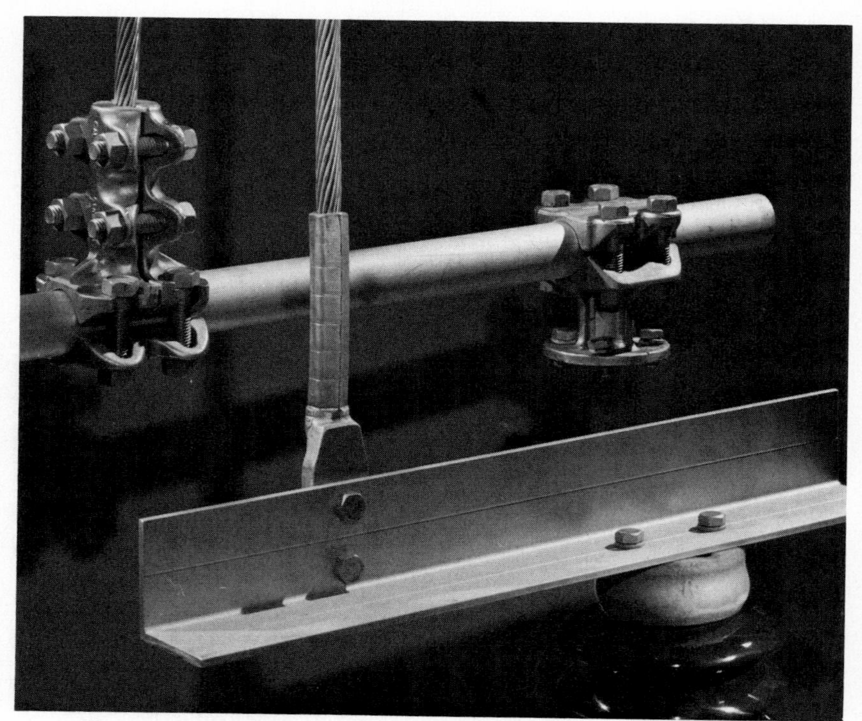

Fig. 6. Installation ease of taps and supports for UABC (universal angle bus conductor), in the foreground, is contrasted with fittings used for conventional tubular bus.

rent capacity is obtained readily merely by adding one or more flat bars, properly spaced, between the webs of the two channels. For enclosed station buses where the space occupied by the conductor is critical, channel of uniform section thickness may be desirable. This type has a small inside corner radius, providing maximum inside flat surface for connections.

Integral web channel bus (IWCB) is an extrusion of EC or 2EC in which two channel-shaped conductors are connected by a ventilated crossweb (Fig. 5). It is particularly suitable where short-circuit forces are high, because of its high section modulus both in the plane of the crossweb and of the channel webs. Its principal use is for generator leads and substation conductors.

Universal angle bus conductor (UABC) is an extruded shape having equal legs and flat surfaces that facilitate the making of bolted electrical connections (Fig. 6). It is used principally in low-voltage distribution substations. The economy of angle bus construction is derived from the elimination of expensive fittings required with tubular bus construction.

Bus conductor size usually is selected on the basis either of temperature rise, minimum voltage drop, or cost of power loss. Tables of current-carrying capacity of various bus sizes for standard temperature rise are given in suppliers' handbooks. For practical purposes, copper bus bar size can be converted approximately to aluminum bus bar size for equal temperature rise by either of the two following methods:

1 Increase the width of the aluminum bar 25%. For example, a 5 by ¼-in. aluminum bar is equivalent to a 4 by ¼-in. copper bar.
2 Increase the thickness of the aluminum bar about 50%. A 4 by ⅜-in. aluminum bar is equivalent to a 4 by ¼-in. copper bar.

The ratio of cross-sectional area required for equal direct-current voltage drop is inversely proportional to conductivity. For the same voltage drop, an EC aluminum conductor should have about 1.6 times the cross section of a copper conductor. Unless voltage drop is critical, it is practical to use a figure of 50% for the cross-sectional area increase for aluminum.

The cost of energy lost through resistance is important where high currents are involved, as in the electrochemical industry. In such applications, economy may dictate the use of conductors at less than their temperature limits. That is, selection of conductor size may be based on compromising between power loss and conductor cost. The most economical conductor, in terms of Kelvin's law, is the one that makes the annual cost of the I^2R losses equal to the annual interest on capital cost of the installed conductor plus the allowance for depreciation.

Magnet Conductors

Magnet wire of aluminum is a relatively new product; it utilizes EC aluminum. Its cross-sectional area must be 1.6 times that of copper wire to achieve equal direct-current resistance. Although this is a disadvantage in coils where space is a major consideration, aluminum wire has several economic advantages that often outweigh space considerations.

In AWG sizes 8 to 20, film-insulated aluminum magnet wire costs less than equivalent copper conductor. Insulation materials for aluminum are generally the same as for copper.

Aluminum conductor weighs half as much as equivalent copper conductor. The lighter weight is attractive for small transformers, coils, motors, and portable equipment, especially in aerospace applications where reduced component weight allows a highly important increase in payload.

The lower mass of aluminum-wound coils results in lower inertia, improving the performance of a wide variety of equipment. Low mass simplifies dynamic balancing of rotary equipment. It also results in higher sensitivity and response in many coil applications, as in instruments and acoustical devices.

Because aluminum magnet wire has a yield strength of only about 4000 psi, little strain energy is required to conform it to an arbor. This quality is beneficial in practice: Rectangular coil sides have less bow than similar copper coils, turns on a motor stator are shorter, all coils are more compact, and operator fatigue is reduced in hand-winding operations. The most striking benefit of this lower springback is reduction in winding tension. Even though aluminum wire is larger than copper, winding machines run faster; they function readily with aluminum wire four sizes larger than the largest copper gage they can handle.

Designing with aluminum magnet wire is fundamentally the same as with copper. In changing from copper to aluminum, the designer often must find space to accommodate the larger wire. Frequently, an existing unit has sufficient unused space. In other units, modification of the existing design may be sufficient. Various measures are available for minimizing the size of wound coils: coils can be precision wound instead of random wound, bobbins can be made smaller, or even eliminated.

Some engineers may prefer to develop an entirely new coil design. Because increase in cost for manufacturing special cores is small, redesign is usually justified. In redesigning transformers and similar items using scrapless laminations (fabricated without scrap generation), it may be necessary to increase stack height to accommodate an aluminum coil of fewer turns of the larger wire, or a different type of core lamination may be required. For devices using wound cores, the modification is nearly the same. Optimum designs for aluminum wire require different core dimensions than those for copper. A typical design for copper has a window area 0.5 times its central core area, a stack height 1.5 times core width, and a window length 1.5 times window width. In the finished product, coil weight is about 33% of the total, and material costs are about minimum for a given performance rating. For aluminum wire transformers, the window area is approximately 75% greater than core area, stack height 2 to 2.5 times core width, and window length 2 to 2.5 times window width. In the finished product, the weight of the aluminum coil is approximately 40% of the total. This design, a complete departure from standard practice, is practical with tape-wound cores.

Many classes of motors can be redesigned readily to utilize aluminum magnet wire. Shaded pole types often have sufficient unused space for easy substitution of aluminum wire. Induction motors may have space for an increase in wire size of 1 or 1½

Table 8. Formulas for Calculating Weights and Resistances of Aluminum and Copper Wire at 20 C (68 F) (a)

Item	Aluminum	Copper
Weight, lb per 1000 ft	$9.199A \times 10^{-4}$	$30.25A \times 10^{-4}$
Length, ft per lb	$\frac{0.09203}{A} \times 10^{7}$	$\frac{0.03305}{A} \times 10^{7}$
D-c resistance, ohms per 1000 ft	$\frac{16.727}{A} \times 10^{3}$	$\frac{10.37}{A} \times 10^{3}$
D-c resistance, ohms per lb	$\frac{18.18}{A^2} \times 10^{6}$	$\frac{3.428}{A^2} \times 10^{6}$

(a) A = nominal cross-sectional area of the wire in circular mils.

gages; when used together with shortened end turns, this may be sufficient for a simple substitution. As with transformers, stack length can be increased or a larger lamination used if more winding room is needed.

In general, these design suggestions for transformers and motors apply also to all other electromagnetic devices.

In many electromagnets wound with copper, the design flux density of the pole piece often is conservative, and the pole-piece diameter can be reduced safely by 10 to 15% to provide the extra space required for larger gage wire. Reducing the inside diameter of the coil, which lowers the mean turn length, is better than increasing the outside diameter.

Formulas for calculating weights and resistances of aluminum and copper magnet conductors are shown in Table 8.

Magnet Strip. With the development of aluminum strip conductors during the last decade, a new concept in electromagnetic coil design and winding technique has been exploited. Strip conductor coils can be wound with higher space factors and less layer-to-layer insulation than coils wound with round wire. With proper selection of strip insulation and coil design, it is possible to produce an aluminum strip-wound coil having the same physical dimensions and electrical characteristics as a coil wound with round copper conductor. The finished aluminum coil may weigh only half as much as the equivalent copper wire coil.

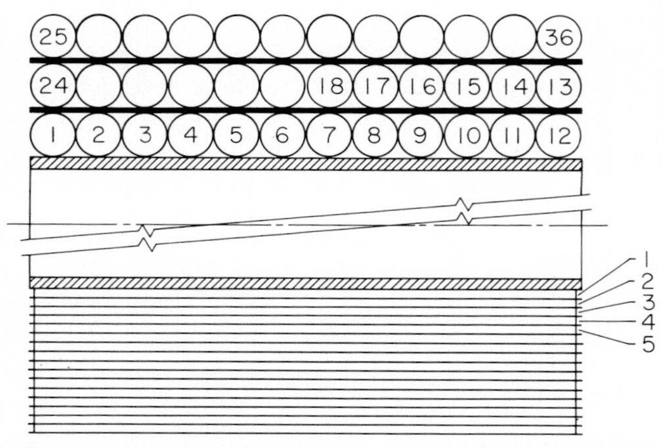

In the wire-wound coil, wire must be insulated for turn-to-turn voltage (1 to 2), and also layer insulation must be provided for layer-to-layer voltage (1 to 24). In the strip-wound coil, the layer-to-layer voltage is the turn-to-turn voltage (1 to 2).

Fig. 7. Insulation requirements of wire-wound and strip-wound coils

Perhaps the most significant advantage of the aluminum strip-wound coil is cost. In many cases, an aluminum strip-wound coil costs considerably less than its round copper wire equivalent because of the savings in manufacturing cost and the lower initial cost of the aluminum conductor.

Conventional wire-wound coils must be wound with particular attention to proper placement of layer insulation and to spaces for cooling and bracing at crossover points, considerations that retard the winding operation and increase the possibility of costly winding errors. With magnet strip, coil winding is faster and greatly simplified. Crossovers are eliminated and the winding spindle need not be stopped to apply interlayer insulation.

With strip winding, space factors of 90% and higher are obtainable, because the vacant space between turns of round wire is eliminated, and because layer-to-layer insulation is not

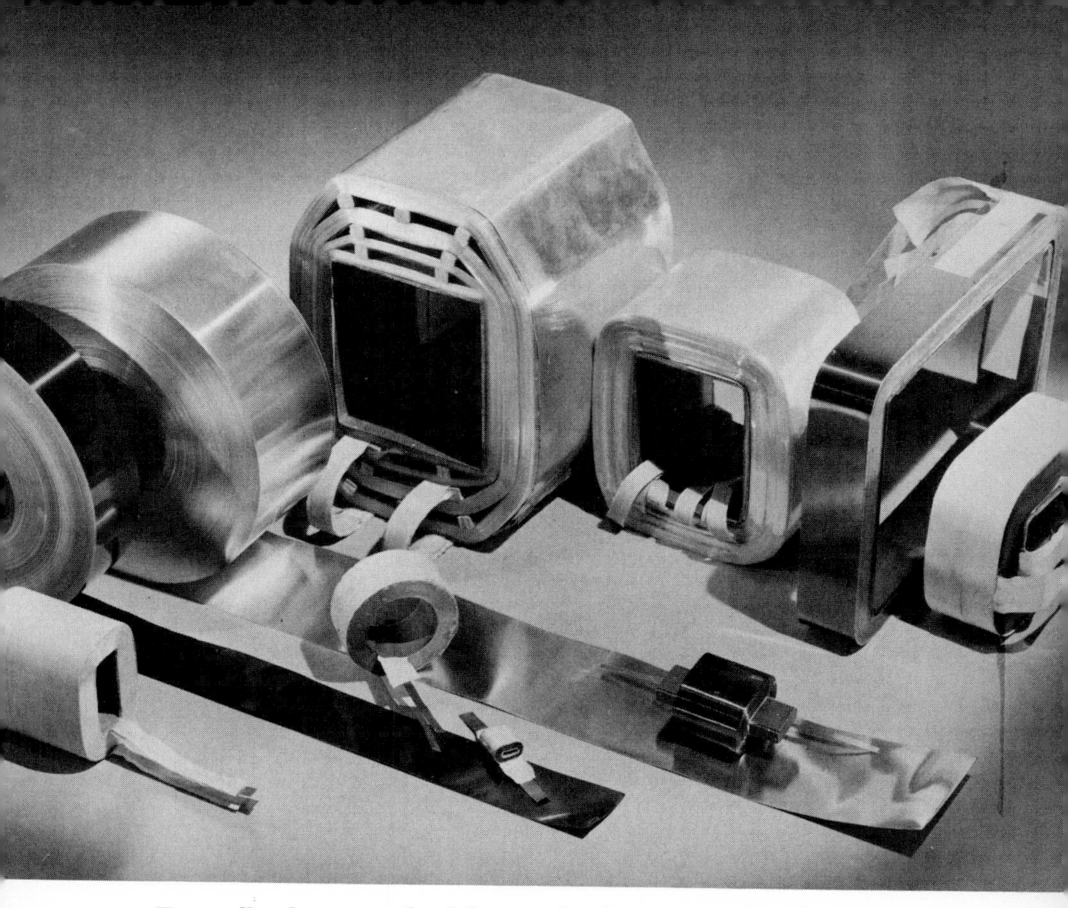

Two rolls shown at the left are aluminum magnet strip. Typical applications of coils using film-insulated strip or wound with interleaving are distribution transformers (larger coils), alternators, and solenoids and relays (smaller coils).

Fig. 8. Coils wound from aluminum magnet strip

required. Figure 7 illustrates why a conventional wire coil must be insulated for layer-to-layer voltage, whereas a strip-wound coil requires only turn-to-turn insulation. The only insulation needed is analogous to turn-to-turn insulation in wire-wound coils. Because there is less danger of insulation cut-through and considerably lower layer-to-layer voltages, the turn-to-turn insulation can be thinner than for wire. Thus, insulation bulk is reduced in two ways.

Higher power ratings can be given to strip-wound coils because they have more rapid heat radiation characteristics than wire-wound coils. The thinner insulation between turns increases turn-to-turn heat transmission and the magnet strip provides a direct conductive path to the outer edges of the coil. Thus, hot spots are prevented, and cooling ducts can be reduced or even eliminated.

Although most strip-wound coil designs presently utilize separate interleaved insulation, such as kraft paper or polyester film, methods of applying insulating coatings have been developed (6). On heavier gages with film insulation, the space factor is improved, as is the over-all coil dimension.

Strip conductors in which an anodic coating is the insulator are used in some applications, such as large lifting magnets. An aluminum-wound magnet is lighter than an equivalent copper-wound magnet; the reduction in dead weight means greater payloads or smaller cranes. Other applications of anodized magnet strip include direct-current magnetic brakes and certain dry-type transformers.

Magnet strip is produced as EC sheet 0.006 to 0.096 in. thick and 3 to 36 in. wide. Edges are specially treated and contoured to eliminate shearing burrs that could puncture interleaving insulation and thus short-circuit adjacent turns, and that would prevent application of satisfactory insulating coatings. For thinner strip, precision-sheared EC foil is produced 0.0011 to 0.0059 in. thick and 1 to 61 in. wide. Figure 8 shows typical coils.

Generating Systems Equipment

Electrical Applications. Isolated-phase bus is the most widely accepted method for connecting generators to transformers. Aluminum bus is cheaper than copper, and easier to handle and install. Because aluminum conductors are welded easily in the factory or field, the number of bolted joints needed to install isolated-phase bus systems is reduced significantly.

Integral web channel bus is ideal for low-voltage outdoor bus; square, tubular and structural-shape bus are also used. Integral web bus also is best for low-voltage underground conductor, because the special shape provides the stiffness needed to resist short-circuit forces, avoiding damage or distortion.

Aluminum is used widely for high-voltage switchyard bus, as tubular aluminum conductors provide a very favorable combination of mechanical and electrical characteristics.

Mechanical Applications. Aluminum's resistance to corrosion contributes major economies in condensate storage tanks, because no maintenance is required inside or outside and no iron is introduced into the boilers. Other applications of aluminum include control tubing, tanks, covers, boiler lagging, jacketing, panels, and canopies.

Boiler lagging, a covering installed to keep boiler insulation dry and in place, represents an outstanding example of the economic advantages of aluminum. The lightweight aluminum sheet, typically alclad 3004, 0.040 in. thick, is easy to install at the plant site, and has a long maintenance-free life. Patterned sheet generally is selected, providing a pleasing appearance.

Much of the aluminum used in generating stations cannot be seen. Some examples of such applications are pistons in reciprocating engines or compressors, bearings and rotors in centrifugal compressors, and rotors in squirrel-cage motors.

Atomic Power

In atomic power generating plants, some of the properties of aluminum are of particular interest. Applications such as fuel cladding, boral sheet, and steam-side components, and the effect of radiation, are described in Chapter 12 in this volume.

Power Transmission and Distribution Equipment

Substation Bus. Tubular bus is the most widely used form of conductor in electric power substations (7).

The most popular tubular aluminum bus alloy is 6063-T6, which has a typical conductivity of 53% IACS. Its current rating, based on temperature rise, is 75% of a copper conductor of the same size. For the same current rating, a tubular aluminum conductor is larger than its copper equivalent. For example, 3-in. IPS aluminum conductor is equal in current capacity to 2.5-in. IPS copper conductor; the aluminum conductor is considerably stronger and more rigid. It weighs less than half as much as the copper product and costs less than one quarter as much.

Although tubular bus is the most efficient carrier of alternating current, it sometimes is not the most economical conductor for high amperages if the heat produced by the I^2R losses is a limiting condition. Hence, structural channels or structural angles often are used for large loads because these shapes have substantially greater surface area than tubular bus. This increased surface allows heat to be dissipated more rapidly, providing a lower operating temperature. Use of integral web channel bus eliminates the need for lacing or spacers normally applied to channel bus, permitting a substantial reduction in the installed cost of the system.

Switchgear. Aluminum buses are extensively used in low-voltage, 5 and 15-kv metal-clad, station-type cubicle switchgear and in metal-enclosed rectifier switchgear. The aluminum conductors are usually extruded rectangular bars of 6101 alloy. Because this alloy is comparable in strength to copper, little, if any, additional bracing is required. The bars generally are silver plated to facilitate the assembly of bolted joints, although units having unplated bars with welded joints are sometimes used. Although welded electrical joints are of highest reliability, properly made bolted joints are reliable, efficient connections.

High-Voltage Switches. Among the newer electrical applications of aluminum are high-voltage and extra-high-voltage switch components (Fig. 9). The manual effort or mechanical power required to operate these switches with their necessarily long blades is reduced considerably by the application of tubular aluminum. Alloy 356-T6 castings weighing less than half as much as those of copper alloy are used for the jaw supports, crank, forklink, and hinge support. The resulting lighter unit makes possible the employment of smaller, less-expensive insulators. Aluminum switch bases with flanges on the outside are easier to drill and to bolt to supporting structures than are conventional steel bases.

Transformers. In oil-filled power and distribution transformers, changing to aluminum conductors results in an increase in the size of the core and associated components, which requires a larger tank and a greater volume of oil. Thus, conventional aluminum magnet wire is generally considered impractical. Aluminum strip conductor (EC), however, has gained considerable acceptance in oil-filled transformers, particularly in the low-voltage windings of distribution and small power transformers (8). In these applications, strip-wound coils offer several advantages over aluminum or copper wire-wound coils: (*a*) almost linear surge voltage distribution across a continuous winding, (*b*) higher strength, particularly under short-circuit conditions, and (*c*) superior adaptability for use of fully automated coil winding techniques.

Aluminum EC magnet wire is used extensively in dry-type transformers and current-limiting reactors. These devices have no liquid-filled tanks to affect cost, and most reactors have no core, so the use of the larger aluminum conductors is economically feasible. The aluminum conductors, although larger, cost considerably less than their copper equivalents. Square or rectangular wire is selected for maximum space efficiency.

The employment of aluminum bus in power transformers presents little or no space problem, but the reluctance of the industry to rely on bolted joints has retarded its acceptance. The

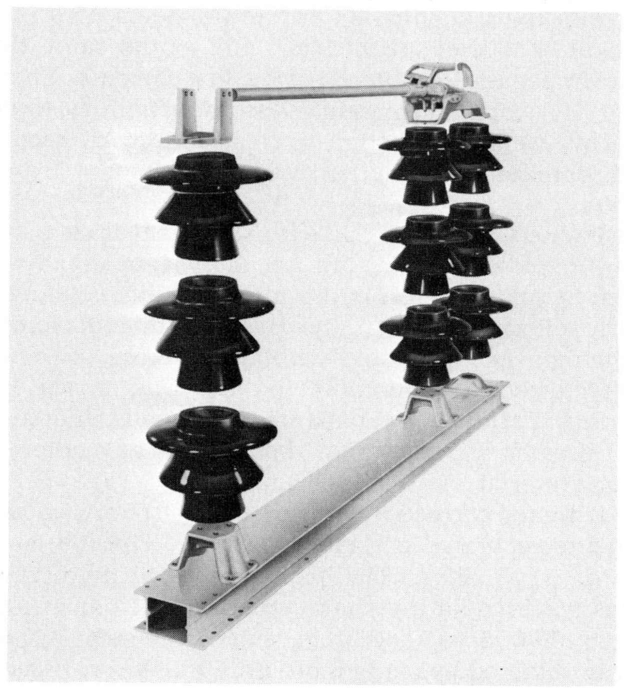

I-T-E Circuit Breaker Co.

Fig. 9. Aluminum and alumina elements of high-voltage disconnect switch, including tubular aluminum blade, extruded aluminum base, various cast components, and alumina-porcelain insulators

recent use of welded joints, which are economically feasible and reliable, has led to an increasing utilization of aluminum bus in these transformers.

Aluminum tanks are used on distribution transformers where exceptional corrosion resistance is required. The aluminum tank shell generally is roll formed and welded, typically in 5052 or 6061, but it can be made in other ways, as from a one-piece extrusion, an assembly of several extrusions, or as a drawn shell. Painting normally is not required for protection against corrosion, but it is recommended as a means of improving emissivity. The light weight of aluminum tanks has added significance for mobile power transformers, a number of which have been produced in recent years.

Line Traps. Aluminum carrier-current line traps are inserted in series with the transmission line to provide a high impedance over a band of carrier frequencies, and at the same time offer negligible impedance to the 60-cycle line current. These traps, employing EC conductor, weigh less than half as much as in copper. This weight reduction decreases support requirements and often eliminates the necessity for employing a crane during installation.

Power-Factor-Correction Capacitors. Foil-paper capacitors used in power-factor correction are an important application for aluminum. Aluminum foil is the most suitable conductor material for capacitors, being both inexpensive and sufficiently strong to permit high-speed winding without breaking. Aluminum foil can be produced commercially in very thin gages (down to 0.00017 in.), permitting capacitors to be made lighter, smaller, and with greater capacity than those using any other practical conductor material.

A power-factor correction capacitor consists of two aluminum foil elements separated by layers of paper. The foil is generally 0.00025-in. 1145 alloy. The paper is pure, high-grade kraft, which has good insulating characteristics. The paper normally is only about 0.0005 to 0.0030 in. thick; the required dielectric strength is obtained by using more than one layer. In assembling the unit, the two layers of foil are wound into a coil, with appropriate connections and separated by an adequate thickness of paper to withstand the design voltage. The coil is inserted into a metal container and the top, containing a small hole, is applied with a hermetic joint. The unit is then evacuated, filled with a high dielectric oil of the chlorinated diphenyl type, and the seal completed. Foil should be free from rolling lubricant, to prevent contamination of the impregnating oil.

In these capacitors, which cover a wide range of capacity values, the capacity is a function of the foil area, the dielectric constant of the oil, and the thickness of the paper separator. To obtain large capacities, foil widths up to 22 in. are used in appropriate lengths. The working voltage at which the capacitor performs satisfactorily is limited by the dielectric strength of the insulation separating the foil sheets.

Soldered connections frequently are employed to establish electrical contact to the foil plates in a capacitor. Alternately, narrow high-purity aluminum strips, commonly ¼ or ⅜ in. wide and 0.003 to 0.010 in. thick, are inserted in the capacitor during winding, making electrical contact through pressure. Clean, smooth edges are required on this strip, known as "tab stock".

Although 0.00025-in. foil is generally accepted as a standard gage for the manufacture of paper-foil capacitors, engineering considerations sometimes indicate a need for other gages. Where space is a limiting factor, lighter gages are resorted to, the most common being 0.00023 in. In some capacitors, gages as light as 0.00017 in. are specified.

Stainless steel capacitor cases have become popular in recent years, because of their resistance to corrosion. Aluminum cases in alloys 1100 or 3003 provide the same level of corrosion resistance at a significantly lower cost and in addition utilize the benefits of lower weight and higher thermal conductivity. For these reasons, aluminum cases often are preferred; at least two manufacturers now offer power-factor-correction capacitors with aluminum cases. An aluminum case should have a wall about 50% thicker than a stainless steel case for the same rigidity.

Insulators. High-strength alumina porcelain insulators (9) are a relatively new development, dating from the late 1950's. Alumina porcelain is at least twice as strong as the conventional wet-process silica porcelain in tension, compression, shear, and, most important, impact strength (10). Thus, with alumina porcelain, insulators are double strength for a given size, or smaller for a specified strength. In addition, alumina porcelain has superior electrical properties for equal size.

At least three manufacturers offer air switches incorporating 3-in. bolt-circle alumina insulators (Fig. 9). The following advantages are claimed: (*a*) light weight and high cantilever strength of the alumina insulators permit shipping switch poles completely assembled and adjusted, (*b*) reduction of 40% in weight makes the switches easier to transport, handle at the substation site, and erect, (*c*) lighter supporting structures can be used, (*d*) low weight on the main switch bearing reduces effort required for power or manual operation, and (*e*) there is substantially less insulator breakage from rough handling of the high-strength alumina porcelain (9).

Development of aluminum caps and pins paralleled development of alumina porcelain insulators. Caps cast in A356-T6 or forged in 6061-T6 are considerably lighter than in steel; in most environments, aluminum has higher resistance to corrosion.

Secondary Distribution Equipment

Busway, a system of interconnected prefabricated sections of steel or aluminum duct enclosing bus bars mounted on insulators, is used for exposed heavy capacitor feeder and circuit wiring in industrial plants. It is a well-established application for silver-plated alloy 6101 conductor. The price of aluminum bus is as little as one third that of copper bus; this saving is reflected in the over-all cost of aluminum busway systems. Aluminum busway weighs as little as 40% as much as a copper system having the same rating.

Conduit. Originally, aluminum rigid conduit was used only where its light weight and corrosion resistance justified a cost much higher than that of steel conduit. As aluminum conduit became competitive in price, in the 1950's, its use widened.

With its weight one third that of steel conduit, alloy 6063-T42 conduit is stacked, lifted, and carried with less effort. It is easier to cut, bend, and thread. Thus, installation costs are significantly lower. Schedule 40 pipe is used, in the size range of ½ to 6 in. With aluminum conduit, the operation of fault-current safety devices is more positive due to low impedance resulting from its high conductivity and nonmagnetic characteristics. Aluminum conduit is preferred for food and pharmaceutical plants because it is nontoxic (Fig. 10). It is recommended along the seacoast, in highly industrialized urban areas, and in most locations where the atmosphere is heavily polluted with chemical dust or fumes.

Aluminum (or steel) conduit buried under ground should be protected from contact with the soil, because soil conditions vary widely. Aluminum conduit can be buried in normal reinforced concrete structures and slabs with no special surface protection or coating. However, where the concrete contains added chlorides, either as calcium chloride (for high early strength), coral aggregate, unwashed beach sand, or sea water, electrical conductivity of the concrete is markedly increased. In addition, even a small flow of direct current causes chloride ions to migrate to anodic areas on embedded metals, resulting in local acidity that prevents or destroys normal protective films. These effects of

The Kroger Co.

Fig. 10. Typical installation of large-diameter aluminum rigid conduit. Installation economies with aluminum conduit are greatest with these larger diameters.

chlorides may cause corrosion problems from stray electric currents or dissimilar metal connections. It is therefore necessary to use a suitable organic coating on aluminum (and other metals) when chlorides cannot be avoided.

Aluminum conduit is accepted in all classifications of hazardous locations as defined in the National Electrical Code where "rigid metallic conduit" is the required method of wiring. Aluminum rigid conduit has been listed since 1922 by Underwriters' Laboratories, Inc. It is recognized by the appropriate specifications standards and codes as the equivalent of any other rigid metallic conduit.

Enclosures. Aluminum switchgear enclosures generally are fabricated either from a system of interlocking 6*xxx* series extrusions or a combination of extrusions and sheet, frequently

Philadelphia Electric Co.

Fig. 11. Lightweight aluminum cage for three utility reactors is assembled from mill stock forms of aluminum, and is handled as a single unit in the field. The nonmagnetic properties of aluminum are advantageous in this application.

patterned sheet. Both methods are versatile; many sizes can be made by varying the number of standard panels.

Aluminum reactor cages (Fig. 11) employ an unusual extruded aluminum angle member to form panels for front and back sections. Sheets of expanded mesh aluminum are placed in the channels of the extrusions and held in position by crimping the channel edges. The sides of the cage are aluminum sheet.

Isolated-phase bus enclosures are almost universally made of aluminum. It is nonmagnetic, eliminating hysteresis losses. Its low resistivity results in low I^2R losses from induced eddy currents. It is practical to use relatively heavy-gage sheet that does not warp or bow when used in large panels. Alloys for these bus enclosures include 1100, 3003, 5052, and 6061.

Power Utilization and Conversion Equipment

Motors. The majority of squirrel cage induction motors employ an integrally cast aluminum rotor. This incorporates the conductor bars, end rings and cooling fan, eliminating welding or brazing and minimizing the use of bolts, screws and other pieces typical of assembly. Heat transfer from the conductor bars to the sheet steel laminations is excellent, minimizing local overheating within the rotor during a severe overload peak.

The choice of alloy for the rotors depends largely on the operating characteristics of the motor. A particular rotor design may require an aluminum alloy having a high, low or intermediate conductivity. Values for rotor alloys range from 60.5% IACS for a high-conductivity type to 28% for 380-F.

Rotor diameters are approximately 1 to 30 in. Several casting methods are used. One procedure is to use a conventional cold-chamber die casting machine. Another method employs a modification of this equipment, utilizing pressure from a vertical hydraulic or pneumatic press. Centrifugal casting and the permanent mold process also are applied, but to a lesser extent.

Cast aluminum frames often are employed in series motors and small shaded-pole motors to obtain rigidity, low noise levels, and economical one-piece construction. End frames of cast aluminum are used to improve portability and reduce machining requirements. Cast housings have integral cooling fins.

Appliance motors with aluminum wire stator windings have been on the market for more than 10 years.

Rectifiers. The major applications of aluminum in rectifier equipment are electrical conductors, heat sinks, and enclosures.

Aluminum offers several advantages that explain its frequent selection as a heat-sink material, even though its volume thermal conductivity is less than that of copper. The extrudability of aluminum permits versatility in the design of aluminum heat sinks with extended surfaces. Configurations ideal for heat dissipation can be produced economically (Fig. 12). Extruded sections, usually of 6*xxx* series alloys, can be color anodized to increase the emissivity of the radiating surfaces, where required by design or service conditions. An extruded aluminum section often functions both as a heat sink and an electrical conductor.

Communications and Electronics Equipment

Antennas. Aluminum is utilized extensively in radar and microwave antennas for air-borne and naval electronic equipment, primarily because of its high strength-to-weight ratio and the rigidity resulting from the large sections permitted. Structural shapes and large-diameter pipe and tube are used in the supporting structures. Parabolic reflectors, spun from alloy 1100 sheet, are supported by a frame of extruded or structural shapes, or pipe. Castings are common for corners, bases and covers.

Virtually all outdoor television antennas are constructed of drawn or welded aluminum tube, usually in 3003 or 6063 alloy. Aluminum dominates this application because of its combination of light weight, electrical conductivity, and resistance to weathering.

Paper and Thin-Film Capacitors. Phenomenal growth of the electronic industry, and of radio and television in particular, since 1940, has been accompanied by corresponding expansion in the manufacture and use of capacitors for electrical devices. Important applications of capacitors are in electronics, power generation and transmission, electric motors, automotive applications, telephone circuits, and fluorescent lighting.

Fig. 12. Heat sinks demonstrate effective use of design flexibility of aluminum extrusions. Several of these designs perform as structural components in addition to radiating heat.

Aluminum capacitors are divided into two categories, according to the type of dielectric. One group, which employs thin layers of paper or thin plastic films, is known either as paper or thin-film capacitors. The other group are electrolytic capacitors, which have a layer of anodically formed aluminum oxide as the dielectric. This group is described in the subsequent section.

Paper capacitors generally are similar to, but much smaller than, the power-factor-correction capacitors described. They consist of two strips of unetched aluminum foil separated by strips of paper, which serve as the dielectric. The maximum voltage at which the unit can operate is a direct function of the number of layers or thickness of the paper. The capacitance of a unit is proportional to the area of the foil elements and inversely related to the thickness of the paper.

Paper capacitors generally are wound on automatic equipment, which meters the lengths of foil and paper. The foil windings are overlapped so that the turns of the two windings extend to opposite ends. The ends of the windings then are flattened, and wire leads connected, usually by soldering.

Thin-film capacitors are of similar construction except that plastic films of a variety of types are used as the separating dielectric. These capacitors generally are sealed in a paper or plastic case and are not impregnated. Capacitance generally is low, because plain (unetched) foil is used and because the dielectric films are comparatively thick.

Electrolytic capacitors have very high capacitance per unit of volume. Their initial use can be traced to the latter half of the nineteenth century, when it was discovered that an oxide film formed electrochemically on aluminum exhibited unidirectional conductance. Two early applications were in the starting of single-phase induction motors and for correction of power factor in alternating-current circuits.

Later, electrolytic capacitors became important in the growth of the radio and electronics industry. Their use in radio circuits made it possible to operate radios from alternating-current sources. The high-capacity filter units of convenient size required for this application, however, could be obtained only through etching the foil to increase its surface area.

An aluminum electrolytic capacitor consists of two aluminum foil electrodes, an electrolyte, and a dielectric film of aluminum oxide. The oxide film is created from the surface layer of one aluminum electrode by an anodic oxidation treatment and is an integral part of the electrode. The film has rectifying characteristics, opposing current flow when the aluminum base is the anode and passing current freely when the aluminum is the cathode. As a result, most electrolytic capacitors must be operated only on direct current and with the correct polarity (oxide-coated element as anode). An exception is where both foil elements have an oxide film, in which case the unit can be operated with either polarity or on alternating current.

Although two metal surfaces are required for a paper-insulated capacitor to function, an electrolytic capacitor uses only one metallic surface and the electrolyte, which becomes in effect the cathode of the capacitor unit. The cathode foil, which is used merely to establish contact with the electrolyte, may be of lower purity than the anode foil.

Electrolytic capacitor anodes are made from foil that is generally 0.003 to 0.004 in. thick. The higher-purity grades containing 99.80 to 99.99% Al are used, because, during anodizing, they readily develop a thin oxide film possessing high dielectric strength and low leakage values. Leakage is related inversely to metal purity, and so the higher purities of foil are employed to produce capacitors that must have low leakage.

Foil composition and characteristics affect the quality of the dielectric film, because the capacitor dielectric is formed from the surface layer of the foil. If the electrode were 100% Al, without a trace of other elements, a continuous film of aluminum oxide could be formed. Aluminum foil generally used for electrolytic capacitors, however, contains up to 0.2% of other elements. These consist mainly of iron and silicon with small amounts of copper, although traces of other elements can be detected spectrographically. The iron-containing constituents usually degrade the dielectric film and its behavior in service. For this reason, higher-purity aluminum foil is being used increasingly. Because capacitance is inversely related to the distance separating the electrodes of a capacitor, it increases as the dielectric anodic film is reduced in thickness.

There are two types of electrolytic capacitors employing anodically coated aluminum foil: those using plain foil and those with etched foil. The plain foil capacitors generally are of relatively low capacity for a given physical size, because the surface area of the foil is equal only to its projected area. Plain foil 0.0005 to 0.002 in. thick is used in this type.

The surface area of foil can be increased substantially by

etching, either chemically or electrochemically. In commercial practice, gains in surface area by a factor of seven to eight commonly are obtained with etched foil used for high-voltage applications. Gains by a factor of 16 or more are achieved with etched foil for low-voltage applications. Thus, it is possible by etching to produce electrolytic capacitors having a much higher capacity for a given physical size. Because of increased surface area from etching, plus the relative thinness of the oxide coating, the electrolytic capacitor is capable of storing very much larger quantities of electricity for the same unit volume than is the paper-insulated capacitor.

Selenium rectifiers have aluminum back plates, frequently alclad 2024-T3, or 6061-T6, which serve as terminals to the selenium layers, while supporting them and radiating heat. The aluminum plates, typically 0.040 in. thick, are coated with selenium by evaporation in a vacuum. The flatness, thickness, and surface texture of the aluminum plates are critical.

Recording disks are used to produce master-copy recordings and high-quality transcription records for the recording industry, as well as for data recording and storage for memory units. The disks are made of aluminum flat sheet circles having a high degree of surface smoothness and flatness.

Wave Guides. Aluminum wave-guide tubing, made of 1100 alloy in special tempers, is lighter and less expensive than brass tubing. Extremely close dimensional tolerances are required. In aluminum systems, flanges and corners are premium-tolerance C355 or A356 castings with a T6-type heat treatment. The interior surfaces of both the tubing and the castings must be very smooth. In certain applications, the interior surfaces are silver-plated for higher electrical conductivity.

Heat sinks for semi-conductors are often extruded aluminum sections. The complex shapes necessary for efficient heat dissipation are made economically by extrusion. Aluminum's high thermal conductivity is a definite asset. The emissivity of the aluminum surfaces can be increased by anodizing.

Enclosures. Aluminum enclosures house a variety of communications and electronics equipment and components. Impact-extruded alloy 1100 cans and drawn shells house small capacitors and other components.

In the past few years, enclosure designs incorporating extrusions or die castings, or combinations of both, have resulted in versatile modular cabinet systems. In some designs, provisions are made for mounting power transistors on the cabinet itself, so that the aluminum cabinet also serves as a heat sink. Interlocking or tongue-and-groove extruded shapes simplify assembly.

The familiar aluminum outdoor telephone booth demonstrates the advantages of aluminum enclosures in outdoor applications.

Interior Distribution and Illumination

Wiring Devices. Metal shell lamp holders made from aluminum coiled sheet consume approximately 60% of the aluminum used in wiring devices. Non-heat-treatable alloys, such as 3004 or 5050, generally are employed, because of cost and formability. The transition from brass to aluminum for metal shell lamp holders was made simply because aluminum fulfills the requirements at a lower cost.

Aluminum cold headed items and screw machine parts (bushings, knobs, eyelets, pins and screws) are used in various devices, but not for current-carrying parts that make or break contact, as the natural oxide film on aluminum increases electrical resistance. Aluminum wall plates, competing with stainless steel and brass, offer long life and attractive appearance at a lower cost.

Lamp bases, the section of lamps or bulbs contacting the shell, require metals having satisfactory electrical conductivity, good formability, adequate strength, solderability, and an acceptable appearance. Aluminum and brass are the two most popular materials for this application, aluminum offering a significant cost advantage. Developed in the 1940's, aluminum bases gradually acquired the larger part of this market. Non-heat-treatable alloys, such as 3004 and 5050, are used primarily in three applications: medium screw bases for general lighting lamps of 150-watt rating and below, bayonet bases for photoflash lamps, and hot-cathode fluorescent end caps. The fluorescent end cap provides only mechanical protection and appearance, brass pins serving as electrical contacts.

Aluminum is superior to brass in electrical conductivity, but the natural nonconductive oxide coating on aluminum is thick enough to prevent its use in some low-voltage applications. Aluminum has a high coefficient of friction, and inserting an aluminum screw base into a socket can cause oxide particles to flake off and abrade the base and the socket screw shell. For this reason, a lubricant is employed on aluminum screw-base lamps.

The satisfactory electrical conductivity listed as a necessary characteristic of incandescent lamp-base materials is a relative term. For example, the conductivity of 3004, a common lamp-base alloy, is relatively low (42% IACS) compared to some aluminum alloys, but higher than that of brass.

Lighting Reflectors. Aluminum reflectors are used in all types of indoor and outdoor lighting applications. Special grades of aluminum sheet are processed to produce superior-quality reflecting surfaces. Processing includes chemical or electrolytic brightening of the surface, followed by anodizing (Volume III, Chapters 18 and 19).

In the visible light spectrum, the reflectance of quality aluminum reflectors is approximately 78 to 84%, depending on wave length. In the near infrared region, reflectance is 75 to 91%. Aluminum reflectors are superior to those made of other commercially available materials for light of short wave length.

A quality reflecting surface is virtually permanent for interior applications. Dust and dirt, although they reduce reflectance, have no deleterious effect on the dry reflector. Quality reflectors can withstand temperatures of about 300 to 400 F without deterioration. The performance of an aluminum reflector in outdoor applications depends on the weight or thickness of the hard oxide coating. For coatings meeting established specifications, durability increases with increase in thickness.

Special grades of aluminum sheet are necessary to achieve desired light control and permanence of reflectors. For diffuse-type reflectors, supplied with an etched surface, reflector sheet of alloy 1135 clad with 1135 often is used. Cladding with the same alloy promotes uniform appearance and controlled etching characteristics. Specular-type reflectors, which are polished prior to finishing, frequently are fabricated from sheet of alloy 1100 or 3003 clad with 1178, a high-purity alloy of controlled composition that permits development of a uniform, mirror-like finish.

Most aluminum street lighting luminaires are made from die cast shells, but some are fabricated from formed sheet.

Joining Methods for Aluminum Conductors

The rapidly growing use of aluminum conductors of all types has spurred development of joining processes and techniques.

To establish and maintain low resistance on the contact surfaces of mechanically secured aluminum electrical joints, techniques must be provided to disperse and prevent full re-formation of the natural oxide film. This can be accomplished by abrading the contact surfaces and applying a suitable electrical joint compound. An electrical joint compound is an unctuous substance that assists in forming and maintaining a low-resistance electrical connection. Proprietary materials commonly used as joint compounds, all grease-type, can be divided into:

1 Materials that serve as a sealer to protect the metal-to-metal conducting areas from moisture and oxygen
2 Vehicles containing particles that fracture the surface films by deforming the conductor surfaces
3 Substances containing active chemicals that dissolve the oxide film and retard its re-formation, thereby facilitating the establishment of many conducting spots

The use of a joint compound is essential to produce and maintain low contact resistance in all types of bolted electrical contacts, including bolted connectors and bolted bus joints, where aluminum surfaces contact each other or other metals.

Platings of other metals on aluminum contact surfaces constitute another method of joint preparation (Volume III, Chapter 20). Silver-plated contact surfaces are used extensively on aluminum (and copper) conductors, especially bus conductors, because the compounds formed on silver in ordinary atmospheres have relatively low electrical resistances. Most aluminum busway conductors are silver plated, and silver-plated bus is common in switchgear.

Silver plating of aluminum contact surfaces has one potential disadvantage. Silver is cathodic to aluminum and may cause galvanic corrosion of aluminum in the presence of moisture. Therefore, the silver plating should be uniform and relatively thick, to minimize the occurrence of voids. The use of protective greases or waxes is essential for optimum performance of silver-plated joints that are exposed to moisture or high humidity.

Aluminum magnet wire most often is spliced or terminated by machine-applied compression terminals having serrated barrels. Of alternate methods for joining aluminum magnet wire, percussion welding and pressure welding appear to be the best. Soldering is a secondary method, because special solders and fluxes are required.

A properly welded joint is the most reliable electrical connection for aluminum, because there is an essentially homogeneous union resulting in maximum joint efficiency; this sometimes is reduced slightly by lower-conductivity filler metal. Inert-arc gas welding methods (Volume III, Chapter 12) are used extensively, both in the shop and field, to join bus conductors and to terminate stranded conductors.

Although brazed joints in bus conductors have given good service for many years in both indoor and outdoor applications, brazing (Volume III, Chapter 13) is not a common method of joining aluminum conductors.

Soldering (Volume III, Chapter 14), a popular method of joining copper conductors, is employed to a much smaller extent with aluminum conductors. Soldered joints in aluminum are very good electrically, but the possibility of galvanic corrosion must be considered. The high-temperature, high-zinc-content

Clockwise from upper left: steel box to aluminum sheet; copper to aluminum plate; copper strap to aluminum winding (also shown in cross section); four examples of ferrule joints combining stranded copper and solid aluminum wire.

Fig. 13. Electrical joints combining aluminum and another metal are arc spot welded.

solders have a much greater resistance to corrosion than the lower-temperature solders, but fluxes used with high-zinc solders are very active, and the flux residues should be removed thoroughly if the joint will be exposed to moisture.

There are, in addition to soldering, several other methods for joining aluminum to copper. Flash welding is well established for making aluminum-to-copper butt welded transitions. Both lap and butt welds can be made by the pressure welding process; applications range from butt welds in small wire to butt welds in bus and lap welds in sheet. Ultrasonic spot and seam welding also are employed to join aluminum to copper. Arc spot welding is a new process for joining aluminum to copper (Fig. 13). All of these methods, which are also suitable for joining aluminum to aluminum, are discussed in detail in Volume III, Chapter 12.

References

1 "Electrical Transmission and Distribution Reference Book", 4th edition, Westinghouse Electric Corp., East Pittsburgh, Pa., 1950

2 Power Cable Ampacities, "Aluminum Conductors", Vol II, Insulated Power Cable Engineers Association and American Institute of Electrical Engineers, IPCEA Publication P-46-246, Montclair, N. J., 1962

3 "Rubber-Insulated Wire and Cable for the Transmission and Distribution of Electrical Energy", Insulated Power Cable Engineers Association and National Electrical Manufacturers Association, IPCEA Specification S-19-81, Montclair, N. J., 1964

4 "Thermoplastic-Insulated Wire and Cable for the Transmission and Distribution of Electrical Energy", Insulated Power Cable Engineers Association and National Electrical Manufacturers Association, IPCEA Specification S-61-402, Montclair, N. J., 1961

5 J. D. Edwards, F. C. Frary, Z. Jeffries, "The Aluminum Industry", McGraw-Hill Book Co., New York, 1930

6 F. R. Roubik, R. R. Cope, "A Progress Report on the Development and Application of Aluminum Strip Conductors", AIEE District Conference Paper DP 62-713, Fort Wayne, Ind., April 1962

7 Substations Committee, Power Div., IEEE, Use of Aluminum for Substation Buses, IEEE Transactions, Power Apparatus and Systems, Special Supplement, 1963, p 72

8 E. A. Goodman, "Characteristics of Sheet Windings in Transformers", AIEE Conference Paper CP 63-1139, Toronto, Canada, June 1963

9 H. W. Graybill, "Application of High-Strength Alumina Porcelain Insulators to Outdoor Air Switches", IEEE District Paper DP 63-717, Davenport, Iowa, May 1963

10 H. W. Graybill, D. E. Alexander, "The Current Revolution in Outdoor Apparatus Insulators", AIEE Conference Paper CP 62-1248, Denver, Colo., June 1962

Chapter 22

Home Appliances, Housewares, Furniture and Other Consumer Products

A. J. Haygood and R. M. Smith

MANY of the earliest commercial uses for aluminum were in consumer products, such as cooking utensils, household notions, and novelties. These have endured and expanded, and modern consumer products — home appliances, housewares, furniture, and recreation items — are a major field of application.

Major Appliances

The vacuum cleaner, one of the first motor-operated work-savers in the home, was from the beginning largely aluminum, with a cast base and tubular handle. From the earliest models, washing machines employed tubs and spin baskets made of aluminum sheet. Gas and electric ranges use aluminum for a variety of parts in the form of sheet, extrusions, tube, and castings. Most other major appliances also contain aluminum (1).

Refrigerators and freezers utilize more aluminum per unit than any other appliances, exceeding 18 pounds in some models. Many applications depend on the rapid conduction of heat by aluminum. Uses include evaporators, shelves, ice cube trays and grids, compartment doors, and trim. Upright freezers have shelves of aluminum sheet with an aluminum refrigerant tube on the underside. In many models of chest freezers, inner liners are formed from aluminum sheet with the aluminum evaporator

The authors are with the Application Engineering Div., Aluminum Company of America, New Kensington. A. J. Haygood is manager for consumer durable goods. R. M. Smith is manager for transportation.

tube fastened to the outside of the liner by brazing or by spot welded clips. Figure 1 illustrates various methods for providing aluminum refrigerant passages in domestic evaporators.

The ice tray and grid were among the first uses for aluminum in refrigerators, dating from 1927. Trays of copper or copper-base alloys, which have higher thermal conductivity on a volume basis, can form ice slightly faster, but cost more. The anodized coating applied to aluminum parts protects their original appearance indefinitely with no maintenance, and can impart ice-release characteristics that make the trays easier to use. The open pores of a newly formed, unsealed anodized coating accept certain materials, including many dyes and pigments, to give special surface properties. Wax formulations applied to seal the pores in

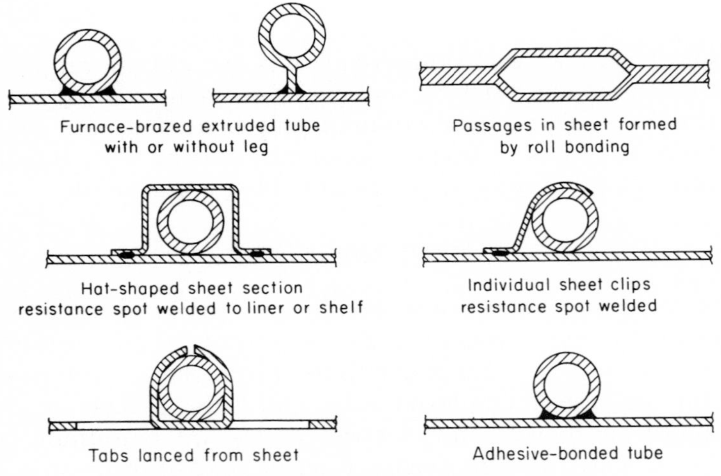

Fig. 1. Methods for providing aluminum refrigerant passages in domestic evaporators

ice-cube trays permit the cubes to break away freely. Trays are drawn from 1100 and 3003 alloys; the grids and operating mechanism, requiring greater strength, are usually stamped from 5052.

Although aluminum shelves have been used in refrigerators for 25 years, it was not until the humidity in the cabinet was increased to present-day levels and rusting of steel shelves became more of a problem that the use of aluminum became significant. Early shelf designs employed alloy 1345 wire (99.45 Al min) in a hard-drawn temper. Straight lengths were upset near their ends, and headed after being inserted through punched holes in an extruded aluminum frame. The frame was generally alloy 6063-T42, chosen for its good finishing characteristics and adequate strength.

Wire shelves remain popular, but sheet models also are employed for a large number of refrigerators and freezers. For refrigerator shelves, the sheet is lanced and formed into ribs that stiffen the panel while permitting air circulation. These shelves are anodized to maintain good appearance. Alloys such as 5005 are used, with certain models adopting the brighter-finishing 5357 sheet. Aluminum die castings are sometimes employed for structural members of rotating shelves; these are painted before the sheet overlay is installed on the shelf.

Freezer shelves are often solid pieces of aluminum sheet, since no air circulation is required. The refrigerant tube is fastened under the shelf, with hat-shaped sheet sections resistance spot welded to the shelf. One model uses tabs pierced and formed from the sheet to hold the serpentine of aluminum tube in thermal and structural contact with the shelf (Fig. 1). Many freezer shelves are made from embossed or coined pattern sheet with no additional finishing, typically of alloy 3003.

A furnace-brazed tube-on-sheet design was adopted for refrigerator evaporators (2) shortly after the second World War, and soon this approach was used to make the entire liner of a chest freezer. Alloy 3003 sheet in a stucco-embossed pattern is used with extruded 1100 alloy tube.

With the development of the roll-bonding process in the early 1950's, aluminum evaporators became the industry standard. Roll bonding produces integral refrigerant passages in a sheet, eliminating the tube and the brazing operation. A stop-off pattern is painted on a sheet to provide selective bonding to a cover sheet in a rolling operation, and the nonbonded passages are subsequently expanded hydraulically.

One European manufacturer employs an aluminum sheet sandwich in making an evaporator. A thin layer of zinc is rolled and bonded between aluminum sheets to provide a low-melting parting material for a hot die expansion operation. The finished panel has an appearance similar to an evaporator made by roll bonding. Aluminum tube is also adhesive bonded to aluminum sheet for freezer liners.

Finned coils are utilized in evaporators for frost-free refrigerators, freezers and combinations. Alloys 1100, bare and alclad (outside) 3003, and 7072 are used for the fin stock, refrigerant lines, and defroster tubes.

Prefinished aluminum sheet with a baked vinyl finish is used as liners for several models of refrigerators. The finish permits the necessary forming and provides good stain resistance. This material offers a savings in tooling costs, compared to steel liners that are porcelain enameled after fabrication and assembly.

Trim parts and accessories form the last category of aluminum applications in domestic refrigeration, excepting compressors, which are discussed in Chapter 20 of this volume. Compartment doors, drip trays, and door racks employ mostly 5*x*57 sheet in the O or H25 tempers, and 6063-T42 extrusions. Automatic ice-maker bodies are die cast, usually in alloy 13, A214 or 360. Aluminum, unlike many plastics, is completely odor-free and does not absorb food odors.

Air Conditioners. Fins on the evaporator and condenser coils are the largest single application of aluminum in air condition-

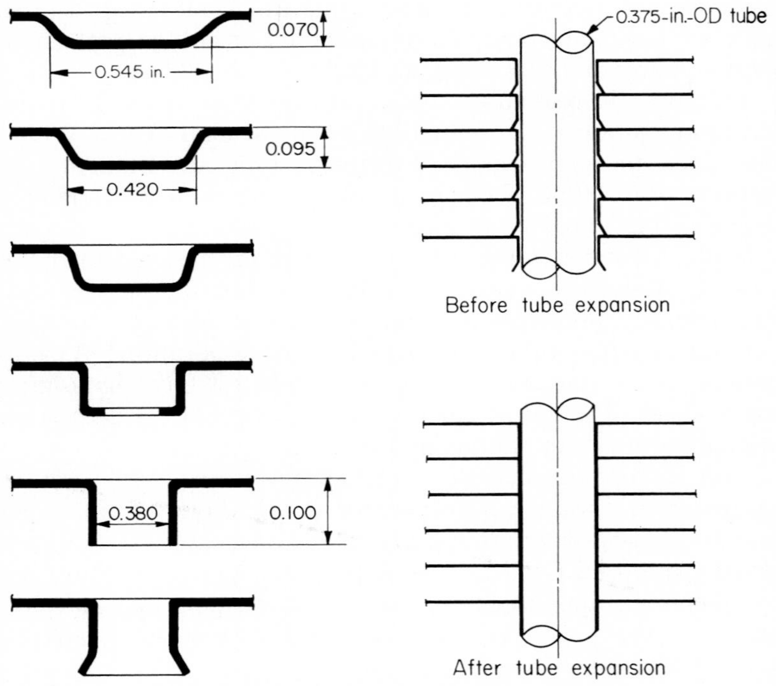

Fig. 2. Typical forming sequence for air conditioning fins, showing assembly on tube

ers. Fin stock is made from the higher-purity commercial alloys, principally 1100 and 1145, because of their higher thermal conductivity. Thickness range is 0.005 to 0.008 in. Intermediate cold worked tempers, such as H11 or H22, are used for fin stock, to provide as much strength and resistance to mechanical damage as possible while retaining sufficient formability to make the fin. Most fins are drawn in several operations, to produce collared or extruded holes through which the refrigerant tubes pass (Fig. 2). These collars space the fins on the tube and also provide extra contact area for improved heat transfer. The forming is fairly severe, and the collars must be free of radial cracks; otherwise, the collar splits during the tube-expansion operation and poor thermal conductivity results.

Aluminum tube in finned coils has had about seven years of satisfactory experience in automotive air conditioning. Tubing for coils is also entering the residential and commercial central air-conditioning field because of the cost savings available. Alloy 3003-O tube, ⅜-in. OD with 0.035-in. wall, is used in some 3 to 5-ton air-cooled condenser coils in residential and commercial units. This application is expanding as manufacturers gain confidence in soldering aluminum refrigerant tube joints with high-zinc filler materials (Volume III, Chapter 14).

The room air conditioner, however, presents a special corrosion hazard to aluminum tube because of the method used to dispose of condensate (3). One suggestion for preventing corrosion is the use of a fin that galvanically protects the tube. Alloys recommended for the tube are 1100 and 3003; alloy 7072, used as fin material or cladding, provides electrolytic protection to the tube. Alloy 7072 also has the same level of strength, conductivity, and formability as conventional fin alloys, at the same cost.

An alternate solution, which adds to the cost of the condenser but provides maximum resistance to perforation, is to use alclad (outside) tube. Figure 3 shows the performance of 1100 alloy condenser tube under 1100 and 7072 fins, and the performance of alclad (outside) 3003 tube in the identical severe environment. Alloy 7072 fins were used on the alclad tube, so that the tube cladding would not have to protect the fin.

The fan at the wet condenser of a window unit is made of aluminum. It has better resistance to corrosion than a steel fan, and is less expensive than one fabricated from copper-base alloys. In the axial fan, a formed aluminum sheet ring around the periphery (Fig. 4) lifts the condensate water from the sump

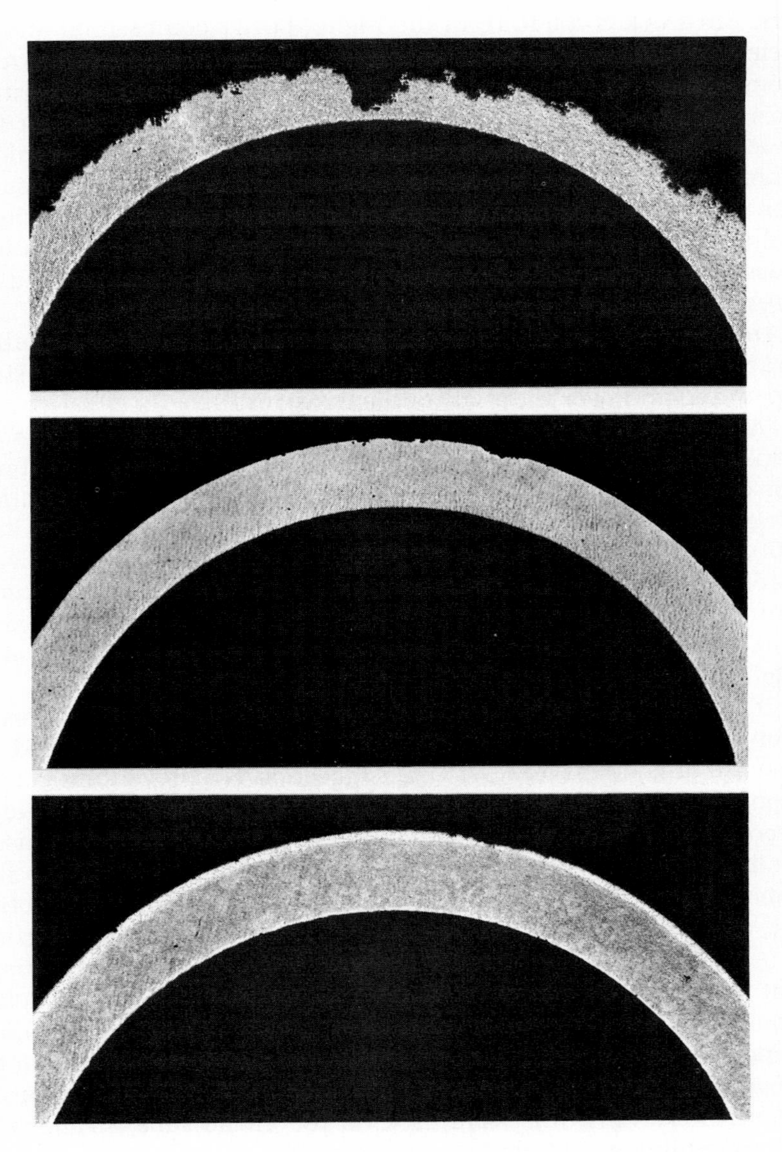

(Top) 1100 alloy tube, 1100 alloy fins. (Center) 1100 alloy tube, 7072 alloy fins. (Bottom) Alclad (outside) 3003 tube, 7072 fins.

Fig. 3. Cross sections of aluminum tube from wet condenser of window air conditioner, showing effect of fin alloy on corrosion resistance of tube and comparing bare tube with alclad (outside) tube. Same service in each test.

and throws it onto the condenser. Alloys 5050 and 5052 are selected for fan blades, because these alloys have higher fatigue strength than 3003. Light weight makes aluminum blades easy to balance.

Air conditioner cabinet components utilize the good weatherability of aluminum alloys. Both in industrial and seacoast environments, unprotected aluminum alloys develop shallow sites of attack, usually 0.002 to 0.004 in. deep, in from six months to two years (4). Then the corrosion in each pit virtually stops; after 20 years of exposure, these same pits are not

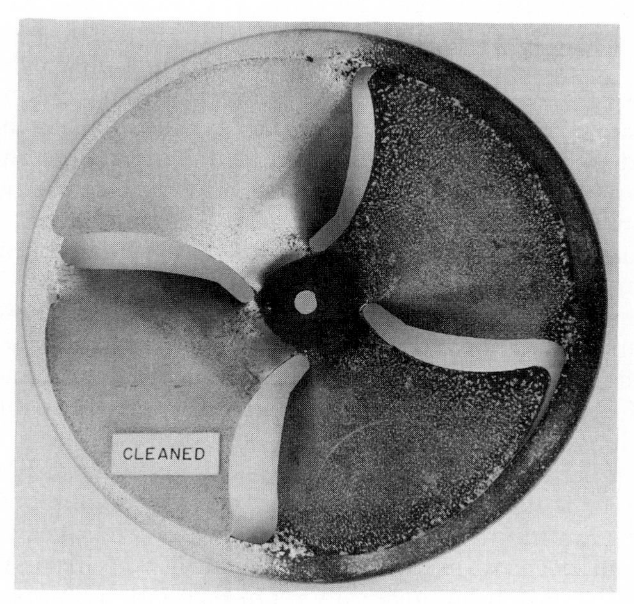

Fig. 4. Aluminum slinger ring fan from air conditioner, showing the shallow corrosion pits on the cleaned side. Ring portion operated in water contaminated with industrial gases and airborne dirt.

appreciably deeper. This type of corrosion, characteristic of aluminum, is termed self-limiting or self-healing (see Volume I, Chapter 7). Any products of corrosion on an aluminum cabinet are white or colorless, and do not appear as stains on the cabinet or streaks down the side of a house under a window air conditioner. Therefore, some cabinet manufacturers employ unpainted 3003 aluminum sheet 0.040 to 0.051 in. thick in an embossed pattern for outdoor components.

The split-system air conditioner is a good example of this application. The condenser cabinet, which is placed outdoors, need not be painted for appearance on the sales floor, as is generally necessary for a window unit. On a window unit, a portion of the cabinet is seen from the room side, and customers expect a painted product. Here, prepainted aluminum sheet can be used. It is available in coils (from the sheet mills), and provides a lower per-square-foot painting cost than does postpainting a completely fabricated and assembled cabinet in the manufacturer's plant. Assembly of a prepainted part must be completed with mechanical fasteners, and this has limited the acceptance of prepainted stock to a few models. One manufacturer's economy line of window air conditioners uses unpainted cabinets.

The rear panel (back) of the cabinet is more commonly of aluminum, because this louvered part is normally mechanically fastened to the cabinet. This permits the use of an aluminum panel on a conventional steel cabinet; and because the back does not show from inside the room, it can be left unpainted.

Manufacturers of room air conditioners provide mounting kits to accommodate a unit in a variety of window widths. The kits are assembled of alloy 6063 aluminum extrusions, sliding one inside another, acting as a frame. Flexible membranes or screens that fold or roll to the side are attached to the expandable frame, and fill the window opening on each side of the cabinet. An interlocking, self-hinging aluminum extrusion design was introduced for the folding screen, but a less expensive accordion-folded plastic part is more common. At least one model employs narrow slats of aluminum sheet for a roll-type screen. These kits use aluminum because of the design versatility of extrusions and because the aluminum generally requires no maintenance.

Dehumidifiers and air filters also use aluminum. Electric dehumidifiers have a small-capacity refrigeration system to remove moisture. On many models, the evaporator coil, which condenses water vapor from the air, is of alloy 1100 or 3003 tube with an outside diameter of ⅜ in. and a wall thickness of 0.035 in. A formed serpentine of tube or a flat concentric-wound coil is normally employed, without fins. Aluminum gives good service in this wet environment, and it is less expensive than other materials having comparable thermal conductivity.

Air filters are made with aluminum media and light-gage sheet frames. The 3003 alloy frame, usually assembled by metal stitching, supports the media, which is most often expanded

1145 alloy foil. Top and bottom layers of the expanded metal are made from material about 0.010 in. thick to support the 0.001 to 0.005-in. inside layers, which provide most of the extended surface needed to clean the air. Aluminum wool machined from alloy 3003 stock is also used as media and is supported between wire screens in a frame. Layers of woven aluminum wire are also employed as a filter. Most aluminum filters can be washed and re-used, affording an advantage over the initially less-expensive disposable glass-fiber filters.

Automatic laundry washers and dishwashers contain a large amount of aluminum in both cast and wrought forms. Cast aluminum agitators are used in premium-quality laundry washers, where resistance to impact and abrasion are demanded. The aluminum-copper alloys are chosen for their good foundry characteristics, which are required to produce permanent mold castings with very thin sections that are only 0.115 to 0.135 in. thick over large areas. A ball-burnish type of finish is most generally used (Volume III, Chapter 16).

Centrifugal water pumps, in both laundry washers and dishwashers, employ cast aluminum alloy housings and impellers, because of the high water temperature and the corrosive conditions. Aluminum-silicon alloys, such as 13 and 360, are generally recommended rather than aluminum-copper alloys, because of their superiority in resisting the general corrosion encountered in the internal passages of water pump housings. Die castings are most frequently used, because of the economies offered and the fine detail and surface smoothness necessary for efficient pump operation.

Aluminum die castings are used extensively for various structural components of clothes washers and dishwashers. These are invariably high-production items, so that the die casting process is normally justified. Examples are transmission housings, tub supports, drive-shaft housings, and base plates. Alloy 380 is the most common for these and other die cast parts, such as pulleys and impellers, because it is economical to produce and has good serviceability.

Wrought products, in the form of sheet and extrusions, are employed in the manufacture of dishwashers and clothes washers. Sheet is used for clothes washer tubs because of the outstanding corrosion characteristics of alloys available in this form and the economic benefits of eliminating costly protective coatings. Although the aluminum surface may become stained

Welbilt Corp.

Fig. 5. Untrimmed die casting in alloy 380 for range top shown in inset. Finished part is given a brushed satin finish.

by alkaline detergent solutions, no corrosion that would impair the serviceability of the products has been observed.

For exterior components where a painted surface is desired, prepainted sheet can be utilized. Other exterior applications of aluminum include decorative trim, doors and frames, and instrument panels, which can be anodized to provide a variety of attractive finishes (Volume III, Chapter 19). Trim items can be either sheet or extrusions. The most common extrusion alloy is 6463; sheet of bright-finishing 5*x*57 alloys is frequently used.

Other appliances, such as ranges, vacuum sweepers, disposers, and sewing machines, also use aluminum extensively.

Disposable oven liners and burner drip pans made from 0.001 to 0.003-in. foil in alloy 1145 solve a once difficult cleaning chore. Removable burner reflectors or drip pans are formed from 3004 alloy sheet 0.015 to 0.025 in. thick. Although pans are sometimes anodized, this is not recommended, because the anodic coating becomes crazed by the heat and spilled food may be baked into the coating. Cleaning is easier with a bare pan.

Extrusions in alloys 6063 and 6463 are used for moldings and handles on appliances. Some manufacturers combine plastics with aluminum extrusions or foil, or vacuum-deposit aluminum on plastic, to enhance styling and color schemes. Anodizing is employed to produce bright, wear-resistant aluminum surfaces that can be cleaned with minimum effort. Griddles with cast-in heating elements are produced as die castings or permanent mold castings in alloys 43 or 344. Deep-well units and broiler pans are usually drawn from 3003 alloy sheet. Figure 5 shows a complete built-in range top made as a die casting of alloy 380.

Gas ranges use 3003-O aluminum tube for gas lines. Couplings and fittings for these lines usually are aluminum screw-machine products in alloy 2011-T3, 2024-T4, 6061-T6, or 6262-T9. Oven thermostat control housings are 380 alloy die castings.

Vacuum cleaners employ aluminum castings, either permanent mold or die cast. They are buffed to a high luster, and are popular for nozzles, frames, and housings. The aluminum-magnesium alloys provide the good impact resistance and finish required for these parts. Wands of 3003 or 6063 alloy tube and drawn canisters of 3003 alloy sheet are used in many models.

Aluminum die castings are used for low-cost, durable components for garbage disposers. Housings, and also the flanged drain-pipe adaptor, are generally die cast in 13 or 360 alloy. Galvanic corrosion, possible at the disposer housing when other metals are used for this drain connector, is thus eliminated. If corrosion occurs at the junction to the trap inlet, it is relegated to the small, inexpensive, aluminum adaptor casting.

All the complex mechanisms involved in a household sewing machine must be contained in a rigid, durable, lightweight housing that can be produced by economical manufacturing procedures. At the same time, the design must be appealing and functional. Aluminum die castings of alloy 13 or 380 satisfy these requirements. They are used for the structural components, and sheet and extrusions are used for access opening covers. All sewing machines currently produced with aluminum die castings have a baked enamel finish, in a variety of colors.

Equipment for Food Preparation

In addition to major appliances, the average kitchen contains many small work-savers to assist in preparing, cooking, serving and storing food.

Cooking Utensils. The same advantages offered by aluminum in the 1890's in the first cast or spun utensils, which weighed less and cooked more evenly and faster than their cast iron counterparts, are still available in present-day utensils.

Most conventional aluminum cooking utensils are formed from sheet of alloy 3003 by deep drawing or stamping, but certain configurations or small production runs are spun. Cast utensils of alloys 43 and 344 are also used, as this process offers design and functional details not easily obtained from sheet. Large griddles, for instance, are cast to provide integral mounting brackets, feet, and stabilizing ribs. Some pressure cookers are cast with a heavy rim, which is machined to incorporate a locking feature for the top. A socket for the handle is also provided in the casting.

Stamped or cast handles are fastened to the pans by riveting or spot welding, or a special fastener is stud welded to the pan for subsequent attachment of the handle. Some pans use a handle fastened into a socket that is flame brazed to the pan body, often automatically. Brazing produces a small, uniform fillet that requires no grinding, as might a gas or arc welded joint. Spouts are frequently formed from one piece of sheet and require welding to close the joint, as does a two-piece spout. Gas welding is commonly used for this type of joint and to attach the spout to the body. Gas welding gives the operator good control of the weld, which has critical appearance requirements, helping to reduce finishing costs on the completed part.

Most aluminum utensils are marketed with a mechanical finish and no protective coating. The inside is usually scratch brushed. Boiling alkaline water stains a bare aluminum pan, but the finish can be readily restored with appropriate kitchen cleaners, such as scouring pads containing soap. Mechanical finishes, such as an outside burnish, remove forming-tool marks and produce a brightened, uniform appearance. Some utensils are buffed on the outside for maximum luster.

The more expensive utensils are given a variety of protective or decorative finishes. Anodizing is used, mostly on covers, for the decorative effect. Porcelain enamel is also used, but it is limited to the outside of pans and the covers. The porcelain frits satisfactory for aluminum contain lead or other low-melting metals that can be toxic, and therefore they are not used for applications involving contact with food. Pans coated with Teflon resins provide a nonsticking surface, permitting foods to be cooked without greasing the pans and reducing cleaning time.

Some bimetal pans designed to combine the advantages of more than one material employ aluminum to distribute the heat evenly and retain the light weight. A good example is the stainless-clad aluminum utensils that have thin stainless steel sheet on the inside bonded to a thicker outside layer of aluminum sheet. This product combines the excellent cleanability of stainless steel with the good thermal qualities of an aluminum

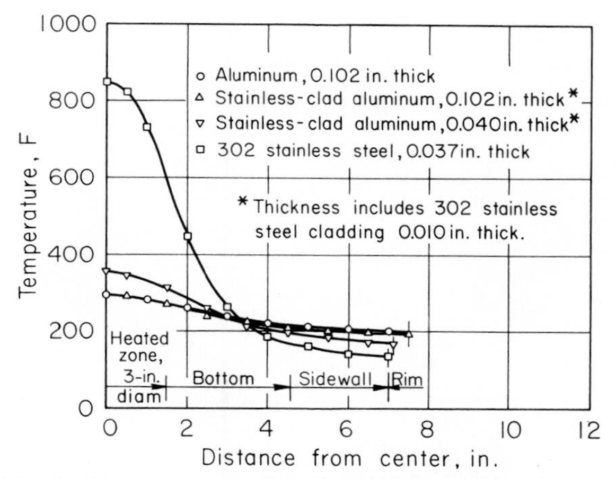

Fig. 6. Temperature distribution in 10-in. frypans fabricated from aluminum, stainless steel, or stainless-clad aluminum, exposed empty for 30 min to heat from a shielded 3-in.-diam electrical resistance unit (550 watts controlled at 1525 F), located 1 in. below the bottom center area of the utensils

pan. The hot rolled bond between the two metals withstands the forming, joining and finishing operations needed to produce quality cookware.

The high rate of heat conductivity of this bimetallic sheet is indicated in Fig. 6. These curves plot the temperatures from center to rim of 10-in. frypans made of aluminum, 302 stainless steel, and stainless-clad aluminum, exposed to a central 3-in.-diam electric heater. This localized heating, representative of top-of-stove cooking, produced a low thermal gradient between the center and rim of the all-aluminum pan and a much higher gradient in the all-stainless steel pan. The difference in gradients was caused primarily by the tenfold difference in thermal conductivity (0.34 Btu per sec per sq ft per in. per °F for aluminum, compared to 0.029 for 302 stainless steel). The two stainless-clad aluminum pans were similar to the all-aluminum pan in temperature distribution.

Although the difference in thermal conductivity caused a large difference in temperature gradient, other thermal properties of aluminum and stainless steel are sufficiently similar or compensating so that approximately the same average temperature per unit of area was obtained in the four test pans. This indicates

Fig. 7. Drawn aluminum frypan with aluminum-cased electric heating element flame-brazed to pan bottom. Thermostat well is also brazed to pan for efficient heat sensing. Method is also used with stainless-clad aluminum sheet.

that the pans had approximately the same total heat transfer characteristics under the test conditions. However, excessively high local temperatures, such as were encountered with the stainless steel pan, can cause burning of food when a minimum of moisture or fats is employed in the cooking operation. Under these conditions, the high thermal conductivity of aluminum or stainless-clad aluminum provides freedom from burning.

Small electric appliances employ many forms and finishes of aluminum. Electric frypans are produced both by the permanent mold and die casting processes, typically in alloys 43, 344, or 380. The heating element is cast-in, eliminating a subsequent brazing operation. Bosses for fastening feet, handle, and thermostat unit are integrally cast. A mechanical finish, such as sanding or brushing, is common for the cooking surface, with polishing and buffing applied to the exterior to enhance the appearance. Covers are usually formed from 3003 alloy sheet.

Electric frypans have been produced also by use of a pressure-bonding process. In this technique, the heating element encased in 3003 aluminum tube is furnace brazed to a 344 alloy permanent mold casting that is first pressure bonded to the bottom of a 302 stainless steel formed pan. Aluminum sheet and stainless-clad aluminum sheet are also applicable to electric frypans with brazed or welded-on heating elements (Fig. 7).

Deep fat fryers, griddles, waffle irons, and warming trays are made by the same casting techniques as electric frypans. With fryers and waffle irons, the cooking units are then built into attractive housings of formed and embossed aluminum, stainless steel, or chromium-plated mild steel sheet.

Mixers and blenders use aluminum die castings of alloys 13 and 380 for motor housings and bases. Paint finishes are usually applied, and ribs and handles are highlighted for contrast by buffing or sanding.

Coffee pot shells are deep drawn from alloy 3003 or 5357 sheet 0.040 to 0.051 in. thick. Aluminum-cased heating elements are assembled into the shell with a locknut. Handles and spouts are welded or brazed on. Finishes range from natural aluminum in a variety of mechanically applied treatments to colored anodic coatings or chromium plate.

Large coffee makers in the 12 to 75-cup range are produced from 0.032 to 0.040-in. sheet using lock-seam construction or a drawn shell. Aluminum-enclosed heating elements with threaded bases are installed with a locknut. Handles and bases are usually riveted or spot welded to the shell.

Household foil consumption has grown from 23.5 million pounds in 1954 to 105 million pounds in 1965. The physical, chemical, mechanical and dimensional characteristics of aluminum foil are discussed in detail in the following chapter, on packaging. Most household foil is annealed 1100 alloy, 0.0007 in. thick, sold in rolls 12 in. wide by 25 ft long; economy rolls range up to 200 ft. Rolls are also available in 8 and 18-in. widths. Interfolded sheets 12 by 10.75 in. in the 0.0007-in. gage are standard. Most foil is sold in the as-fabricated finish, but patterned foil is available.

Foil for commercial kitchens is sold in rolls of 5 to 50 lb, and special sheets are available. For example, sheets to wrap potatoes for baking are made from 0.0005-in. foil, and are marketed with a gold lacquer on one side for decorative effect. Another product uses 0.00035-in. foil laminated to paper, with the laminate containing small slits. Hot sandwiches are wrapped with these sheets for take-out delivery, and the slits let moisture out, preventing sogginess while retaining heat.

Preformed pans stamped from foil are produced both for the consumer market and the commercial or institutional user. These include broiler trays, pie and cake pans, pizza pans, and many other special-purpose containers. Metal gages are thicker than for general-purpose foil — 0.003 to 0.005 in.; many of these products are produced from alloy 3003 hard-rolled foil for required strength (Chapter 23 in this volume).

Commercial food-handling equipment is made of aluminum for the same reasons that aluminum is popular for domestic kitchen utensils. Light weight is especially important for the large pots and pans because of ease in handling and cleaning.

Applications for aluminum begin where the food supplies enter the storeroom. It is used for two-wheel and four-wheel hand trucks, for maneuverability and ease of cleaning. Wood trucks can harbor bacteria and do not permit steam cleaning. Aluminum tote boxes are used to deliver ground meat or dressed poultry. Bulk ingredients, such as flour and sugar, are stored in undercounter bins fabricated from aluminum sheet, castings and extrusions. These covered containers are sometimes on aluminum casters; also aluminum dollies are available to facilitate movement of conventional bins.

In food preparation and cooking, aluminum is used for measuring and mixing containers, scoops, paddles, a variety of stove-top pots and pans, and ovenware. Steam-jacketed kettles and gas-fired kettles for large-quantity cooking are made of aluminum alloys. Serving equipment likewise utilizes aluminum; this category includes carts, trays, buffet service, plate covers, and pitchers.

Bakeries and other food processors employ specialized equipment, much of it in aluminum. Chapter 12 in this volume discusses aluminum in the food processing industry, and aluminum in food packaging is covered in Chapter 23.

Much of the food-handling equipment is fabricated from 3003 alloy sheet, although many items are made in 3004 or 5052 because of their higher strength. One line is made almost entirely of alclad 2024 sheet for an outstanding combination of strength and resistance to corrosion. Typical extrusion alloys are 6061 and 6063; most castings are of 43 or 344.

Fabrication follows the techniques described previously for cooking utensils. Most of the larger products are not given any finish coating; roasting and baking pans, generally anodized, are exceptions. This coating increases the surface emissivity of the aluminum from below 10% to about 75%, causing faster cooking in the oven and more uniform browning of the contents. Some serving equipment, because it is seen outside the kitchen, is anodized to protect the original appearance. Trays are sometimes made from sheet with a polyvinyl chloride film laminated to one or both sides for scuff resistance and to maintain appearance.

Housewares

In the kitchen, grinders, slicers, and juicers employ aluminum die castings, for their attractive appearance and minimum overall cost. These hand-operated food preparation devices are ball burnished, as are many smaller tools and gadgets, such as ice cream scoops, bar sets, and lobster crackers. Alloys 43 and A214 are frequently used for these parts.

Canister sets are deep drawn in alloy 3003, and often have a scratch-brushed finish. Bread boxes and cake pans are lock-seamed on the side and bottom and are generally painted for decoration. Ice buckets are similarly fabricated, and are frequently embossed on the sides and top for appearance effects. The unfinished exterior reflects heat effectively from these insulated containers because of aluminum's infrared reflectivity of over 90%. Lunch-box hinge leaves are sometimes made of aluminum sheet, and are joined to the box with aluminum rivets in alloy 1100, or 6053 if more strength is required. It is not good practice to make the hinge pin of aluminum, because of potential galling; steel wire usually is selected. Other aluminum containers around the home include waste baskets and garbage pails.

Tubular aluminum mop and brush handles are lighter than wood and more durable. Car washing brushes that connect to a garden hose have long aluminum tube handles, which give added reach with minimum effort. This long-life tool also has attachments for washing windows and gutters, and for scrubbing basement floors. Extruded, drawn, and welded tube are all used for handles; tube sizes are 0.75 to 1-in. diameter with a wall thickness of 0.030 to 0.045 in. Alloys generally employed are 6063-T6 and 6063-T832 for extruded and drawn tube, respectively. Alloy 3003-H18 is also used for drawn tube. For welded tube, the harder, cold worked tempers of 3003, 3005, and 5040 sheet are commonly employed.

Sponge mops have aluminum parts in the head to withstand the corrosive environment. Dust pans, including the long-handle models, are aluminum, and other floor-treating devices, such as carpet sweepers, rug shampooers, and waxers, employ aluminum components for ease of handling.

Collapsible clothes-drying racks have been made entirely of aluminum tube and extrusions for good portability and resistance to corrosion. Permanent clotheslines are made of alloy 1100 wire ⅛ to $\frac{3}{16}$ in. in diameter; the wire maintains its integrity outdoors and does not have to be taken down each washday for long life. The uncoated aluminum is sometimes accused of smudging the clothes, but the smudge is caused partly by dirt that collects on the surface between uses. Wiping the wire each week reduces smudging, and a thin coating of wax on the rack or line eliminates it. Aluminum clothes hangers are made of 0.25-in.-diam wire in alloy 5357-H36, usually have an anodic finish, and are available in colors. Damp shirts and sweaters are not stained during drying on this type of hanger.

Dry irons and steam irons have cast aluminum soleplates. One model employs a stainless steel-clad aluminum soleplate, but other hand irons use conventional aluminum permanent mold or die castings. Permanent mold cast soleplates are generally in alloy 138, developed for maximum surface hardness at elevated temperatures, whereas die cast plates are usually 380 alloy. The permanent mold cast plates were originally the more popular, but the lower-cost die cast product is prevalent today. Both designs have the steel-encased heating element cast in the plate. Cast design also permits incorporation of lugs to assemble the hood and attach the thermostat and other controls. Steam passages can be included, and the casting can be shaped either to heat the water reservoir or to minimize the contact, depending on design requirements.

Aluminum is used for soleplates principally because its high thermal conductivity rapidly brings the ironing surface to temperature, and maintains a uniform temperature, avoiding scorching. Aluminum's lightness reduces work in ironing, and its resistance to corrosion is important in steam irons. The rough casting is polished to produce the ironing surface, and this finish gives satisfactory service. Finishes that would provide a greater degree of scratch resistance than bare aluminum have been considered, but surfaces such as chromium plate increase the cost more than the value of the benefit they provide.

The water reservoir in many models of both boiler and flash types of hand steam irons is made from alclad 3003 alloy sheet 0.019 to 0.032 in. thick. In most models, the reservoir is inside the hood, although at least one brand uses the top of the boiler as the hood. This manufacturer furnace brazes (Fig. 8) the drawn hood to the stamped tank bottom, and finishes the iron by polishing the hood. In other designs, the flanges of the tank halves are crimped together, using a sealant to obtain the

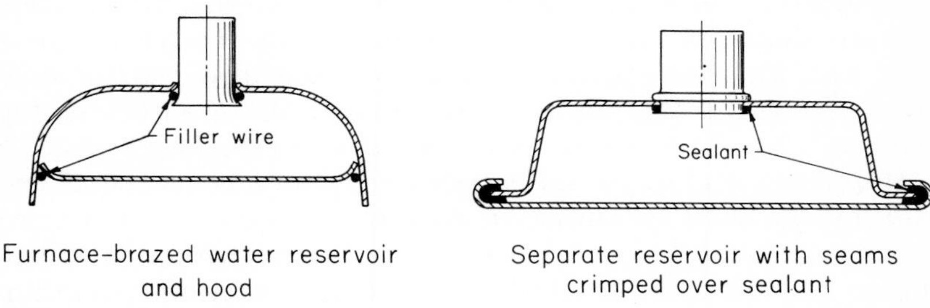

Fig. 8. Methods for joining aluminum steam-iron water-reservoir parts

watertight joint. In this design the reservoir is left in the as-fabricated sheet finish, and a separate hood in a bright finish covers the water chamber. In one brand, this hood is drawn from 5357 sheet, buffed, chemically brightened, and anodized in a copper color.

Home hair dryers include aluminum components to improve portability. Alloy 3003 sheet stampings are used for covers on the blower housing and heating mechanism. Vaporizers utilize aluminum for water tanks, to reduce the possibility of corrosion. Houseware fans and heaters employ aluminum for blades and reflectors. Fan blades are usually made from alloy 5050 sheet, rather than 3003, because of its higher fatigue strength. The blades require no special finish, and their low density makes them easy to balance.

Reflectors in portable electric heaters are aluminum because of its high infrared reflectance. Mill-finish aluminum sheet ranges above 90% in these wave lengths, and bright-rolled products measure 97%. An anodized coating reduces the efficiency in the infrared region (5), although anodizing is frequently used to maintain a bright reflector. The customer expects a reflector to be specular, and one-side-bright 1100 sheet with a thin, 0.1-mil anodic coating is a typical choice. Chapter 20 in this volume discusses aluminum applications in air-moving and heating equipment.

Serving carts, snack tables, and decorative trays are aluminum to achieve high portability and good appearance. Hot-plate pads and stove mats use aluminum sheet over asbestos or rubber to distribute the heat and provide an easily cleaned surface. In one line of rubber-base mats, a thin pattern sheet of aluminum is bonded to the rubber in the vulcanizing process, to insure a nonpeeling laminate. Syphon bottles for carbonating beverages in the home consist of an impact-extruded can and a die cast top, both of aluminum, principally because of the design features these two processes permit. The impact-extruded can incorporates ribs on the side for decorative effect, and the die cast top includes a handle and a recess for the carbon dioxide cylinder.

Mail boxes and house numbers of aluminum sheet require no painting for good resistance to weathering. Alloy 3003 pattern sheet is frequently used for this application. Automatic fire alarms and extinguishers for the home are housed in aluminum containers that present an attractive appearance for wall mounting. Kitchen step stools and small ladders for the home are made of alloy 6063 extrusions and 3003 sheet. These items are rugged, yet easy to move and store. Use of aluminum for large, heavy-duty ladders is discussed in Chapter 10 of this volume.

Furniture

Consumer Furniture. In dinette tables and chairs, aluminum tube, sheet, and extrusions are used in combination with wood, glass, plastic, and fabric to produce functional, maintenance-free, attractive items. The alloys used are generally 6061 and 6063 for tube and extrusions, and 6061 for sheet. Various finishes are applied, including chemical etching, scratch brushing, painting, and anodizing (Volume III, Chapters 16 to 22).

Contemporary home furniture has permanent mold or sand castings for chair and table bases, where contours cannot be economically produced by other processes. Alloys A108, B195, and 356-T6 are utilized extensively because of their strength and finishing characteristics.

Utility chairs and tables have die cast legs in alloys 218 or 380, where design permits and production volume is sufficiently high. Aluminum castings generally are given a mechanical finish and then lacquered or painted. Premium-quality lines are often anodized; for these, low-silicon alloys, such as A108 and B195, are selected to obtain a bright finish.

Modular units, such as kitchen cabinets, room dividers, and book shelves, use aluminum extrusions in combination with other materials for shelving, paneling, and doors. Decorative trim is usually 6063-T42 alloy, while structural or other functional parts are generally 6063 in the T5 or T6 temper. The extrusion process enables the designer to build into his system unique interlocking features, not only for assembly of the extrusion joints, but also to receive the paneling. The usual finish, a chemical etch, has low cost and a pleasing appearance.

For utility storage cabinets and lockers, sheet in the 3*xxx* and 5*xxx* series alloys is used for good formability with satisfactory strength. Aluminum rivets or other mechanical fasteners, in combination with resistance spot welding, are employed in the assembly. When prepainted sheet is used, adhesive bonding or indirect spot welding can be employed.

Lawn and porch furniture uses welded, drawn, or extruded aluminum tube for structural components, with sheet, extrusions and castings for fittings and accessories. Aluminum is combined with plastic webbing, cushions, wood slats, or canvas to provide a large variety of furniture items.

Welded tube, generally produced from the 3*xxx* and 5*xxx* series alloys, is used more extensively than drawn or extruded tube, because of lower cost. The common alloys for drawn tube are 3003 and 6063. Furniture tube is made from the higher-strength cold worked or heat treated and strain-hardened tempers of these alloys. Alloy 6063-T6 is the common choice for extrusions for lawn and porch furniture.

Tube diameters vary from ⅝ to 1 in. OD, depending on the application. The most popular diameter for outdoor furniture is 1 in. The average wall thickness is 0.035 in., although aluminum as thin as 0.027 in. is specified for certain components. Thicker walls are used where design and quality dictate.

Aluminum tube can be formed into short-radius bends, as well as the commonly used knuckle or crushed bend. The tube is frequently tapered by spinning or swaging, and the tube end may be spun closed.

Square tubing, mostly welded, is finding increased application in the outdoor field. Die cast hinge elements and fittings are used on some models; however, most of these parts are made from sheet. A wide variety of mechanical fasteners, usually plated steel, are almost universally employed to join the components. Although the use of aluminum or stainless steel fasteners avoids corrosion problems, stainless fasteners are expensive and aluminum frequently lacks the required mechanical properties. The finish supplied on outdoor furniture tube generally is as-fabricated, because the tube manufacturers have learned to provide a bright surface at the mill that eliminates the need for buffing. The more expensive models are frequently color anodized.

Commercial furniture for restaurants, offices, and institutions uses both cast and wrought aluminum products extensively. The alloys, processes, and finishes are similar to those employed for consumer furniture. The extruded products, however, are mostly 6061-T6 with some 6063-T6, and much of the sheet is 6061-T6. These alloys provide the required strength and weldability. Where forming requirements are severe, 6061-T4 sheet or tube is often used and then, after fabricating, the product is artificially aged to the T6 temper.

Generally, commercial furniture is inert-gas tungsten-arc welded, despite the fact that welding anneals the heat treated members at locations that may be highly stressed. Many products are reheat treated after welding, or designed to accommodate the reduced properties at the welds. Much of this quality furniture is anodized to retain its initial appearance; proper selection of weld filler alloy is critical to insure minimum visibility of the weld zone after the anodizing treatment.

Recreation Products

Camping and sporting equipment utilize aluminum's light weight, weatherability, and durability. Photographic equipment, which includes many intricate parts requiring close dimensional tolerances, is made of aluminum die castings and screw-machine products. Swimming pools use chiefly sheet and plate products, to combine strength, resistance to corrosion, and good portability during construction. Home entertainment products use many forms of aluminum, particularly for trim.

Camping, Fishing, and Hunting Supplies. In camping equipment, sheet and tube are the common aluminum forms. Typical sheet alloys are 3003, 3105, and 5052. Drawn parts such as mess kits, canteens, and flashlight cases are of annealed alloys. Camp stoves, portable ice chests, and folding tables use harder tempers of sheet for these brake-formed parts. Some of these items are made of patterned sheet and are not painted. Aluminum tube is employed for folding stools, camping cots, back packs, and tent frames, pegs, and poles. Welded tube is the most economical product for the intermediate level of strength required, and alloys 3003 and 3005 are frequently used. Diameters are 0.5 to 1.25 in. and wall thicknesses, 0.030 to 0.062 in. Drawn and extruded tubes are also common in alloys 3003-H18, 6061-T6, and 6063-T832. As with sheet parts, aluminum tubular components are usually supplied in the as-fabricated finish.

Camp stoves, operating on propane or white gasoline, are formed of sheet, while many portable charcoal grills are made of aluminum castings. The cast firebox and hinged cover incorporate lugs to support a steel grate, wire grill, and hinge brackets, as well as sockets for tubular aluminum legs.

Although some aluminum flashlight cases are made as impact extrusions, most models are deep-drawn sheet. An impact extruded shell is usually lower in cost than one requiring five or six drawing and ironing operations. However, many flashlight manufacturers prefer to utilize their existing multiple-draw equipment to retain more flexibility in design of the product. Flashlight cases in alloy 3003 are often chromium plated, and some anodized models are made of 5050 or 5357.

Fishing accessories in aluminum include tackle boxes and bait buckets in alloy 3003 sheet of about 0.032-in. gage, and creels woven of 1100 wire of $\frac{1}{16}$-in. diameter. Rods and reels use aluminum in the form of tube, die castings, and screw-machine parts. In a fishing rod, aluminum is normally combined with steel or reinforced plastic. Reel covers and ends are die castings of alloy 218, and the spool is machined from rod of alloys 2011 or 6262. Reels are frequently anodized to impart added resistance to corrosion. Aluminum tube of alloy 3003 is used for the handle and frame of fish-landing nets that float. Many fishing lures have aluminum parts in the form of sheet, extrusions, and forgings.

Firearms employ aluminum for receivers, barrels, sights, and frames. Rifle receivers are made as die castings in alloy 380;

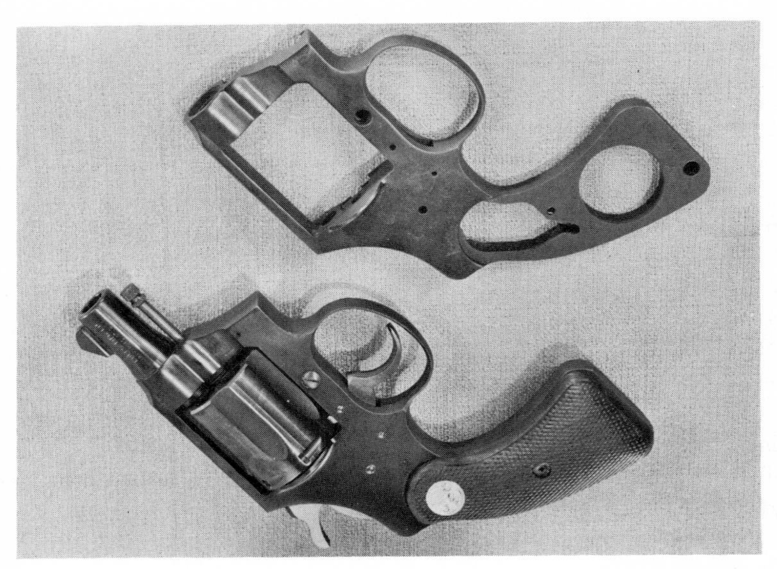

Colt Industries, Inc.

Fig. 9. Alloy 2014-T61 forging was used to make frame for revolver. After machining, part was anodized and dyed black.

shotgun receivers, as forgings in 6061-T6. An aluminum receiver reduces the weight of the weapon and permits a choice of colored protective coatings by anodizing procedures. One shotgun has a steel outer barrel with an aluminum tube liner. The gun is unique in that several aluminum liners are provided to change the gage quickly. Both open and telescopic gun sights are made of aluminum. Conventional open sights are machined from 2024-T4 extrusions or 6262-T9 bar stock. Telescopic sights use 6061-T6 aluminum tube and impact extrusions for the body, and machined parts for eyepieces, lens holders, and mounting mechanism. A gray or black anodic finish is popular for these parts to reduce reflectivity. Air pistol frames are die cast in 380 alloy. The frame for one model of revolver is a 2014-T61 forging (Fig. 9).

Aluminum arrows are recognized as the best available because of consistent performance and durability. They do not have the warping problem or strength limitation of wood arrows. Arrow stock is made from alloy 2024, drawn after heat treatment to close tolerances and a high level of strength. Popular sizes are ¼-in. OD with 0.018-in. wall, 9/32-in. OD with 0.018-in. wall, and 5⁄16-in. OD with 0.022-in. wall. Arrow manufacturers use hand straightening because it is better than roll straightening and stretching. The nocks, feathers, and tips are affixed by adhesive bonding.

Collapsible carriers or racks to transport big game out of the woods utilize aluminum tube assemblies. These units can be carried in as a conventional pack, and expanded into a wheeled cart for bringing out big loads.

Compass parts are made of aluminum because of its nonmagnetic quality. Case halves are frequently machined from aluminum bar stock, and the face is stamped from aluminum sheet. Certain models are anodized black.

Sports Equipment. Badminton racket frames are made from 6061-T6 or 7178-T6 tube or extrusions. They do not warp like wood frames, and can be restrung an indefinite number of times.

High-quality skis, requiring controlled flexibility, employ alloys 7178-T6 or 7075-T6 in sheet form in a lamination with plastics and edge-grain plywood (Fig. 10). The high strength-to-

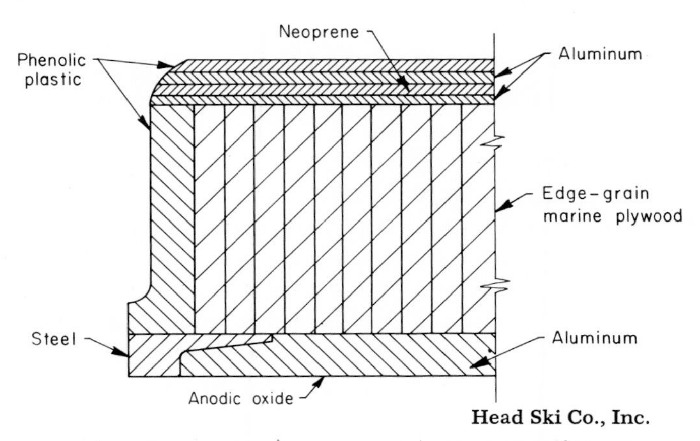

Head Ski Co., Inc.

Fig. 10. Competition skis are laminated using high-strength aluminum alloy sheet. The anodized aluminum running surface requires virtually no waxing.

weight ratio of aluminum is the reason for its inclusion in the adhesive-bonded laminate. Ski poles use 7178-T6, 2014-T6, or 6063-T832 alloy, are amply strong, and weigh only about half a pound each. Steel points are sometimes inserted in the aluminum poles. Tube sizes are usually 5⁄8 or 3⁄4-in. OD, with wall thicknesses from 0.035 to 0.049 in. The 3⁄4-in.-diam tube is generally tapered most of its length by swaging or spinning. When the ⅝-in. tube is employed, only the point is tapered.

Golf carts, where lightness is almost a necessity, employ 6063 alloy tube in various diameters. Some vaulting poles use 7178-T6 alloy tube, for maximum strength-to-weight ratio; diameters are about 1.5 in. and walls approximately 0.070 in. Javelins are usually swaged from alloys in the 6*xxx* series. Light, sturdy hurdles have aluminum tubular bases, and fittings formed from sheet. Shuffleboard cues are generally 6061 or 6063 alloy tube. Pool cues are swaged from 3003-H14 alloy tube, and are usually made in two pieces with a twist-joint in the middle. Color-anodized finishes are applied to enhance appearance.

Automatic pinsetters utilize aluminum to minimize inertia loads and over-all weight. The reciprocating main frames are produced as aluminum permanent mold or die castings (see Fig. 1 in Chapter 2, this volume) or as laminates of 6061-T6 alloy sheet and plywood. The large gear boxes are permanent mold or die castings, usually of 356-T51, A356-T6, or 380 alloy. Forged aluminum arms and levers are 2014-T6.

Roller-skate shoe plates with integral wheel-truck mounting bosses are aluminum castings or forgings. Alloy 6151-T6 forgings are the usual choice for the high-quality models, and 218 alloy for lower-cost die cast designs.

Swimming pools and accessories have been made of aluminum to a limited extent for several years.

Above-ground pools are typically circular, composed of a structural steel frame, a metal sidewall, and a plastic liner. Aluminum sheet in alloys 3003 and 3105 is widely used as the sidewall. The wall, about 0.020 in. thick, provides some rigidity to the frame and sides of the pool and serves as protection against accidental puncture of the plastic liner. Bare pattern sheet is normally used, although painting is also common.

The large institutional in-ground pools are welded of aluminum alloy sheet and plate $3/16$ to $1/4$ in. thick. Subassemblies, particularly the sides, are joined in the factory and shipped to the pool site, where field welding completes the job. The inside surface is painted to provide the desired blue-green color associated with swimming pools. Alloy 5050 is generally used because of its good weldability, resistance to corrosion, and satisfactory stength. In installations where severely corrosive soil conditions are anticipated, alclad 3004 sheet is recommended. Aluminum has a special advantage in large pools in that the light weight makes cost-saving factory subassembly practical.

Composite pools have an aluminum sidewall and a concrete floor. An aluminum wall is not damaged by expansion and contraction associated with temperature changes, nor by the stresses resulting from minor movement of the earth backfill. In composite construction, aluminum wall panels are completely finished in the factory in a size for installing at the pool site with hand labor. The sheet panels are prepainted or laminated with an organic coating on the water side, and may be back coated or made from alclad sheet for soil-side protection, a good practice in any pool installation. The panels are 0.080 in. or more in thickness, depending on structural requirements, and are designed to be joined mechanically. Bolting is generally used; a sealant in each joint provides watertightness.

In-ground pools utilizing a vinyl liner also have aluminum panel construction, to support the liner and to form the pool shape. Sheet panels 0.080 to 0.125 in. thick in alclad 3004 are commonly used, and sandwich panels composed of a foamed plastic core and aluminum skins are sometimes employed. The panels are assembled mechanically in a variety of ways, since the joints do not need to be watertight.

Pool ladders, diving boards, cleaning equipment, and furniture use aluminum in several forms. Extrusions in 6061 and 6063 reinforce the pool walls. Extruded or drawn tube is employed in ladder rails; the ladders have cast steps and fittings. Aluminum castings of alloys 214-F and 356-T6 are utilized in pool cleaning equipment. Extruded sections are used for diving boards, to provide the necessary strength, stiffness, torsional rigidity, and consistent spring action. During a dive, the modulus of elasticity of aluminum of 10 million psi provides the required deflection without excessive stresses in the board. Alloys 6061, 6066 and 6070 are employed; sections are joined by welding, adhesive bonding, or mechanical fasteners. One (Fig. 11) 16-ft-long board

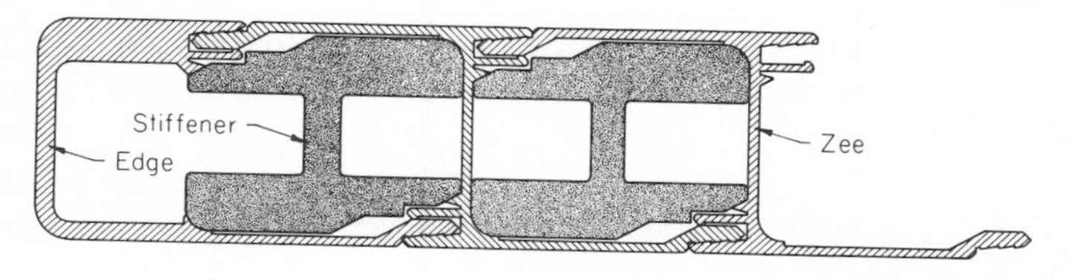

Swimquip Inc.

Fig. 11. Partial section of an aluminum diving board designed with extrusions. The reinforcing stiffeners are used only in the area of the fulcrum.

employs ten extrusions that are assembled utilizing a snap-lock design. Extruded stiffeners of varying lengths are inserted in the fulcrum area to distribute the stress evenly over the entire board.

Photographic Equipment. The complex housings of movie and slide projectors are engineered into aluminum alloy die castings.

The high thermal conductivity of aluminum contributes to the cool running of a projector and prevents local hot spots around the projector bulb that would affect dimensional stability. Die castings also are used in grills, louvered lamp housings, sound-head covers, reel arms, and condenser mounts. Alloy 380 generally is selected for die cast projector components.

Premium-quality movie cameras use aluminum die castings for rigid frames and shutter mounts. Dimensional stability after machining is important, as slight distortion affects focus and camera speed.

Still cameras, from 35-mm up to large plate models, use aluminum die castings, screw-machine parts, sheet, and extrusions for controls, frames, covers, and lens mounts. Tripods are of telescoping tube in 6063 alloy. Because the elastic modulus of aluminum is about 10 million psi, tube diameter or wall thickness or both must be increased to attain rigidity equal to brass (15 million psi) or steel (30 million psi). Some examples of size substitutions for equal rigidity are given in Table 1. Natural, scratch brushed and lacquered, or chemically etched finishes are employed. Swivel heads are die cast in 380 alloy.

Economical containers for packaging or storing movie or strip film are drawn in 1100 alloy sheet or produced as impact extrusions in 3003 alloy. Protective slide frames are also made from sheet. Aluminum reflector sheet, brightened and anodized, is applied in flash reflectors.

Home entertainment products encompass items such as radio and television sets, record-playing equipment, musical instruments, and the general field of games and toys.

When portable television sets were first produced, most of the manufacturers used aluminum sheet for the cabinets to reduce the weight; the aluminum was painted after fabrication. In some instances, a vinyl-plastic laminate with 3003-H14 sheet was used to form the cabinet, eliminating any need for finishing subsequent to forming. After a few years, the weight saving was sacrificed for economy and sheet steel cabinets were adopted.

The chassis of radio and high-fidelity equipment are sometimes made of aluminum sheet, partly to reduce the weight and partly to help dissipate the heat generated. There are no critical alloy requirements; 3003 or 5052 generally is used, in an intermediate work-hardened temper to permit brake forming. Much of the trim on cabinets is aluminum sheet and extrusions, including the anodized nameplates and instruction panels. Alloy 5357 is selected for bright sheet trim.

Aluminum is used for knobs and handles on this type of equipment. Knobs are die cast, and handles are made from forgings, extrusions, castings, or sheet. The pickup arm on record players is frequently an alloy 380 die casting. Outdoor

Table 1. Dimensions and Weights of Brass and Aluminum Tubes Having Rigidity Equal to That of a Specific Steel Tube

Example No.	Outside diameter, in.	Wall thickness, in.	Weight, lb per ft
	Steel		
...	0.750	0.035	0.267
	Brass		
1	0.750	0.086	0.659
2	0.936	0.035	0.335
3	0.875	0.045	0.431
	Aluminum		
4	0.750	0.220	0.431
5	1.067	0.035	0.133
6	0.875	0.074	0.219

television antennas are made from aluminum tube in both 3003 and 6063 alloys. The tube is roll formed or extruded, usually ⅜-in. OD with a wall thickness of about 0.040 in. Aluminum antennas weigh less than steel, facilitate installation, and have much longer life, with no maintenance regardless of weather.

In the musical instrument field, aluminum is used in xylophones for the vibrating bars. These are made in a variety of sizes from extrusions or plate. Heat treated alloys are used, because a dampened tone was obtained with strain-hardened material, probably because of the type or magnitude of the residual stresses. An electric organ has aluminum for trim and for structural components in such places as the music rack and the keyboard panel. These parts are alloy 6063 extrusions, color-anodized for decorative effect. Drum cases are made from aluminum by rolling sheet into a cylinder and welding. Aluminum is particularly important for the large bass drums in marching bands, because of minimum weight.

Piano plates have been cast in 319 alloy to reduce weight compared to cast iron. However, lower costs have led to the current utilization of cast iron for these components.

A number of toys use aluminum components. Walking stilts of aluminum tube are lighter and stronger than wood stilts. Certain types of model airplanes have aluminum sheet wing components, and the small engines are usually machined from die castings, bar stock, or a special extrusion in alloy 6063. Model train components are made as aluminum die castings. Dished sheet circles are used for sliding in the snow.

Tools and Garden Equipment

Although aluminum is used extensively in many types of hand tools, a more dramatic growth in applications for aluminum has occurred in power tools for home and industry. For example, castings are now widely used as housings for portable units. Aluminum is prominent in gardening equipment where small, air-cooled gasoline engines supply the motive power. Castings again predominate, being used for many engine components.

Hand and Power Tools. Hand levels are an example of good die casting design. Stable, flat working surfaces require only rough grinding for a finish. Hand grips and bosses for the bubble vials are easily cast in. Manufacturers' identification and other lettering are sharp and clear on the casting. Alloy 380, in the as-cast finish or highlighted by grinding, is the common choice. Premium-quality levels are anodized for increased resistance to corrosion and wear.

Masonry finishing trowels utilize forged aluminum alloy handle bodies, for high strength and impact resistance. Steel blades are riveted to the forgings, with the rivet heads ground flush with the steel work surface. Wood handles are assembled on the tang provided on the forging. Alloy 6061-T6 in the as-fabricated finish is common for this application. Die cast 218 alloy trowel handles are used on less expensive models.

Utility handles for files, saws, and knives, where durability and hand-fitting design are of importance, are aluminum alloy die castings. Finishing is held to a minimum; coring eliminates any machining requirement for component assembly.

Pipe wrenches, especially in the 18 to 60-in.-length range, where light weight and high strength are primary requirements, are forged of alloy 2014-T6. The jaws on both handle and hook have hard steel inserts pinned to the work-contact surfaces. The adjusting nut is a 2014-T6 alloy screw-machine product. Ratchet wrenches with 0.75 and 1-in. drives are forged in alloy 2014-T6, with steel inserts pressed in to carry ratchet assembly loads.

Aluminum alloy hammers are employed in assembly operations where denting or marring of the work cannot be tolerated. Hammer heads, or complete one-piece units, sand or permanent mold cast in alloy 43 are in general use.

Power tools, with requirements of streamlined styling on housing exteriors and assembly bosses on the inside, are well suited to aluminum die casting techniques (Fig. 12). Drills, routers, sanders, and saws are in this category. These portable but rugged units are economically produced in 380 alloy. The high thermal conductivity of the aluminum prolongs tool life. Mechanical finishing by polishing is common.

Sears, Roebuck & Co.

Fig. 12. Three aluminum die castings form the structure of lightweight portable saber saw. Rear housing incorporates handle and control supports as integral elements of the casting.

Lawn and garden equipment can be classified as hand-operated or power-operated. Hand equipment includes landscape rakes, pole saws, trowels, tree trimmers, utility carts, and snow shovels. Landscape rakes employ extrusions with punch-outs to leave tines on 26 to 42-in. heads. Handles are generally 6063-T832 or 3003-H18 alloy drawn tube. Pole saws and tree trimmers with telescoping handles in 3003 hard-drawn tube are light and maneuverable. Utility carts with 3003 sheet bodies and aluminum tube handles are maintenance-free. Snow shovels and pushers use 3004-H38 or 3105-H16 sheet for blades and 6063-T832 alloy tube for handles. Steel wear strips usually are riveted to the working edge.

The major application of aluminum in power-operated lawn and garden equipment is in small, air-cooled, two and four-cycle gasoline engines, ranging from 1 to 10 hp. Aluminum die castings are universally used for such parts as cylinders, cylinder heads, pistons, connecting rods, crankcase covers, and carburetor bodies. Alloys 13 and 380 in the as-cast condition are in general use. However, all pistons and connecting rods are stabilized with a T5-type heat treatment (see Volume I, Chapter 5). Iron cylinder liners are cast in, except in one major engine that has flash-chromium-plated aluminum-copper-silicon alloy pistons operating in a bare, honed bore of the same alloy.

Usually, aluminum alloy connecting rods are run direct on steel at both crank and pin ends. This applies for four-cycle engines of up to 5 hp and for two-cycle engines with displacement of 2 cu in. per hp or more. Steel crankshafts and camshafts run direct in the aluminum crankcase and cover. Valve-guide inserts are not required, but ferrous valve seats are pressed in.

Four-cycle engines of up to 5 hp use virtually all the engine components and practices mentioned. Engines of 5 to 10 hp generally utilize aluminum only for pistons, cylinder heads, and connecting rods. Iron cylinders and crankcases are preferred because of the lower production volume and the fact that weight limitation is not necessary. Forged aluminum connecting rods in 2014-T6 alloy, when employed in engines in this higher horsepower range, are operated direct on the piston pin bearing. However, the crank end may be tin immersion coated, have babbitt cast in, or use replaceable bearing shells. Pistons are permanent mold castings in F132-T5 alloy, cam ground, and normally tin immersion coated. Cylinder heads are permanent or semipermanent mold castings in 333-T5 alloy, unless production volume warrants a 380 alloy die casting from a cost standpoint.

Two-cycle engines find application not only in the low-horsepower range but also are highly favored for chain saws, because of their low weight per horsepower. Die cast 380 alloy cylinders, generally with integral heads, and F132-T5 alloy permanent mold pistons are used in conjunction with magnesium die cast main frames and crankcases to produce maximum maneuverability. Although some chain-saw engine manufacturers use cast-in iron cylinder liners, others chromium plate the aluminum cylinder bore for additional weight saving. The environment of high temperature and borderline lubrication in which connecting rods must survive makes ferrous rods with needle bearings the choice in these high-output units.

Miscellaneous small permanent mold, sand, and die castings are used for carburetors, air-cleaner horns, and flywheel fans. Power lawn mower housings are made extensively as alloy 380 die castings and to some extent as permanent mold cast parts in alloy 333-F. Stamped sheet in alloys 3003 and 5052 has been evaluated, but the aluminum casting can be designed to incorporate more structural and assembly features. Many powered garden equipment units have handles formed of aluminum tube.

Other Products

Some of the many consumer items that utilize aluminum but cannot be readily classed in the categories previously discussed are treated briefly in the following paragraphs.

Artificial Christmas trees are made of bright-rolled aluminum foil. For the tree branches, the fringed foil is wrapped on straight wires. The branches generally are 5005-H19 wire 0.100 to 0.110 in. in diameter. The foil is used in a 3-in. width, and the coil is slit into ⅛-in. strips across the width leaving a ⅛-in. edge. This edge is spirally wrapped around the wire branch and adhesive bonded or taped at the end. The “needles” stand out around the branch, and can be made to stay straight, twist, curve, or bunch into a flower shape at the end of the branch, according to the pattern of cutting and wrapping.

Alloy 1145 foil was used in the first Christmas tree models, but the need for higher strength progressively changed the alloys used to 1100, 3003, and 5052. The standard alloy now is 5050-H19, chosen for high strength and retention of brightness. The thickness is 0.0015 to 0.002 in. Some trees use colored foil, but the majority depend on the bright aluminum surface for the sparkle that is most often accentuated with a spotlight, which is considered more effective and safer than lights on the tree itself.

Eyelets and ferrules of many types are deep drawn from aluminum sheet in alloys 3004 and 5050. The largest single application is for shoe eyelets, with the metal thickness varying from 0.010 to 0.016 in. Aluminum is used because of its low cost and freedom from corrosion problems. Annealed alloys generally are used because of the multiple draws, and the cold work applied gives the finished product adequate strength. Aluminum does not work harden as rapidly as steel or brass in this application, permitting most aluminum eyelets to be completed without an intermediate anneal. Generally, the tubular portion of an aluminum eyelet is not ironed between the punch and die; all of the depth is obtained by extra draws. This practice eliminates excessive thinning of the eyelet wall, producing a stronger part. The extra draws are not objectionable in high-speed, multiple-station eyelet presses.

Eyelets and grommets are also used to reinforce fastening holes in products such as tents and shower curtains. Resistance to humid environments is the reason for using aluminum in such products. The principal use of aluminum ferrules is on furniture legs. Drawn tube is often used to make the longer ferrules; and the alloys used are 3003, 5052, and 6063. These are sometimes tapered by swaging or spinning, or an intermediate-diameter tube may be forced into a tapered die with a punch that expands the large end and supports the small end that is being compressed.

Slide fasteners (zippers) are made from aluminum sheet and round or flattened aluminum wire. These fasteners consist of scoops crimped onto the beaded edge of cloth tape halves, which interlock to provide the closing feature. The movable member, which opens and closes the scoops, is the slider body, and its handle is called a pull. Stops are attached to the top and bottom of the length of scoops to prevent the slider body from leaving the assembled fastener.

Aluminum scoops are made of either round or flattened wire in alloy 5056. Round wire is formed longitudinally into a Y cross section, after which it is sliced into short lengths. These small pieces, or blank scoops, are then formed to produce the interlocking contour, and each finished scoop is crimped to the fastener tape by closing the Y over the beaded edge. Scoops made of flattened wire are die cut to the Y shape, and then formed and joined to the tape as in the round-wire process. The temper of the 5056 alloy varies from annealed to H14, with most manufacturers selecting soft tempers, such as H111 or H112.

The slider body generally is not made of aluminum where aluminum scoops are used; galling could become a problem even if a lubricant were applied, because dry cleaning solutions tend to remove the lubricant when the clothing is cleaned. Aluminum slider bodies, made as die castings, work well on nylon fasteners, but the pull is the only aluminum part on most sliders. Pulls can be made of aluminum sheet or flattened wire, and 5056 alloy generally is used. Many styles of stops are made of aluminum sheet. These parts require considerable forming and are sometimes annealed after fabrication to eliminate excessive springback after clinching to the fastener tape.

Alloy 5056 is used because it work hardens to higher strength than most non-heat-treatable aluminum alloys. Aluminum slide fastener components are often anodized; some are subsequently painted to match garment colors.

Aluminum jewelry is made from super-purity alloys because of their bright finishing characteristics. Aluminum of 99.99% purity is normally alloyed with varying small quantities of magnesium, to increase the strength and to improve the surface appearance, both by refining the grain size and by imparting higher hardness, which improve the mechanical finishing characteristics. The magnesium has only negligible effect on the color of bright-anodized parts. Most other alloying elements commonly added to aluminum alloys impart some tint to the anodic coating. Lurium is the name of four alloys imported for manufacturing jewelry and related items, and 5405 is the common domestic alloy.

Eyeglass frames and temple bars are made from these jewelry alloys; light weight and freedom from warpage are advantages. However, light weight is not always esteemed in jewelry, as consumers generally associate jewelry quality with weight.

Cosmetic cases, cuff links, and cigarette lighters are made from sheet and impact extrusions and are usually buffed, chemically or electrochemically brightened, and anodized either in the natural finish or in color. Super-purity alloys are also available in wire, and this form is used to make decorative chains for necklaces and handbags. The anodized aluminum does not tarnish and is less expensive than competitive metals.

Miscellaneous applications in consumer products include such items as giftware, smokers' supplies, and luggage. Aluminum ash trays, candy dishes, and fruit bowls are examples of giftware. These sheet items are often decorated by embossing or coining and are normally anodized to maintain the polished or matte-finished surface. Proper selection of alloy, surface finish, anodic coating, and color makes it possible to produce aluminum items having the appearance of brass, silver, or gold.

Gift wrapping made of 0.00035-in. aluminum foil laminated to paper is popular because of the variety of bright colors and patterns printed on the foil. The foil base causes the colors to appear brighter because of the metallic luster, and uncolored areas in bright or matte aluminum add to the decorative effect.

Aluminum tube is used to make certain cigarette holders and pipe stems. It is also formed to make the body of mechanical pencils, the tube often being drawn to a hexagonal shape. Impact extrusions and deep drawn shells in 5050 alloy are used for pen and pencil parts. Knitting needles in large sizes are produced from alloy 3003-H18 tube; aluminum wire is more common for smaller needles. Alloys 1100, 3003, 5052 and 5056 are used, and the temper is normally full hard, although some headed needles are half hard.

Aluminum hardware on luggage employs die castings for latches, and extrusions for frames and edging. Edging is clipped over the wood or leather shells to both decorate and protect the sides. Aluminum frames are used in conjunction with plastic or cloth cases to give shape and durability to the luggage. Some luggage bodies are drawn from 2024-T4 sheet 0.040 to 0.050 in. thick and given a clear anodic finish. Extrusions usually are 6063-T6 and die castings are alloy 380.

References

1 Brightening Outlook for Aluminum in Appliances, Modern Metals, 21, No. 3, 30–35 (April 1965)

2 J. N. Woolrich, Furnace Brazing Aluminum Refrigerator Parts, Iron Age, 163, 62–65 (May 26, 1949)

3 D. G. Vandenburgh and A. J. Haygood, Performance of Aluminum in Air Conditioners, Refrigeration Engineering, 66, 42–76 (Sept 1958)

4 C. J. Walton, D. O. Sprowls and J. A. Nock, Jr., Resistance of Aluminum Alloys to Weathering, Corrosion, 9, 345–358 (1953)

5 C. S. Taylor and J. D. Edwards, Some Reflection and Radiation Characteristics of Aluminum, Heating, Piping, and Air Conditioning, 11, 59–63 (Jan 1939)

Chapter 23

Packaging Applications

J. A. Lake, A. B. McKee and R. C. Reed

THE FIRST packaging use of aluminum, closures on glass bottles, dates to the early 1900's. This was a successful application primarily because the closure could be made to hold tightly to the somewhat irregular glass threads. Aluminum foil was adopted for packaging shortly after its initial production in this country in 1913. Candy-bar and chewing-gum wraps took advantage of many of the desirable properties of aluminum foil. Impact-extruded collapsible tubes of aluminum were introduced in the United States in 1921. In the late 1950's, there was a trend toward adoption of aluminum for a broad range of rigid containers. The fabricating characteristics of aluminum permitted production of such containers by impacting, drawing, and adhesive bonding, as well as by spiral winding of foil laminates. Extensive development efforts are now being directed toward using strong aluminum alloys, to achieve gage reductions and lower costs, in applying aluminum to cans. In some applications, such as large containers, steel, with its high modulus and greater strength than applicable aluminum alloys, enjoys an advantage.

Foil consumption in packaging continues to expand. Aluminum collapsible tubes are popular in the United States for toothpaste, cosmetics, and pharmaceutical items, but are not accepted for food packaging as extensively as in Europe.

Aluminum for packaging is preponderantly in the form of

J. A. Lake is a section manager, Packaging Div., Alcoa Process Development Laboratories, Alcoa Technical Center, Pittsburgh. A. B. McKee is chief, Packaging Div., Alcoa Research Laboratories, New Kensington. R. C. Reed was formerly manager, Packaging Div., Alcoa Process Development Laboratories.

sheet or foil. Considerable commercially pure aluminum is employed, although non-heat-treatable alloys of the aluminum-magnesium and aluminum-manganese types are also used for higher strength. With both commercial-purity aluminum and alloys, broad ranges in mechanical properties are available through varying degrees of work hardening.

The uses of aluminum in packaging are identified by the industry in four categories:

1 Flexible wraps and laminates (incorporating foil)
2 Rigid containers (made from sheet, foil laminates, or drawn heavy-gage foil, or impact-extruded from slugs)
3 Closures for bottles and jars (made from sheet or foil)
4 Collapsible tubes (fabricated from slugs by impact extrusion)

Flexible Packaging

In the Packaging Institute's glossary of packaging terms, flexible packaging is defined as involving the use of flexible materials such as foil, films, paper, and sheet, to form the container. However, in this chapter, containers based on foil made rigid by laminating to a stiff material such as paperboard or by drawing heavy-gage foil are generally classed as rigid containers. Similar heavy-gage products that are merely pressed into wrinkled shapes, such as the familiar throw-away pie pan, are designated formed containers.

Aluminum foil* has become firmly established as one of the major flexible packaging materials. In the United States, estimated total foil shipments in 1965 were about 200,000 tons, which was more than double that produced in 1954 and more than the entire output of primary aluminum in 1935. In 1965, about 85% of all aluminum foil produced was used in some form of packaging. The three major packaging applications are household foil, 35%; laminated foil, 30%; and formed containers, 28.5%.

Aluminum foil is sheet less than 0.0060 in. thick. It can be rolled commercially as thin as about 0.00017 in. An important characteristic of aluminum foil is its high covering area per unit of weight. For example, 0.00035-in. foil has a covering area of 29,300 sq in. (203 sq ft) per pound. This is equivalent to 14.8 lb per 3000-sq-ft ream. At a price of 84¢ per lb, foil in this gage costs approximately 3¢ per 1000 sq in.

* Additional information on foil is given in Chapter 2 of this volume.

Aluminum foil is outstanding in its low permeability to water vapor and gases. Extremely small pinholes are unavoidable in thicknesses less than 0.001 in. However, even in the lighter gages of foil — such as 0.00035-in., used extensively in packaging — the water vapor transmission rates (WVTR) are negligible when coatings or laminated structures are applied (1).

Foil is tasteless, odorless, nontoxic, and hygienic. A special advantage of annealed foil is that it is substantially sterile because of the temperature (over 650 F) of annealing (2). Foil is greaseproof and nonabsorptive to liquids, and hence is especially suited for packaging medicinal oils, ointments, grease-base cosmetics, and similar products. Foil remains dimensionally stable during exposure to oils and greases.

Foil is an effective barrier to light and is used extensively to package photographic materials and other light-sensitive products. Ultraviolet radiation accelerates the development of rancidity in certain foods; foil is a good barrier to this radiation, retarding loss in flavor and appearance, and inhibiting development of rancidity and staleness.

Because it is an efficient reflector and low emitter of radiant heat, aluminum foil is employed for packaging where the thermal insulating properties imparted by these characteristics are advantageous (3). Despite these insulating effects, the good thermal conductivity makes it possible to chill or heat aluminum packages more rapidly than those with nonmetallic covering.

Aluminum foil is not combustible under the conditions encountered in packaging applications. Annealed foil has excellent "dead-folding" characteristics, which permit crimping or folding without springback, an important property in forming overwraps (flexible sheet wraps applied as the outer cover of a paperboard box or carton).

Aluminum foil resists corrosion by a wide variety of packaged products. Resistance to attack by oils, greases, and organic solvents is excellent. Intermittent contact with water generally has little or no effect. Some hygroscopic products packaged in foil may have a corrosive action, particularly if the product contains chloride salts in combination with mild organic acids, such as are present in cheese, ketchup, and mayonnaise. When corrosion is a problem, it is usually possible to control the attack by means of a protective coating or inhibitor (4).

Alloys used for foil in packaging applications include 1100 (99.0 to 99.3 Al), 1145 (99.45 to 99.60 Al), 3003 (Al – 1.25

Mn), and 5052 (Al – 2.5 Mg – 0.25 Cr). Annealed or soft foil is identified as O-temper. Annealing is accomplished by heating the metal to above 650 F. This softens the foil, removes traces of lubricants left from rolling, and effectively sterilizes it. For many years, all the aluminum foil marketed commercially was in either the annealed or the full-hard H19 temper. Foil gages above 0.002 in. are now also available in the intermediate, partially annealed tempers H25 and H27. Lighter gages in intermediate tempers are available from a few foil sources.

The hardest temper of foil, available in any gage and designated H19, is an extra-hard temper that has received a high degree of cold work.

The mechanical properties of aluminum foil are of considerable interest for flexible packaging applications. Tensile strength and elongation for 1100, 1145, 3003, and 5052 alloys in the O

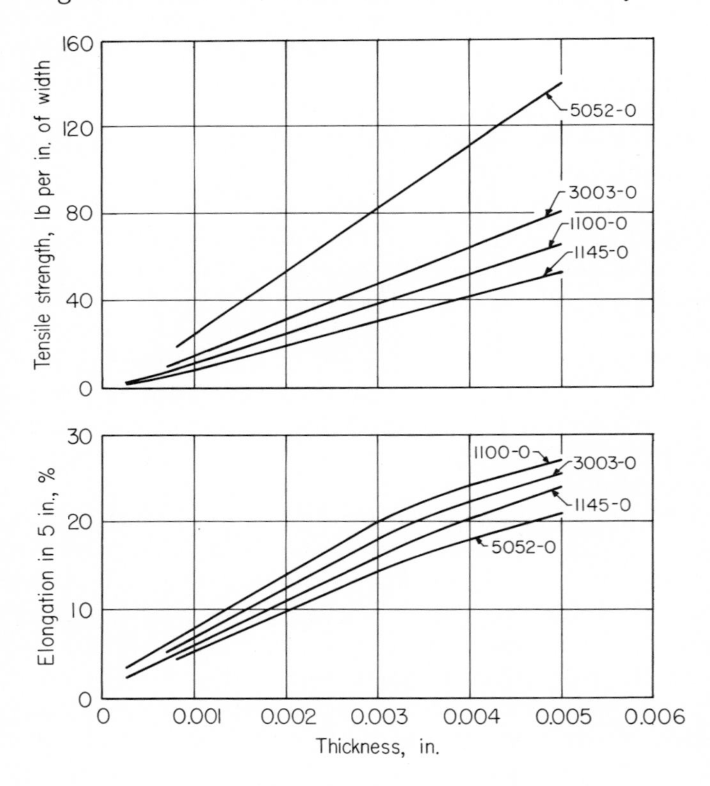

Fig. 1. Tensile and elongation properties of annealed aluminum foil

and H19 tempers are given in Fig. 1 and 2. Economic considerations generally dictate the use of thin foil, relying for strength on plastic films or papers laminated to the foil. Increasing interest in storage of food products at low temperatures brings to the fore aluminum's increase in strength and ductility as the temperature is lowered (3% increase between room temperature and −20 F) (see Chapter 13 in this volume).

Laminating, Coating, and Printing Materials. Unsupported foil in the light gages used for packaging often lacks the ruggedness to withstand abuse encountered during shipping and handling. For this reason, foil gages less than 0.001 in. are generally laminated to paper or plastic films. In many instances, the foil also is coated for protection, decoration, or heat sealing; usually, the laminate is printed for product identification and appeal. Heat sealing unites two or more surfaces by fusion,

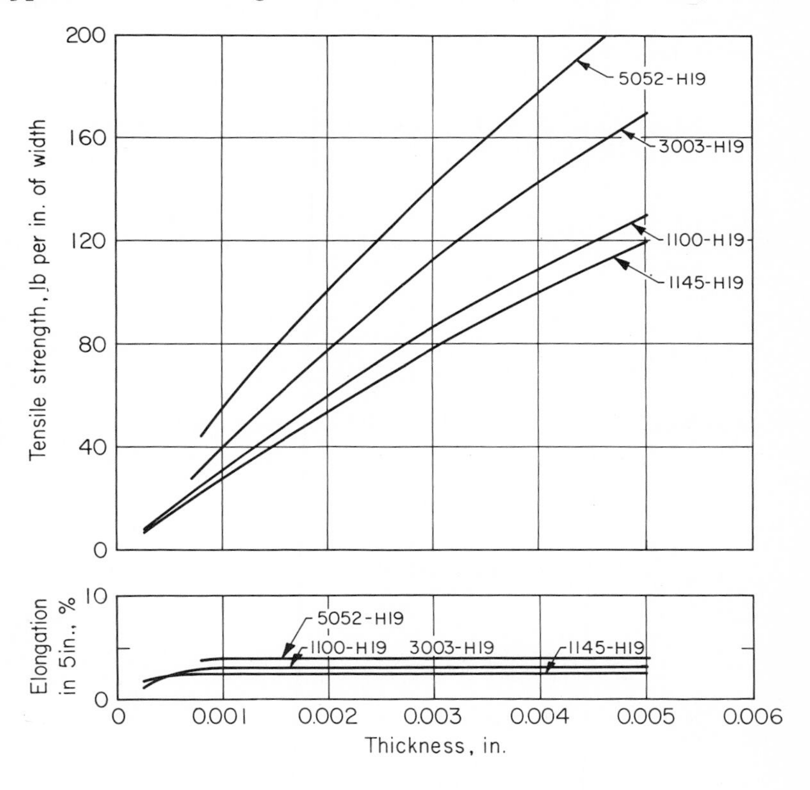

Fig. 2. Tensile and elongation properties of H19-temper aluminum foil

either of the base materials or of coatings that have been applied, using controlled temperature, pressure, and dwell time. The bond between the heat-sealed surfaces may be one of complete fusion or may be partially fused to allow easy separation of the two surfaces. Laminated structures with various types and weights of paper or plastic film perform satisfactorily under a wide variety of conditions (Table 1).

Kraft (sulfate) papers are employed where high strength

Table 1. Commercial Laminated Structures Made With 0.00035-In. Foil

		Structure(a)	End use
Foil, Adhesive, Paper or film	1	Foil/silicate adhesive/30 to 40-lb kraft paper	Reflective insulation
	2	Foil/casein-latex adhesive/30-lb ground wood paper	Label stock
	3	Foil/casein-latex adhesive/25-lb kraft paper	Canister labels
	4	Foil/asphalt/30 to 60-lb kraft paper	Insulation vapor barrier
	5	Foil/micro wax/8-lb porous tissue	Overwrap
Paper or film, Adhesive, Foil, Film	6	25-lb pouch paper/casein-latex adhesive/foil/polyethylene	Pouch stock
	7	Cellulose acetate or cellophane film/solvent-type adhesive/foil/polyethylene	Pouch stock
Paper or film, Adhesive, Foil, Plastic film	8	25-lb pouch paper/casein-latex adhesive/foil/solvent-type adhesive/plastic film	Pouch stock
	9	Cellulose acetate or cellophane film/solvent-type adhesive/foil/solvent-type adhesive/plastic film	Pouch stock
Foil, Adhesive, Wax, Paper	10	Foil/water-base adhesive/15-lb tissue/micro wax/8-lb porous tissue	Overwrap
Foil, Wax, Paper	11	Foil/micro wax/15-lb tissue/micro wax/8-lb porous tissue	Overwrap

(a) The term "lb" used in these structures indicates lb per 3000-sq-ft ream.

and rigidity are required at moderate or low cost; bleached krafts, where whiteness also is needed. Sulfite papers impart moderate mechanical properties and a high degree of surface smoothness. Low-cost groundwood papers are selected where low strength and slight color are acceptable. Glassine, greaseproof, and parchment papers represent the more expensive types and offer high resistance to oil and moisture.

Plastic films laminated to foil for commercial use include cellophane, cellulose acetate, rubber hydrochloride, vinyls, polyvinylidene chloride, polyesters, and polyethylene.

A wide range of water-base, organic-solvent, and hot-melt adhesive materials are employed with foil laminated structures; the individual requirements of each application usually restrict the selection. Requirements include color, odor, toxicity, and resistance to heat, cold, and moisture.

Water-soluble and water-emulsion adhesives are low in cost and excellent for bonding foil to papers or other fibrous materials. Since water wets papers readily, the water base aids in establishing a good bond. Sodium silicate solution is used in laminating foil to paper for cigarette and soap wrappers and certain types of labels. Casein-latex formulations and resin emulsions are somewhat more expensive, but they are widely used because they are less brittle than the sodium silicate solutions; consequently, the foil is less likely to fracture and become permeable to moisture.

Organic-solvent-based adhesives, such as vinyls, are used chiefly to laminate plastic films to foil, and also, in some cases, for less water-wettable papers, such as glassine and flameproof kraft. These adhesives are usually applied to the foil and heated to evaporate the solvent prior to hot laminating. Disadvantages are high cost and flammability, and toxicity of some solvents.

Hot-melt adhesives (waxes and thermoplastic resins) contain no water or organic solvents, and so they must be heated to liquefy them for use. Having no solvent, they do not require subsequent tunnel drying. Wax-base hot melts generally provide additional resistance to water vapor transmission. Certain low-molecular-weight grades of extruded polyethylene resins can be considered a special type of hot melt, but normal extrusion-grade polyethylene resins are quite different and are important as adhesives, coatings, and free film.

Coatings used on aluminum foil for protection can be formulated for resistance to chemicals, heat, or scuffing. Resistance to chemical attack or to mechanical abuse can be provided either by protective coatings or by various plastic films. In many applications, a protective coating serves also as a heat-seal surface, as discussed subsequently. To provide effective protection against chemicals and aggressive food products, both polyolefin and vinyl-type coatings are commonly used. In addition, films of polyvinylidene chloride, vinyl chloride–vinyl acetate, and rubber hydrochoride (laminated to foil) are used to obtain a specific type of protection. Where these are inadequate, curing epoxy resins, epoxy-phenolic blends, or vinyl-phenolic blends are applied.

Fig. 3. Laminated-foil overwraps

These coatings should be applied at a weight of at least 2 to 3 mg per sq in. (1.9 to 2.9 lb per 3000-sq-ft ream). For products having severe corrosive action on aluminum, coating weights of 4 to 6 mg or more may be required. For applications where coatings may come in contact with food products, it is essential that the coatings be nontoxic and free of residual odor or taste.

Decorative lacquers applied to foil are commonly nitrocellulose formulations containing resins and plasticizers. They are colored with dissolved dyes, dispersed lake colors, or ground pigments. Decorative coatings often require resistance to color fading, good formability, and good resistance to heat.

Of the available heat-seal coatings, the vinyl type is considered to be the most satisfactory for aluminum foil. Those commonly employed are the copolymers of vinyl chloride and vinyl acetate. Since the middle 1950's, polyolefinic coatings have been used in volume because of their versatility and ease of application by the extrusion coating method. Because of their good chemical resistance, these thermoplastic coatings are also utilized extensively as protective coatings, performing a dual function. Other heat-seal coatings used satisfactorily on foil include nitrocellulose, ethyl cellulose, methacrylates, chlorinated rubbers, rubber polymers, and polyvinylidene chloride.

Printing on aluminum foil can be accomplished by any commercial process, including rotogravure, flexography, lithography, and letterpress. The foil generally is coated with a washcoat or a primer prior to printing. Shellac washcoats normally are used for gravure or flexographic printing, which utilize rapid-drying organic-solvent-base inks. Vinyl washcoats are used for gravure printing when unusual resistance to grease, oil, or chemicals is specified. Vinyl and nitrocellulose primers are employed for lithographic or letterpress printing, which involve oil-base inks that harden by oxidation (5). Inks are formulated specifically for use with foil and for each printing process.

Applications. Aluminum foil laminations have proven successful for a great variety of applications. Overwraps, such as item 10 in Table 1 (page 602), are used widely on cartons for packaging cookies, crackers, butter, oleomargarine, detergent powders, tobacco, and dehydrated or other dry products. Intimate (inner) wraps are employed for candy bars, chewing gum, butter, oleomargarine, and cheese. Several commercial packages illustrating overwraps and intimate wraps are shown in Fig. 3.

Heat-sealed foil pouches find extensive application in packaging dehydrated foods, detergent powders, sugar, coffee, drugs, pharmaceuticals, and chemical products. Gusset or square bags are especially suitable for marketing potato chips, pretzels, and cereals, either foil alone or as an innerwrap. Multiwall bags are used for handling chemicals, cement, animal feed, flour, fertilizers, and similar bulk products.

Foil combined with paperboard is the basis for heatable trays for baked goods. Foil-lined fiber cans, drums, and boxes package products such as viscous oils, greases, hygroscopic chemical powders, self-rising flour, cake mixes, and confections in bulk. Printed paper-backed foil labels and printed heavy-foil name plates are used where high-quality appearance justifies the cost. In addition, substantial amounts of aluminum foil are consumed for closures, milk-bottle hoods, gift wraps, and florist wraps.

The largest single use of aluminum foil is for household foil.

Fig. 4. Typical formed foil containers

Two thicknesses are common: 0.0007-in. for regular household foil, and 0.001-in. for heavy-duty foil. Both 1100 and 1145 alloys are employed.

Formed all-foil containers of the type illustrated in Fig. 4 have proven highly successful for packaging a wide variety of products. Included are pans for pie, cake and other bakery products, trays for frozen dinners and meats, and containers for specialty foods, such as waffles, pizza, candy, popcorn, cheese, sandwich spreads, and various snack and gourmet foods.

Rigid Containers

Rigid containers are stiff packages, usually of metal sheet and usually round in shape. This type, known familiarly as "cans", originated in the days of Napoleon. Some rigid containers employ foil laminated to a stiff nonmetallic backing sheet. Others are smooth-wall containers drawn from heavy-gage foil. Rigid containers should protect the product and withstand reasonable handling without deformation or breakage.

The can industry is the largest segment of the packaging

complex (6). Cans are generally made from steel, tin-coated steel, aluminum, a combination of fiber and aluminum foil, or plastic. In 1965, the industry consumed an estimated 5.1 million tons of metal to produce a total of about 52 billion containers ranging from 2 to 6 in. in diameter and 1 to 9 in. high, in all combinations of diameter and height.

Most rigid containers are cylindrical. This shape utilizes the container material efficiently, but the greatest advantage is that it permits manufacturing, filling, and closing at high speeds with exacting control. Almost all beer, beverage, vegetable, fruit, dog food, and motor-oil containers are cylindrical.

In 1965, an estimated 95,000 tons of aluminum was consumed for cans and can ends in the United States, principally for citrus, beer and motor oil.

Aluminum Alloys and Tempers. The aluminum alloys commonly used are 1100, 3003, 5052, 5082, 5086, and 5154. The tempers employed vary from the annealed condition, used for impact can slugs, to the strain-hardened, extra-hard H19 temper for beer and oil can ends. Intermediate work-hardened tempers are used where appreciable forming is required. Gages range from 0.003 in. to 0.018 in., except for impact or drawn-and-ironed bodies, which start as slugs or disks up to 0.125 in. thick (Volume III, Chapters 4 and 6).

Mechanical properties of these alloys are given in Volume I, Chapter 9 and temper designations in Volume I, Chapter 4. The alloys are cold worked during forming and may be partially annealed while organic coatings are being cured. Yield strengths range from 5000 psi for 1100-O to 57,000 psi for 5086-H19, depending on the application and on forming requirements.

The alloys with low yield strength and high elongation are easy to form, whereas those with high yield strength and low elongation can be used only for simple forms such as can ends. A satisfactory alloy-temper-gage combination can be selected for almost any type of container. For example, an end for a pressure beer can, where formability is not a restricting factor, is made of the strongest alloy in the hardest temper, using the minimum gage for satisfactory performance. Figure 5 illustrates the alloy-temper combinations for some common applications.

Rigid container sheet stock generally is furnished in "mill finish". This is typically clean, reflective, and moderately bright, although foil stock normally is brighter. The surface is attractive whether uncoated or coated.

Characteristics. Aluminum sheet of equal gage is approximately one third as heavy as the tin plate commonly used for cans, and offers considerable freight savings on some commodities. However, the recently introduced thinner tin plate reduces aluminum's weight advantage to a 2-to-1 ratio. Table 2 compares weight per thousand cans for various structures in use for frozen citrus juice. If the transportation cost for an average shipment is

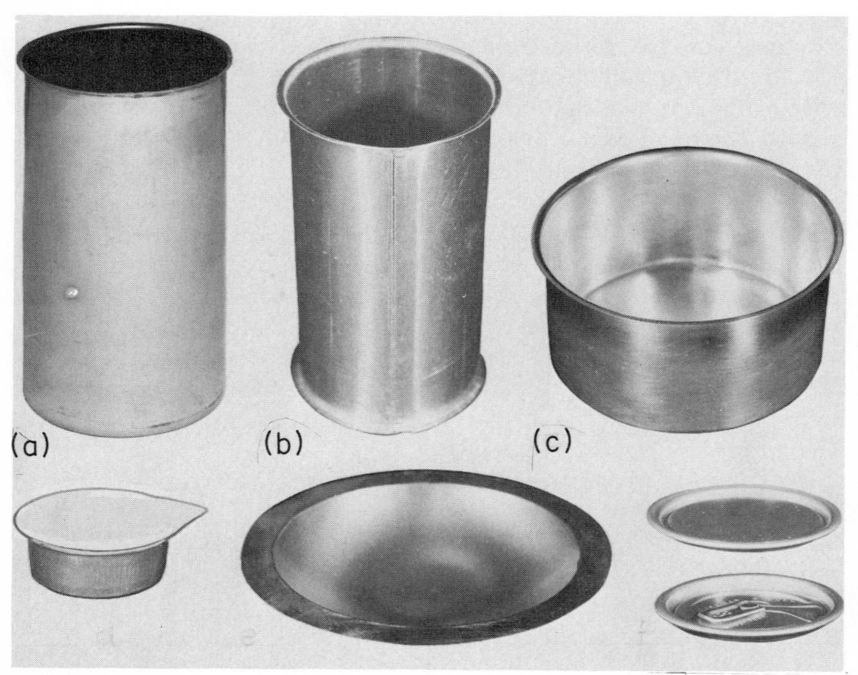

(a) Impact can, alloys 1100-O and 3003-H14. (b) Cemented side seam and flanged body, alloy 5052-H26. (c) Shallow-drawn can, alloys 3003-H14 and 5052-H26, H34, H36. (d) Drawn-foil cup, alloy 1100-O. (e) Air-formed tray, alloys 1100-O and 3003-O. (f) Can ends, alloys 5052-H28, 5082-H19 and 5086-H36, H18, H19.

Fig. 5. Typical aluminum containers

assumed to be $2 per 100 lb, the difference in weight between the all-aluminum can and the lightweight tin-plate can in the 6-oz size represents a cost saving of $74,000 for 100 million cans shipped, a representative annual shipping schedule for a large cannery.

Since aluminum conducts heat rapidly, it is particularly

Table 2. Weight of Empty Citrus Cans, Pounds per 1000 Cans

	6-oz size ($2\frac{1}{8}$-in. diam by $3\frac{7}{8}$ in.)	12-oz size ($2\frac{11}{16}$-in. diam by $4\frac{7}{8}$ in.)
Lightweight tin plate (55-lb tin-plate body, 60-lb tin-plate ends)	67.5	101.5
Aluminum body and ends, 0.008-in.	30.5	...
Aluminum body and ends, 0.009-in.		50.5
Composite can (two aluminum ends, 0.00035-in. aluminum-foil label, and liner with two layers of paperboard)	33.0	56.6
Composite can (two 60-lb tin-plate ends, aluminum-foil–paperboard body)	45.0	72.0

desirable for thermal operations. Almost all food products are either cooled or heated after the can is filled and closed.

Although aluminum is basically nontoxic and odor-free, most containers require a protective coating on the inside surface to insure satisfactory shelf life. This is particularly true with wet food products containing considerable chloride salts in combination with organic acids. Some spice ingredients lead to corrosion by attacking the coating; most spices are essential oils, which have a solvent action on the coating. For most dry products, no protection is required.

The internal coatings used for aluminum rigid containers are generally thermosetting organic materials cured in hot-air ovens after application. Various resins are utilized, such as epoxies, phenolics and acrylics, along with modified vinyls developed specifically for aluminum substrates. Less frequently employed are thermoplastic materials, which are used subsequently to heat-seal together several parts of a rigid container. Colored pigments and dyes are sometimes added.

Coatings and decoration can be applied by commercially available techniques with slight variation from tin-plate practice. The high reflectivity of aluminum promotes wide use of clear or translucent, colored base coatings for decorative purposes.

Decorating of rigid-container sheet is currently accomplished by lithography, but rotogravure printing is being considered. A clear or colored exterior base coat may be applied before the decorative inks. The inks are protected by a clear top coat. This lithographic procedure, also used to decorate tin plate, can be applied to aluminum as easily as to other materials.

When containers must be sealed hermetically to protect a product, a gasket material or compound is introduced between the body and end. This gasket plugs or seals any small passageways that might prevent complete sealing. The gasket materials commonly used, elastomeric in nature, are based on dispersions of natural or synthetic rubbers, or both, ranging up to 50% in total solids. They are produced as either an organic or water dispersion. These materials vary only slightly from those used for tin-plate ends. The gasket material is placed in the end as shown in Fig. 6. The mechanical interlocking of the end and the

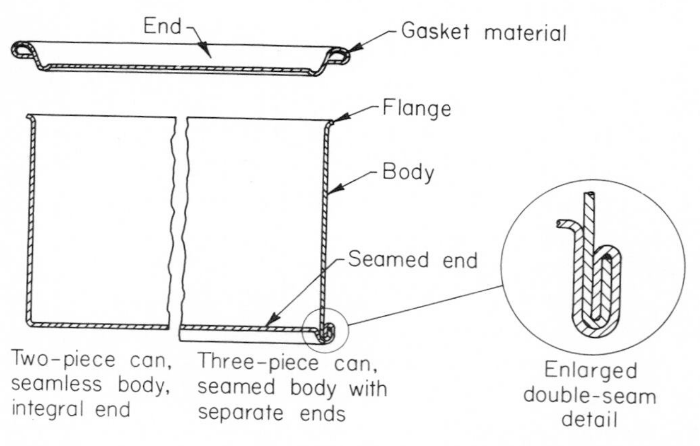

Fig. 6. Two-piece and three-piece can constructions

can body is achieved by properly designed seaming rolls and chuck, as is typical with all-steel can practice. Figure 6 also illustrates can end and body before and after double seaming.

Types. Rigid containers are classified as two-piece or three-piece, depending on the number of component parts required to contain the product, as shown in Fig. 6.

Impact-extruded cans and drawn-and-ironed cans are two-piece containers. The former are made in the desired untrimmed shape from slugs (disks) of aluminum with one stroke of the impact press (Volume III, Chapter 4). The drawn-and-ironed body is made from a sheet-circle blank that is first drawn into a cup. The sidewalls are then thinned by passing the cup through a series of dies with diminishing bores (Volume III, Chapter 6). The polishing effect of the ironing produces a very bright, reflective exterior surface. The severity of the forming requires that coating and decorating operations follow forming. Both the impact and drawing methods can make bodies with a length-to-diameter ratio as high as 2 to 1.

Shallow-drawn can bodies generally are coated before forming. The coating is formulated to withstand the forming and not lose continuous coverage. The sheet thickness remains substantially unchanged during forming. Temper normally employed is H14, H26, H34, or H36; anticipated refinements in drawing techniques would permit using harder tempers.

Another type of two-piece container is produced by "air forming", in which air pressure is used to deform foil into a cavity die to produce a formed pouch or shallow tray (Volume III, Chapter 6). The thickness of the material in the formed area is reduced as much as 10%. This container generally is coated prior to forming with a thermoplastic material, such as a vinyl copolymer, that provides for heat sealing a cover to the body (7).

"Tin" cans traditionally have been three-piece — two ends and a body. From a formability standpoint, aluminum is especially suited to this type of container. The first significant utilization of aluminum in a rigid container was in a body made with a

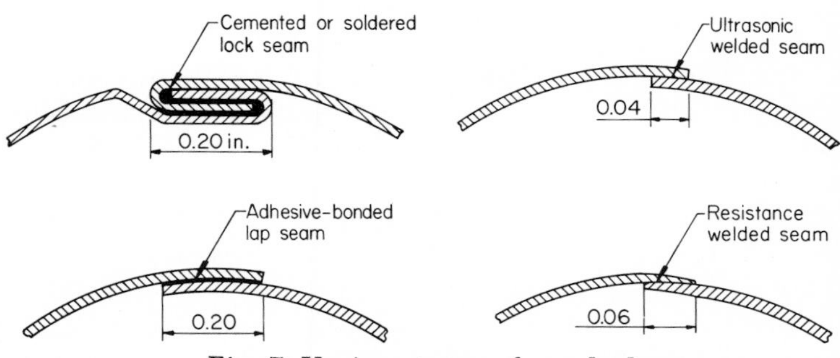

Fig. 7. Various types of can-body seams

cemented, mechanically locked side seam (Fig. 7). This container holds unheated products such as frozen citrus juice or motor oil effectively, but it has not yet been adapted successfully to operations involving heat.

Most tin-plate bodies employ soldered side seams, a process presently not developed for aluminum bodies. This seam is similar to a cemented side seam, except that it is filled with solder, which produces a strong mechanical joint. Excellent joints can be achieved in aluminum by resistance or ultrasonic welding, although neither method has yet been automated sufficiently for high-volume production. In this construction, the lock seam is avoided and there is a metal saving in the body blank, in addition to eliminating the cost of the solder (Fig. 7).

The aluminum foil-fiber (kraft board) body is one of the lower-cost structures. Containers made with a sidewall structure as shown in Fig. 8 successfully hold lubricating oils and greases, a variety of dry foods, and refrigerated products. Most foil-fiber bodies are made by spiral winding, although some are of simple wound (convolute) construction. Aluminum foil is used for both the liner and the label.

Can ends and covers account for most of the aluminum used in rigid containers. The design of ends is influenced by factors such as internal pressure or vacuum, resistance to shipping and handling damage, double-seaming requirements, and production

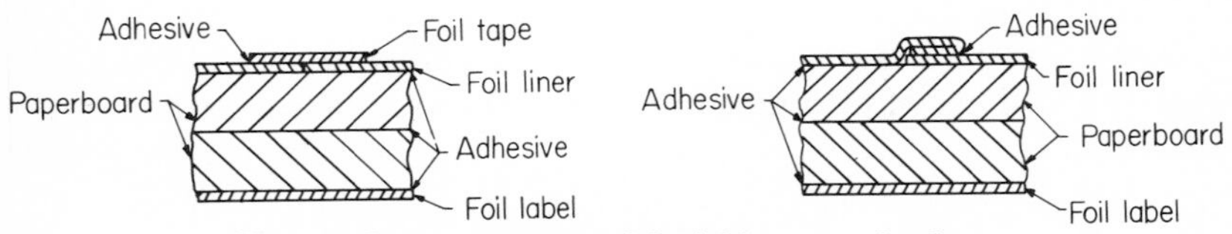

Fig. 8. Cross section of foil-fiber can bodies

problems. The shape or profile of the end is thus of considerable importance. For example, the countersunk annular ring around the inner edge of the end, shown in Fig. 6, reduces the center panel area and strengthens the end. Sharp radii in this location are desirable. Properly formulated coatings permit smaller radii than with uncoated or separately lubricated stock. The final selection of alloy, temper, and gage for the can end is a resolution of these design, production, and service requirements.

Aluminum ends are blanked and formed on conventional press equipment at rates up to 600 per min. In handling aluminum, vacuum systems are used, since aluminum does not respond to the magnetic systems used for steel. Beer-can filling and seaming lines operate at speeds of 1000 per min when tin-plate ends are used; when aluminum ends are used, equivalent speeds are possible with proper design.

Applications. Two-piece aluminum cans are extensively used for shallow ($3\frac{7}{16}$-in.-diam by $1\frac{13}{16}$ in.) drawn tuna and sardine cans, as well as double-drawn, deep cans ($2\frac{1}{2}$-in.-diam by 2 in.) used for sausage and dehydrated soups. The beer industry has utilized large quantities of experimental impact-extruded, impacted-and-ironed, and drawn-and-ironed two-piece cans in the $2^{11}/_{16}$-in.-diam by $4^{13}/_{16}$-in. size.

In the 1940's, three-piece aluminum composite cans, made with two sheet ends and foil for the liner and label, were introduced in volume for packaging refrigerated biscuit dough. In the 1950's, all-aluminum three-piece cans, made with a cemented, mechanically locked side seam, were adapted for packaging frozen citrus juices and motor oils. After several years, these were largely displaced by the composite type previously mentioned, which are now common also for other materials, including caulking compounds, greases, cleaners, grated cheese, and toys.

Aluminum ends are used extensively for beer cans, motor-oil cans, and 6 and 12-oz cans for frozen citrus juices. Aluminum ends for beer cans improve the shelf life of the product by reducing iron pickup in the beer. In a six-month, room-temperature aging test, beer in tin-plate cans with one aluminum end showed iron and tin concentrations 31 and 23% lower, respec-

Fig. 9. Easy-open or convenience can ends

tively, than in all-tin-plate cans; with both ends aluminum, the concentrations were 55 and 51% lower (8).

A popular advantage of aluminum for can ends is its adaptability to designs that improve the opening of the container. These designs are generally designated "easy open" ends, because the consumer needs no tool to open them (Fig. 9). The workability of aluminum permits forming integral rivets to attach tabs or keys to a scored section on the can end. This is generally accomplished without a significant reduction in the structural integrity of the end. Breaking the scored area permits all or part of the end to be removed easily.

Closures

A glass container consists of a glass body and a closure. Many years ago the closures were cork, or a glass stopper, usually with a rubber-type gasket. Today, closures are made from aluminum, tin plate, steel, plastic, or, sometimes, paper. Ideally, a closure must be hermetically sealable, easily applied, and readily removable and recloseable. Attractive appearance is advantageous for sales appeal. The cost should be low, but more important in many applications is the need to protect the product. Furthermore, it is often desirable to make the closure tamperproof.

Crowns are an important segment of closure production. A crown is a fluted metal closure employed for bottles of small neck diameter; it is found most commonly with beer and carbonated beverages. Current consumption (1965) is about 51 billion crowns per year (presently all made of steel in this country) compared to 21.3 billion units for the rest of the closure market. Of these 21.3 billion closures, approximately 3.75 billion are made from aluminum.

Closures were among the earliest applications of aluminum, dating to 1897 with Goldstein's invention of the Goldy closure. This use of aluminum is based on its easy formability, resistance to corrosion, compatibility with food products, and potential for decoration.

Aluminum Alloys and Characteristics. For many years, aluminum closures were manufactured principally from 1100 alloy. During the 1920's, alloys 3003 and 3004 were adopted, to take advantage of their higher mechanical properties with satisfactory adhesion for the coatings then used. The H14 and H34 tempers have been used most frequently.

About 1950, the aluminum-magnesium alloys, such as 5050 and 5052 in H36 temper, were introduced for the larger-diameter closures, where higher strength is required. Stronger alloys in full-hard or extra-hard tempers allow a reduction in metal gage. Gages commonly used for closures are in the range of 0.006 to 0.012 in. for 3003 alloy and somewhat thinner for 5052. For example, a closure normally made in 0.0095-in. gage of 3003 may be satisfactory at 0.0085 in. with 5052-H19, providing a reduction in gage of 10% and almost as much in cost. Advances in drawing techniques are expected to promote greater use of the stronger tempers of 5052, including the extra-hard H19.

In the past, it was thought necessary to use the more formable alloys for deep drawing of a closure shell; today, some of the

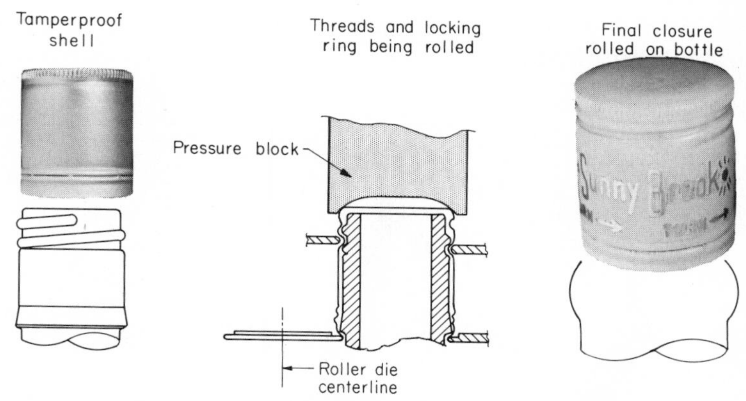

Fig. 10. Tamperproof closure

stronger alloys draw well, and it is possible to make large-diameter closures within the economical gage range required to compete with tin plate.

The "rolled-on" tamperproof closures, requiring good formability, are especially adaptable to aluminum. They can be formed against a glass surface under moderate pressure, with rollers that depress the metal into the area between glass threads or beneath annular locking rings, without breaking the glass. This produces a tight seal when performed in conjunction with sufficient downward pressure on the top of the closure. The rolled-on process individually fits each closure to each container. Poor fit because of the dimensional variations normally present in separately made closures and glass containers is eliminated.

Another significant aspect of aluminum's formability utilized in producing closures is its ability to be scored and yet retain appreciable strength. This is advantageous in tamperproof closures where the hold-down ring has been slit, leaving bridges of metal. The bridges are broken when the tamperproof cap is twisted (Fig. 10).

Controlled scoring, plus a pull-and-tear tab, is the basis for both the pioneering Goldy closure and the new beer-bottle closures. In each instance, adequate strength must be combined with ease of tearing to provide a dependable but readily removed closure. The Goldy closure is shown in Fig. 12.

Because most closures are round, high scrap results in stamping blanks from sheet. The higher value of aluminum scrap compared to tin plate is a significant economic factor in the production of closures.

Coating and gasket materials are applied to almost all closures during their production. The coating serves the functions of

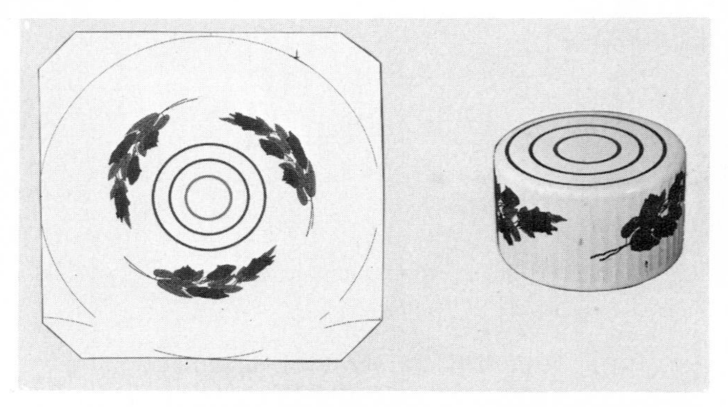

Fig. 11. Decorated closure disk before and after forming

protecting against corrosion, providing a base for printed decoration or messages (Fig. 11), and serving as a lubricant during the forming operation. Effectively cleaned and coated aluminum is highly resistant to corrosion by most food products.

Another critical part of the closure is the gasket or sealant material introduced between the closure and the edge of the glass. This gasket material can be die cut from extruded vinyl-type sheet, or produced from other synthetic elastomers, such as butyl rubber. Another widely used form of gasket material is a plastisol compound, applied in much the same way as the gasket material is applied to a can end, and then fused in an oven to produce a highly resilient gasket. However, the type of gasket employed in the majority of threaded closures is a plastic-coated or varnish-coated paperboard disk, or a foil-paperboard laminated disk, inserted in the cap.

Types and Applications. The rolled-on closure is the most popular, and probably the most responsible for the extensive use of aluminum in closures. Many variations of closures employ the rolled-on principle.

In addition to the various rolled-on designs, aluminum closures are made as screw cap, hidden-thread screw cap, tumbler cap, and pry-off (England).

In the 1961–1963 period, over a billion closures were used annually in the whiskey and wine industries. The majority of these were the tamperproof design; the remainder, mostly the short-flange, hidden-thread type with a smooth exterior appearance. In this same period, the ketchup industry consumed over 300 million rolled-on closures — half the closures used by this industry. As yet, lug-type caps in aluminum have not been widely used, but the high mechanical properties of 5052-H19 should make it practical for this application. Aluminum is also used for ordinary foil capsules or overcaps.

Parenteral closures (for hypodermic solutions), used in great volume by the drug industry, employ a natural-rubber plug where the hypodermic needle is inserted; this is held in place by the primary closure, which in turn is protected by an overcap — either a screw cap or a dust cover plus a scored aluminum ferrule — to hold the assembly.

Another form of closure used in great quantity is the milk-bottle hood, which may be employed as the primary closure or as an overcap. The 0.0033-in. 1145-O foil usually is laminated to 0.007 in. paperboard; the coated side of the paperboard is placed next to the milk, to permit control of release characteristics. A lower-cost version employs 0.0035-in. 1145-O coated foil without backing. Figure 12 illustrates various types of aluminum closures and the accompanying table lists the products for which they are popularly used.

The aluminum crown closure has been popular in Europe, and there is a strong trend toward its use in the United States. The regular fluted crown appears to be feasible, and a tear-off type is in production.

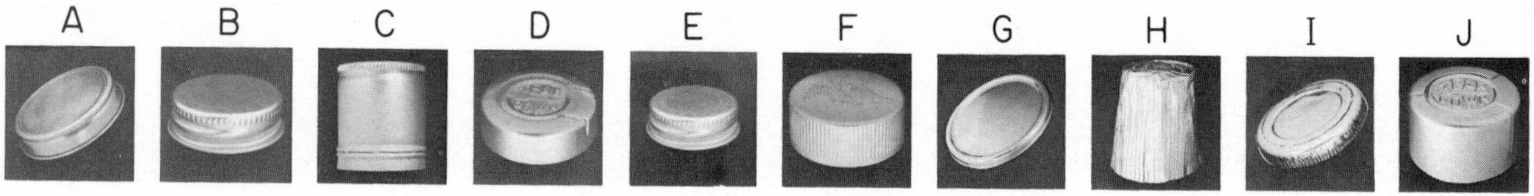

Products	A Wide-mouthed rolled-on	B Rolled-on thread	C Tamper-proof rolled-on	D Goldy	E Screw cap	F Concealed preformed thread	G Tumbler cup	H Foil capsule	I Dairy closure	J Parenteral closure
Vegetables	X	...	...	...	...	...	...	...	...	...
Fruits	X	...	...	...	...	...	...	...	...	...
Juices and beverages	X	X	X	...	...	...	...	X	...	...
Dry food products	...	X	X	...	X	X	...	...	...	...
Dairy products	X	...	...	...	...	...	X	...	X	...
Meats	X	...	...	...	...	...	...	...	...	...
Baby foods	X	...	...	...	...	...	...	...	...	...
Relishes and pickled products	X	X	...	...	X	X	...	...	...	...
Toppings, syrups, sauces and spreads	X	X	X	...	X	X	...	X	...	...
Salad dressings and oils	X	X	X	...	X	X	...	X	...	...
Condiments	X	X	X	...	X	X	...	X	...	...
Wine and alcoholic beverages	...	X	X	X	X	X	...	X	...	...
Proprietary medicines	...	X	X	...	X	X	...	X	...	...
Ethical drugs, injectables	...	...	...	...	...	...	...	...	...	X
Cosmetics and toiletries	...	X	X	X	X	X	...	X	...	...
Household	...	X	X	X	X	X	...	...	...	...
Chemicals	...	X	X	X	X	X	...	...	...	...

Fig. 12. Closures and their uses

Collapsible Tubes

A collapsible tube is defined as a cylinder of pliable metal that can be sealed in such a manner that its contents, although readily discharged in any desired quantity, are protected from contact with air or moisture. Products so packaged must flow under pressure low enough not to damage the tube, but must be sufficiently viscous not to spill out of the tube. Commercial production of aluminum collapsible tubes by impact extrusion began in Switzerland in 1914 and in the United States in 1921 (9). Between 1940 and 1950, the production of metal collapsible tubes in this country doubled; by 1955, annual production reached 1 billion tubes. More than half of these were aluminum; the remainder were lead or tin.

Design. The terminology for the various parts of a collapsible tube is shown in Fig. 13 (10). In the United States, 99.7 Al

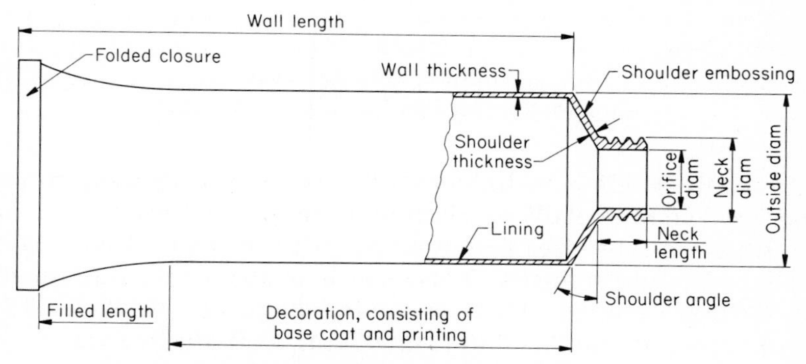

Fig. 13. Nomenclature for metal collapsible tubes

(1170 alloy) is preferred for collapsible tubes; in Europe, 99.5 Al is more generally used (11). The manufacture of collapsible tubes by impact extrusion is described in Volume III, Chapter 4. After extrusion, the tubes are annealed to remove the work hardening and provide the softness or limpness needed for good collapsibility. The degree of hardness that remains in the annealed condition is needed for the tube to maintain its shape and to hold the crimped fold at the closed end.

Various types of folds are used to close the open end of tubes. Sealing compounds often are introduced in the folds, to insure gastightness and prevent loss of volatile components from the contents. Welded end-closures employing electric resistance and

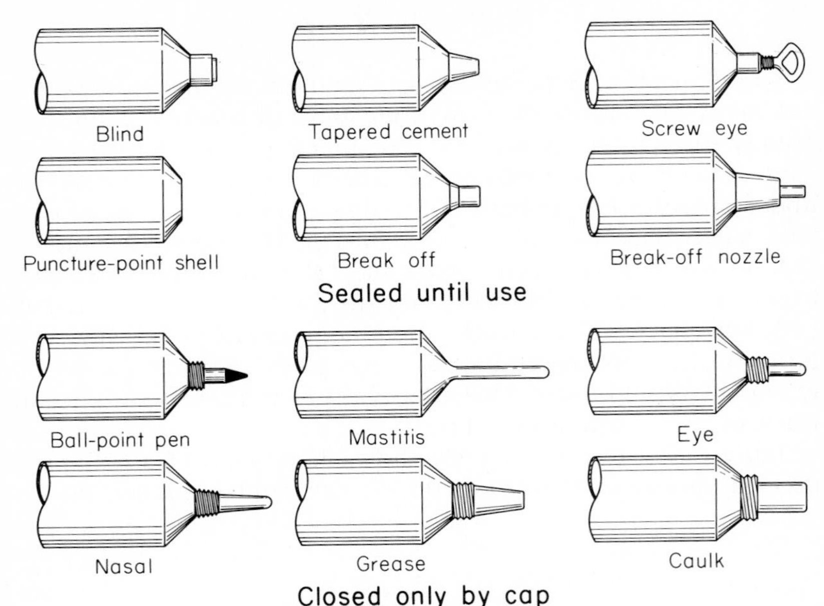

Fig. 14. Special tips for collapsible tubes

ultrasonic welding techniques have been investigated, but are not used commercially on aluminum tubes.

Standard tube sizes and dimensions have been adopted by the collapsible-tube industry. Tubes are available commercially with 2 to 10-in. lengths, 0.375 to 2.0-in. diameters, 0.188 to 15.5-fl-oz capacities, and 0.0048 to 0.0077-in. wall thicknesses.

Necks and orifices are available in a range of standard dimensions (12). The common neck and orifice is a straight cylinder, threaded on the outside, whose size is designated by the number of sixty-fourths of an inch of orifice. Standard sizes are No. 8, 10, 12, 16, 20, and 28. Nonstandard orifices are available, the most popular being the rectangular orifice that dispenses the product in a ribbon shape. Nonstandard tips are available for special purposes such as to provide better visibility at the point of application, to permit application inside a small opening, or to control the shape of the ejected product. Some special tips in common use are shown in Fig. 14.

Coatings are required inside some aluminum collapsible tubes to prevent corrosion by certain products. Even a superficial amount of corrosion, which might be tolerated for other applications, is objectionable in the tubes, because gas produced by the corrosion reaction causes the tube to swell. Consequently, coatings that provide a high degree of protection against corrosion are required. Good adhesion and maximum coating flexibility also are essential, because of the severe deformation encountered as a tube is collapsed and rolled to expel the contents. Thermosetting enamels of the epoxy type are the most commonly used.

External coatings are applied for decorative purposes only. Printing is by offset lithography.

Applications. The largest single market for aluminum collapsible tubes is for toothpaste. Fluoridated toothpastes require an especially protective interior coating; suitable coatings have not yet been developed for use with aluminum tubes. Other major areas include medicinal ointments, cosmetics, shaving creams, adhesives, paint colorants, printing inks, caulking compounds, and greases. In this country, less than 1% of the collapsible tubes are used for packaging food; in Europe, over half the tubes manufactured are employed for food. The current use of aluminum tubes for high-altitude and space feeding (13) may provide impetus to commercial adoption of aluminum tubes for civilian food packaging.

References

1 M. A. Miller, J. E. Stillwagon, and D. B. Strohm, WVTR of Aluminum Foil Laminates, Package Engineering, 6, 36–40 (Feb 1961), and 70–72 (March 1961)

2 C. J. Sanborn and R. S. Breed, Methods for Bacteriological Examination of Milk Bottle Caps, Hoods and Closures, 14th Annual Report, New York State Association of Dairy and Milk Inspectors, 317–324 (1940)

3 A. B. McKee and D. B. Strohm, Aluminum Foil's Thermal Properties Offer Packaging Advantages, Package Engineering, 6, 76–80 (Oct 1961)

4 Helen Goerig, Corrosion Need Not Mar Your Food Package, Package Engineering, 5, 35–38, 73, 92 (May 1960)

5 M. A. Miller and E. M. Eiland, Lithography on Foil, Modern Packaging, 33, 162–164, 221–222 (July 1960)

6 The Advancing Metal Can, Modern Packaging Encyclopedia, Packaging Catalog Corp., 38, No. 3A, 324–327 (1965)

7 R. C. Reed and R. J. Zoeller, Air Forming of Foil, Modern Packaging, 37, 186–188, 190, 282 (Sept 1963)

8 J. E. Hall and T. R. Mulvaney, Aluminum Ends for Beer Cans, Brewers' Digest, 38, 48–52 (Nov 1963)

9 H. H. Hall, Aluminum Collapsible Tubes, Modern Packaging, **5**, 32–34, 74 (May 1932)
10 U. S. Government Research Reports, **38**, No. 3, 101 (Feb 5, 1963)
11 E. Elliott, Aluminum Collapsible Tubes; Production, Testing and Application, Metallurgia, **66**, No. 397, 203–213 (Nov 1962)
12 Collapsible Metal Tubes, Modern Packaging Encyclopedia, Packaging Catalog Corp., **37**, No. 3A, 338–340 (1964)
13 D. E. Reed, G. H. McDonnell, and R. S. Schultz, Use of Aluminum Tubes for High Altitude and Space Feeding, Activities Report, Quartermaster Food and Container Institute for the Armed Forces, **14**, Second Quarter, 117–121 (June 1962)

Chapter 24

Uses in Pigments and Paints

K. E. LUYK

ANNUAL shipments of aluminum paste and powder for organic coatings and allied uses increased from 18½ million pounds (metal weight) in 1956 to an estimated 24 million pounds in 1965. These figures exclude atomized powders and other particulates for metallurgical, chemical, explosive, rocket propellant, and exothermic reaction uses; shipments for these uses were an additional estimated 31 million pounds in 1965. Although consumption of aluminum pigments has grown continuously, the emphasis has shifted from maintenance paints, traditionally the major market, to roof coatings and product finishes.

Aluminum Pigments

Forms. Air-atomized granules and flake powders are used as pigments. The more important is flake pigment, made by wet ball milling. These flakes are sold either as hydrocarbon-containing pastes or dry powders, and are classified as leafing or nonleafing, depending on the type or condition of milling lubricant utilized. Stearic acid adsorbed on the flake produces leafing, which enables the pigments, when mixed with a varnish and applied to a surface, to float on the varnish film in a nearly continuous, flat layer. This layer gives the highly reflective metallic brightness that is characteristic of aluminum paint. The special particle placement can occur with only a small part of the pigment. Most of the flakes become arranged in parallel layers beneath the upper sheath of metal, producing a homogeneous,

The author is a research engineer, Finishes Div., Alcoa Research Laboratories, New Kensington.

multilayered barrier to the ingress of moisture, fumes, and film-destroying oxygen and light. Figure 1 is a magnified cross section through a well-leafed paint film.

Other lubricant acids, such as oleic, do not cause the flakes to leaf; these pigments are called nonleafing. However, to some extent they also become aligned throughout the film in layers parallel to the painted substrate. In masstone (the visual effect of a paint film in which a single pigment is incorporated in a binder), nonleafing pigments appear metallic gray.

Nonleafing pigments also are produced from leafing pigments by deleafing with lead naphthenate or other metallic soaps, or by treatment with polar solvents such as ketones, esters or alcohols. Organic acids that occur naturally in many resinous vehicles also

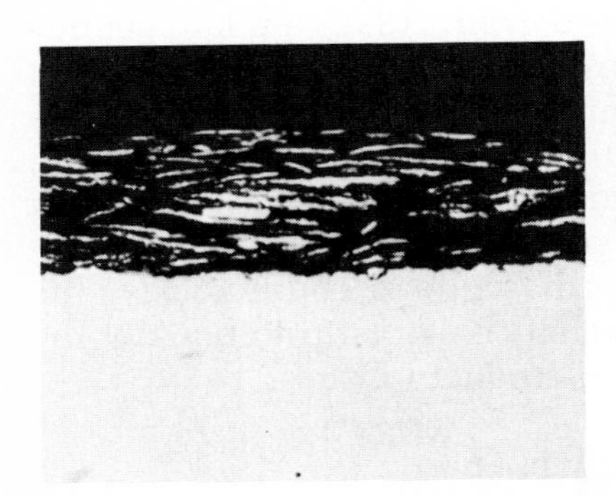

Fig. 1. Cross section of two-coat aluminum paint film, showing the layering effect of flake aluminum pigment. 500×.

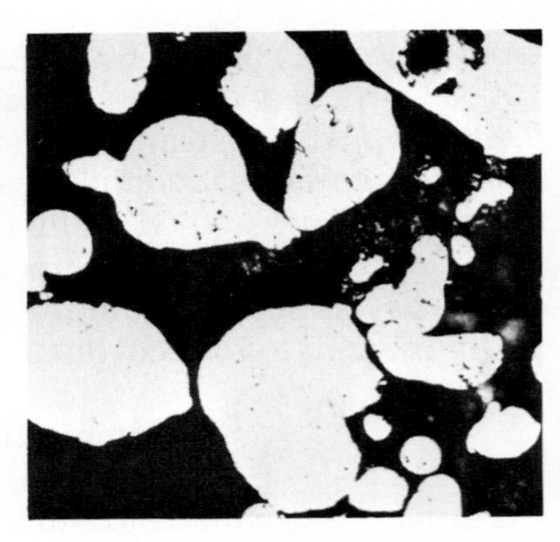

Fig. 2. Air-atomized 99.5+ aluminum powder. Cross section, unetched. 500×.

can cause deleafing, which is troublesome when leafing is desired. This can be combated with chemical leaf stabilizers such as amines.

Most aluminum pastes are sold with 65 to 75% nonvolatile content (metal flakes plus lubricant). They contain mineral spirits, sometimes also mixed with aromatic naphtha, so that they disperse readily in paint vehicles without further grinding or other high-shear mixing. Special-use pastes are compounded with plasticizers such as dioctyl phthalate, with wetting aids for easy dispersion in water, or with rust-inhibitive pigments, such as strontium chromate (1).

Pastes, when incompatible with specific vehicles, are replaced with flake aluminum powders. They are composed of up to 99.9% nonvolatile aluminum flakes coated with as much as 5% milling lubricant. Use of aluminum powders usually is avoided because they are inconvenient and may be hazardous.

Sizes and Shapes. Flake metallic pigments differ greatly from granular pigments, as do the methods of analysis employed. Microscopic examination of atomized or flake aluminum well dispersed in a resinous medium readily reveals the difference between the two types (Fig. 2 and 3). In cross section, atomized metal appears as irregular granules, whereas the flakes are thin laminar particles with a greatly increased proportion of fines. If photographed by reflected light (Fig. 4), flakes appear wrinkled from the impacts and indentations during milling.

The size and distribution of particles are determined from micrographs by standard measuring and counting techniques. The time and skill required for this method demand more practical ways to indicate aluminum pigment size. Covering capacity on water is one such test developed for leafing aluminum pigments. The flakes, as a powder freed from excess milling lubricant by solvent extraction, are dusted onto the surface of a rectangular tray of distilled water. The edges of the tray have been waxed to permit the water to rise above them without overflowing. Two waxed glass barriers at opposite ends are moved toward and away from each other along part of the length of the rectangle, confining the powder between them. When a maximum area of the water is covered (representing a film one

Fig. 3. Fine aluminum flake. Cross section, unetched. 500×.

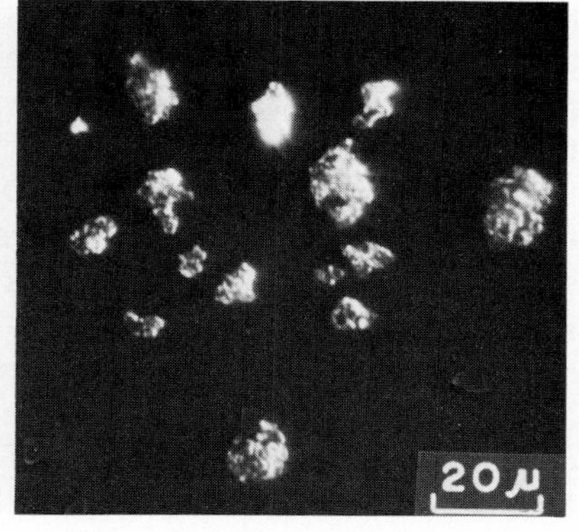

Fig. 4. Fine aluminum flake. Surface view. 500×.

flake thick), it is measured and the "covering area" is computed in square centimeters per gram. For coarse pigments, the values are low (4,000 to 12,000), and for the finest, high (24,000 to 32,000). Pigments of medium fineness (12,000 to 24,000) are commonly used for maintenance paints.

Covering area or covering-on-water (not to be confused with paint coverage in square feet per gallon) permits an approximate calculation of the thickness of flake. Thickness so determined ranges from 0.1 to 2 microns. Determination by an interference technique gives values that range from 0.3 to 1.2 microns. These figures are of the same general magnitude, making the approximations appear valid. Figure 3 clearly reveals the relationship of thickness to diameter (length).

Screening of aluminum pigments is another method to indicate size, although not useful for size distribution finer than 325-mesh. For flake pigments, the screen sizes are commonly expressed as the amount retained on a 100, 200 or 325-mesh sieve. Fine pigments of the high-covering types pass 100% through a 325-mesh sieve. Pigments of medium fineness usually have a maximum of 0.5% retained on a 325-mesh sieve. Coarse pigments are approximately 5% on 325-mesh and 0.5% on 100-mesh. However, with nonleafing powder of coarse types, as much as 15% may be retained on a 325-mesh sieve. As most aluminum pigments sold are pastes, wet screening is the usual method of sizing. This is described in Federal and ASTM specifications. Proper technique and experience in testing are vital.

From covering-on-water results, an approximation of the total surface area of flake aluminum is gained. The results must be multiplied by two for total surface, because the water-covering test measures only one of the flat surfaces. However, the doubled figure introduces an error twice the area of voids in the covering film (from failure of the flakes to touch at all points because of their irregular contours). It also does not account for the area of the edges of the flakes, or the area produced by the irregularity of surfaces. Gas-sorption methods are employed for more precise measurements of total surface (2). They confirm the usefulness of the covering-on-water test in defining pigment surface area and relative particle size. Table 1 compares these two methods of determining surface area. The ratio of the surface area to covering increases with fineness, probably due to the greater total length of edges per unit area of flake surface in the fine pigments.

Other Physical Properties. Leafing and nonleafing pastes appear similar as packaged. But when a sample of each is dispersed in a solvent such as xylene, the difference is evident. The leafing particles form a bright metallic mirror over the entire solvent surface, whereas the nonleafing flakes remain submerged in the solvent, showing their metallic character only as points of reflected light. Atomized powder is distinguished visually by the granular character and smoky gray appearance. If dispersed in xylene, atomized powders soon sink to the bottom, leaving a clear supernatant liquid; the length of time required to settle depends on fineness.

Table 1. Typical Surface Areas of Aluminum Powders

Description	2 × covering area on water, sq m per g	Gas-sorption area, sq m per g
Atomized Aluminum		
Coarse (40-mesh designation)	..	0.15
Fine (200-mesh designation)	..	0.25
Dust-collector fines (325-mesh designation)	..	0.90
Leafing Aluminum Flake From Pastes		
Coarse	2.4	2.9
Medium	3.8	5.2
Fine	6.5	9.7
Nonleafing Alumini m Flake Powders		
Coarse	..	2.4
Medium	..	4.7

SOURCE: W. C. McGrew, Alcoa Research Laboratories, and T. E. Fitzgerald, Alcoa Fabricating Works.

Flake aluminum pigments provide different masstone shades depending on the dispersion medium and whether they are leafing or nonleafing. Aluminum pigments are opaque to visible, infrared and ultraviolet radiation. Leafing pigments reflect 65 to 75% of all incident light, depending on their fineness, and can have the appearance of polished aluminum. The finer pigments have a darker, more specular look, whereas the coarser ones are brilliant and more diffuse.

Nonleafing pigments behave similarly; the coarser grades are the brighter, but the total reflectance in masstone approaches a maximum of 50%. The tone and luster produced depend on the type and amount of pigment and the nature of the vehicle.

Density is important in packing and handling aluminum particles. With powders, the relevant density measurements are: apparent density (weight per unit volume of uncompacted powder), tapped density (weight per unit volume of compacted powder), and real density (inherent weight per unit volume of powder particles). For pastes, the measurements are the density of the paste itself and the real density of the particles free of solvent. The published data for the real density of powders can be applied to particles of equivalent type and size in paste. Real densities of flake powders range from 2.5 to 2.6 g per cu cm. This value is used to calculate pigment volume concentration in a dried paint film or in a plastic mass. Paste density, at 1.47 to 1.49 g per cu cm for 65% nonvolatile materials, is important only for computing the volume occupied by paste entering mixing tanks or packing units. Apparent density of a powder is a value useful for estimating volume. When transferred with a minimum of agitation, a powder may show a value as low as 0.15 g per cu cm. By tapping to obtain maximum packing, as high as 0.68 g per cu cm may be obtained for flake pigments. Complete typical values are given in Table 1, Chapter 10, Volume I.

Because aluminum in massive form is a good thermal and electrical conductor, the same properties frequently are mistakenly presumed for aluminum powders. Flake aluminum powders actually act as thermal insulators because of the blanket of air surrounding each particle. When dispersed in plastic, rubber or paint films, aluminum particles improve the thermal conductivity, a property utilized in aluminum-filled plastic dies for metal forming. Electrical conductance, however, is not increased when aluminum pigments are dispersed in a paint or plastic medium. The film of aluminum oxide and milling lubricants surrounding each metal particle prevents current flow. For this reason, aluminum pigments are not useful in conductive coatings, and do not function galvanically when employed in metal-protective paints. Atomized powders at high concentrations in paints, however, can be welded through by resistance welding at sufficient voltage and welding tip pressure.

Chemical Properties and Reactivity. Chemical properties of aluminum are discussed in Volume I, Chapter 1, and chemical applications of aluminum particles are discussed in Chapter 25 of this volume. Pertinent information on chemical reactivity and corrosion appears in Volume I, Chapter 7. Chemical reactivity of packaged pigment or paint is outlined here.

Finely divided aluminum, with its increased surface area, reacts more readily with water, oxygen and chlorinated hydrocarbons than might be predicted from the reactivity of aluminum in massive form. The natural oxide film occurring on bulk aluminum stops further oxidation. However, aluminum powder covered with oxide can oxidize further. With some combinations of oxygen, powder and an initiating spark, dust clouds of aluminum powder can ignite with explosive violence. The maximum safe concentrations of aluminum powders in air depend on particle size, on the energy available for ignition, and on other factors, some of which have not been adequately evaluated.

Aluminum powders and pastes form oxide in the presence of water as liquid or vapor. Atomized aluminum exposed to moisture-saturated air at room temperature slowly forms beta alumina trihydrate and hydrogen; stearic-acid-coated powder does not. Unless an inhibitor is introduced, all aluminum pigments dispersed in organic vehicles react with as little as 0.15% water to produce hydrogen. When confined, such mixtures can generate enough pressure to bulge or blow the lid off a metal can. All stages in the manufacture of aluminum pigments thus are stringently controlled to limit moisture.

Methylene chloride, carbon tetrachloride, and chlorinated rubber resins in paint formulations may also react with aluminum pigments, even under anhydrous conditions. With such materials, the possibility always exists that free hydrogen chloride may be released slowly, resulting in a reaction with aluminum. The reaction products may cause formation of more hydrogen chloride and a continuing reaction. The most effective means of combating this is with scavengers, such as zinc dust, zinc oxide, zinc stearate, or epichlorohydrin.

Except for special chemical-resistant grades, aluminum pigments in paint films are attacked by certain mineral acid environments, especially hydrochloric and hydrofluoric. This reactivity is used in the automotive industry to discriminate between metallic finishes with different resistances to acid. Drops of 0.5% solution of hydrochloric acid on the painted surface are evaporated to dryness (room temperature, ambient humidity) and the finish evaluated for discoloration. Spot-discolored finishes are rejected. During 1965, one major automotive manufacturer completely changed to acid-resistant grades of nonleafing aluminum pigment, and others made substantial use of them. Because of the reactivity with alkali, aluminum pigments are not used for coatings requiring good resistance to alkali, although in paints they are not affected by washing with ordinary soap solutions.

Handling and Storing. Aluminum pastes or powders should be stored in closed containers at 60 to 80 F (well away from steam pipes, radiators or other sources of heat). They must be free from any sources of moisture and in tightly covered containers. Open containers permit evaporation of hydrocarbon from pastes, resulting in changes in composition and serviceability. Also, storage should be in fireproof rooms away from other combustibles, such as organic coatings, that require different fire-fighting methods. When handling powders, excessive dusting must be scrupulously avoided and all potential sources of ignition must be eliminated. In case of fire, neither water, carbon dioxide, nor carbon tetrachloride should be used. Sprays or splashes on burning powder can spread the fire and increase the possibility of explosion. Clean, dry sand, sprinkled gently on smoldering aluminum powder will extinguish the fire. In containers, fires should be smothered by covering, and the surrounding area cleared of other powder or paste.

The use of pastes eliminates the dust hazard associated with powders and makes mixing more convenient. It also reduces the storage area needed for the same weight of flake particles, because of the difference in the bulk densities of paste and powder. Because liquid contained in paste does not flow readily from breaks in a container, fire hazard from the storage of paste is less than from the storage of mineral spirits.

Aluminum Paints

Aluminum paints have been used successfully as protective finishes for more than 40 years. A simple classification of the types of aluminum paints for the many surfaces to be painted has evolved. It includes paint for: (*a*) metal, masonry and interior wood; (*b*) weather-exposed wood; (*c*) nonweathering surfaces that may be heated up to 600 F; (*d*) metal heated above 600 F indoors or out; (*e*) water-immersed metal; (*f*) metal or composition roofs. The best pigment and vehicle for the surface depend on material to be painted, exposure (indoors or outdoors), and special conditions (heat, moisture, submersion).

Selection of Pigments. The first consideration in selecting an aluminum pigment is intended use. This immediately dictates whether a granular or flake particle is required, and if flake, whether leafing or nonleafing. The choice of particle size is similarly governed. If bulk properties of aluminum are needed, as in plastics, atomized particles usually are required, although coarse flake pigment may also be suitable. If brightness and metallic luster are desired, as in decorative enamels, roof coatings, or maintenance paints, leafing pigments are used. If the need is admixture with color, as in automotive finishes, or easy mixture with water, as in paper coatings, nonleafing pigments are chosen. The vehicle dictates whether paste or powder is best.

In selecting specific pigments from the groups of leafing or nonleafing types, the two most important factors are the appearance desired and service required. The qualities that influence selection include texture, gloss, hiding or opacity, durability, moisture permeability, reflectance and color. Coarse flakes produce the coarsest texture, the lowest gloss, hiding and durability, and the highest reflectance, moisture permeability and color purity. Medium flakes yield smoother texture, higher gloss and hiding, optimum outdoor durability and moisture permeability, and lower reflectance and color purity. Fine flakes result in smoothest texture, highest gloss and hiding, less durability and moisture resistance than the medium size, and lowest reflectance and color purity. The optimum durability and resistance to moisture permeation with the medium flakes result from the greater mean free path around the medium flakes than around the coarse or fine. This is because of the size, shape, and distribution of particles.

The amounts of leafing pigments per gallon of vehicle vary from 1 to 1.25 lb of "extra fine lining" paste (fine) for chromium-like, heat-resistant enamels to as much as 3.5 lb of "standard lining" paste (medium fineness) for high-heat-resistant exterior silicone paints. Maintenance coatings usually are made with 2 lb of "standard lining" paste, whereas asphalt roof coatings may have from 1.25 to 3 lb of "standard fineness" paste (coarse). Considerable latitude exists in choosing the type of leafing pigments for roof coatings; some pigments having covering values as high as 22,000 sq cm per g are used. Paints for wood usually contain somewhat less pigment than metal-maintenance paints, allowing for the penetration of the vehicle into the pores: 1.75 lb of "standard lining" paste is common. These pigmentations are generally based on the vehicle having 50% nonvolatile binder, although as low as 35% vehicle solids (binder) may be used in some enamels and asphalt paints.

When mixed with color pigments, nonleafing pigments are used frequently in smaller concentrations than are leafing pigments. For example, in polychromatic enamels for automobiles, only 1 to 2 oz per gal is used. A variety of particle sizes is employed to achieve various distinctive color effects. However, for colored aluminum roof coatings and maintenance finishes of maximum durability, concentrations of nonleafing pigments almost equal those for leafing aluminum maintenance finishes (3). This also applies to intermediate maintenance coats for contrast with leafing top coats on bridges and oil storage tanks. For optimum durability, aluminum pigments of medium fineness are preferred.

Selection of Vehicles for Maintenance. Exposed wood surfaces must be coated with very flexible paints to withstand the extensive variations in dimensions from weather and season changes. Long-oil varnishes or alkyd resins are best. Indoors, wood does not demand this flexibility, because moisture conditions are more uniform. Thus, varnish or alkyd resin vehicles made with less oil (less flexible) are suitable. Identical vehicles are used for metal and masonry surfaces, indoors and out, permitting reduced inventory. In painting steel, one or two coats of a rust-inhibitive primer should be applied under two coats of aluminum paint, for maximum performance. If this is not desirable, aluminum can be combined with a rust-inhibitive pigment, such as strontium chromate or basic lead silico chromate, for a one-coat or two-coat application. Water-immersed steel requires more resistant vehicles, such as phenolics, epoxy esters, catalyzed epoxies, or vinyls. For fresh-water immersion service on both steel and aluminum, aluminum and zinc chromate pigment mixtures in phenolic varnishes are effective.

On interior metal or wood surfaces needing only improved appearance, enamel varnishes low in oil (high in hard resins) may be used for service up to 600 F. Because of the use of low-cost resins and small amounts of drying oils, they are economical.

For heat resistance above 600 F, and for combined heat and weather resistance, silicone or silicone-modified vehicles are best. Straight silicones provide best heat and weatherproofing, but at higher cost. Modification with compatible resins reduces the cost, but generally at some sacrifice in performance. For maximum resistance to outdoor heat and weather, a zinc dust silicone primer is often applied beneath a top coat of silicone aluminum paint.

The binder most often used for roof coatings is asphalt. Usually employed are cutback asphalts (dissolved in solvents) that have a middle range of viscosity. If too soft, they "cold flow" in a cellular pattern resembling alligator hide. If too hard, they inhibit the mobility of aluminum particles in the wet coating. This prevents full utilization of the desired properties of the metal flakes in protecting the asphalt. Leafing aluminum asphalt paints or roof coatings, well-formulated and applied, show no evidence of their dark binders. Two types of leafing aluminum asphalt are available: fibered and nonfibered. The ingredients are comparable, including aluminum pigment, asphalt binder, and solvent, except that the fibered ones are mechanically fortified with short asbestos fibers, giving the coating a heavy, buttery consistency.

Nonleafing aluminum pigments have afforded effective use of color in asphalt. Aluminum flakes subdue asphalt blackness and act as tiny reflectors against which color pigments can be seen. Asphalts discussed above are suitable in these colored finishes and are commonly used with asbestos fibers for uniform application. Coatings of this type are sold as colored black-top or pavement dressings. In Germany, coarse aluminum particles have been used in asphalt paving; a result claimed is greatly improved night visibility at a cost premium.

Selection of Vehicles for Product Finish. Aluminum pigmentation enhances the beauty of many product finishes, ranging from automobiles to tackle boxes. Unusual tasks of product protection may be accomplished, such as improving organic coatings on the inside of cans to prevent food juice penetration, and coating paper sacks for frozen food for reflective insulation.

Colored finishes containing small amounts of nonleafing aluminum pigments are termed "polychromatic". They are used widely as interior and exterior automotive finishes and for a variety of decorative purposes on appliances and other metal products. Vehicles usually consist of heat-curing alkyds modified with urea-formaldehyde or melamine resins and nitrocellulose or acrylic lacquers. These finishes are available in many hues and are bright and clean when used with transparent colored pigments, such as phthalocyanine blue or green, quinacridone red or violet, or lightfast vat dyes. Appreciable application is made of vinyl plastisols containing leafing or nonleafing powder to produce polychromatic fabrics. Such fabrics are suitable for automobile upholstery, golf bags and other products.

Architectural finishes containing nonleafing aluminum are available in several colors. They are similar to the polychromes in composition; vehicles include vinyl, acrylic, and alkyd-amine resins. The aluminum pigments employed are the same as those used for automotive finishes. Generally, these finishes are roller coated on strip lines, but they may be sprayed for special applications.

Hammer finishes, which create the illusion of hammered metal when sprayed, are used effectively for many metal and nonmetal fabricated products, especially where a minimum surface preparation is desired. On sealed wood or composition materials, the nonleafing pigments in hammer finishes impart a metallic appearance. Suitable binders are styrenated alkyds and epoxy esters, as well as some other enamel and lacquer resins if treated with 0.3 to 1.0% of a special silicone polymer additive. For best hammer patterns, viscosity of the paint must be carefully controlled.

Wide employment of water-borne resins in coatings prompted the development of aluminum pigments and pigment systems to achieve optimum water dispersibility and chemical inhibition of the reaction between aluminum pigment and water. Traditionally, nonleafing litho powders were mixed with casein or protein binder solutions. Enough material was prepared for application within a day; otherwise, reaction evolving hydrogen degraded the mix and appearance of the coating. However, several water-dispersible pigments are now available, including some inhibited against the water-aluminum reaction (9). This permits satisfactory storage of industrial coating systems for as long as several weeks. A dihydrogen ammonium phosphate treatment for aluminum powders can be used; with this the pigment surface develops a phosphate coating more resistant to the water-aluminum reaction than untreated flakes (4).

Many latex vehicles — such as butadiene-styrene, polyvinyl acetate, and acrylic — can be used with aluminum pigments to produce both colored and bright aluminum finishes. However, storage stability may vary considerably among these vehicles, and even from batch to batch of one vehicle. Although the major application for water-dispersed resins is in paper coatings, these vehicles are not the only ones employed for this purpose. Nitrocellulose lacquers are useful where more water resistance is required than is offered by casein or protein binders. Although only medium or coarse nonleafing powders or special leafing pigments are included in water-dispersed systems, medium or fine leafing powders can be employed in the lacquer vehicles.

Textiles are coated with leafing aluminum coatings for reflective and weatherproofing properties. For canvas awnings, decks, and tarpaulins, paint containing a flexible vehicle, such as a vinyl lacquer or phenolic resin varnish, is useful. Vinyl sheeting pigmented with fine leafing powder is employed extensively for rainwear. Other fabric-like sheeting is made in attractive pastel "metallescent" finishes (5). Fabrics coated with aluminum flake powder in a quick-drying binder are used as reflective insulation for garment and quilt linings, ironing board covers, and draperies. Here some application of emulsion coatings is made. Reflective window shades are coated similarly. Very fine aluminum pigments may be added to filament-forming solutions or plastics before extrusion, to avoid application of coatings. Filaments containing aluminum pigment can be spun into thread for weaving into cloth.

The addition of leafing and nonleafing aluminum pigments to coatings for cans has aided protection and decoration. Fine pigments of both types are suitable. Where the coating is in contact with food, food-grade pigments must be used. Most applications are by roller coating; sometimes it is beneficial to add small quantities of soya lecithin to promote uniform appearance. Suitable vehicles are oleoresinous varnishes and butadiene-styrene, epoxy-urea, and epoxy-phenolic resins.

Specifications. Aluminum paints and vehicles have been specified by many groups and agencies. In addition to the U. S. Government, specifications are issued by the American Water Works Association, American Association of State Highway Officials, Association of American Railroads, and the Steel Structures Painting Council.

Methods of Application. Although any of the usual methods of applying paints — brush, spray, roller, or dipping — can be used to apply aluminum paints, several specific conditions should be recognized. Brushing of leafing paints requires the same care normal to achieve a uniform appearance for any glossy paint. During hot weather, lapping may be noticeable if the solvent is not adjusted properly to maintain a wet edge. Also, final brush strokes must all be in the same direction and away from the laps for best uniformity.

Because aluminum paint is light, fine drops or wet overspray may be carried a long distance by wind. This is avoided by using a very-fast-drying vehicle that produces dry overspray, which is dusted easily from other surfaces.

Specialized methods, such as airless spray or electrostatic application, present unique conditions necessitating application care. The extremely fine orifice utilized in airless spray may not be suitable for aluminum pigments of large particle size. When using electrostatic equipment with some aluminum paints, difficulty may be experienced and special formulations may be necessary, for reasons that have not been clearly established

Table 2. Visible Reflectance of Paints Made With Different Grades of Leafing Aluminum Pigments

Grade of pigment	Aluminum pigment concentration, %	Total reflectance(a), %	Apparent directional reflectance(b), 45, 0
Coarse paste	16.6	75.5	0.220
Coarse powder	16.6	74.5	0.172
Medium paste	13.7	71.0	0.188
Medium powder	14.2	71.0	0.161
Fine paste	9.3	65.5	0.163
Fine powder	11.7	68.0	0.133

(a) Taylor-Baumgartner Reflectometer. (b) Hunter Multi-Purpose Reflectometer.

SOURCE: J. D. Edwards and R. I. Wray, "Aluminum Paint and Powder", Reinhold, New York, 1955, p 110

(6). In electrostatic spraying, some differences may be experienced between leafing and nonleafing pigments.

Properties of Aluminum Paint Coatings. Aluminum pigments impart reflectance, opacity and impermeability to a paint. Paint binders are disintegrated by sunlight, moisture and oxygen. Thus, aluminum pigments in a paint film oppose these destructive forces, improving durability in outdoor service.

Reflecting up to 75% of sunlight striking the surface, leafing aluminum pigments protect the binder from degradation by ultraviolet, visible and infrared radiation, thereby increasing paint life. Reflectance values for various types of radiation are listed in Tables 2, 3 and 4. Table 2 records the effect of particle size on both total and apparent reflectance. Apparent directional reflectance is measured on an instrument having a light source at 45° and a receptor photocell perpendicular to the surface, and it indicates the relative degree of diffuseness and specularity. The coarse pigments are relatively brighter and more diffuse (higher apparent), the fine ones less reflective and more specular (lower apparent).

Tables 3 and 4 emphasize the relative constancy of reflectance for leafing aluminum paints over the spectral range of interest: ultraviolet, visible and infrared. The reflectance of nonmetallic pigments decreases rapidly as wave length shortens.

The ability of thin-film aluminum paints to hide an undersurface results in high coverage and low paint cost. The opacity of leafing aluminum paint can be compared with white paints when both are applied over black iron or over black and white paint charts. Aluminum paint can be applied to a greater area per gallon and still produce satisfactory hiding. In one coat, aluminum paint achieves almost 99% the reflectance it attains in two coats. A white lead – zinc oxide paint reaches only 91% of two-coat reflectance in the first coat; a titanium dioxide paint, 93%. The second coat of aluminum paint is not necessary to hide the undersurface, whereas the second coat of white paint often is, a significant benefit where only one coat is preferred.

Table 3. Reflection of Various Materials for Visible and Ultraviolet (0.2967-Micron) Radiation

Surface	Reflectance, % For white light	At 0.2967 micron
Aluminum paint	75	65
White enameled metal	65 to 75	5 to 8
White lead paint, flat	80	27
White plaster	90	50

SOURCE: A. H. Taylor, J Opt Soc Am, 24, 192 (1934)

Table 4. Emissivity and Reflectance of Aluminum Paints for Infrared Radiation(a)

Aluminum pigment grade	Emissivity, %	Reflectance, %
Coarse paste	18	82
Medium paste	28	72
Fine paste	36	64

(a) Emissivity at surface temperature of 100 F. Reflectance for radiation from black body at 100 F, which has dominant wave length of about 9 microns.

SOURCE: J. D. Edwards and R. I. Wray, "Aluminum Paint and Powder", Reinhold, New York, 1955, p 111

Flake shape produces opacity and resistance to moisture and gas penetration (7). Because the flakes arrange in layers parallel to the painted surface, they lengthen greatly the path that moisture, oxygen, and fumes must follow to pass through the paint film. This significantly retards penetration by these film destroyers. Moisture permeability is lower with pigments of medium particle size than with coarser or finer ones, as shown in Table 5.

Numerous advantages for the aluminum-pigmented layered structure can be cited. Painting stained or creosoted wood or bituminous materials with white or light colors usually results in

Table 5. Effect of Powder Fineness and Content on Water Vapor Resistance of an 80-Gal Varnish Applied as a One-Coat Film

Aluminum pigment, lb per gal of vehicle	Water vapor resistance(a)		
	Coarse leafing (flake) powder	Medium leafing (flake) powder	Unpigmented varnish
0	...	...	0.28
0.5	0.34	0.43	...
1.0	0.40	0.50	...
1.5	0.52	0.64	...
2.0	0.67	0.83	...
3.0	1.10	1.36	...

(a) Water vapor resistance is 1/WVT. WVT (water vapor transfer) is given in grains of water vapor transmitted per square foot per hour. Values here were obtained with films 1 mil thick at 80 F and 95% relative humidity.

SOURCE: J. D. Edwards and R. I. Wray, "Aluminum Paint and Powder", Reinhold, New York, 1955, p 138

bleeding (staining outward from the undersurface). By interposing a leafing-paint base coat, a light paint can be used subsequently without bleeding. If preferred, the aluminum coating can remain unpainted.

Sulfide fumes that darken lead-containing paints have no effect on aluminum paint; they are prevented from penetrating the film by the layers of aluminum flakes. Mirrors are back-painted with aluminum paint to prevent sulfide fumes from destroying the silvered surface.

Zinc chromate primer paints on aluminum and steel are beneficial in salt-water service; when they are exposed in fresh water, the topcoats soon blister from osmotic pressure created by the diffusing water. Addition of aluminum pigment to such a primer greatly retards the water penetration rate. Similarly, aluminum pigments enhance water resistance of films of coal tar ship-bottom paints, and vinyl and phenolic underwater paints for dam gates. Nonleafing pigments are used for ship paints; leafing, for the others.

Protective organic coatings on steel surfaces are loosened by moisture, oxygen and corrosive gases. Flake aluminum pigment in a paint film serves a dual purpose: prolonging the life of the resinous film-former, and maintaining the integrity of the adhesive bond between paint film and protected surface.

Similar mechanisms operate in protecting weather-exposed wood. Properly formulated aluminum paints impede moisture penetration into the porous cell structure, appreciably reducing the swelling and shrinking that lead to rupture of the bond between wood and paint. Likewise, elasticity of the paint film is maintained through oxidation impedance provided by the lamellar distribution of aluminum flakes in the paint film.

Other aluminum pigment applications depend on these same characteristics. In paper coatings, the reflectance, opacity and impermeability may contribute advantages. In coatings for cans, opacity is important for the exterior and impermeability for the interior. In automotive finishes, the brightness of the nonleafing pigments is essential for their appearance, while opacity and resistance to moisture penetration are important for durability. In roof coatings, the opacity and reflectance provided by aluminum pigments facilitate production of highly reflective coatings and light metallic colors not otherwise achievable with asphalt, and also increase resistance of asphalts to moisture penetration.

Except for paints pigmented with titanium dioxide, aluminum paints have the highest visible reflectance of any commonly used maintenance paints. Generally, the higher reflectance of titanium paints is associated with continuous erosion of the paint film, as the paints are designed to chalk to maintain their reflectance. This erosion or chalking requires more frequent painting. Where a difference in reflectance between aluminum and titanium white may have an economic significance (as in reducing evaporation losses from oil-storage tanks), cost of material lost by evaporation should be weighed against the higher labor costs resulting from more frequent painting.

Resistance to moisture permeation differs between granular (for example, titanium dioxide or zinc oxide) and flake pigments. Flakes, with their overlapping layers, offer a greater barrier to moisture penetration and corrosive gases than do grains. The latter depend on close packing of various-sized particles for a dense film. However, the path for vapor or gaseous penetration between environment and protected surface is much shorter through the granular particles than through a lamellar film of flake pigment. Therefore, a more direct attack on the underlying film or surface can occur where granular pigments are employed. On steel, this often leads to spotty rusting at thin parts of a film with corrosion expanding from that spot. This is hastened by more rapid loss of inhibitor-pigment ions from the primer through the more permeable thin spots. With flake aluminum paints, even where thin, the primer and underlying surfaces are more effectively protected from this action because of the lower permeability.

Aluminum hides because the metal pigment particles are opaque. Titanium dioxide and other crystalline pigments hide because of a high refractive index and the light-scattering effects of fine particles.

Despite the many merits outlined, aluminum paints are less widely employed for some purposes than might be expected. High opacity makes for good hiding in thin films; but, if the paint is not applied thickly enough, moisture can penetrate due to holidays and brushmarks in the film. High metallic luster may not be a virtue when an aluminum paint is overcoated with a material of comparatively low hiding power and high contrast, such as a white over aluminum-primed wood. The aluminum showing through the contrasting topcoat, especially if the latter is thin, is difficult to hide. Two or three topcoats may be needed, increasing the cost of the system. Use of nonleafing aluminum paint reduces this effect to some extent.

Additional Uses for Aluminum Pigments

Structural. Atomized powders are useful as fillers in plastic dies used for stamping and forming steel where runs are limited to 4000 to 5000 parts. Flake powders are not satisfactory because their shape and high surface area cause too rapid a change in consistency with increasing concentration. Resins such as epoxy, polyester and phenolic have proved suitable, with the epoxies being applied most widely. Hardening is accomplished by addition of a suitable curing agent. For casting, the commonly used proportions by weight are two parts of atomized aluminum powder to one of resin. Somewhat less aluminum is used for laminations. Particle size affects both viscosity and settling rate of the aluminum in the resin-aluminum mix, and must be selected to maintain a balance of these two qualities, especially in bulky sections that require a long time to cure. This use of aluminum powder results in a number of benefits:

1 Cost is lower than with the unfilled resin.
2 Heat transfer is improved to the extent that charring of the resin is materially reduced during melting.
3 Shrinkage is only about 0.1%, compared to 0.7% or more without aluminum.
4 Impact strength, toughness and malleability are increased.
5 Appearance of finished parts is greatly improved.

Cold plastic "solders" are also made from aluminum powder and resins. Up to 70% atomized powder (minus-100-mesh) is blended with vinyl chloride-acetate copolymer resin, plasticizer and solvent. Suspending aids and extender pigments may be included. When the solder is applied to wood, metal or plastic, the solvent evaporates, leaving a dense film of aluminum particles tightly bound by the resin. These plastic solders, which are widely employed for filling dents, cracks and seams, can be filed, sawed, sanded or polished. When sufficient aluminum powder is present, the dried and polished material looks like aluminum metal. The product is widely sold in tubes as a paste, although thermoplastic sticks and thin sprayable coatings are also available.

Aluminum-pigmented, resinous, auto-body "solders" and fillers are in wide use for repair work; they have also been employed to a limited extent in new work. Epoxy-polyamide and polyester types are available. Both require final mixing of separately packaged components prior to application. These are superior to the vinyl type, because upon curing they become hard and insoluble. With the epoxy type, separate fluid resins are each pigmented with atomized aluminum. When needed, equal volumes of the pigmented resins are mixed, preparing enough for about 4 hr of use. The workable life of the mix is increased by refrigeration and decreased by warming. Often the polyamide portion (the hardener) is tinted black for easy differentiation.

The polyester type of auto-body solder is a unique aluminum-pigmented molding composition suitable for patching (8). It is sold in two separate containers. One contains coarse (120-mesh) aluminum flake packaged with benzoyl peroxide catalyst absorbed in inert fillers such as kaolin, mica or asbestos. The second package contains the polyester resin solution, which hardens after mixing with the pigmented component.

These aluminum-pigmented compounds offer several advantages over the conventional lead solders and fillers. Application is made by putty knife, squeegee or paddle, after the repair area is prepared by sanding and heating with lamp or torch to remove surface grease and moisture. Some efforts have been made toward adapting these materials to gun application of ribbons into seams, eliminating the need for lead fillers. They require no heat, and can be applied around glass, rubber, or synthetic fabrics without damage; also, large, flat areas of metal will not warp. When fully cured, they are finished easily with a rasp and sander, requiring only moderate skill.

Aluminum pigments also can be utilized in a variety of caulks, putties, and cements. Leafing powders or pastes confer an aluminum appearance to caulks and putties while providing added resistance to moisture, oxygen, and sunlight, and thus prevent premature deterioration. Coarse grades of powder or paste are usually incorporated at about 10% metal weight.

Other uses of aluminum pigment include:

1 Printing inks and other graphic arts materials
2 Colored decorative powders for inks and coatings
3 Mold wash coatings for improving the surfaces of cast ingots
4 Electrosensitive recording paper (as back coatings)
5 Rubber, fabric and plastic compositions
6 Vinyl plastic "mothballing" preparations
7 Unique identifications for felt roofing, coal and lubricants

References

1 R. B. Dowell, Aluminum Pigment Improvement, Official Digest, **36**, 244–255 (March 1964)
2 J. Beresford, W. Carr and G. Lombard, Surface Area of Pigments, Journal of the Oil and Colour Chemists Association, **48**, No. 3, 293–307 (March 1965)
3 K. E. Luyk and Rolf Rolles, New Vehicles for Fibered Colored Aluminum Roof Coatings, Official Digest, **37**, 1055–1070 (Sept 1965)
4 A. F. Knoll and L. C. Hurd, U.S. Patent 2,858,230 (Oct 28, 1958)
5 V. E. Luzena, U.S. Patent 3,057,749 (Oct 9, 1962)
6 J. W. Merck and L. L. Spiller, U.S. Patent 3,210,316 (Oct 5, 1965)
7 A. E. Claxton, Lamellar or Flake Pigments in Finishing Paints for Structural Steelwork, Official Digest, **36**, 268–285 (March 1964)
8 R. L. Gorick, British Patent 885,461 (Dec 28, 1961)
9 M. H. Brown and Rolf Rolles, U.S. Patent 3,244,542 (April 15, 1966)

Chapter 25

Uses in Metallurgical and Chemical Reactions

P. T. STROUP

ALUMINUM has many applications based on its chemical or metallurgical reactions. In some applications, the effect (heat, light, deoxidation, propulsion or explosion) is produced by the mechanism of the reaction and not from the products; in others, it is the final product of a chemical or metallurgical reaction that is used (alloys or aluminum compounds).

Aluminothermic Reactions

Thermic reactions are those in which an oxide of one metal is reduced by reaction with another metal having a higher heat of formation for the oxide. The excess heat of formation of the products is evolved as heat; hence, the name "exothermic" is often used loosely for many such applications. Thermic or exothermic reactions include carbothermic, sodiothermic, magnesiothermic, and aluminothermic. The widespread use of aluminum results from its great chemical affinity for oxygen, whereby most metallic oxides are reduced by aluminum, freeing the metal. Of equal value is the high temperature produced from the large amount of heat that is generated by the aluminothermic reactions.

Smelting is practiced by aluminothermic methods, where it is desired to form an aluminum alloy or to avoid the presence of carbides or silicides in the extracted metal.

The author is an assistant director of research, Alcoa Research Laboratories, New Kensington.

In operation of the process, the most important factor is to maintain a self-propagating but controlled reaction throughout the charge of intimately mixed, finely divided aluminum powder and metal oxide (1). The reaction must produce sufficient heat to melt the products of reaction and to facilitate separation of the metal and the slag. The reaction vessel must be well insulated thermally, to conserve the heat evolved. The reduced molten metal settles to the bottom, while the molten slag floats to the top, where it provides a protective cover that prevents reaction of the metal with the atmosphere.

Two methods are available for adjusting the "oxygen balance". In the first, the oxygen ratio of the oxide or ore is adjusted by reducing or oxidizing roasts prior to aluminothermic reduction. In the second, the oxygen ratio either is increased by adding to the charge oxygen-rich salts such as peroxides, bichromates, chlorates, or nitrates, or is decreased by adding reduced metal in a dispersed form.

Two practices are employed to carry out the reduction. In the first, the entire mixture that forms the charge is placed in a suitable container and ignited at the top with a highly reactive mixture of barium peroxide and aluminum powder. The reaction gradually spreads downward through the mass, becoming progressively more violent, often accompanied by ejection of molten slag. As much as a ton of charge may be melted in a period as short as 50 to 90 sec. The disadvantage of this procedure is the great contraction in volume that occurs on melting the powdered charge, leaving the container only about one third full at the end of the reaction.

In the second, more common method, the unreacted charge is placed in containers near the reaction vessel, and the reaction is started with only a small quantity of the charge at the bottom of the vessel. The charge is fed in gradually, and the reaction is controlled by the charge feed rate. The advantage is that charging can be continued until the container is full.

In either procedure, the metal is allowed to solidify and cool under cover of the slag, which protects it to a considerable extent from atmospheric oxygen and nitrogen. The metal ingots, weighing up to a ton, are cooled for about 24 hr.

Many metal products are produced by aluminothermic processes, as shown in Table 1. These include pure metals, where absence of carbon and silicon is desired, and several ferroalloys and aluminum alloys. These alloys are used as "hardeners" or rich alloys added to iron and aluminum alloys. Aluminothermic methods are used to a greater extent in Europe than in the United States.

Welding is a well-known application that is concerned more with the heat generated by aluminothermic reactions than with the chemical or metallurgical products. A temperature of 5590 F is theoretically possible during the well-known thermit or Goldschmidt reaction between aluminum and iron oxide; in practice, the maximum attainable temperature is considered to be about 4600 F, because of heat loss to the reaction container. Additions to adjust the metal product for composition in welding and to obtain the desired fluidity of the slag may further reduce the maximum temperature to about 3800 F. The reaction is nonexplosive, but requires under a minute for completion. An initiating temperature of more than 2200 F is required for ignition. To start the reaction, a special ignition powder is used. It contains peroxides, chlorates, or chromates as oxidizing agents plus aluminum powder; the fuse is magnesium ribbon.

Table 1. Metals and Alloys Produced by Aluminothermic Smelting

Metal product	Metal oxide	Metal product	Metal oxide
Barium	BaO(a)	Strontium	SrO(a)
Boron	B_2O_3(b)	Tantalum	Ta_2O_5(f)
Calcium	CaO(a)	Vanadium	V_2O_5(g)
Cesium	Cs_2CO_3(c)	Ferroalloys of Cr, Mo, V, Ti, Zr, B, W, Cb, and Ta	Fe_2O_3 + oxides or combined oxide ores (columbite, ferberite)
Chromium	Cr_2O_3(d)	Aluminum alloys of Ti, B, Zr, Cb, and Ta	Double fluorides or oxyfluorides alone or mixed with oxides
Cobalt	Co_3O_4		
Columbium	K_2CbOF_5		
Lithium	Spodumene(c)		
Magnesium	MgO(e)		
Manganese	MnO_2		
Molybdenum	MoO_3		
Rubidium	Rb_2CO_3(c)		

(a) Vacuum, 2200 F. (b) Product contains aluminum boride. (c) Vacuum, 1600 F. (d) Extra oxidizer ($Na_2Cr_2O_7$) added. (e) Vacuum, 2100 F. (f) CuO added to agglomerate metal particles. (g) Fluoride as flux.

The commonly used mixture contains one part aluminum powder to three parts by weight powdered iron oxide. Mixtures for welding often contain other materials in addition to the iron oxide and aluminum, to control the time and temperature of the reaction and the composition of the produced weld metal. Steel punchings are added to augment the supply of weld metal.

The welding method most frequently used is fusion, utilizing both the heat and the molten metal produced by the reaction. Another method joins the parts through pressure, utilizing only the heat from the reaction. A third uses the heat merely to melt a brazing alloy. Success in welding by this process requires proper attention to joint preparation, mold construction, quantity of thermit mixture, preheating, gating and risering, crucible tapping, and cooling.

Among products commonly joined by thermit welding are railroad rails, oil-drill stems, large pump housings, stern frames of ships, heavy machinery castings and forgings, steel mill roll necks, crankshafts, rudder stocks, crossheads, pinion teeth, and crane runways.

Local metallurgical heating is a relatively recent application of the heat evolved from aluminothermic reactions. The aluminothermic mixture is placed to fit in or around the product to be heated. Exothermic mixtures are formulated to produce reaction temperatures as high as 3300 F. This type of controlled local heating is ideally suited for extensive use in the field and in foundries; it permits metallurgical heating operations without the expense of furnaces. Local heating can be employed for such practices as heat treating, annealing, stress relieving, pipe straightening, and preheating.

In casting steel ingots, exothermic reactions are used for hot tops and sideboards. Some types of topping formulations not only have moderate exothermic reactions but supply a layer of insulating material over the top, extending the feeding period by keeping the metal at the top molten for a longer time. Foundries have found many advantages in adding a controlled amount of heat to promote directional solidification. Feeding patterns are improved by the use of exothermic riser sleeves and cores.

Aluminum as an Alloying Addition

Aluminum is an important alloying addition in almost all metal systems. It is essential to alloy systems of magnesium, zinc, and titanium to obtain age hardening. Addition to ferrous alloys causes many beneficial results.

Table 2 summarizes the metallurgy and applications of alloys in which aluminum is present as an alloying addition.

A recent and active development is the incorporation of sapphire (aluminum oxide) wool and whiskers into composites of metals (nickel, silver, aluminum) to provide mechanical strengthening (13). The whiskers are made by any one of several chemical methods involving controlled oxidation of aluminum or $AlCl_3$. Special surface pretreatment of the whiskers is employed to make the metal adhere to them.

Steel Deoxidation and Grain Size Control

The most potent of the elements commonly used as deoxidizers for molten steel is aluminum, which gives the most nearly complete removal of dissolved oxygen. Aluminum is also the most important single factor in the control of grain size (2, 3).

In commercial deoxidation practice, aluminum added as ingot, shot or grain to rimming and semikilled steels diminishes the content of active FeO and controls the action in the molds. For rimming steels, the amount of aluminum ranges from 0.15 to 0.4 lb per ton of steel in the ladle; for semikilled, 0.15 to 0.7 lb per ton in the ladle; and, frequently, in addition, as much as half these amounts in the molds. The amount will vary with the carbon and manganese content of the steel, the composition of the slag, the size of the heat, and the size of the mold. In general, the rimming action contributes to the removal of the products of deoxidation. The residual metallic aluminum is virtually nil in rimming and semikilled steels. Up to 5 lb per ton may be added to produce fine-grained deep-drawing properties. For steel castings, 2 to 3.5 lb per ton is added. Addition of silicon reduces the aluminum requirement, especially in low-carbon steels.

Care is required in adding aluminum to steel to avoid undue loss by oxidation. Common practice in the United States is to add it in the ladle, where high losses may occur at the surface of the steel. A special effort must be made to keep the aluminum completely submerged, not only to prevent high loss of aluminum but also to avoid the formation of large aluminum oxide inclusions in the steel.

Aluminum as shot or granules is added to the slag in high-alloy steel production to recover alloying elements — chromium, molybdenum, tungsten, vanadium — that would otherwise be lost in the slag as oxides.

Inclusions are inevitable in the melting and refining of steel in contact with air or combustion gases. The action of aluminum as a deoxidizer may result in the formation of inclusions as oxides, nitrides, and sulfides of aluminum; most are sulfides.

Table 2. Metallurgy and Applications of Alloys Containing Aluminum Additions

Alloy system	Al, %	Metallurgy	Applications
Antimony	18	AlSb compound formed	Semiconductors
Beryllium	15 to 45	High strength by age hardening; improves fabrication	Supersonic aircraft parts
Copper	8 to 9.5	Aluminum bronze castings; cannot be heat treated unless over 2% Ni or Mn is present (a).	Valve nuts; cam bearings; impellers; hangers in pickling baths; agitators; crane gears; connecting rods
Copper	9.5 to 14	Aluminum bronze castings; heat treatable above 9% Al	Rolling mill screwdown nuts and slippers; worm gears; bushings; slides; impellers; nonsparking tools; valves; dies
Copper	5 to 12	Wrought bronzes develop surface film of Al_2O_3, which has high resistance to impingement corrosion; heat treatable above 9% Al	Condenser tubes; gold bronze powder; marine hardware; beater blades
Copper	9	Propeller bronze; 82 Cu–9 Al–4 Fe–4 Ni–1 Mn	Marine propellers; hubs
Copper-zinc	2	Aluminum brass; high resistance to impingement corrosion; 76 Cu–22 Zn–2 Al	Tidewater power plants; parts exposed to turbulent sea water
Iron-chromium	4 to 12	Aluminum is the most effective addition for suppressing the scaling of iron—even more resistant with iron containing 20 to 30% Cr; such alloys are difficult to fabricate and sensitive to damage of the oxide film (b).	Heating elements—particularly useful at 2100 to 2350 F where Ni-Cr alloys are not suited because oxidation is too great and temperature is too close to melting point
Iron-nickel	8 to 12	Alnico alloys, Fe-Ni-Co-Al-Cu (c)	Permanent magnet parts
Iron-silicon	3 to 8	Aluminum and silicon increase resistivity and eliminate allotropic transformation with retention of good magnetic properties.	Low-cost, low-power magnetic steel parts; transformer cores
Magnesium	3 to 8	Forgings; extrusions; sheet	Luggage; ladders; shovels; hand trucks

Magnesium	7 to 9	Castings—presence of aluminum permits higher strength from heat treatment; increase in corrosion resistance as aluminum increases	Major use in aircraft and missile structures; portable tools; machinery parts; conveyors
Nickel	1 to 2	Heat-resistant nickel alloys containing 10 to 20% of Cr, Co, Mo, or W are strengthened by precipitation of Ni_3Al in a solid solution hardened by molybdenum and chromium.	Used in high-temperature range of 1400 to 1800 F; more resistant to oxidation than the Fe-Ni-Cr alloys or stainless steels
Nickel	3 to 5	Corrosion-resistant nickel alloys containing aluminum are age hardenable and retain strength at elevated temperatures.	Duranickel, 94 Ni−4.5 Al, and K Monel, 66 Ni−29 Cu−3 Al. Used as pump rods, springs, shafts, etc, in exposures to dilute mineral acids, salt water, and steam; poor resistance to oxidizing acids.
Nickel	2	Alumel, Ni−2.5 Mn−2 Al−1 Si; presence of manganese and aluminum provides resistance to oxidation.	Chromel-Alumel thermocouple, best known and universally used thermocouple for oxidizing atmospheres at 1200 to 2200 F
Nickel-chromium	3	Ni-Cr-Al electrical resistance alloys (d)	Heating elements
Stainless steel	1	One variety of precipitation-hardened stainless steel is obtained by addition of 1.15% Al to 17 Cr−7 Ni or 15 Cr−7 Ni−2 Mo.	Mechanical properties can be increased to over 200,000 psi tensile strength.
Titanium	2 to 8	Aluminum is a strengthener (e).	Structural parts in aircraft and missiles
Zinc	4 to 6	Necessary ingredient of all zinc casting alloys to obtain high strength	Major use is die castings (f).

(a) Contain 0.75 to 4.0% Fe to refine grain; narrow solidification range; resist corrosion by pickling solutions. (b) Fe-Cr-Al alloys have higher electrical resistivity and lower density than the conventional Ni-Cr alloys, with excellent resistance to oxidation, but are brittle and require adequate support; can be hot worked. (c) Produce more energy per unit volume than most other magnet alloys; available only cast or sintered; grinding is only means of shaping. (d) More resistant to oxidation than other electrical resistance alloys; have resistivity 2.5 times that of Manganin, with superior temperature coefficient and mechanical properties. (e) Aluminum is the most effective strengthener, especially at elevated temperatures; hot working becomes difficult above 6% Al. (f) Where close dimensional limits, low cost, and excellent finishing are important; for automobiles, housings, business machines, tools, toys, and electrical applications.

Aluminum oxide inclusions exhibit a wide variety of shapes and microstructures. A typical diameter for most inclusions is about 0.001 in. Forms such as corundum clouds, and iron and iron-manganese aluminates are recognized. Typically, 0.015 to 0.020% alumina is found in all steels deoxidized by aluminum. This very low content of residual alumina is independent of the original oxygen content of the steel and of the amount of aluminum added, indicating effective alumina elimination.

Grain size control is an important and desirable result of the use of aluminum in steel. The grain-coarsening temperature becomes higher as the residual aluminum content increases to a range of 0.02 to 0.05%. Above this concentration, the grain-coarsening temperature is lowered.

A theory of the mechanism by which aluminum raises the grain-coarsening temperature proposes that finely dispersed particles of oxide and nitride function as grain growth inhibitors. As the temperature is increased, the oxide and nitride particles are finally dissolved or coalesced, and grain growth occurs. Because it is now established that the alumina content of all aluminum-deoxidized steels is the same regardless of grain size, it is concluded that the most important grain inhibitor is aluminum nitride.

The minimum amount of residual aluminum required to produce a fine-grained steel has not been determined with accuracy. Fine-grained steels containing as little as 0.01% Al have been reported. A residual content of 0.02 to 0.03% Al is usually recommended. To attain this residual concentration, addition of 1 to 1.5 lb per ton is normally required. Steel made in the basic electric furnace usually requires smaller additions than that made in the open hearth furnace, depending on the character of the charge and the type of slag used.

Aluminum-killed steels are widely used for both cold rolled and hot rolled sheets. They are particularly desirable for cold rolled sheets subjected to severe forming or drawing, and for sheets to be stored for long periods before use. An advantage for killed hot rolled sheet is the achievement of superior mechanical properties by retaining a finer grain after welding.

Notch sensitivity is improved as a result of the effect of aluminum deoxidation on low-temperature, ductile-brittle transition behavior. Aluminum nitride present in aluminum-killed steels decreases strain sensitivity and lowers the transition temperature. Aluminum is more effective than calcium, silicon, titanium, or zirconium in lowering the transition temperature of steel. The effect is more noticeable in low-carbon steels. It disappears in high-carbon steels when the carbon exceeds 0.50%. The deoxidation composition most commonly added for the greatest improvement in notch toughness is composed of 0.15 to 0.30% Si and 0.02 to 0.05% Al.

Aging is controlled by adding aluminum to molten steel to prevent strain-age embrittlement. The increase in strength and hardness, and accompanying decrease in toughness and ductility, caused by aging is thought to result from precipitation of nitrides, carbides, or oxides from supersaturated solution in alpha iron. For this reason, formation of stable nitrides by such elements as aluminum or titanium favors the use of these as deoxidizers where strain-age embrittlement would otherwise be a hazard in use of the steel part.

For deep-drawing applications, where stretcher strains are important considerations, deoxidation should be supplemented by a stabilizing heat treatment. Aluminum is now added widely as a deoxidizer in low-carbon, deep-drawing steels in amounts of 3.5 to 5.0 lb per ton, since it improves drawability and eliminates susceptibility to stretcher strains. A unique, elongated grain structure is characteristic of aluminum-killed, low-carbon steels. This grain structure is particularly desirable in bright-annealed and temper-rolled sheets used for unsymmetrical deep drawing applications such as forming automobile fenders. In rimming grades, the grain structure is almost invariably equiaxed. In comparison with rimmed steels, aluminum-killed steels have a much lower recrystallization rate and a lower hardness after annealing at equivalent temperatures.

Graphitization is an important secondary result of the use of aluminum as a deoxidizer. This is demonstrated by the accelerated spheroidization or graphitization of cementite, which occurs upon long exposure of steel to high subcritical temperatures. The effect is especially pronounced at welded joints. The graphitization occurs readily when more than 0.5 lb of aluminum per ton is added, but rarely when less is used.

Nitriding. Steels containing aluminum can be nitrided. The aluminum nitride that is formed is more stable than the nitrides of chromium, iron, molybdenum, silicon, tungsten, and vanadium. Aluminum also inhibits formation of a eutectoid of iron and nitrogen that causes spalling of the nitrided case. Molybdenum and chromium are usually present in nitriding steels. Nitralloy steels contain from 0.85 to 1.50 Al, 0.9 to 1.8 Cr, 0.15 to 1.0 Mo, 0.2 to 0.4 Si, 0.4 to 1.1 Mn. The high hardness obtained by nitriding is attributed by some to the precipitation-hardening effect of a critical dispersion of chromium and aluminum nitrides, while others believe it is caused by formation of complex iron-aluminum-chromium nitrides.

Steels are nitrided with a minimum of distortion, because of the low temperature of 930 to 1000 F at which the parts are case hardened in an ammonia atmosphere and because no quenching is required.

A graphitic nitriding steel for lubricated wear applications contains 1.35 Al, 1.25 C, 0.25 Cr, and is graphitized by the proper heat treatment prior to nitriding.

Cast irons containing from 1.0 to 1.5% Al and up to 1.5% Cr are nitrided for use as cylinder liners.

The properties imparted to steel by nitriding include great wear resistance, retention of hardness at elevated temperatures, increased endurance limit, and resistance to certain types of corrosion. Applications of nitrided steels include aircraft exhaust valve stems, the moving parts of dies to be used for die and permanent mold casting, and gears.

Aluminum-Coated Steel

Aluminum coatings are applied to steel to obtain improved behavior in the following types of service:

1 Where the primary concern is utilization of certain beneficial properties of aluminum: good resistance to corrosion, bright metallic appearance, receptiveness to finishes, high reflectance, and good electrical conductivity
2 Where the aluminum-iron alloy is required for resistance to oxidation, scale formation, and abrasion, and for high hardness
3 Where the primary objective is to provide a protective coating for steel—obtaining the mechanical properties and weldability of steel for low-cost, nonrusting products to which finishes peculiar to aluminum surfaces can be applied

In volume of products, the automobile muffler market is the largest consumer, fencing second, and roofing and siding third.

Resistance to corrosion of aluminized steel is superior to that of galvanized steel in many environments. However, in salt spray and seacoast exposures, there is little or no difference in the degree of protection provided by the two coatings, because both metals provide galvanic protection to steel.

Aluminum provides galvanic protection to steel under any circumstances in which zinc is effective, although there may be variations in the degree of protection. Because the potential difference between zinc and steel (0.6 v) is greater than that between aluminum and steel (0.3 v), zinc provides better protection initially but is consumed faster. With zinc coatings, rusting of the steel will start much sooner, as is illustrated in Fig. 1.

A large-scale evaluation of metallic coatings was initiated by the American Society for Testing Materials in 1929 (4). Aluminized coatings showed better protection than galvanized after 10.3 years at Pittsburgh, Pa.; 12.3 years at Altoona, Pa.; 23.2 years at Sandy Hook, N.J.; and 29.6 years at State College, Pa. Galvanized coatings gave better protection after 22.0 years at

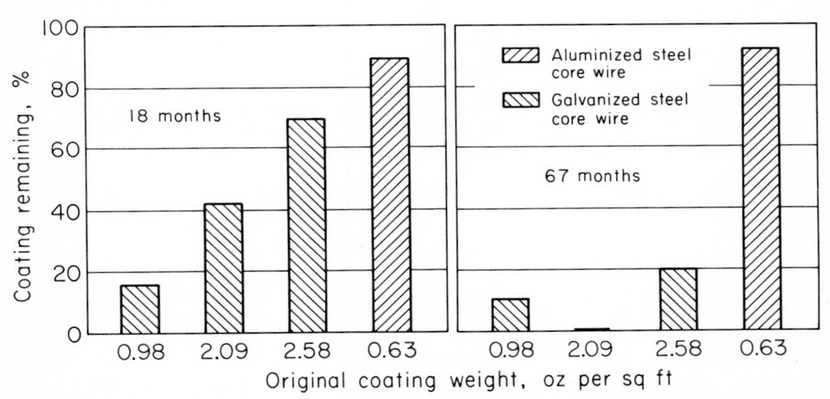

Fig. 1. Coating remaining on steel core wire of No. 2 ACSR *6/1 after exposure to severe Pacific seacoast atmosphere*

Key West, Fla. The ASTM started another test of metallic coatings in 1958, but exposure is yet too brief for comparisons.

Conclusions from the American Welding Society program (5) on metallized coated steel after 6-year exposures were that the life of aluminum coatings is definitely longer than that of zinc coatings at the thinnest coating thickness for each (0.003 in.). For protection of steel in sea water, metallized aluminum sealed with clear vinyl was the best coating system tested.

A golden stain frequently appears on aluminized steel during exposure. The appearance of this "patina", as it is called in the steel industry, is alarming to the inexperienced. However, the

Table 3. Typical Outdoor Applications for Aluminum-Coated Mild Steel

Product and method of coating	Applications
	Fabricated Bar, Strip or Fasteners
Batch hot dip	Anchor bolts for aluminum railing, lighting posts; fasteners for aluminum fabricated items; pole-line hardware for electrical transmission
	Sheet or Strip
Continuous hot dip (Vapor deposition is used when steel is thinner than 0.0149 in.)	Air conditioner housings; awnings; building panels; corrugated roofing and siding; ductwork; outdoor signs; roof decking; tractor muffler outer sheets; truck body rocker panels; weather shields; welded tubing for fence posts; rolling doors; boiler casings; silo roofs; porcelain enameled products; automobile mufflers
	Welded Assemblies
Batch hot dip, or spray	Agricultural implements; clothes driers; frames for air filters; furnace-heater casings; oil coolers; heat reflectors; toasters; electric heaters; trash burners
	Wire Products
Continuous hot dip	Chain-link fencing; cores for aluminum electrical transmission lines; barbed wire; farm fencing
Batch hot dip	Nails

SOURCE: Metals Handbook, 8th Edition, Vol 2, American Society for Metals, 1964, p 490

resistance to corrosion of the coating is unaffected by this staining, which usually reaches a maximum within 30 to 60 days.

Performance superior to that of galvanized steel has been obtained with aluminum-coated products in the following environments: industrial atmospheres containing sulfur compounds; rural atmospheres containing nitrate-phosphate fertilizers; automobile exhausts; air at elevated temperatures; organic acids in food wastes; and grass fires.

Examples of outdoor applications of aluminum-coated mild steel are given in Table 3. These are designs requiring the high modulus and strength of steel with resistance to corrosion approaching that of aluminum.

In long-time corrosion tests in an industrial atmosphere, aluminized steel panels are still intact after 25 years of exposure, while galvanized panels showed rusting after 6 years (6). Results of many exposure tests are shown in Table 4.

Painting of aluminum-coated products is seldom done except for decoration. This is one of the cost-reducing advantages in the use of this material for products exposed to weathering. However, if paint is desired, the aluminum coating provides a good substrate. For strip and shop applications, surface pretreatments used conventionally for aluminum alloys should suffice (see Volume III, Chapter 21). For painting in the field, it is necessary only to remove oily films and nonadherent soil prior to painting. The weathered aluminum surface generally provides a satisfactory surface for most exterior organic coatings. Organic finishes of the alkyd, acrylic, and vinyl types are all suitable.

Porcelain Enameling. Aluminum-coated steels make use of lower-melting porcelain enameling frits and thus sag and distort less on firing. One successful use is for chalk boards.

Oxidation resistance at elevated temperatures is an outstanding characteristic of aluminum-coated products. For most elevated-temperature applications the aluminum is diffused into

Table 4. Appearance of Aluminized and Galvanized Products After Various Exposures

Product	Exposure	General condition Aluminized	Galvanized
Wire	8 years, New Kensington atmosphere	Good	Very poor
ACSR	67 months, Pacific Coast atmosphere	Good	Very poor
Fencing	2 years, 3.5% NaCl intermittent spray	Fair	Fair
Fencing	2 years, 100% relative humidity at 125 F	Good	Very poor
Fencing	4 years, Point Judith, R. I., atmosphere	Fair	Fair
Fencing	8 years, New Kensington atmosphere	Good	Poor
Sheet	10 years, New Kensington atmosphere	Good	Very poor
Pole-line hardware	8 weeks, 3.5% NaCl intermittent spray	Good	Good
Pole-line hardware	8 weeks, 100% relative humidity at 125 F	Good	Very poor
Bolts	6 years, New Kensington atmosphere	Good	Good
Bolts	1 year, 3.5% NaCl intermittent spray	Very poor	Poor
Bolts	1 year, 100% relative humidity at 125 F	Fair	Fair
Rivets	8.5 years, New Kensington atmosphere	Fair	Very poor

SOURCE: E. T. Englehart, Alcoa Research Laboratories

Table 5. Typical Applications of Diffused Aluminum Coatings for Resistance to Oxidation and Corrosion at 850 to 1800 F

Product (and typical basis metal)	Type of service
Heat Treating Equipment	
Burner pipes (5 Cr–0.5 Mo)	Oxidation (1600 F)
Fixtures (mild and medium-alloy steels)	Carburizing; carbonitriding
Flue stacks (mild steel)	Oxidation; sulfur corrosion
Furnace insulation supports (mild and medium-alloy steels)	Oxidation (1000 to 1200 F)
Pyrometer protection tubes (types 310 and 316 stainless steel; mild steel)	Oxidation (1800 F)
Heat-Exchanger Components	
Boiler soot blowers (1 Cr–0.5 Mo)	Oxidation; sulfur attack
Boiler tubing (2 Cr–0.5 Mo)	Oxidation (1000 to 1100 F)
Cylinder barrel, air-cooled engine (nitralloy)	Oxidation (to 900 F)
Preheater tubing (1 Cr–0.5 Mo)	Oxidation (1200 F)
Tubing (mild steel; 1.5 Cr–0.5 Mo)	Hydrogen sulfide gases
Miscellaneous Equipment	
Chemical reactor tubing (mild steel)	Carbonization; iron contamination
Chimney caps (mild steel)	Oxidation and corrosion
High-temperature fasteners	Oxidation (to 1400 F)
Recuperator tubing (2.5 Cr–0.5 Mo)	Oxidation and sulfidation
Refinery heater tubing (type 304 stainless steel; 2.25 Cr–1 Mo)	Oxidation and sulfidation
Sulfuric acid converters (5 Cr–0.5 Mo)	Sulfur dioxide corrosion (1300 F)

SOURCE: Metals Handbook, 8th Edition, Vol 2, American Society for Metals, 1964, p 490

the steel by heating, either prior to use or during use. Such a product, obtained by heat treatment subsequent to coating by any one of the several coating methods, is metallurgically similar to those made by pack calorizing. Some items produced in this manner are listed in Table 5.

The advantage of using aluminum-coated carbon steel for complicated heat treating fixtures subjected to temperatures up to 1600 F is demonstrated by Fig. 2. Over-all cost may be less than for the highly alloyed austenitic steels normally used for this application. Similar reasons have prompted its use in barbecue equipment, home incinerators, and oven and furnace liners. American Gas Association requirements permit the use of aluminum-coated steel for operating temperatures up to 1030 F in heating elements of gas-fired appliances.

The greatest increase in the use of diffused aluminum coatings is in ultrahigh-temperature applications for automotive and aircraft components, some of which are listed in Table 6.

Coated automotive exhaust poppet valves show improved durability, because they resist high-temperature erosion from high-velocity exhaust gases containing sulfur dioxide and combustion products from tetraethyl lead. Aluminum coatings are also useful in reducing scaling oxidation of medium-alloy steels used for intake valves subjected to the temperatures generated in high-compression engines. In a similar corrosive environment, but with temperatures in excess of 1500 F, blades and nozzle vanes for gas turbine engines are coated with aluminum

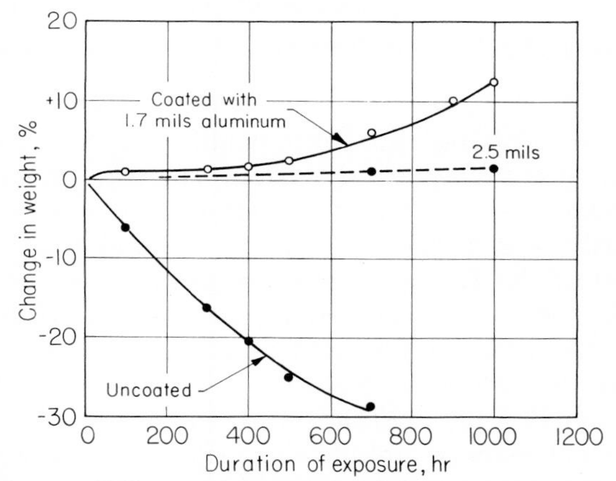

Fig. 2. Effects of coating thickness on oxidation resistance at 1600 F of coated and uncoated heat treating fixtures made of 1020 steel

for effective resistance to thermal shock and erosion. The most common method of aluminizing in this case involves spraying with aluminum and fusing the layer by heating in a molten salt bath or by induction (12).

Aluminized sheet, now used in more than 60 different automobile muffler designs, has achieved a successful reduction in failures from "rust out". It was estimated that, by 1963, 90% of the mufflers were fabricated with aluminized steel.

In petroleum refineries, surfaces protected by aluminum offer more resistance to hydrogen sulfide attack than solid stainless steel. One set of test data (7) indicated that both aluminized and calorized carbon steels are more than 100 times as resistant to pure hydrogen sulfide as 18–8 stainless steel at 1110 F; other results showed that they were 25 times as resistant as straight chromium steels.

Table 6. Typical Parts Aluminum Coated for High-Stress High-Temperature Applications

Part (and typical basis metal)	Type of service	Coating method
Exhaust poppet valves (Silcrome XB)	Oxidation and corrosion by leaded fuel combustion products at 1400 F	Spray and diffuse
Intake poppet valves (8640)	Oxidation	Spray and diffuse
Turbine blades (Inconel 713, GMR 235)	Oxidation and thermal shock at 1500 to 1700 F	Hot dip and diffuse; spray and diffuse
Turbine vanes (HS-31)	Oxidation and thermal shock at 1650 to 2100 F	Spray and diffuse; pack diffuse

SOURCE: Metals Handbook, 8th Edition, Vol 2, American Society for Metals, 1964, p 490

Methods of applying aluminum coatings include batch or continuous hot dipping, pack diffusion, slurries, metal spraying, cladding, vapor deposition, gas plating, and electroplating, all of which will be described. Choice of method is determined by composition of the ferrous metal, importance of the interfacial layer, application of the coated product, size and shape of the product, production volume, and cost. Hot dipping is the dominant process at present (8, 9, 14).

Well-established commercial types of aluminum coatings on ferrous metal products include: (*a*) sprayed coatings, built up to required thicknesses of 3 to 15 mils, usually consisting of pure aluminum, which can be applied with or without a subsequent diffusion heat treatment; (*b*) dipped coatings, with thickness about 7 mils maximum; and (*c*) pack diffusion coatings, usually 15 to 20 mils thick. Similar but thinner diffused coatings are obtained by heat treatment of any other type of coating.

Sprayed coatings are mechanically bonded; without a subsequent heat treatment for diffusion bonding, they are the least effective coating method because of porosity in the coating. Spraying to a coating thickness of 9 mils eliminates continuous pores. Diffusion heat treatment of the sprayed component, particularly in an inert atmosphere, markedly increases its adherence and effectiveness.

Dipped coatings (aluminized) provide an inner zone and bonding layer of a diffused aluminum-iron alloy, and a thin overlay of pure aluminum, but there are limitations on the size and shape of the parts that can be coated.

Calorized coatings usually have a totally diffused layer thicker than that obtained by aluminizing but no pure aluminum overlay. The calorized layer thus may last longer than the thinner pure aluminum layer, because of its greater thickness, particularly if there is erosion; if it is not totally diffused, it becomes more susceptible to cracking and spalling as thickness increases.

Slurry or powder paint methods of coating are widely used for high-temperature processing equipment employed in the chemical and petroleum industries and for aircraft parts exposed to combustion gases. Aluminum is diffused from the dried slurry into substrates of steel, stainless steel, nickel, or cobalt superalloys by direct diffusion, by melting with flux, or by vapor-phase subhalide reactions.

In a small volume, cladding has been used to produce various combinations of laminated sheet structures without formation of an interfacial layer. Thin aluminum sheet or foil is rolled onto steel or stainless steel. Another practice is to bond aluminum plate to thick gages of steel by pressing or explosive bonding prior to rolling. Wire with thick aluminum coatings is produced by extruding aluminum powder around a steel rod that is subsequently drawn; it is used for high-strength electrical conductors. Aluminum powder is used for cladding steel hardware; it is applied by a peening action in a ball mill.

Electrolytically deposited coatings of aluminum have been examined as a substitute for tin plate. Aluminum coatings containing 20 to 35% Mn can be electrolytically deposited to produce a bright appearance without any treatment subsequent to electrodeposition. One process includes continuous electrophoretic deposition of aluminum powder on strip, consolidating the powder by rolling and then heating, which sinters and bonds the compacted powder to the steel.

Vacuum (or "vapor") deposition is practiced experimentally for continuous coating without formation of any interfacial layer, to replace tin plate can stock. The process is particularly useful for steel sheet too thin to coat by hot dipping because of attack by the molten aluminum. Vacuum-deposited coatings 2 mils thick are applied to hot component parts for aircraft engines and noses. This process is also used for depositing thin decorative coatings on plastics, glass, and novelties.

Gas plating depends on thermal decomposition of such compounds as triisobutyl aluminum or diisobutyl aluminum hydride at temperatures as low as 300 to 450 F. A continuous coating with a brilliant appearance is obtained on intricate and threaded parts without shadow effects. Aluminum can be gas plated, to form a pore-free layer up to 2 mils thick without formation of any aluminum-iron interfacial alloy.

Two important factors in successful coating by any method are: (*a*) proper preparation of the steel surface, and (*b*) controlling formation and growth of the aluminum-iron alloy that forms at the interface of the aluminum coating and the steel substrate. Although there are many possible methods of preparing the surface, the method selected must (*a*) remove the iron oxide, either mechanically or chemically, and (*b*) remove adsorbed moisture and gas from the surface.

The formation of aluminum-iron alloy is undesirable except in those products that are to resist scaling or abrasion. This alloy forms on heating aluminum and iron in intimate contact above 1000 F for short periods of time or above 900 F for prolonged periods. This occurs in any hot dipping, heat treating, or annealing step, but not in spraying, cladding, vacuum deposition, gas plating, or electroplating processes. The extent of formation is reduced by the presence of silicon, beryllium, or chromium in the aluminum or steel (10, 11). Very thin coatings on the steel of phosphate, chromium, or molybdenum permit bonding and coating, and inhibit growth of the interfacial layer.

Joining of aluminum-coated parts is accomplished by many methods. Mechanical fasteners of aluminum, stainless steel, aluminized steel, and galvanized steel are suitable and available. Welding is accomplished by arc and oxyacetylene torches using

Table 7. Uses of Products Formed by Chemical Reactions of Metallic Aluminum

Product	Applications
Acetate	Antiperspirant; astringent; mordant; fireproofing; embalming disinfectant; waterproofing; lake manufacture
Alkyls	Cocatalysts for manufacture of polyethylene, polypropylene, polydibutanes, long-chain alcohols, alpha olefins
Chloride	Organic chemical manufacturing; petroleum refining; deodorant; wool processing
Isopropoxide	Selective reducing agent to produce primary alcohols from aldehydes and ketones
Metal	Reduces ferric to ferrous compounds to produce white titania pigment; inhaled to bind silica to prevent and reverse lung changes from silicosis
Oxide	High-purity alumina catalyst base for gasoline production
Nitride	Inert refractory for high temperatures
Nickel alloy	Raney catalyst used in hydrogenation of unsaturated vegetable oils

the same practices employed with steel. For best quality welds, it is recommended that the aluminum coating be removed adjacent to the joint area, to prevent alumina inclusions in the weld. Special fluxes are available to dissolve or float the alumina. The best arc welds are obtained by the tungsten inert-gas (TIG) method, using a stainless steel filler for corrosion-resistant welds. When fluxes are used, it is essential to remove the flux residues. The raw steel weld should be metallized with aluminum or coated with aluminum paint to prevent rust staining of that area.

Spot welding is easily accomplished when surfaces are clean. Brazing may be done using practices suited to either steel or aluminum. Excellent soldered joints in aluminum-coated steel are obtained employing the zinc-base solders used for aluminum.

Aluminum in Galvanizing

Aluminum in amounts of 0.1 to 0.3% is added to hot dip galvanizing baths to inhibit the formation of a brittle iron-zinc alloy layer, thus improving the forming properties of galvanized steel sheet. The aluminum provides a brighter finish on "hand dip" products.

Where a layer of chloride flux must be maintained in the process, a reaction occurs between the aluminum and the chlorine compounds that removes the aluminum and obviates any fluxing action. To retain the benefits of aluminum, a reducing atmosphere has replaced the flux layer in continuous galvanizing.

Chemical Reaction Products

Products resulting from chemical reactions of aluminum are utilized in a variety of applications, as shown in Table 7.

Dry cells with aluminum anodes are attractive because the potential for the couple $Al = Al^{+++} + 3e^-$ is reported as $E° = -1.66$ v, while for the couple $Zn = Zn^{++} + 2e^-$, $E° = -0.763$ v; thus, a cell with an aluminum anode should have a potential approximately 0.9 v higher than the corresponding zinc cell. However, the theoretical potential for aluminum is rarely attained, and a working value of −0.83 to −0.93 v is a more practical figure.

The most favorable electrolytes contain chlorides of aluminum or chromium, usually with chromate inhibitors. The potential of these cells on open circuit may vary from 1.58 to 1.65 v, depending on the electrolyte mix.

Aluminum dry cells have excellent room-temperature shelf life. After eight years' storage at room temperature, cells have 75 to 90% initial capacity. There is no perforation of the anode during this period.

References

1 A. H. Sully, "Metallurgy of the Rarer Metals", Vol 1, Academic Press, New York, 1954, p 21

2 S. L. Case and K. R. Van Horn, "Aluminum in Iron and Steel", John Wiley and Sons, New York, 1953

3 Metals Handbook, 7th edition, 1948; 8th edition, Vol 1, 1961, American Society for Metals

4 Proc ASTM, 44, 92–109 (1944); 52, 118–122 (1952); **60**, 116–123 (1960)

5 "Corrosion Tests of Metallized Coated Steel — 6 Year Report", American Welding Society, New York, 1962

6 "Armco Aluminized Steel", Armco Steel Corp., Middletown, Ohio, 1961

7 Metals Handbook, 8th edition, Vol 1, American Society for Metals, 1961, p 603

8 P. T. Stroup and G. A. Purdy, Aluminum Coating of Steel — A Comparison of Various Processes, Metal Progress, **57**, 59–64 (1950)

9 Metals Handbook, 8th edition, Vol 2, American Society for Metals, 1964, p 489–497

10 D. O. Gittings, D. H. Rowland, and J. O. Mack, Effect of Bath Composition on Aluminum Coatings on Steel, Trans ASM, **43**, 587–610 (1951)

11 K. G. Coburn, Aluminum-Coated Steel Sheets, ASM Symposium on Developments in Carbon Steels, Cleveland, Ohio, October 24, 1963, Tech Rept 21.6

12 E. S. Nichols, J. A. Burger, and D. K. Hanink, Comparative Evaluation of Protective Coatings for High Temperature Alloys, SAE Air Transport and Space Meeting, New York, April 27, 1964, No. 843E

13 A. Kelly and G. J. Davies, The Principles of the Fibre Reinforcement of Metals, Metallurgical Reviews, **10**, No. 37, 1 (1965); D. Cratchley, Experimental Aspects of Fibre Reinforced Metals, Metallurgical Reviews, **10**, No. 37, 79 (1965); "Fiber Composite Materials", American Society for Metals, 1965

14 Better Protection for More Products, Steel, **157**, 65 (Aug 23, 1965)

Index

Following this alphabetic index are numerical indexes of aluminum casting alloys and aluminum wrought alloys. Symbols used after entries tell whether information is in a figure (F), table (T), or whole chapter (C).

G

H

Alloy Index

Alloys are arranged in numerical order. Alloys with specific heat treatments follow the listing of the alloy without heat treatment designation. Thus, 3003, 3003-F, 3003-H14, 3003-H18, 3003-H19, 3003-O, and alclad 3003 appear in this order.

Casting Alloys

Wrought Alloys